A GEOGRAPHY

of

EUROPE

Edited by

GEORGE W. HOFFMAN

DEPARTMENT OF GEOGRAPHY
UNIVERSITY OF TEXAS

CONTRIBUTORS

NELS A. BENGTSON

W. GORDON EAST

ERIC FISCHER

F. KENNETH HARE

GEORGE W. HOFFMAN

VINCENT H. MALMSTRÖM

ALAIN PLÉNEL

HENRY H. SCHLOSS

THEODORE SHABAD

GEZA TELEKI

THE RONALD PRESS COMPANY ⸜ NEW YORK

PREFACE

Europe at mid-century is in the process of rebuilding its economy for the second time within one generation. Inherent in this struggle are many basic problems, all of which are rooted in the continent's long and tumultuous history and its divergent geographical environments. The purpose of this regional geography is to present, as a background to a discussion of these problems, an authoritative description of the physical and cultural landscapes which are characteristic of each geographic region.

The organization of the book is simple and is the outgrowth of two basic ideas gained from the experience of the editor and his colleagues in teaching the geography of Europe. First, it has become clear that the student must be given a general grounding in the continent's historical geography and its complex physical geography. This essential background is provided by Chapters 1 and 2. The second basic idea was our selection of the regional divisions. The presentation of an integrated picture of the European scene requires the use of subdivisions derived from political boundaries, from the boundaries of recognized natural regions, and from the boundaries of broad cultural areas. All are used in the seven regional chapters. Each of these is the work of a specialist who is thoroughly versed in the problems of his region. The order of the regional chapters follows the logic of beginning with the British Isles, a region which is in many ways peripheral to the rest of Europe, of grouping together the three regional chapters which share the Alps, and of closing with the chapter devoted to the U.S.S.R.

The summary chapter brings the geography of each region into perspective and gives the reader a chance to assess the total importance of the regional problems which confront the major compartments of Europe: Western Europe which is struggling to regain its former position in the world's economy, and Soviet Europe which is undergoing a remarkable and rapid industrial development.

The text is closely integrated with the maps, nearly all of them especially drawn for this book, and based on sketches submitted by the contributing authors. The illustrations, many of them originals, were selected by the editor and his colleagues. The reader will also note that the climatic graphs and statistical material are organized as Appendices, and thus give a far more comprehensive picture than would be the case if they were distributed throughout the text.

It would have been easy for a book with ten authors to become a collection of essays. To make sure that our labors produced a broadly uniform text the manuscript of each chapter was critically read by every other contributor. To each contributing author goes the editor's thanks for his cooperation and for his patience. Especial mention should be made of the extra responsibilities assumed by Mr. Shabad, who strove to have all names properly spelled, and by Professor Schloss, who is chiefly responsible for the statistical appendix.

For their help in reviewing one or more of the chapters, the editor and his colleagues thank many friends and associates: Professor Donald D. Brand, University of Texas; Professor Chauncy D. Harris, University of Chicago; Professor Robert E. Dickinson, Syracuse University; the late Professor Johann Sölch, University of Vienna; Professor Fridtjov Isachsen, University of Oslo; Professor Herman F. Otte, Columbia University; and Professor J. Carter Murphy, Washington University. Grateful acknowledgment is made of the invaluable help received from various government agencies in this country and in Europe, from the United Nations, from the staff of the American Geographical Society, and from the embassies of nearly every European country. Last, but not least, the editor thanks his wife, Viola, for her unfailing encouragement and help throughout the long months this book has been in preparation.

GEORGE W. HOFFMAN

Austin, Texas
    January, 1953

CONTENTS

APPENDIX

MAPS

A GEOGRAPHY OF EUROPE

chapter 1

THE HISTORICAL
BACKGROUND

Often the key to the present—or at least one key—can be found in
history, in what lies behind. Again, depth and relative completeness
of understanding in many cases are realized only when historical and
geographical research are blended.

—Isaiah Bowman

As a home of man, Europe has been long
in the making. As we see it now, it reflects the outcome of a long
history, geological and human. The intelligent student will not
conceive this habitat, man-made though it is in part, as something
wholly distinct from the physical setting into which it is firmly and
inseparably welded. The physical elements of Europe are the contribution of a very long geological history, a history which straddles
the whole length of geological time. In contrast, the human history which has contributed the cultural elements of the European
landscape is very short, although much longer than that of the
Americas and comparable in length with that of Asia. The fact
that man inhabited Europe during part at least of the Great Ice
Age [1] has had, however, but little influence on the development of
the present Europe, for it was not until Neolithic times, four or
five thousand years ago, that the human factor became an effective
agent of geographical change. When, after an almost endless period of cultural standstill, Neolithic colonists introduced the practices of cultivation and stock breeding and, although still in a
seminomadic state, attempted to group themselves in small rural

[1] For geologic terms, see Appendix I.

3

settlements, they began also to mold their environment in ways broadly recognizable and to an extent not wholly irrelevant to the geography of modern Europe. Indeed, these Neolithic colonists were the true pioneers in the long process of evaluating and exploiting the natural resources of the continent, and, by clearing its forests for cultivation, the first to alter its vegetation cover.

Some reference to prehistory is therefore necessary for a full interpretation of the geography of Europe. It is, however, the time-span of history proper, and not merely its more recent phases, which has major significance. This history is very rich, especially since Europe, as an appendage of Asia, was continually exposed to the movements of peoples and ideas from Asia, notably from its south-western part. In tracing the lineaments of the present continent, continual recourse has to be had to historical events and processes, i.e., to the migrations of peoples, to the rise and fall of empires, to the colonizing and state-building achievements of the Middle Ages, to the wars and statecraft of modern times, to the growth in navigational competence, and to the striking economic and technological changes of the so-called Agricultural and Industrial Revolutions.

Thus, the geographical individuality of Europe does not spring simply from the variety of its climates, of its rocks, and of its land forms, although all these make their contribution. Rather, it springs from the prolonged efforts which have been made by many different peoples to use its surface and to develop its resources with varying success and intensity from one period and one area to others. France, wrote Vidal de la Blache, is "a medal struck in the effigy of a people"; Europe is an assemblage of many such medals.

Any attempt merely to glance at the many sharply distinguishable cultural landscapes of Europe, or to consider the many elements compounded in any one such landscape, emphasizes how clearly the handwriting of history appears on its map. Dissected plateaus of wooded and pastoral aspect have become populous regions of coal mining and of heavy industry. Wide areas of steppe, which linked like areas of Siberia and Central Asia with south Russia and the Danube Basin, have passed from the control of the nomad horseman to that of the settled agriculturist and of the town-dwelling industrialist. The geographical values attaching to different parts of the continent show continual change throughout history: the Mediterranean lands, for example, no longer dominate in population numbers, in political energy, and in civilization generally. One quarter of the world's population has found its home in Europe, and distributed itself there in a very unequal manner: here densely concentrated in specialized industrial or intensively developed agricultural areas, there thinly spread over a rural landscape of mountain valleys, widespread forests, heath, moor, or marsh.

The countryside of Europe reveals the many varieties of rural settlement and of urban forms. It contains some metropolitan giants which mask with their buildings and their transport lines the nature and form of the underlying rocks, yet which they dare not wholly ignore. The landscape of the "conurbation," a term used to describe those continuously urban areas which have arisen through the coalescence of two or more towns mainly during the last hundred years, must also engage attention. And away from the towns of whatsoever size and function, villages, hamlets, and single farms scatter all over the continent, their distribution posing intricate problems to the solution of which agrarian history, related as it is to the variety of physical environments, can contribute much.

Many other features of the human geography have also grown out of the past; for instance, the ports and resorts of the coastlands, and the patterns of inland transport by rail, road, and water. And, if attention is turned to the inhabitants of Europe themselves, these are still separable into ethnic, linguistic, national and state groups, the locations of which were first sketched long ago.

Confronted by the wealth of Europe's history, the student of human geography may well wonder what is his precise task in turning back to the past for the light which it can throw on the present. In essence, he is concerned with the study of groups of people and their settlements, of their forms of economy, and of their means of travel and of transport. Under each of these three main heads—settlement, economy, and "circulation"—a set of problems arises for separate discussion. Thus consideration of the peoples of Europe will refer to the growth and distribution of population, to rural and urban settlement, and to the ethnic types, languages, nations, and states as they are distributed over the continent. Similarly, attention will be turned to the variant patterns of agriculture, industry, and commerce, and to the patterns of transport on which they depend: all these will be noted in relation to their physical background and to their development through time.

The Peoples of Europe

Prehistoric Settlement. Geography need concern itself little with the Paleolithic period which, despite its long duration of perhaps 500,000 years, has left virtually no mark on the landscape of the continent. The interest attaching to the study of the first human occupants of Europe and notably to the Neanderthal man, relates rather to the story of man in Europe than to that of the European countryside. Paleolithic man inhabited those parts of the continent which were not invaded by the Fenno-Scandian and Alpine glaciers, where probably a tundra-like climate prevailed or, at best, humid oceanic conditions, as in the Mediterranean peninsulas. An archaeologist has estimated for the earlier or Lower Paleolithic period that the total energy at man's disposal in Europe—and all of it was human—did not exceed that of a four-engined bomber: as an agent of geographical change, therefore, Paleolithic man can be ignored.

That transitional phase between the Upper Paleolithic and Neolithic cultures which has been termed "Mesolithic" deserves passing notice. When the North German Plain and the Baltic area had been abandoned by the glaciers and were being colonized by trees, some immigrants from the South, Mesolithic in culture, settled along its seacoasts and along the banks of its numerous lakes and rivers. From about 8000 B.C. until about 3000 B.C. these prehistoric tribes still lived by hunting, fishing, and food collecting, and were presumably ignorant of cultivation and of metals, and had no domesticated animals except the dog. Their tools and weapons were still fashioned of unpolished stone, flint, and bone; they had not yet learned to polish stone but only to flake and chip it; nor, with few exceptions, were they familiar with pot making. And this way of life lingered on, especially in Northwest Europe, long after the Neolithic culture, based on agriculture and pastoral husbandry, had become established in Egypt, Mesopotamia, and Northwest India.

The climatic and vegetational background to the Mesolithic period and the succeeding cultures of post-glacial Europe is now being revealed in clear outline, thanks above all to the microscopic study of pollen grains preserved in datable layers of peat and other organic or semiorganic sediments.[2] It is now possible to envisage in relationship not only the main fluctuations of climate since the final retreat of the Fenno-Scandian and Alpine glaciers, but also the various stages in the spread of forest-forming trees and the corresponding culture-periods of the archaeologist. Four successive climatic phases have been distinguished: the Boreal, Atlantic, sub-Boreal and sub-Atlantic, although the third of these is less clear.

---

[2] On pollen analysis see H. Godwin, "Pollen Analysis, An Outline of the Problems and Potentialities of the Method," New Phytologist, XXXIII (October 1934), 278-305, and Stanley A. Cain, Foundations of Plant Geography (New York: Harper & Bros., 1944), especially chap. x.

Compared with the cold pre-Boreal period which preceded it, the Boreal period was dry and increasingly warm; the Atlantic wet and warm; the sub-Boreal was cool but perhaps not so dry as was formerly believed, while the sub-Atlantic, which lasted into the historical period of the Roman Empire, was marked by cold and moist conditions. Precise calendar dates for these periods are as yet difficult to determine. Nor is it clear that the specified climates apply farther afield than Northern, Western, and Central Europe. But the succession of climatic changes is by now broadly established, and so also is that of the corresponding changes of the vegetation cover.

In contrast to North America, Europe has relatively few indigenous tree species and even fewer today than it had during the Tertiary period. This scarcity is not the result of its present climate nor of the adverse conditions of the Great Ice Age. It is due to the two barriers aligned west-east: the middle mountain ranges and the Mediterranean Sea, which checked the retreat of tree species as climate worsened with the onset of the Great Ice Age. Fewer species were therefore able to immigrate into the continent from the southwest and southeast as the climate improved in the post-glacial period. In the Boreal phase spruce (*Picea*), fir (*Abies*), pine (*Pinus*), birch (*Betula*), and hazel (*Corylus*) established themselves as far north as central Sweden and Finland. In the succeeding Atlantic phase, these gave pride of place to mixed forests of oak (*Quercus*), elm (*Ulmus*), linden (*Tilia*), and common alder (*Alnus*). The beech (*Fagus*), especially sensitive to temperature and traveling fastest by way of river valleys, spread into Western and Central Europe from the Danube Basin during the sub-Boreal and sub-Atlantic periods. Both Mesolithic Europe, which may be dated to the late Boreal and Atlantic phases, and Neolithic Europe, which falls within the late Atlantic and the sub-Boreal phases, must be thought of as thickly clad with trees and undergrowth, excepting only those areas where tree growth was precluded by high altitude, bad drainage, or exposure to persistent gales. Even the considerable areas stretching from south Russia across the continent to the English Channel, where layer upon layer of *loess* had been deposited by wind during glacial periods, are now known, thanks to pollen analysis, to have been covered, not with a steppe-heath flora, but with beech, hawthorn (*Crataegus*), juniper (*Juniperus*), yew (*Taxus*), box (*Buxus*), and ash (*Fraxinus*). Also, the Mediterranean peninsulas had then an abundance of forest and scrub, rooted in an ample soil which, as a result of forest destruction by man and beast, has since been largely lost.

Attention can be paid here only to three particular aspects of the Neolithic and Bronze ages: the route-ways (i.e., natural routes) used, the areas occupied, and the mineral sources exploited—since these are directly connected with the development of Europe as a home of man. It was by the diffusion of men and techniques from certain primary centers of progressive culture in Egypt and Southwest Asia that Europe learned in turn, and adapted to its very different environment, the Neolithic and Bronze Age ways of life. The Neolithic culture, as it developed between 6000 and 3000 B.C. in its original homes, marked a major revolutionary change in man's use of his habitat. Its economic basis was food production by cultivation and stock rearing, and its social expression was, at first, the village and, later, the town. It brought technical inventions and new crafts: wheel-turned pottery, kiln-fired bricks, spinning and weaving, building, writing, trade, social organization, and the fashioning of works of art. All these new triumphs of human ingenuity, to which the beginnings of metallurgy were later added, characterize the Neolithic culture or civilization. Given the original location of the homelands of the Neolithic culture, it is not surprising to find that the new culture was first to appear within the European realm in Crete and the other islands and coastlands of the Aegean Sea, whence it spread by sea and by overland routes. The area which, chiefly on climatic ground, Ellsworth Huntington found most favored for civilization in Europe—the Northwest, including the British Isles—was the last to receive it.

Figure 1 illustrates the land and water routes by which, on the basis of the distribution of known prehistoric sites and artifacts, men and ideas seem to have spread into and throughout the continent. The general point worth noting here is that already at that early time, the prehistoric peoples were outlining the main areas of human settlement and linking them by sea and land channels of communication which have since then tended to remain in continual use.

It is doubtless highly dangerous to generalize about the areas occupied by European peoples in the various stages of the Neolithic and Bronze cultures, for several millenniums are involved and the evidence cannot claim to be complete. There is, however, a striking correspondence between the areas settled by Neolithic peasants and certain areas of porous or pervious rocks. This applies particularly to the loess lands, but also to areas of sand, gravel, loam, limestone, and sandstone, all of which were not only well drained, but developed light-textured soils, easy to work with simple stone or wooden hoes.

The relative facility of cultivating such soils would seem to have been their main attraction; the absence of forest cover and its replacement by a steppe-heath type of flora under an allegedly dry sub-Boreal climate can no longer be offered as the explanation. Rather, it is now clear that the Neolithic peasants often settled in village groups at the wooded margin of the steppe, and made the first big clearance of forests by firing, in order to win land for agriculture and pasture. It is remarkable, too, that the lowlands and plateaus, once conquered in this way, have continued to be defended for the plow against a reinvasion of forests by a historical succession of colonists. Thus the Neolithic men of Europe and their livestock of the third millennium B.C. played a part in fashioning European downlands, steppes, and heaths from original woodlands. It is believed, for instance, that the great extent of heath in northwest Germany owes its origin to the agency of men and their grazing animals which, in the course of the sub-Boreal period (i.e., during the later Neolithic and Bronze Age), entirely destroyed the former forests.

The Bronze Age in Europe, which may be dated from about 1800 B.C., called attention for the first time to the mineral wealth of the continent. This wealth was found for the most part outside the areas selected earlier for their agricultural possibilities, and principally in those places where rocks of Hercynian folding were exposed. Among the regions which were then important for their minerals were Transylvania with silver, gold, and salt; Bohemia with tin and copper from the Erzgebirge (Ore Mountains); Spain with tin and copper; Ireland with copper and gold; and Brittany and Cornwall, the mineral resources of which included the scarce metal tin necessary, with copper, for bronze-making. The knowledge of bronze first reached Bohemia and Hungary to be diffused therefrom by nomad intruders from South Russia. New trade routes by land and sea were then opened up, including those along which amber was brought overland to North Italy from the Baltic. Ireland, then remotely placed, assumed for a time a leading role in metallurgical industry and European commerce. The sea route from the Mediterranean through the Irish Sea to the Orkney Islands and Scandinavia, which is inferred from a study of tomb plans and vases to have been in use in the third millennium B.C., was clearly an established trade route by about 1500 B.C., as is shown by the finds of traded products of known origin. The development of agriculture continued during the Bronze Age with a few local changes, some of which are known with surprising accuracy. Thus, in Denmark, expert studies of the impressions of grain still

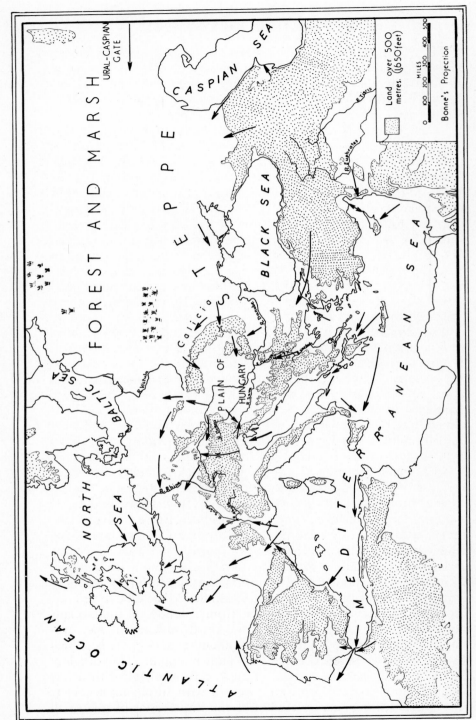

FIGURE 1. The natural routes of prehistoric Europe. (This and the remaining maps in this chapter were prepared by the author.)

detectable on the prehistoric pottery and of carbonized cereals found in peat, reveal that barley was by far the most important crop there in the late Bronze Age, although several varieties of wheat were no less prominent in the Neolithic period.

It was during the Bronze Age that immigrants from the steppe lands north of the Black and Caspian seas brought to the rest of Europe the domesticated horse, which was used for pulling war chariots and only later for riding. These immigrants spoke the Indo-European language, and it would seem that for a time, during the latter part of the second millennium B.C., a single speech prevailed in Europe. If for no other reason than this, the European Bronze Age is geographically memorable, as it is from the language introduced then that, by a process of regional differentiation, most of the present languages of Europe have developed.

Our sketch of the prehistoric settlement in Europe should conclude with a reference to the expansion of Iron Age peoples into western Europe during the last thousand years before the birth of Christ. The knowledge of the working of iron had penetrated into the Danube Basin from the East, and once again it was from a Danubian area that a new technique was rediffused. From the upper Danube Valley between Bavaria and the middle Rhine in Alsace, Iron Age culture was carried into France, Iberia, Scandinavia, and the British Isles. Several waves of migration ensued. In Britain, for example, three can be distinguished and broadly dated, and these appear to have consisted of Celtic-speaking peoples who were bringing with them successive Iron Age cultures. These immigrant "Celts"—this term has only a linguistic meaning—were the ancestors of the many peoples established in North Italy, Iberia, Gaul, Bohemia, and Britain with whom the Romans later fought when, leaving peninsular Italy, they launched their career of conquest. Numerous Celtic river names in Europe, such as Rhine, Danube, and Thames still attest their former presence.

As its climate improved and fluctuated with the retreat of the glaciers of the Great Ice Age, Europe, we have seen, became a "pioneer" or "colonial" field, occupied and exploited by a succession of immigrants of different cultural attainments. The temperate forested lands of Europe owed this initial development to the inflow of men and ideas from the precociously civilized countries situated in lower latitudes, above all Mesopotamia, Egypt, and even Turkestan. In these movements we may note the important roles played by the island of Crete and the steppe of South Russia, and parts of the Danube Basin. In the course of the first millennium

B.C., the prehistoric period in Europe gives place to the historical period which is illuminated by literary records. They reveal, as is known also from archaeological evidence, that the Mediterranean lands of Europe reached the highest degree of social and political organization, of commercial activity, and of civilization in general: the Phoenicians, the Greeks, the Etruscans, and the Romans of classical antiquity focus the attention of the historian, while in Europe beyond the Mediterranean lake-land world more primitive conditions of life prevailed.

The Nations and States. Even though present-day Europe still shows traces of its prehistoric past—Neolithic grave mounds, Bronze Age trackways, Iron Age contour camps, and much else—the main features of its human geography are explained above all by processes operative during the historical period. The peculiar patterns of "nations" and "states" in Europe, to which we now turn our attention, are clearly the results of such processes. It is a remarkable fact that Europe, occupying only one twelfth of the habitable earth, contains about one half of its independent states. No less does Europe house a high proportion of the self-conscious and articulate nations of the world. Time has served only to intensify the trend toward the creation of more and more so-called "nation states," and to produce what must appear to Americans, familiar with larger and simpler state-and-nation patterns, a parochially organized continent. This appears particularly true of Central and East Central Europe since nations and states are much more simply arranged peripherally to these regions, in Western, Northern, and Eastern Europe.

As a glance through the pages of a historical atlas shows, state territories and the boundaries of states have changed continually. In contrast, the distribution of national groups shows marked stability. To define what constitutes a "nation" is not easy: like the concepts of "space" and "electricity" in physical science, it resists exact definition. But it is something more fundamental than the state which, as twentieth-century history has shown, can be made and unmade. Social groups, bound together by common traditions and culture, have tended to become acutely conscious of their own individuality and have often, but not invariably, sought separate statehood, whether or not they possessed a single common language. But national self-consciousness and the idea of the "nation state" are relatively modern developments. Let us look back in time to see where and how the nationalities of Europe first appeared. It will be convenient to start this discussion by reference to the foundation and fortunes of the Roman Empire in the early centuries of the Christian era.

At its maximum extent in the second century A.D. (Figure 2) the Roman Empire extended northwards from the shores of the Mediterranean Basin to the Rhine and Danube and bestrode these rivers along parts of their courses—in the upper Rhine, and in both the upper and lower Danube. Within this large part of the continent Rome established centralized political organization and

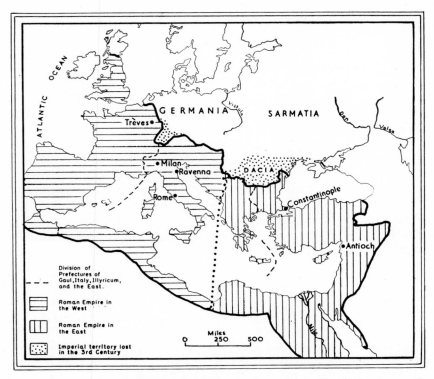

FIGURE 2. Division of the Roman Empire in 395 A.D. Imperial capitals are named.

maintained the peace, security, and ordered life of her provinces by fortifying the imperial frontiers and by building a system of well-engineered roads. The Roman Empire achieved remarkable success as a multinational state: its citizenship provided a common bond to many different peoples—Gauls, Iberians, Illyrians, Greeks, Britons, and others—and its language, the Latin of the hillmen of Latium, was widely adopted except in less accessible areas, and in the eastern basin of the Mediterranean where Greek speech maintained its cultural ascendancy. While there were many distinct peoples or nations and many forms of native speech, the several nation-groups had not, nor did they seek, separate statehood. Indeed, the political pattern of Europe in the second century was one of greater simplicity than any other of later time: there was the extensive, well organized, and highly civilized Empire, and beyond it, in regions which were only loosely and lightly occupied, the "barbarian" world, so-called by the Greeks, not to express loathing or contempt, but because its inhabitants made in their speech "bar bar" noises unintelligible to them.

The cultural gradient between these two worlds was steep, yet they did not fail to react on each other. Finds of Roman coins, as far east as the Vistula and as far north as central Sweden, point to trade relations. There were military engagements on both sides of the frontier. Barbarian peoples were, moreover, permitted at times to settle as colonists within the Empire, as were Germans, for example, in the plain of Alsace.

From the third century onwards, the Empire weakened and for military and administrative convenience was divided in 395 A.D. into two parts, the eastern part being ruled by an emperor at Byzantium, renamed Constantinople (now called Istanbul), and the western by another emperor ruling from Rome or elsewhere as defense needs dictated (Figure 2). The Eastern Empire, in which Greek or Hellenistic culture prevailed widely, succeeded in absorbing Slavic and other immigrants and in maintaining some semblance of imperial organization for another thousand years; known as the Byzantine Empire, it was overthrown only by the Ottoman Turks in 1453. The western half, which included Italy, Iberia, Gaul, Britain, and North Africa, collapsed under barbarian pressure in the fifth century. It was then that the more vigorous peoples from the barbarian world took the future of Europe in their hands, and among them can be seen the forerunners of the principal nations of present Europe—notably those of the German (or Teutonic) and of the Slavic groups.

The collapse of Roman power in Western Europe opened wide the floodgates to conquering barbarian peoples who sought new homes within the Empire, in lands richer, because more effectively exploited, than their own. These movements, not just of armies but of whole peoples, are known as "the barbarian invasions of Europe" or the *Völkerwanderung*. Peoples of Germanic stock were the protagonists; in their wake pressed the Slavs, while there were also some intruding peoples from Asia and North Africa.

The earliest known homeland of the German people, where they had been established since the second millennium B.C., lay in the glaciated lowlands and hills between the lower Rhine and the lower Oder, the Danish peninsula and islands, and southern Sweden. For a long time stock-rearers and fishermen rather than tillers of the soil, they increased in numbers and pressed southwards from their difficult environments of forest, marsh, and heath, and in the course of time comprised a number of distinct nations, more or less settled and attached to the soil by their practice of stock-rearing and shifting agriculture. One branch, the East Germans, migrated from the lower Oder across the basin of the Vistula to establish themselves on the steppe to the north of the Black Sea, whence some were allowed to settle in the lower Danubian lands of the East Roman Empire and others moved westwards to Italy, southern Gaul, and Spain. The other branch, the West Germans, more civilized through closer contact with the West Roman Empire, included the Angles, Saxons, and Jutes who colonized the English Lowlands, and the Franks who, under Charlemagne, re-created for a time the Roman Empire in the West and have left their name in the state of France.

The long-term effects of the barbarian invasions, conquests, and settlements were to replace the Western Roman Empire by a number of smaller states in Italy, Gaul, Iberia, Britain, and the Rhineland, while political patterns began to appear too in the broad area of Central Europe, between the Rhine and Vistula and the Baltic and the Danube, which the Romans had labeled *Germania* on their maps. The history of the Franks from the fourth to the ninth century explains how, by no means inevitably, the kingdoms of the West Franks and the East Franks—to become respectively France and Germany—originated within particular territorial frames. Charlemagne's empire, formally created in 800 A.D., did not last long. In extent, it was both more and less comprehensive than the West Roman Empire of earlier days; more because it included considerable areas beyond the Rhine, less because most of Spain and Britain and part of Italy were not included. The partition of Charlemagne's empire among three of his grandsons, by the Treaty of Verdun in 843 A.D. (Figure 3), was the most important of many such divisions of the period because it had permanent effects. It outlined a kingdom, much smaller than Gaul, which was to become France; another, east of the Rhine, became Germany and grew greatly by eastward expansion. Between these two, a third elongated middle kingdom, based mainly on the Rhine and extending from the North Sea to the Apennines, lacked the possibilities of political unity apart from surviving Roman roads. It could not survive troubled times. This territory proved indeed a bone of contention between its two neighbors right down to the present century; it contained, too, the "nuclear" or "core" areas for the states now known as Switzerland, Luxembourg, the Netherlands, and Belgium.

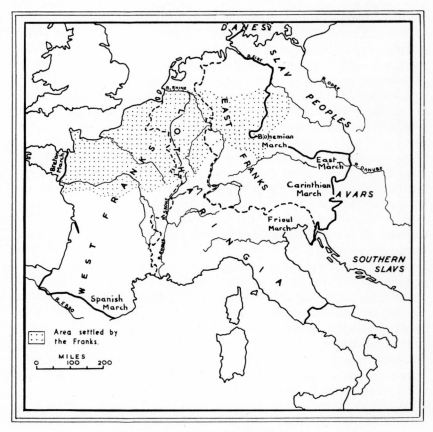

FIGURE 3. The partition of the Carolingian Empire in 843 A.D.

In the British Isles, the conquests and settlement of the Germanic Anglo-Saxons, Danes, and Norwegians brought political subdivisions which, in west Britain and Ireland, included those of Celtic-speaking peoples. The newcomers established their speech in the English lowlands, thus effacing the Latinized speech which developed and persisted in most of the former imperial territories of the West. Only after yet another conquest, by the Normans—

French in speech but Germanic in blood—was political unity rees-
tablished at least in the most settled and productive part of the
British Isles, namely England, the wealth of which William the
Conqueror astutely investigated by his famous Domesday Survey
of 1086 A.D.

Italy suffered a succession of barbarian invaders. As in earlier
and in later times, the Alps proved defensively useless, a "splendid
traitor"; their passes served not to prevent but only to canalize
ingress into the land which offered glittering prizes to the conqueror. Italy became a mosaic of states, including city-states, and
so it still appeared in the mid-nineteenth century, on the eve of
its unification as a kingdom under the House of Savoy, with its base
in the Piedmont. In the centuries which preceded this unification,
north Italy was largely bound politically to trans-Alpine powers,
notably the Holy Roman Empire and the Austro-Hungarian Empire;
the Papal States stretched across peninsular Italy; South Italy and
Sicily, caught in the stream of Mediterranean seapower, passed
in part or as a whole first into Arab and then in turn into Norman
and Spanish hands. But political disunity did not preclude the
reflowering of city life—at Venice (Venezia), Genoa (Genova),
Siena, Milan (Milano), Pisa, Florence (Firenze), Palermo, and
elsewhere—nor high attainment in the industrial arts and in trade
by land and by sea.

The Iberian Peninsula, "Spain" as the Romans conceived it,
was occupied also by Germanic intruders:—Suevi, Vandals, and
Visigoths from across the Pyrenees—and Moslem Moors and Arabs,
the former the more numerous, from North Africa. In their revival of classical learning, in their successful application of irrigation to agriculture, and, above all, in their architectural legacy at
Cordoba, Granada, and Seville (Sevilla), the Arabs have left memo-
rials of their conquest. But they never held permanently the northern provinces of Iberia, from which was waged against them the
Christian Crusade which led to the establishment of the kingdom
of Portugal in the thirteenth century and that of united Spain in
the fifteenth century.

During the thousand years which followed the fall of Rome
(476 A.D.), new nations and states emerged within the peninsular
and formerly Roman territories of Western Europe. Farther afield,
in the broad lowlands of East Central and Eastern Europe, the
contemporaneous movements of the Slavs have left their imprint
on the map of the nations and states of the continent. The Slav
peoples of Europe, who are conveniently classified into Eastern,
Western, and Southern groups, make up one third of Europe's

population and one twelfth of mankind. The Slavs in no sense constitute biologically a "race," nor indeed do they conform to a single "ethnic type." They remain divided in religion, a result of geographical location and orientation in medieval times. Russians, Serbs, and Bulgarians belonged to the Greek or Eastern Orthodox Church; Poles, Czechs, Croats, Slovenes, and Dalmatian Slavs fell within the orbit of the Roman Catholic Church. Similarly, although it is language which provides the main bond between all the Slav peoples, the Russians, Serbs, and Bulgars have adopted the Greek Cyrillic alphabet, while others, notably the Poles, Czechs, Croats, Slovenes, and Dalmatian Slavs, use the Roman alphabet.

The original homeland of the Slavs cannot be precisely located. Tacitus, writing in 98 A.D., locates the Venedi (or certain Slavs) east of the Vistula and refers to their habit of wandering far and fast on foot, in the course of plundering forays, between East Prussia in the north and the Galician plateau in the south. As the Germans vacated Central Europe during the Völkerwanderung the Slavs pressed as far westwards in their wake as the lower Elbe and its tributary the Saale. They also moved eastwards into the mixed-forest region of the Great Russian Plain, then lightly occupied by Finnic peoples; and southwards into the Danubian and Balkan lands of the Byzantine Empire.

The economy of the early Slavs was primitive and their political organization weak. Swine-rearers, hunters, and fishermen, they grew flax and hemp for clothing and for oil, gathered honey from the wild bees of the forest and made intoxicating mead from it. They had no horses or cattle, no heavy plow, no vines or grain fields. In view of the high status of the Slavs in the world of music, it is of interest to note that, already in the ninth century, they had a variety of musical instruments, including those made from marsh-grown reeds. Indeed the Slavs in their way of life clearly owed much to environmental influences; they suffered too from their geographical position in the eastern marches of Europe. Like a "soft anvil," they were exposed to the blows of two hammers which were as hard as steel: one the recurrent waves of mounted nomads from the East, and the other the German pioneers and colonists from the West.

We can only briefly indicate here the shape of the present patterns of Slavic Europe and how they were formed. The Slavs long remained an inland people, cut off from the seas by the Balts (Old Prussians), Lithuanians, Germans, and Swedes in the north; and by steppe nomads and the Byzantine Empire in the south. A broad wedge of non-Slav peoples remained within the Danube Basin: the Germans in Charlemagne's Ostmark (East March), which was to become Austria and the coreland of an empire; the Magyars, a mixed people, mounted horsemen from Asia and Finno-Ugrian in speech, who occupied the basin of Hungary toward the year 900 A.D.; and the Romanians, who developed their Latinized speech in the aloofness of their habitats in the Transylvanian Alps.

The eastward colonial movement of the Germans after the year 1000 A.D. into the lands between the Elbe and the Oder largely effaced or at least obscured the Slavs, but they have held their own in Bohemia and Moravia. Within the forested basin of the Vistula the Poles found and maintained their homeland, although the boundaries of Poland have fluctuated widely during the last thousand years. In the south, Slovenes, Serbs, and Croats have preserved their identity, now recognized in the federal structure of the Yugoslav state. Greece, although it was overrun more than once by the Slavs, resisted Slavic influences. Slavs, however, form the major element in the Bulgarian nationality, which takes its name from the Finno-Ugrian Bulgars, nomadic intruders from the steppe in the seventh century.

From the Russian forests, other Slavs—the Great Russians— ranged far afield to the White Sea, the Caspian, and, beyond the Ural Mountains, to the distant Pacific. But it was the invading Scandinavians (Varangians) of the ninth century who forged the earliest Russian states and it is only in the fourteenth century that Muscovy, shaking off the Mongol tutelage, launched the expanding Russia which we know now as the federated Soviet Union or U.S.S.R.

Many of the patterns of the nations and states of Europe thus begin to emerge from the conquests and settlements which followed the fall of Rome. The student of particular nations and states will direct his attention to their original "nuclear" areas which are often geographically significant: the Elbe plain of the Czechs in Bohemia, the Paris Basin of the French, and the upland plains (*polja*) of the Serbs, to cite three examples. Minor shifts of national groups and changes in the territorial content of states have been continual, and many European state patterns are of twentieth-century origin. We may note that the populations of these states are seldom strictly homogeneous; everywhere there were or are still "inliers" or "outliers" of other nationalities. These two geological terms can be usefully applied to such minority groups—the former to indicate that the groups were established before, and the latter after, the nationalities by which they are at present surrounded. Thus the Basques and Bretons form "inliers" in France, just as the Volga Germans formed an "outlier" in the U.S.S.R. In the so-called "Shatter Belt" of East Central Europe (see Chapter 8), the distribution of nationalities is more complicated, and was much more so before World War II than now.

For many centuries before the French Revolution, when it was exceptional to believe or assert that each nation should seek separate statehood, imperial regimes attempted, not always with success, to subject different nations to a common rule. But this twentieth century, notably during World War I, witnessed the eclipse of several empires established on European soil: the Ottoman Turkish, which once reached west to include much of Hungary; the Russian; the Austro-Hungarian, which tried not ineffectively to hold together Austrians, Hungarians, Czechs, and other Slav groups of the Danube Basin; and the German, created only in 1871 by Prussian arms and statecraft. Out of the fallen empires and in pursuance of the principle of national self-determination, Poland, Czechoslovakia, Yugoslavia, Austria, Hungary, and Finland were either created or re-created. The Baltic states of Estonia, Latvia, and Lithuania won their independence for a short time but now find themselves constituent republics of the U.S.S.R. Romania, Bulgaria, and Greece have maintained the independent statehood which they won from the Turks with foreign aid in the nineteenth or early twentieth century, although there, as elsewhere in the politically unstable and ethnographically complex "Shatter Belt," boundaries have undergone much change. From one angle, the political pattern of Europe in 1953 shows a certain simplicity broadly similar to that of Roman times, with the Soviet Union and its satellites on the one hand and the "Western" states on the other. Only Yugoslavia, Spain, and Sweden stand somewhat apart from this alignment.

Races and Ethnic Types. The European has yet to be born; European peoples abound. "A great multitude, which no man could number of all nations, and kindreds, and peoples and tongues . . .": these words from the Book of Revelation may fittingly be applied to a continent whose human complexity is as great as its area is small. The peoples of Europe can be allocated to distinct groups on the basis of ethnic type, language, political allegiance, and in other ways. The findings of physical anthropology, archaeology, history, and linguistics help substantially to explain the present patterns, but part of the story of Europe's peoples, who during four or five millenniums fashioned the habitat we now know, remains obscure.

Much has been lightly if feelingly written about the "races" of Europe, yet very little that is strictly scientific can as yet be said. We leave aside here the popular and politically tendencious conceptions of racial origins, racial traits, and racial superiority which are seldom related to "race" as the anthropologist's concept. As such this implies biological relationships, especially genetic ones. It would be scientifically tidy and satisfying if the existing peoples of Europe could be classified into clearly marked racial groups and if these could be shown to be derived from early historical or prehistoric races, no less distinct. The idea of originally pure races from which present Europeans are descended, however convenient it would be, has no authority in known fact. Since all the existing varieties of mankind belong to one species, and since man has always been the most adaptable and the most mobile of all animals, the quest for the geographical habitats of originally separate racial groups is a false trail. Certainly the anthropometric study of present Europeans has thrown no clear light on their genetic relationships, although physiological studies of blood groups may achieve more success.

It is wise therefore to turn to other aspects of the European peoples—to their ethnic types and their linguistic and national groupings—which can be discussed with more assurance and, indeed, are matters of everyday significance. For it must be confessed that, while "racial theories are still potent destructive agencies," the racial history of Europeans, were it ever fully revealed, would be a matter of purely academic interest. We have no grounds for believing that "race" divides the population of Europe into neat compartments as do languages and, above all, states.

Although the racial history and racial classification of Europeans remain obscure, it is possible to describe their ethnic characters and even to speak of specific ethnic types. The existing populations are studied as they appear, in respect to physical characteristics, such as head and nose forms, stature, hair texture and color, and eye color. Using such criteria, Deniker [3] postulated the existence and showed the broad geographical distribution of six principal ethnic groups and four subgroups. The six principal ones he called "Northern," "Eastern," "Ibero-insular," "Cevenole or Western," "Littoral," and "Adriatic or Dinaric." Later writers emphasized the prevalence of three distinct types called "Nordic," "Alpine," and "Mediterranean." This classification is clearly too simple to

[3] J. Deniker, *The Races of Man: An Outline of Anthropology and Ethnography* (New York: Charles Scribner's Sons, 1900), pp. 325-34.

cover the numerous varieties present even in small areas of the continent, although it points to some major contrasts of types and distributions. Indeed it is clear that the humble task merely of describing (let alone accounting for) the physical variety of Europeans, has not yet been accomplished. Within any area, besides individuals of the main types, there are many others of variant subtypes, for the main types are determined in part by the personal judgment of the anthropologist and in part on the basis of average figures for the ethnic characters used as criteria; average figures in this context are no more significant than they are, for example, in climatology. The task of adequately describing the European peoples, to achieve precision, should involve estimates of the frequency with which the various types occur. Negatively, at least, it can be stated that no correlations appear between the distribution of ethnic groups and those of languages and nations.

We can here only allude to the distributions of a few selected ethnic characters as shown cartographically in C. S. Coon's *The Races of Europe*. The map of stature shows that the tallest populations in Europe, i.e., those with average heights of between 5 ft. 8 in. and 5 ft. 10 in., occur in the Baltic-North Sea region, in Scandinavia, Finland, the Baltic States, parts of north Germany, the Netherlands, and the British Isles; they occur also in the Dinaric highlands of Montenegro and Albania. In contrast, the lowest average height—5 ft. 2 in. to 5 ft. 6 in.—is found among the Lapps and Samoyeds (Nentsy) in the extreme north of Europe, but also markedly in France, Iberia, and Italy, the area which Sir Halford Mackinder called "The Latin Peninsula" of Europe. In Central and Eastern Europe average stature appears to lie between these two extremes.

The cephalic index, which measures head shape (by dividing head breadth by head length and multiplying by 100), has long been a cherished statistical device of physical anthropologists. Although it is useful for descriptive purposes, it has scarcely proved illuminating as a key to racial problems. No simple patterns emerge from the distribution map of head forms in Europe. The small-headed Lapps are the broadest-headed (with a cephalic index of 88-89) and contrast with the Norwegians and Swedes who tend to be medium- and even long-headed, as also do the peoples of the British Isles. Broad-headedness (shown by an index of 84 or over) characterizes the populations of southern France, notably in the Massif Central; Switzerland; north Italy; the Balkan Peninsula; and most of Central Europe, the northern lowlands excepted. Iberia, south Italy, and the Mediterranean islands except Cyprus, show medium-headedness and some traces of the long- and/or narrow-headedness typical in North Africa and Egypt. In East Central Europe and the European U.S.S.R. the average head form ranges between medium and broad. The lands of the Mediterranean Basin do not appear as a unit on maps showing either stature or head forms; in contrast, the coastlands of the Baltic and North Sea, and especially those of the latter, do show some uniformity in both respects. The following broad ethnic divisions have been recognized:

	Long Head		Broad Head	
Stature	Tall	Short	Tall	Short
Brunette		Mediterranean	Dinaric	Alpine
Blond	Nordic			Eastern European

Finally, the ethnic distribution based on differences in the pigmentation of hair and eyes is not without geographical interest. The area in which a majority of the population has fair to light brown hair and light eye color (e.g., shades of blue or grey) corresponds broadly to the glaciated area of Northern Europe (the southern half of Scandinavia, western Finland, eastern Britain, and the northern European plains from Holland to west central Russia). The "pure" blond type, as distinct from that with tendency to blondness, is not very widespread; only a third of Norwegians and Swedes, who show this trait most, are "pure" blonds. In southern Europe, on the other hand, the more typical features are those of the brunette rather than the blond: black or dark hair, together with brown or black eyes, occurs among more than half the population of Spain, Portugal, peninsular Italy, eastern European U.S.S.R., Greece, the Balkan Peninsula, and the Mediterranean islands. An intermediate zone from France via north Italy to central and southern European U.S.S.R. contains populations about equally fair and dark in hair and eye color.

The Languages of Europe. Certainly today Europe is, for its size, the most polyglot area in the world. Although advances in the means of transportation have virtually erased physical obstacles to the intercourse of the peoples of Europe, very long periods in the past, when movement was difficult, witnessed the sharp differentiation of languages which presents today so formidable an obstacle to European unity. Philological study has established, as a generally accepted hypothesis, that most of the languages spoken from northern India to the extreme west of Europe derive from a single original language called Indo-European. Languages unrelated to this parent speech are spoken by only a small number of European ethnic groups and have not always been established in written form. In fact, these languages occur rather as survivals or as intrusions within a land of Indo-European linguistic parentage. But the family relationship between the tongues has now no practical significance. All the languages of Europe differ to such an extent that it is rare for any two distinct languages to be mutually intelligible. This being so, and in default of any single common language—such as Latin provided for educated Europeans during the Middle Ages and the Renaissance—it is not surprising that language has served more than anything else to foster national consciousness and thus to play a great part in the political subdivision of the continent.

The languages of Europe, most of which fall within the two classifications Indo-European and Ural-Altaic, are listed below:

CLASSIFICATION OF THE LANGUAGES OF EUROPE (see Figure 4)

A. *Indo-European*

   1. Celtic (now confined to the Atlantic coastlands of the British Isles and Brittany): Irish and Scottish, Gaelic, Welsh and Breton. Also includes Cornish (now dead) and Manx (almost dead).

   2. Romance (descended from Latin): Italian, French, Walloon, Provençal, Spanish, Portuguese and Galician, Catalan, Romanian, and various Alpine languages, including Romansch and Ladin. Also the Sardinian and Dalmatian dialects of Italian.

   3. Teutonic (North European group): German (High and Low), Dutch and Flemish, Frisian, English, Danish, Norwegian, Swedish, Icelandic, and Faeroese.

   4. Baltic: Latvian and Lithuanian.

   5. Slavonic: Great Russian, White Russian (Belorussian), Little Russian or Ukrainian (including Ruthenian), Bulgarian, Serbo-Croat and Dalmatian, Slovene, Czech (including Moravian), Slovak, Polish, Sorbian (or Lusatian).

   6. Hellenic: Greek.

   7. Thraco-Illyrian (formerly widespread in the Balkans): Albanian.

B. *Ural-Altaic*

   1. Finno-Ugrian (which includes also many languages spoken in Asiatic U.S.S.R.): Magyar, Finnish and Karelian, Estonian, Lapp, Mordvinian, Komi, Komi-Permyak, Udmurt, Mari, Vogul, Ostyak, Nentsy.

   2. Turkic or Turki-Tatar (mainly in Asia): Turkish (numerous outliers in the Balkan Peninsula), Kazan, Tatar, Crimean Tatar, Bashkir, Chuvash, Kalmyk, Kazakh.

C. *Semitic*
   Maltese (many educated Maltese also speak either English or Italian).

D. *Basque*

In Europe, as elsewhere, language is a mark of social contact
and not of race. Peoples came either to adopt the language of
their conquerors, or imposed their own language on their conquerors. The language that tended to prevail belonged to the higher
material culture. The adopted tongue developed in turn regional
characteristics which often became sharp enough to define a recog-

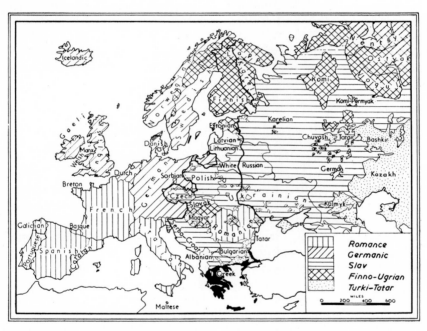

FIGURE 4. Major linguistic patterns in Europe before World War II. Some
subsequent adjustments of this pattern are referred to in the text. (After A. Meillet,
modified.)

nized language. Thus Latin, the speech of the first Romans of
Latium, being the expression of the superior Roman civilization,
was adopted in Western Europe, North Africa, and Danubian
Europe. In the eastern Mediterranean countries, however, Greek
held its own despite Roman conquests, by virtue of its high cultural
tradition. In Western Europe provincial Latin conditioned the
growth during the Middle Ages of languages of the Romance group
(Figure 4): French, Provençal, Italian, Catalan, Spanish, and Por-

tuguese. In the Swiss Alps there are still some small "islands" of Ladin and Romansch, while an "inlier" of Romance speech, containing though it does some Slav elements, occurs in Romania, the territory of which once formed the Roman province of Dacia.

The distribution of Romance languages in Europe falls far short of the extent of Roman territories at their maximum. The areas from which Latin speech disappeared in favor of non-Romance languages were either frontier lands where Roman culture was less firmly established or lands where later invaders succeeded in imposing their language. Thus North Africa lost the Latin speech of its cities with the Arab conquest of the seventh to eleventh centuries, as Egypt lost its former Greek speech. Similarly, southern Britain, where Latin was widely spoken by the Romano-British population, assumed, except in Cornwall and Wales, the Germanic speech of its Anglo-Saxon conquerors. In the Balkan Peninsula, Slav languages developed, except where Greek, Vlach, and Albanian maintained their hold. Finally, within the frontier regions of the Roman Empire, along or astride the Rhine and Danube as well as in Switzerland, the present limits of Romance speech lie well behind the former imperial limits.

The second large linguistic group, the Teutonic, includes several distinct languages, together with others that are clearly akin. When Old German was first recorded (in some inscriptions of the third and fourth centuries A.D.), three distinct forms existed: Gothic, which has died out; Western German, which includes present-day German, Dutch, Flemish and English; and Northern German, of which Danish, Swedish, Norwegian, and Icelandic are the chief subdivisions. The widely distributed High German dialect has become the basis of a literary language current throughout Germany, Austria, and the northern half of Switzerland, but locally there are variations in pronunciation and vocabulary.

English has moved far from the original Anglo-Saxon speech and has undergone much admixture, notably from Norman French, so that its relationship with modern German appears distant. More unity is apparent between the written and spoken languages of the Scandinavian world. There is still enough in common between the spoken languages of Denmark, Norway, and Sweden to permit the nationals of these countries to understand one another. Both Sweden and Denmark have written forms, different in grammar and pronunciation, which go back to the Middle Ages, while Norway employs two literary languages; one is based on Danish and the other derived from old rural Norwegian dialects (Old West Norse) very different in pronunciation from Danish. In Belgium and the Netherlands, Dutch and Flemish are two forms of Low German speech which have a common literary form: Netherlandish, more usually called Dutch.

The Slav languages, which constitute the third group within the Indo-European family, still preserve more in common than do languages of the Romance and Germanic groups, since they developed slowly and retain archaic features. They began to diverge notably from the ninth century onwards, and present today three major varieties. The Eastern (or Russian) variety includes Great Russian, White Russian, and Little Russian. Each of these has a literary and a spoken form. Little Russian has a wide currency over an area now equated with the Ukrainian S.S.R. It has held the status of a literary language only since 1905 and is the official language of the second most important republic of the Soviet Union. Whether spoken or written, Little Russian does not present much difficulty to compatriots of Great Russian speech. White Russian (Belorussian), spoken in the Soviet republic of that name, has little ground for separate status apart from Great Russian, which is by far the most widely used Slav language in Europe and constitutes virtually the *lingua franca* of the whole U.S.S.R. The literary form of Great Russian was established in the eighteenth century, on the basis of the speech of the Moscow region.

The Western Slav languages, now represented by Polish, Czech, and Slovak, were once spoken as far west as the Elbe and its tributary the Saale. The so-called "Sorbian" or "Wendish" spoken, together with German, by over 100,000 people in Lusatia (the hill country southeast of Berlin), survives as a reminder of this former distribution. Polish and Czech are surrounded by other Slav languages and German, Magyar, and Lithuanian speech, but have resisted effacement; indeed, both have literatures dating back to the later Middle Ages. Czech and Slovak show spoken and written differences, although some claim they form only one language and not two.

The Southern Slav languages, separated from the Western and Eastern groups by peoples of German, Hungarian, and Romanian speech, are found in the broad northern part of the Balkan Peninsula between the Adriatic and the Black seas and north of the area in which Albanian, Greek, and even Turkish are spoken. Bulgarian and Serbo-Croat are the two chief languages of the Southern group. Both had late medieval forms but were formalized as written languages only in the nineteenth century. In northwest Yugoslavia, Slovene is spoken by about two million people. Like Serbo-Croat, from which it does not differ greatly, it has been a written language since the later Middle Ages. In the Dalmatian coastlands, Slav speech replaced a form of Romance speech related to Italian. So much variation occurs in Serbo-Croat and Bulgarian speech that in certain areas it is difficult to determine on any scientific principle which of these languages is being spoken; this is well illustrated in Macedonia, a frontier region of languages, where also forms of Greek speech are found.

To the Indo-European languages of the Romance, Germanic, and Slav groups must be added Greek, Albanian, Celtic, and certain Baltic languages. The first has a limited range in the Aegean islands, the Peloponnesus, and the Greek peninsula as far north as Epirus and the coastlands of Macedonia and Thrace; modern Greek, be it noted, has changed so much since the days of ancient Greece that foreign students of classical Greek cannot take modern Greek in their stride! Albanian, the literary form of which was established only in the second half of the nineteenth century, is the sole survivor of Thraco-Illyrian languages once widely spoken in the Balkan Peninsula. It has borrowed much from neighboring languages in the past, especially from Latin. Two forms of Celtic survive in the west of Europe where, at the dawn of history, this language was widely spoken. Gaelic survives in the lightly populated Scottish Highlands and Isles and provides the official language of Eire; Brythonic survives in Wales and Brittany. Welsh and Gaelic possess literatures and owe their survival not a little to national sentiment and stimulus. In the east Baltic lowlands, Lithuanian and Lettish (in Latvia) represent the two languages of the "Baltic" group, a third, old Prussian, having been replaced by German in East Prussia by the sixteenth century. Lithuanian and Lettish are spoken by only a few million people. Although Lithuanian preserves the most archaic features of all the Indo-European languages of Europe, its literature dates only from the eighteenth century. Whereas Lithuanian has lost much ground over the centuries, Lettish has spread among Livonians who formerly spoke a Finnic language.

For the rest, the non-Indo-European languages of Europe can be noted briefly. Maltese represents a survival of Semitic speech from the days of the Arab conquest. Basque is believed, on the other hand, to have survived from the days before the settlement of peoples of Indo-European speech, for its relationship with other languages remains obscure. Before the Roman period, it was used widely in Iberia and in France south of the Garonne and west of the Lower Rhone. Today it is confined to a small area athwart and westwards of the western Pyrenees, and even there educated people speak also either French or Spanish. Today, Basque is a factor in regional consciousness, as witnessed by the formation of a Basque republic during the Spanish civil war of 1936-38, and the provincial organization of Spain recognizes the distinctness of the Basques, the majority of whom occupy the province of Vizcaya.

There remain the numerous languages of the Finno-Ugrian and Turkic families which are spoken by relatively small numbers in Europe, although over a considerable area. Finno-Ugrian is mainly represented by Magyar, which is spoken inside and outside the limits of the Hungarian republic, notably in the towns of eastern Transylvania, once a part of the Hungarian kingdom and now a part of Romania. The languages of the Finns, Karelians, and Lapps also fall within this group, as do several others still spoken in the northeast of European U.S.S.R.: Nentsy, Ostyak, Komi, Vogul, and the rest. Indeed, as river names still testify, Finno-Ugrian speech once prevailed widely in the European area now dominated by Russian speech. Finally, the Estonian tongue spoken by only about one million people, is Finno-Ugrian and closely related to Finnish.

The Turkic languages are spoken in European areas of the Soviet Union which are now organized as autonomous Soviet Socialist Republics, i.e., the Bashkir, Tatar (or Kazan), Chuvash, and Kalmyk. Turkic speech extends also to eastern Thrace (European Turkey) and to the Crimean Peninsula but is spoken by only a minority of the population.

The language map of Europe thus depicts many frontiers or areas of transition through which it is possible to draw boundary lines, often only with much difficulty and rough accuracy. Although linguistic groups are often compactly located, they are seldom homogeneous and in places appear widely scattered. In Western, Northern, and Mediterranean Europe they are relatively compact, but even there islands of other languages and marginal areas of mixed languages occur. In Central Europe, and above all in the "Shatter Belt," the distributions are much more complicated, although less so now than in 1938. Apart from "alien" minorities within the country and the mixture of language groups on the state margins, there are or were until recently, many scattered "outliers." Moreover, areas of great complication occur where very many languages are spoken, and where, as a result, the mapping of the distribution of languages becomes well-nigh impossible. Macedonia, now divided between Greece, Yugoslavia, and Bulgaria, represents the most striking illustration of this complexity so that Gallic humor has coined the expression *Macédoine de fruits* to describe fruit salad.

The explanation of the language map of Europe cannot be found solely in the physical geography of the continent. It has been argued [4] that "language areas . . . have been largely determined by the character of the surface and climate" and that "linguistic lines of cleavage . . . conform to a notable degree with physical features." Only if men, like plants, had specific climatic and edaphic needs, could one expect to find in physical geography a complete explanation of the language map.

Certain physical features or environments do, it is true, help to define the linguistic patterns in Europe. The lower Danube, flanked by a broad belt of marshes on its north bank, does divide Romanian from Bulgarian-speaking peoples. The boundary between French and German passes along the wooded summits of the high Vosges. The area of the Pripet marshes separates Ukrainian and Belorussian speech, and the Pyrenees effectively separate French and Spanish. Areas of scantily settled steppe and rivers which are unnavigable upstream, characterize the frontier region between Portuguese and Spanish. But, in the main, peoples and languages have negotiated physical obstacles such as mountains, rivers, highlands, and marshes. The watershed of the Alps does not neatly divide French and German from Italian; within the Alpine valleys, distinctive languages have developed in semi-isolation; neither do the eastern Pyrenees sharply divide the areas of Catalan and Provençal. As to the navigable rivers of Europe, they commonly serve to unite rather than to divide, so that the Vistula Basin forms the core region of Polish speech while that of the Rhine has become mainly Germanic, yet invaded by French on its western flank. The Danube, in contrast, presents a succession of language areas astride its valley.

In lowlands and hilly country, the frontiers of language bear no obvious relationship to the relief and are clearly the expression of social forces operative long ago. Even so, former geographical features—now erased—may have been significant: thus the former Carbonnière Forest did in medieval times form a zone of separation between Flemish speech in the Scheldt Basin and French speech to the south.

In short, Europe's language map, like those of its nations and states, can be explained only in terms of historical geography, i.e., the movements of peoples, their initial settlements and subsequent

[4] L. Dominian, *The Frontiers of Language and Nationality in Europe* (New York: Henry Holt & Co., Inc., 1917), pp. 2-3.

colonization outwards, and their mutual reactions when brought into contact with each other. By the end of the Middle Ages the language patterns were clearly outlined; one can point to specific linguistic frontiers, notably that of French and German in the Lorraine plateau and that of Walloon and French on the Franco-Belgian border where the boundary has changed but little during the last thousand years. And, since the end of the Middle Ages, the many migrations, colonizing efforts, and compulsory and voluntary transfers of population, especially in the last decade, have modified distributions fixed long ago.

Demographic Considerations

Population Growth, Densities, and Distribution. The population of Europe is estimated at over 550 millions, that is, one quarter of mankind, and is very unevenly distributed. The outstanding areas of high density occur in Italy and in a diagonal zone from the British lowlands and the Low Countries, in the northwest, to the Ukrainian steppe, in the southeast. The highest figure reached in a state-area [5] is 823 persons per square mile in the Netherlands (year 1950). Notably low densities occur in Northern Europe, including Fenno-Scandia and the northern lowlands of Germany, Poland, and the U.S.S.R.; in Iberia; and in the Balkan and Greek peninsulas. Apart from Iceland and the northeastern parts of European U.S.S.R., Norway has the lowest density, 25 persons per square mile. Clearly the present densities and distribution of population, no less than the high degree of urbanization that characterizes Europe, are the result of historical changes, some of the last two centuries or less, and are the particular product of those changes concerned with the increasingly effective exploitation of natural resources and opportunities.

From the dawn of history, Europe has always been one of the most densely populated areas of the world. Historians estimate the population of the Roman Empire, in its heyday, at 70 millions, when that of China, on the basis of its census of 156 A.D., reached an estimated 50 millions. Europe contained only part of these 70 millions, for some of the most populous areas of the Roman Empire lay outside its European boundaries—in Egypt, North Africa, the west coast of Asia Minor, Syria, and Palestine. Outside the Roman frontiers in Europe dwelt Celts, Germans, and Slavs, organized at first into tribes and later into nations. Their economy

[5] For England and Wales, part of the state territory of the United Kingdom, the 1951 Census figure is approximately 750 per square mile.

was so rudimentary as to support only relatively small numbers. Thus in the early Christian era, as today, Europe stood second only to Asia in population numbers, for to the numbers of Chinese must be added tens of millions of Indians and other Asiatic peoples.

The distribution of population in the early centuries of the Christian era differs sharply from that of the present day, and reflects the historical circumstance that progress in material culture, on which increasing numbers have depended, spread from cultural centers in the east and southeast, i.e., Egypt, the Levant, Greece, and Rome. Italy was relatively populous in the Roman Empire, but it was the peninsula rather than the northern plain which then held the greater density of population. Generally, Southern Europe—Italy, Greece, southern Spain, and the Mediterranean islands—shows the highest densities, while population grows scantier further away from the Mediterranean axis of the Empire. Thus Britain, less populous than Gaul, had but an estimated one million people during its centuries as a Roman province (43 A.D. to about 400 A.D.), while Central and Eastern Europe—the so-called "barbarian" world beyond the Rhine-Danube frontiers—and still more Scandinavia, can scarcely have accounted for more than a few millions.

Although the demography of medieval Europe is still very much a matter of research, it would appear that its population doubled between 1100 and 1300 A.D., fell sharply during the following century and a half, partly as a result of the Black Death, and rose to its former high level by 1500. Central Italy appears to have had the densest population about the year 1300, when notable increases in density also occurred in France and the Low Countries, in northern Italy, in the English Lowlands, and, to a lesser degree, in the German-settled lands between the Rhine and the Neman (Niemen). In other words, the pattern of well-populated lands had extended to the northwest since Roman times. Farther east in Europe, in Bohemia, Moravia, the Vistula-Bug basin and in the forests of north and central Russia colonization, principally by Slavs, must have led to greater though still scattered settlement and higher densities than those obtaining at the time of Rome. The Iberian Peninsula in the mid-fourteenth century appears not to have advanced in numbers since Roman times: warfare between Christian princes and Moslem conquerors, carried on in the south, may well have served to check the growth of population.

For the early eighteenth century, although official censuses were still lacking, it is possible to see rather more clearly the broad outlines of Europe's population map. For the whole continent the population is estimated to have been then about 100 or 110 millions. France, the British Isles, the Low Countries, and Germany had still further increased their relative demographic standing. As compared with today, the continent was but sparsely settled by populations for the most part rural, drawing their livelihood from agriculture but also in some areas from rural woolen industries. The highest densities reached, notably in the English Lowlands, central Lombardy, Westphalia, the Rhineland, and Saxony were of the order of only 100 to 175 persons per square mile.

Soil fertility was one important physical factor behind population densities, but not the only one. Urban concentrations were evidently related to industrial, commercial, and administrative activities, while some of the potentially best arable soils of Europe, notably the black earths of the Ukraine, the steppe soils of eastern Hungary, and those developed on the loess of Lower Silesia and Galicia, were as yet virtually unexploited.

A significant feature of the early eighteenth-century map of the distribution of population is the semivacant tract which extends across the continent from the Baltic to the area between the Danube delta and the Don. Of this sharp break in the settlement pattern between Western Christendom and Russia there are many complementary explanations: the extensive Pripet marshes discouraged and diverted settlement; the Tatar (Mongol) invasions of the fourteenth century and many other wars had caused much destruction; the steppe lands were still subject to the mastery of the nomad; the material culture lagged far behind that of Western and Central Europe. It was in this zone that, from as early as the fourteenth century, Jews escaping from persecution in Germany and Western Europe increasingly sought refuge. They created what became known as "the Jewish Pale." The Baltic coastlands, covered widely with boulder clay and studded with small lakes, remained in 1720 very scantily populated, while in Northern Europe only the Swedish Midlands (but not Scania and Småland), and the southern littoral of Finland were really populated. The upper Volga-Oka basin, where lay the old province of Moscow, and the area southwards to Kiev were clearly the demographic core of Russia, although its density of population fell well below the highest figures of the time reached in Saxony, the Rhineland, the Low Countries, Italy, and England.

Attempts have been made to estimate roundly the population of European countries in the early eighteenth century; some estimates for the years 1720, 1820, and 1930 are given below. Josef

Haliczer's figures [6] for the separate countries have been grouped here to fit the major regions discussed later in this book. The areas of the named states, totaled for the several regions, are those of 1930.

ESTIMATED POPULATIONS OF THE MAJOR DIVISIONS OF EUROPE
IN 1720, 1820, AND 1930

Regions	Areas (in thousand sq. miles)	Estimated Population (in millions)		
		1720	1820	1930
SOUTHERN EUROPE (Spain, Portugal, Italy, San Marino, Trieste, Greece, European Turkey)	411	25	41	79
WESTERN EUROPE (France, Low Countries, Luxembourg)	239	22	36	59
BRITISH ISLES (United Kingdom, Eire)	121	8	21	49
NORTHERN EUROPE (Denmark, Norway, Sweden, Finland, Faeroes, Spitzbergen)	485	3.5	6	16
EUROPEAN U.S.S.R. (including Estonia, Latvia, Lithuania)	1,800	17	39	125
EAST CENTRAL EUROPE (Poland, Czechoslovakia, Hungary, Romania, Bulgaria, Albania, Yugoslavia)	445	..	38	94
CENTRAL EUROPE (Germany, Switzerland, Austria, Liechtenstein)	176	18	28	75
EUROPE (estimates)	3,700	110	210	500

What do these round figures show? The British Isles, together with Western and Central Europe, as defined in this book, although they occupy only one seventh of the continent's area, accounted in 1720 for between two fifths and one half of its population. This proportion, however, fell to 36 per cent in 1930 and continues to fall. In contrast, European U.S.S.R. and East Central Europe, which dominate in area (about 60 per cent), were so retarded in exploitation and settlement in 1720 as to contain less than one third of Europe's population. This proportion markedly increased by 1930 to 42 per cent, thus exceeding that of the British Isles and Western and Central Europe. Moreover, it is still increasing, reflecting as it does much higher fertility rates than those prevailing in the west. The least settled major division of the continent, Northern Europe, maintained over the last three

[6] Josef Haliczer, "The Population of Europe, 1720, 1820, 1930," *Geography*, part 4 (December, 1934), 261-73. This article contains generalized distribution (dot) maps for the selected dates.

centuries its small proportion of the European population, namely about 3 per cent. Southern Europe's share has clearly decreased, from nearly one quarter in 1720 to rather less than one sixth in 1930.

In general, these estimates show the remarkable increase in Europe's numbers, notably during the period 1820-1930, even though net emigration was then very considerable. They also illustrate that, over the whole period 1720-1930, rates of estimated increase were lowest in Western and Southern Europe, higher in Central Europe, Northern Europe, and the "Shatter Belt," and highest in the British Isles and European U.S.S.R. Further, they draw attention to the tilting of the demographic balance toward East Central and Eastern Europe, where the long-delayed evaluation of natural resources has been and is still being increasingly achieved. The demographic race, it would seem, is being won— in Europe at least—by the late starters.

Emigration and Migration. Some reference must be made to these dynamic aspects of Europe's population, notably during the last hundred and fifty years. There was an unparalleled exodus of population from Europe to lands overseas during this period; and there were also numerous smaller shifts of population, not always voluntary, within state-territories and between states. The effects of the great outflow of Europeans have, of course, been written indelibly into the geography of settlement and the economic development and nation-building in countries which not so long ago were either virtually empty or only scantily peopled, notably the Americas, Australia, southern Africa, and New Zealand. The internal redistributions of population within Europe after the end of the Middle Ages, although continual and numerous (and excepting those redistributions of the last eight years), have produced only relatively minor changes in the distribution of population and of nationalities.

At least 60 millions are estimated to have moved from Europe to North America and Australasia alone, during the hundred years preceding 1924. Others in smaller numbers migrated to South America, South Africa, and elsewhere.[7] Although probably more than one third returned to Europe, the movements were clearly on a grand scale, stimulated as they were by the new steamship facilities and by the labor demands of agriculture as it expanded overseas in response to growing demands for imported foodstuffs in the

[7] For a short account see J. S. Huxley and A. C. Haddon, We Europeans (London: Jonathan Cape, 1935), chap. viii, "Europe Overseas," by A. M. Carr-Saunders.

populous and industrial countries of Western Europe. It was the peoples of Northwest Europe [8] with their established interest in the sea routes as avenues of commerce and/or of imperialism, who made the greater contribution to emigration in the nineteenth century as in earlier centuries, while those of Southern, East Central, and Eastern Europe dominated only during the first fifteen years of this century.

Since certain countries, especially Great Britain, Ireland, Italy, Germany, Spain, and Austria-Hungary sent large numbers overseas, this fact bears on the interpretation of the differential rates of increase inferred from the summary on page 35. So also does the fact that there was a substantial outflow of Russians into their Asiatic territories (over six million persons moved there during the period 1901-1914), where they found new lands for colonization and exploitation.

Despite Europe's long tradition of political division, no period in the continent's history has been without some movement of national groups, voluntary or enforced, from one state territory to another. While such movements were healthy in fostering economic developments, for instance, when German ironworkers, Flemish weavers, Dutch dikers, and Jewish traders applied their skill in new areas, they produced innumerable local political problems. With the growth of acute national consciousness particularly evident in this century, the presence of minorities of alien population was more and more resented in some national states.

The migration of the Germans, which was the most remarkable dispersion of people in Europe, continued long after their major colonial effort of the later Middle Ages. Between the sixteenth and the nineteenth centuries, they pressed into the lands eastwards and southeastwards of Germany where less effectively organized states were unable to oppose their entry and settlement. Before World War II, German minority groups were to be found in Poland, the Baltic States, Hungary, Romania, Yugoslavia, Czechoslovakia, north Italy, south Ukraine, and the middle Volga region. The problem of the alien groups within would-be national states, characteristic particularly of the countries of the "Shatter Belt," was not restricted to Germans, for there were, for example, large Russian populations in Poland; Hungarian minorities in Romania, Yugoslavia, and Czechoslovakia; and Yugoslavs in the Istrian area of Italy. Wartime and postwar expedients have had marked success in effecting, either by forcible means or by voluntary action

[8] The peoples of Northern and Western Europe contributed fully three quarters to the ancestry of the population of the United States in 1920: *Ibid.*, pp. 245-46.

sometimes based on international engagements, many transfers of minority populations. These transfers were usually but not invariably to their national homelands.

Such transfers have been far too numerous for any summary here, but a few striking examples may be noted. Some 400,000 Finns exercised their right under the Soviet-Finnish peace treaty of 1940 to return from ceded areas to the reduced territory of Finland. A similar treaty provision in 1945 permitted Czechs and Slovaks in the U.S.S.R. to move to Czechoslovakia and Russians in Czechoslovakia to move to the U.S.S.R. (Carpatho-Ukraine). Some Germans of the South Tyrol were transferred from Italy to Germany under a Hitler-Mussolini agreement and only a few have returned. The allocation to the post-World War II Polish republic of German territory in East Prussia, Silesia, Brandenburg, and Pomerania was followed by a virtual expulsion of Germans whose lands were resettled by Polish peasants. Similarly, the Czechoslovak republic has sent back to Germany almost all of the Germans (over three million strong in 1938) previously settled within its territories, notably in the Sudetenland. Broadly speaking, the westward expansion of the U.S.S.R., which began with the Nazi-Soviet Pact of August, 1939 and culminated in the territorial annexations at the end of hostilities in 1945, set in train many large-scale shifts of national groups. In contrast to Western and Central Europe, however, the Soviet Union, as a multinational state based on the federation of its major component nationalities, professes no national exclusiveness. Under the pressure of the Nazi invasion of Russian territory in 1941, the Germans of the middle Volga region, some 400,000 in number, were transferred to new homes east of the Urals. Several other national groups—the Crimean Tatars, the Chechens, and the Kalmyks—were also deported. Within Germany, truncated territorially at the end of World War II, in-migration from outside the former Reich boundaries has added substantially to its total population and interzonal migration has increased the density of Western Germany at the expense of the eastern (Soviet) zone (Chapter 6). Thus, in response to national sentiment and in furtherance of the idea of the "nation state," Europe west of the Soviet Union shows closer concordance between its boundaries of states and of nationalities.

Internal migration of a different kind, leading to new patterns of population density, has been active in Britain during the last two centuries, and in much of continental Europe during the last hundred years. The Industrial Revolution and all that it entailed in industrial expansion and in new transport facilities was the major cause. The main effects were the great growth of town populations, the concentration of population in the coal fields and in other industrial districts, and the depopulation of many rural areas and of some highlands and mountain valleys, such as the Massif Central and Swiss Alpine valleys. This depopulation has been offset, in some areas, by the seasonal invasion of the holiday-maker.

The Settlements

The Towns. The town, ranging between the extremes of the country market center and the outsize metropolitan city, characterizes as never before the settlement geography of Europe. The degree to which population is concentrated in towns shows marked regional differences. Europe contains, too, a large proportion of cities of the greatest scale: no less than two fifths of the world's cities of more than one million inhabitants. While the traveler is impressed by the conspicuous antiquity of many European towns, he can scarcely fail to note many centers which have clearly arisen within the last hundred years as a result of the Industrial Revolution. The geographer's study of towns turns attention to many of their varied aspects: their sites, situations, and positions; their spatial growth and areal components; their population numbers; and not least their manifold functions: industrial, commercial, administrative, defensive, residential, and holiday-making—to cite only the chief ones. With these main topics in mind, let us glance at Europe's long urban history for what light it can throw on the geography of its towns today.

The town proper, in a form unambiguously urban, either as a specially organized community or as a built-up area, owed its firm establishment in Europe to ancient Greece and later to the Roman Empire. The town was indeed the hallmark of Romano-Greek culture. The Roman Empire took over many long-established towns—such as Athens (Athenai), Alexandria, and Marseilles (Marseille)—situated around the shores of the Mediterranean, and to the Roman Empire is due the first spread of towns in Europe beyond the confines of the Mediterranean world.

Roman towns, although laid out in accordance with a plan, were very different in shape, this being largely determined by the local topography. They had a checkerboard road pattern, and were often but not invariably girdled by high walls. With only a few notable exceptions, these towns were by our standards very small. *Londinium*, which the Romans established as a port and bridging place at the head of the Thames estuary, occupied only half a square mile although it was the largest town in Britain and the equivalent of large continental cities such as Cologne (Köln) and Mainz. Most towns were much smaller; only a few, notably the imperial capitals of Rome (Roma), Constantinople (Istanbul), and Lyons (Lyon), the capital of Gaul, stood well above the rest. Roman towns enjoyed amenities such as piped water and heated houses; their industries and trade were normally limited. Some urban settlements were roadside stations rather than producing centers, or watering places like Wiesbaden in Germany and Bath in England. Others were ports such as Ostia, the port for Rome, and Marseille, first founded by Greek colonists as early as the sixth century B.C. There were also the prototypes of the later Calais and Boulogne, controlling the passage of the English Channel.

A number of historic towns in Western and Mediterranean Europe occupy sites on or near former Roman towns: we may note here Milan (Milano), Naples (Napoli), Lyon, Bordeaux, Coblenz, St. Albans, Lincoln, Canterbury, Vienna (Wien), Belgrade (Beograd), Sofia (Sofiya), Niš, Dubrovnik, Split, and Salonika (Thessalonike). The continuity of such towns as organized societies from Roman times onward cannot often be demonstrated, although this may fairly be claimed for some at least of the cities of the East Roman Empire, of Italy, and Gaul. Often, as in Britain, there was a marked hiatus in urban life due to the destruction and disorganization which followed the collapse of Roman power in the west. Immigrant conquerors and settlers, either nomadic or essentially agricultural in their economy and unable for some time to establish peace and security over wide areas, had little use for towns, which were reborn later under more favorable conditions and in response to specific social needs. The newcomers were at first content to occupy but a small corner of a Roman town site, plundering its ruined buildings for stone and tiles with which to build their churches, as at Nîmes and Autun in Gaul. At some particular cities, such as Vienna, Belgrade, and Regensburg, it is of much interest to discover that Christian churches were built on the sites of Roman temples and that Roman street patterns survived into later times. In other cities, like London, the Roman street pattern did not survive and the Roman occupation level lies buried a few yards below the present surface.

As the Dark Ages passed into the later Middle Ages, and as growing populations won new areas for the plow, towns on new as well as old sites gradually come clearly into view. Vigorous industrial and mercantile societies, striving to achieve legal privileges from the Crown or from lay or ecclesiastical lords, formed trade associations and established civic self-government. The distinguishing marks of these towns were a charter, a market, and a wall.

We can only hint here at the origin and rise of towns in the different parts of Europe and note that they greatly increased in economic stature, particularly in the thirteenth century. It was as places of industry and trade that they made their mark in an age when power was largely attached to the ownership of land. Site and positional factors help to explain why the urban settlement came into being and why it grew: towns commonly arose, for example, at bridging and navigable points on tidal rivers. An important social and economic factor in the siting and growth of cities was often provided by a royal residence, a monastic foundation, a bishop's palace, or a feudal castle.

A remarkable phase of town building is attested in Belgium and the Netherlands from the eleventh to the thirteenth century. Many towns, often laid out carefully to a plan, arose there for the first time under the protection of a seignorial castle or a religious foundation often, as at Brugge (Bruges), on a navigable river, or along a dike. In northern France a number of towns—Troyes on the Seine, Châlons-sur-Marne, Bar-sur-Aube—flourished during the twelfth and thirteenth centuries because their fairs drew foreign merchants by overland routes from as far afield as Italy, Egypt, Syria, and Persia. With the opening up (in 1317) of the sea route from Italy to the English Channel, such fairs as those of Brugge, Ghent, and Antwerp in Flanders took over the functions of these French fairs as entrepôts for a wide range of commodities of diverse origin.

The deliberate foundation of towns by royal or seignorial authorities, often for defensive purposes, accounts for other settlements, many of which failed to survive as such through lack of economic sinews. Winchelsea and Kingston-upon-Hull in England were thus founded by King Edward I (about 1300 A.D.), while in South France the so-called *bastide* towns (Villeneuve-sur-Lot is one) were laid out on a geometric plan in the thirteenth and fourteenth centuries. In South Germany the important regional capital of Munich (München) was a twelfth-century addition to a number of towns, such as Augsburg, which were originally of Roman foundation. Farther away, on the Great Russian plain, many of the fortified centers (*goroda*) of the Slavs grew into towns in the tenth century thanks to the political and mercantile energy of intruding Scandinavians.

Although certain periods stand out in the urban history of Europe, notably the later Middle Ages and the last two centuries, new towns were arising here and there at all times: one may note, as examples, the Channel port of Le Havre and the ducal capital of Mannheim in the Rhineland, respectively of seventeenth and eighteenth-century origin. Madrid was a creation of the sixteenth century, succeeding as capital of a united Spain the old Castilian capital of Toledo.

To the colonizing efforts of the Germans, notably in the four centuries after 900 A.D., was due the basic distribution of towns in Central and even East Central Europe. Sites already occupied by Slavs as local regional (or *gau*) centers or as fishing settlements were often selected, and some German place-names with Slav suffixes such as *in* and *zig* (e.g., Berlin and Leipzig) recall this association. The new German towns east of the Rhine were distributed differentially within the physically contrasted zones of North Central Europe. Some were established along the North Sea and the Baltic coasts and located at estuary heads, as Hamburg and Bremen; at the heads of bays, as Lübeck and Danzig (Gdansk); or in the shelter of lagoons, as Königsberg (Kaliningrad). Inland there were relatively few towns within the desolate heaths, woods, and marshes of the Baltic Heights, except where major rivers such as the Elbe and Oder cut gaps through the hills, on their way northwards. In the depressed and ill-drained zone farther south, some towns grew up on west-east river routes—Brandenburg on the Havel, Berlin on the Spree, Poznan (Posen) on the Warta among them. It was within the loess-covered foothill belt where the northern plains approach the Hercynian Mountains that town development (and settlement generally) was most marked in a zone of natural west-east communication: Dortmund, Magdeburg, Hanover (Hannover), Brunswick (Braunschweig), Leipzig, Cracow (Krakow) were among the well-known towns founded in this physically favored countryside.

Most of the towns of Central Europe in the later Middle Ages were in size comparable to the nucleated villages of today. Their function was to serve peasants making their way on foot, within a radius of six to thirteen miles. But a small proportion of these towns, well placed on land and water routes, like some of the cities of the Hanseatic League, throve remarkably in the last centuries of the Middle Ages as ports and trading places with widespread relationships.

Early engraved plans of European towns have much to tell about the expansion of medieval towns, as new areas were built up and enclosed by walls. Figures 5 to 8 show how four important towns of today appeared in the sixteenth century. They emphasize

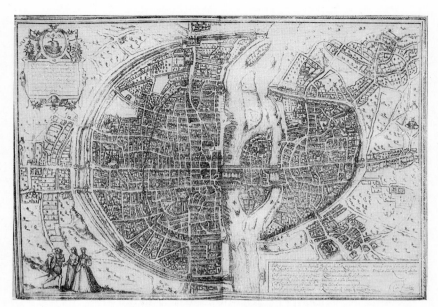

FIGURE 5. Paris in the sixteenth century.

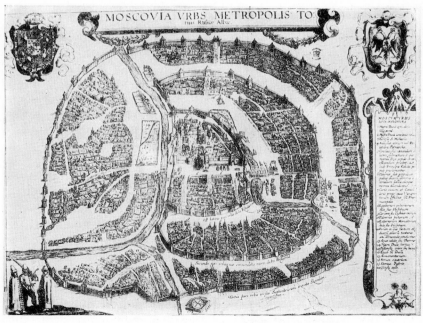

FIGURE 6. Moscow in the sixteenth century.

42

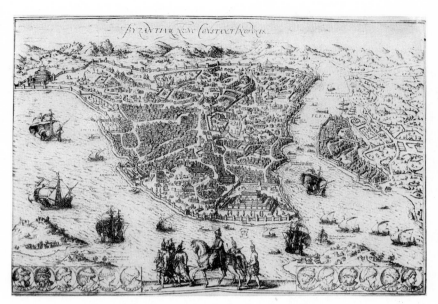

FIGURE 7. Constantinople in the sixteenth century.

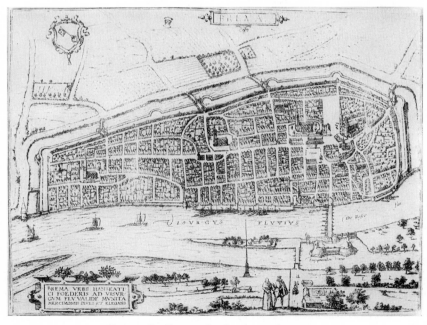

FIGURE 8. Bremen in the sixteenth century.

43

how small were even capital cities like Paris and Moscow (Moskva).
And although the old town walls, elaborately strengthened in the
sixteenth and seventeenth centuries to withstand cannon fire, have
usually disappeared to provide space for boulevards and buildings,
and few medieval buildings have survived, the old sites, as depicted in such plans, provided the nucleus around which European
towns have so widely grown, especially during the last hundred
years.

In present Europe the phenomenon of the "giant" city calls for
explanation. This is essentially a modern development related to
increasing population numbers and transport facilities of the nineteenth and twentieth centuries. In 1700 Europe had only 13 or
14 large towns, nearly all capital cities. London, with a population
of 959,000, was the largest city in Europe in 1801, and only some
19 others, with about 100,000 or more, could then be accounted
as of first magnitude. Chief of these were Paris and Constantinople, each with a population of about a half million. Some of the
largest cities of today are merely those of 1800 grown in size;
London, Berlin, Paris, Moscow, Leningrad, Vienna, Istanbul, and
Marseilles are well-known examples. Others owe their stature to
a development, often hand in hand with that of industry, only
during the last hundred years or less. Some illustrations will make
this point clear:

POPULATION OF SOME SELECTED TOWNS OF EUROPE—1800-1950

	1800	1850	1880	1920	1950
Essen	4,000	9,000	57,000	439,000	605,000
Duisburg	—	—	41,000	244,000	408,000
Düsseldorf	10,000	27,000	95,000	407,000	498,000
Munich	30,000	110,000	230,000	631,000	831,000
Rotterdam	53,000	90,000	148,000	511,000	620,000
Budapest [1]	54,000	178,000	371,000	926,000	1,600,000
Odessa	6,000	90,000 [2]	194,000	420,862 [3]	600,000
Belfast	40,000	87,000	208,000	387,000	443,000
Cardiff	2,000	20,000	83,000	200,000	243,000
Birmingham	71,000	242,000	437,000	919,000	1,184,000

[1] Until 1880 Buda and Pest were separately organized cities.
[2] 1858
[3] 1926

Clearly, behind the population figures for such towns lies an interesting chapter of civic history.

The Rural Settlements. Not the least striking of the marks
which social groups have written on the European landscape
throughout history are the varieties of rural settlement which
visibly symbolize man's appropriation, adaptation, and use of the

land. Not merely have these elements of the European country-side their own intrinsic interest but, in their varying forms and with their associated economies, they also help to create different landscape patterns. Basically different patterns of settlement are found in "champaign" or *champagne* and "enclosed" or *bocage* countryside, as they were traditionally described in England and France. One is characterized by large nucleated villages surrounded by unhedged arable fields in a largely treeless plain; the other by numerous small settlements—homesteads and hamlets—with small fields enclosed by quick-set hedges or dikes, dispersed over a country generally wooded in aspect. (See Figure 128, Chapter 8.)

Rural settlements today are the outcome of many successive phases of colonial activity and of changes in agricultural practice. Some settlements were spontaneous and some were planned; some of the stages are old and relatively obscure while others, notably those since the Agricultural Revolution of the eighteenth century, can be more clearly seen. The geographer's main task is to show the broad distribution of the settlement types and, looking behind the existing patterns, to attempt to explain their origin. While it would seem that the principal explanation of Europe's rural settlement map is to be sought in the agrarian technique and social organization of peoples at specific periods of history, it is evident that conditions of physical and biological geography are also relevant to the discussion.

The complications of the present-day rural settlement map of Europe spring—the point must be emphasized—from the many successive stages of colonization of which it presents the surviving features. Rural settlements appear in prehistory and may in some areas have fixed the sites of modern villages,[9] but it is to historical times that the student largely turns for the explanation of the contemporary map. Although the attribution of the communally organized open-field village with its surrounding unenclosed fields to Germanic influence cannot be accepted as generally and exclusively true, it is nevertheless clear that these features are revealed during the centuries which followed Germanic immigration and colonization in parts of Northwest Europe, notably in the English Lowlands, in northern and northeastern France, southern Belgium, Lorraine, and the Rhineland. In other areas which were also subject to early Germanic settlement, such as Kent (England), and central and southern Gaul, as well as in countries not so affected, such as

[9] A. Demangeon draws attention to the existence of Celtic villages in Roman Gaul and claims for these villages a Neolithic origin. See his *Géographie Economique et Humaine de la France* (Paris: Armand Colin, 1946), Vol. I, p. 187.

Wales and Brittany, settlements of the hamlet and homestead types, with early enclosed fields and *bocage* aspect, became prevalent. Indeed, in some places either Roman or pre-Roman Celtic settlements and agrarian systems survived as an element in shaping the countryside, despite German conquest and settlement. Certain settlement patterns and field systems also developed independently of influence from outside, for example, the communally organized villages and fields of Sardinia.

But if the photographic plate of Europe's rural settlement map begins to "develop" during the Dark Ages which followed the barbarian invasions of Europe, it clarifies and sharpens as further colonization of the later Middle Ages and of the last two centuries goes on. New branches are grafted onto the trunk of primary settlement as population grows and mastery is won over hitherto undeveloped areas of forest, marsh, moor, and steppe. Numerous "marsh" and "forest" villages are created by free-holding peasants and commonly set out in "linear" form along a dike, a stream, or a road, with individual holdings running back at right angles to the village axis. At the same time colonization by single homesteads is also made, as in the drained polder-lands of the Low Countries and in the woodlands of the English Weald. The increase in population in Western Europe, especially between the eleventh and thirteenth centuries, leads to the creation of many "daughter" settlements, i.e., homesteads or hamlets beyond the fields of the parent village. Some such settlements arise from "free lance" action, others—and this was the more usual reason—by the organized efforts of secular, ecclesiastical, and monastic landowners intent on the better exploitation of their lands. The new villages assumed many different forms.[10]

At a much later date, the Agricultural Revolution of the eighteenth century, which brought new possibilities of enhanced productivity from lands enclosed under individual ownership, became the cause of much new dispersed settlement, as tenants moved out from existing villages. The steppe lands of Southeast Europe, notably in the Ukraine and eastern Hungary, began in the second half of the eighteenth century to be transformed from an environment of seminomadic pastoral husbandry to one of settled villages, with cultivation as the basis of their mixed farming. As transportation facilities improved during the last two centuries, wealth won by urban dwellers in industry and commerce has also often been

[10] See R. E. Dickinson, "Rural Settlements in the German Lands," *Annals of the Association of American Geographers*, XXXIX (December, 1949), No. 4, pp. 239-63, for a discussion and illustrations.

used to modify the rural landscape through building of large country houses and the creation of gardens and parks.

The student of rural settlement in Europe should thus be much concerned with the history behind geography. This is true whether he confines attention to any one country, or indeed to part of one country. France still shows striking contrasts, clearly observed by Arthur Young [11] during the years 1787-89, between the *champagne* of large hedgeless villages in the north, the *bocage* of smaller dispersed settlements of the west and center, and the mixed, once mainly nucleated, settlement of its Mediterranean south. Britain, too, shows such contrasts of landscape types and complicated patterns of settlement woven throughout history. The county of Pembroke in Wales, for example, as a result of Anglo-Norman colonization, contains old nucleated villages with fields now enclosed in its southern lowland, and yet older dispersed Welsh settlements in its higher northern parts. Certainly many settlement types have established themselves without strict regard to physical geography. In the waterless limestone plateau of Causses, as in neighboring well-watered parts of the Massif Central, dispersed settlements prevail alike; in the Pays de Caux, despite broadly uniform physical conditions, settlements are dispersed in the west and concentrated in the east. Yet in the more detailed study of the sites, distribution and frequency of villages, correlations with physical conditions are often evident enough: for example, the alignment of villages along the scarp-foot and dip-slope edge of limestone plateaus, along the terraces of rivers, or on dry island sites in former fenland.

A workmanlike guide to the rural settlement map of Europe is provided by Demangeon's genetic classification of settlement types.[12] This provides no easy key, since it assumes much knowledge of rural history. Settlements as they now appear may have changed drastically in form, even in recent times: witness how in Denmark, in the Channel Islands, and in many parts of Ireland [13] and Scotland, present dispersed settlements replaced nucleated villages in the course of the nineteenth century.

Among nucleated villages Demangeon distinguishes three types on the basis of their origin. First, the communally organized "open-field village" which appears widely established in Western and

[11] Arthur Young, *Travels in France During the Years 1787, 1788, 1789* (2 vols.; Bury St. Edmunds, 1794).

[12] A. Demangeon, *Problèmes de Géographie Humaine* (3d ed.; Paris: Armand Colin, 1947), pp. 185-202.

[13] E. Estyn Evans, *Irish Heritage* (Dundalk, Eire: Dundalgan Press, 1942), p. 48.

Central Europe from the Dark Ages onwards, although it is claimed that some originated in the clearings and settlements of Neolithic times. The dwellings of a nucleated village grew up around some or all of the following features: church, manor house, inn, bridge, spring or well, pond and mill; only from this central area could the villagers have convenient access to their scattered holdings in the village fields. These lay open around the village and were cut into strips; its meadow and pastoral waste were communally used. The communal organization lasted on into the nineteenth century; the scattered strips have been by now mostly consolidated into compact units but only exceptionally, as in England, have they been fully enclosed. This farming was proudly acclaimed in the eighteenth century as *la grande culture*, for the open-field system was operated on some of the richest soils of the continent, notably those which overlie the loess although it included, too, some mountain valleys and heavy-clay lands.

The second type is the "village with contiguous fields." To this category belong the linear villages created in forest clearings and drained marshes in the later Middle Ages; from their origin, the lands adjacent to the village were divided into individually owned holdings. Such villages are found in the Low Countries and northwest Germany and in many forest clearings of the Hercynian highlands, for example, in the Black Forest and the Bohemian Forest.

The third type, the "village with dissociated fields," is best represented in Mediterranean Europe, where very large compact settlements perched on high sites, originally chosen in part at least for reasons of defense, stand aloof and distant from their fields, as indeed from their supplies of water. This settlement type is found in association with large estates in south Italy.

Similarly, four kinds of dispersed settlement can be distinguished. The first kind, the so-called "primary dispersion," was effected long ago. It is believed that much of the dispersed settlement of the Massif Central, of Cornwall and of Wales is of this type, as well as that of Norway, the language of which has no word for "village." The second is "intercalated dispersion," which refers to dispersed settlement made subsequently to nucleated settlement, by a process of "filiation" from existing villages as organized clearance of the waste took place. The fifteenth century witnessed much settlement of this kind in France as feudal lords and monastic houses conceded to peasants parts of their demesne. The third kind of dispersed settlement, "secondary dispersion," takes place when, for reasons of agricultural convenience, peasants move out from their village and settle by their lands: the *tanyas* of Hungary and the *bastides* of Provence resulted from such secondary dispersion. Much of the settlement pattern of England is of this type, following the enclosure of the common fields between the fifteenth and nineteenth centuries. Lastly, the "primary dispersion of recent date" can often be easily noted. From the nineteenth century onwards, greater transport facilities and superior water control and water supply permitted widespread dispersion of dwellings.

The Economy, Including Circulation

It has been claimed that man's work and the consequences of that work provide the real link between history and geography. The economy of Europe in all its regional variations and in its diverse visible features has its roots in the distant past, although the effects of the last hundred years stand out with particular clarity. The student's interest in the economic geography of Europe is rightly directed to the maps of its agriculture, its forests, its mines, its industrial concentrations, its transport patterns, and its seaports, which together show the effects on the face of the land of a concerted effort to exploit what Nature has provided.

The peculiar features of contemporary European economy—and notably its interregional and international trade relations—are discussed later in this book (Chapter 10). It is enough here to note its five broad characteristics. First, the industrial and commercial importance in the world of Western and Central Europe, based on the application of a large and skilled labor force to available natural resources in an area geographically well placed for, and historically conditioned to, oceanic commerce. Second, the continuing importance of agriculture throughout the whole continent and its higher relative importance in the broadening lowlands of East Central and Eastern Europe. Third, the well developed railroad network, notably in Western and Central Europe, and the continent's many major seaports related to the routes of world trade. Fourth, the economic contrast between Western and Central Europe on one hand and the remaining greater part of the continent on the other, where industrialization in its modern forms came later and has a more restricted place. Lastly, the political dichotomy between East and West, which has sharpened since the end of World War II and has clearly its economic aspect. The Soviet Communist world, beyond the "Iron Curtain," is now organized to achieve Soviet economic self-sufficiency, whereas the rest of the continent seeks and must seek trade both within the continent and with lands overseas in order to sustain an economy integrated into that of the whole world. In the brief discussion which follows, the reader is invited to consider a little of the history which lies behind Europe's present economic map. For "what is" has sprung from "what was."

Agriculture. Some reference has already been made to the distant beginnings of agriculture in Europe. Agriculture was indeed, in Neolithic days, a very different thing from what it has now become. Long subordinate to stock raising, carried on in small temporary fields, on light shallow soils with the aid of a digging stick or hoe, and in a setting dominated by forest, the earliest agriculture lay technologically remote from modern forms with large permanent fields, tractors, selected seeds, fertilizers, and heavy farm machinery. Yet, technological progress apart, and despite regional specialization in manufacturing industry and in mineral exploitation, Europe remains almost everywhere an area of agricultural productivity. It absorbs in agriculture the greater part of its labor force. European agricultural economy shows little of that broad standardization which characterizes large areas of North America where terms like "cotton belt" and "corn belt" introduce the student gently into the complications of agricultural geography. On the contrary, Europe's agriculture presents great regional and local variety in response to physical conditions of climate, soil, slope and other landform aspects, and to the differential energy and enterprise with which they have been used. In the size and organization of the farm unit, in the range and yield of crops, in the degree of "mixed farming," in the application of capital and mechanization, in the use of irrigation and of artificial fertilizers, in the emphasis on farming for subsistence or for "cash crops," in the manpower required per acre and in the output per man-hour obtained—in all these and in other ways European agriculture is diversified. But thanks to this diversity and thanks, too, to much intensity of farming, especially in Western and Central Europe, the continent produces most of its food, leads the world in the production of wheat, and grows a wide range of other cereal crops including even rice. It also produces some specialized products like olive oil, wine and essential oils; vegetable fibres like flax and hemp, though only a trifling amount of cotton; a wide range of fruits, including citrus; and much cattle fodder, sugar beet, and tobacco.

We may glance at two important background facts to the present-day agriculture in Europe. First, it represents the culmination of an age-long struggle to tame an environment little suited in its primitive state to large-scale agricultural development. The tillage of European soil is marked by prolonged and hard efforts which are devoted to forest clearance, marsh drainage, and soil improvement. Second, since it reflects the outcome of much scientific and technological progress, we should not ignore that outstanding phase of reorganization and improvement which is summed up as the Agricultural Revolution. This was effective at different times in different parts of the continent, between the seventeenth and the nineteenth centuries.

"The country . . . either bristles with woods or festers with swamps": this is how Tacitus described Central Europe in 98 A.D., through which, from the middle Rhine to the Carpathians, stretched the Hercynian Forest, as Caesar named it. The German peoples at first had no inclination to destroy the forests which harbored their divinities and protected their settled islands of farmland. Nor were the Slav and Hungarian peoples to the east, and the Scandinavian peoples to the north, inclined to pit their strength against the vast permanent woods which encompassed them and were useful in providing them with game, timber, fuel, honey, wax, and some marginal rough grazing. When the Germanic peoples had possessed themselves of and settled in former imperial lands, their energies were turned first to the recovery of cultivated fields which had been wasted and abandoned. Only later was the pioneer clearing of forested land undertaken, although, in England, Anglo-Saxons and Danes were quick to launch fresh attacks on the woodlands.

The reign of Charlemagne (768-814 A.D.), however, witnessed the felling of great stretches of primeval woodland, notably on both sides of the middle and lower Rhine, in the Main valley, and in Hesse. More land was needed for settlement, for stock raising, and for agriculture. In later centuries, as the Germans pushed eastwards their conquests and colonization under the leadership of Church and State, forest clearance was made in scale and is recalled by many of the names of their settlements, notably those containing the elements -rod, -reud, -ried, -rath, -rade, -brand, -hain, -scheid, and -grün. The later centuries of the Middle Ages witnessed much forest clearance in France, and Germans and Flemings were called into Hungary to fell trees in Transylvania. Some woodlands disappeared by "assarting," i.e., by clearings made around existing settlements. But great stretches of hunting country, much of it wooded, were carefully preserved by law to gratify the hunting tastes of emperors, kings, and lords. Forest clearance was not wholly deliberate—witness the destructiveness of goats grazing the rugged hills of the Mediterranean countries; sometimes the first cutting led to soil erosion and further destruction of woods, as in the Dauphiné province of France in the western Alps. Nor was forest clearance wholly due to agriculture, a fact attested by the inroads made by seafaring peoples of the Mediterranean Basin and by iron smelters, using charcoal for fuel, in such areas as the Harz, the Weald of England, and the Ural Mountains of Russia.

The clearance of the forests, together with the reclamation of marshland, heath and bog land, the drainage of lakes, and the ploughing up of the steppe—all contributed to the increase of the agricultural area. The increase of the arable area in response to the growth of population must have been continual. Figures available in the nineteenth century show the rapid increase, from 364 to 546 million acres between 1820 and 1880.

These changes markedly altered the face of the country. They produced too, notably in Western and Central Europe, a shortage of timber which in turn led to efforts to re-afforest suitable unused areas. By the Railway Age there were only a few countries, notably Norway, Sweden and Russia, which could offer timber for export. In Norway and Sweden, as in many other countries, forests are now "cropped," i.e., the annual cut is equated to annual replacement. Re-afforestation has meant much change in the character of such woodlands. Thus, in Germany, quickly growing conifers now dominate in afforested areas where formerly deciduous species, useful for grazing as well as timber, held sway.

In addition to the clearing of woodlands, the reclamation of marshland and sea-invaded lowland, and the drainage of lakes have contributed to the agricultural area of Europe. Hollanders and Flemings, with the encouragement of their counts, lords, bishops, and monastic foundations, took the lead in the attempt to make profitable the lands lying near or just below the high-tide water level. In the late Roman period the sea invaded coastal Flanders (where a layer of marine silt covers the Roman occupation level) and submerged large parts of Roman-occupied Holland and Zeeland, where large artificial mounds—terpen or werden—had been previously built to provide dry points for settlements.

The drainage of parts of maritime Flanders, Zeeland, and Holland and their settlement by a free and independent peasantry began early and was going on vigorously in the eleventh century. Further invasions by the sea during periods of high tides or violent storms in the later Middle Ages only intensified the struggle of the Dutch against the sea. Hollanders and Flemings carried their skill into marshlands beyond their own countries—to the English Fenland and to the estuarine lowlands of the Weser, Elbe, Oder, and Vistula. Cities and monastic houses in the North Italian plain similarly started in the twelfth century to drain the marshes which had formed largely through neglect of former Roman measures of water control. Nowadays, along the coasts and rivers of the Low Countries, the *polders*, as the drained and diked lowlands are called, are held safe for dairy cattle and crops with the aid of steam and electric pumps, which have largely replaced the traditional windmills. In recent decades part of the Zuider Zee has been reclaimed and its remainder, enclosed by a sea wall, has become the fresh-water IJsselmeer. The largest surviving ill-drained tract of the continent—a relic of the Great Ice Age—lies in the Pripet marshes of the Belorussian S.S.R., but the Soviet government has plans to effect their reclamation.

Present-day European agriculture owes to the past the expansion of its area of field, pasture, and meadow; it owes to the past also the major changes in agrarian organization and the applications of modern science and technique. The Mediterranean lands of the Roman Empire were the first to lead in the art of agriculture and, despite the shrinking of the agricultural area and the falling off in agricultural practice during the Dark Ages, Roman traditions largely survived, supplemented by Arab innovations—themselves in part based on Roman models—to inform the farming of Western and Central Europe. Within the Roman Empire the "two-course rotation," that is the autumn sowing of either wheat or barley followed by fallowing, was developed to meet the need, under the Mediterranean climate, of "dry farming." Great care was taken by successive plowings of the topsoil of the fallow field to retain moisture for the following crop. To supplement the hoe, the farmers of the Empire used the *aratrum*, a light, wheel-less plow, with or without a colter, although the *caruca*, a wheeled plow which was better adapted to heavy soils, appears to have been invented then in North Italy. Roman agriculture knew, and in some measure grew, fodder crops such as vetch, lucerne, alfalfa, and chick-pea, so valuable for winter feed, while the value of enriching land by the application of stable manure, pigeon dung, wood ash, and vegetable compost, was also well understood. The practice of transhumance, effected by the seasonal movement of sheep between high- and low-level pastures was well established in the Mediterranean lands of the Empire. Nor should we forget the remarkable success achieved by the Romans in irrigation and in the cultivation of the vine, the olive, and other fruit-bearing trees.

Western and Central Europe largely inherited these legacies but made their own modifications to suit the very different conditions of climate and landforms. It was a striking advance when tillage for crops superseded cattle raising as the dominant feature of the economy of the Germanic settlers in the west. It was not less striking when regular crop rotations, adapted to two or three fields, took the place of the former temporary cropping of burnt-over ground. The Roman *aratrum* long prevailed in use, although the *caruca*, much better suited to the northern lowlands and drawn by horses instead of oxen, was increasingly used at the end of the Middle Ages. Marling (i.e., liming) of arable fields was an important northern practice, although one limited by transport deficiencies to areas with easy access to supplies of chalk. But with all its success in expanding the agricultural area and the supply of food and raw materials (wool, flax, etc.), agriculture in Western Europe became in many respects inefficient and resistant to progressive change. What has been called "the Agricultural Revolution of the eighteenth century" was necessary to provide the possibility and means of advance. And, even then, East Central, Eastern, and parts of Mediterranean Europe were little affected: organization and practice there have only changed substantially during the last hundred years.

It is not surprising geographically, that many of the ideas of the new husbandry were derived from north Italy and the Low Countries. That these areas, and in particular Lombardy and Flanders, led in agricultural efficiency was due not so much to physical advantages—although soil and climate were broadly favorable—as to the economic stimulus long exerted on the surrounding countryside by numerous rich and populous cities. The Agricultural Revolution was most marked in England and parts of northern France. It largely brought to an end the old communally organized fields and pastures of the open-field system, led to some consolidation of the strip holdings in the fields and, notably in England, to much new enclosure of fields by hedgerows, walls, and ditches. Individual ownership or holding of farmland brought new initiatives and techniques. It became possible to abolish the fallow field by scientific rotations and, at the same time, to grow winter fodder (roots and clover) for livestock. Especially in England, capital was increasingly applied to agriculture for the production of more grain and meat. Transport by road, river, and canal was much improved. Poor soils were found to be not always useless: by heavy manuring, for example, the sands of central Belgium have become little distinguishable from the intrinsically richer marine clays farther north. By scientific stock breeding cattle doubled, and sheep trebled in weight in the course of a century. The pressure of population, much of which was engaged in industry, was the economic stimulus behind the Agricultural Revolution.

The Americas made their contribution of plants which have now become long established staples in Europe. Chief among these were the potato, corn (maize), and tobacco. The potato was first grown in gardens and later became a field crop. Although at first regarded by peasants as fodder rather than as human food, it became also a foodstuff of great importance, above all in Ireland, and was well adapted to the north European lowlands. The sugar beet is a nineteenth-century innovation, the cultivation of which has been deliberately favored by European governments in order to secure their independence of seaborne supplies of cane sugar in time of war. By the middle of the last century it was being grown in northern France, Belgium, and throughout the loess belt of Germany, Bohemia, Moravia, Hungary, and southern European U.S.S.R.

We may conclude this brief sketch of the antecedents of present European agriculture by noting how agrarian changes, designed above all to break up large estates for peasant holdings, occurred in East Central Europe (except in Hungary) after World War I. The establishment of "collective farming" in the U.S.S.R. brought radical changes, including mechanization, to the Soviet countryside. The extension of this system to the Soviet satellite countries of East Central Europe is now in progress, following the break-up of surviving large estates.

Industry. The numerous industries of Europe may be distinguished into two groups: the extractive and the manufacturing. The extractive industries include mining and quarrying, fishing and whaling, and lumbering, the localization of all being determined by the facts of economic geology or geography. To this category of industries should doubtless be added industrial developments of this century, such as the generation of hydroelectric power and the extraction of nitrogen from the air. The manufacturing industries are legion and, in so far as in most of them goods are made by machines rather than by hand, the term might appear literally misleading. On the one hand are a wide range of light industries, including luxury industries, where the skill of the craftsman is still all-important: French wines, Parisian gowns, Harris tweeds, Belgian lace, and German wooden toys, to name a few. On the other hand are those major industries on which modern industrialized states depend, where power-driven machinery is essential and large-scale plant usual—industries such as steel-making, heavy chemicals, engineering, and shipbuilding.

Industry in Europe is no new phenomenon. In the Middle Ages there were already both urban and rural areas where industry played a dominant part in economy—for example Flanders, with its many cities engaged in making woolen and linen textiles, the Harz, the Thuringian Forest and Siegerland with their iron mines and smelters, and the English West Country, with its worsted manufacture based on the supply of water and of water power from its streams. The novelty resides in the fact that modern industry, using power-driven machinery, much capital, and a large labor force, is operated on a grand scale usually in and around towns and tends to group itself geographically within specific areas. In many parts of Europe today "industrial belts" must engage the interest of the student of geography.

The reasons for this localization spring from considerations of many kinds. The presence of local supplies of fuel and power—especially coal and hydroelectricity—is often the main explanation. The occurrence of either mineral ores or coal seams, in surface outcrops or at accessible levels below the surface, no less clearly explains the localization of mines and quarries and of related industries. The outsize towns like London, Berlin, Milan, Vienna, Paris, Moscow, and Leningrad are big industrial regions for quite different reasons. They provide ample labor, large markets, good transport facilities, and can with ease utilize electrical energy. Some industrial areas find their explanation in history, and their continued importance illustrates what can be best termed "historical momentum." Thus Lancashire, favored by the abundant soft water and supplies of wool from the Pennine moorlands, was traditionally engaged in the manufacture of linen and woolen textiles. But, following a start made in the seventeenth century, it has become a specialized area for cotton textiles, using American cotton imported via Liverpool, and steam-powered machinery. In contrast, other areas which were famous in the past for particular products, failed to compete successfully when coal replaced water for motive power and charcoal for fuel. This happened, for example, to the English West Country, where the manufacture of Witney blankets survives to recall its more famous past, and to the English forests of Dean and the Weald, where iron was dug, smelted, and forged into implements and weapons of war down to the end of the eighteenth century.

We must allude here, also, to the Industrial Revolution which, like that in agriculture, revitalized industry and gave it vastly enlarged scope. The Industrial Revolution had its home in Britain where geographical, economic, political, and social conditions favored, indeed stimulated, industrial progress. In the eighteenth century Britain had built up overseas trade, based on sea power and imperial territories, and was amassing capital. The depletion of her forests focused attention on her resources of coal, of all the chief varieties, some of which were well located for shipment by sea and many of which contained seams of iron ore. Her labor supply was inadequate to keep pace with the growth of her trade in domestic staples—notably textiles, and this presented a stimulus to the invention of machines which could economize on labor. Certainly the application of the scientific ideas to industrial technique, together with the ingenuity of engineers and other craftsmen, were responsible for many remarkable inventions which transformed the organization, scale, and cost of industrial production. Among many triumphs of inventiveness were the steam engine, first used for pumping water from mines, the "spinning jenny" and new weaving looms, the use of coke for smelting iron ore, the Bessemer and Gilchrist-Thomas steel-making processes which enormously increased the range of production and utilization of steel, and the more recent revolutionary developments in the chemical industries. On the basis of these and other technological innovations, notably in the field of transport, Britain became in the nineteenth century the "workshop of the world."

The geographical effects of this industrial activity are here relevant. First, it resulted in the rapid growth of Britain's industrial regions, marked by their high densities of population and high degree of urbanization, by their relation to coal fields—for in the last century even more than today, coal was industrially king—and by their dependence on overseas trade. This overseas trade brought in essential raw materials such as cotton, flax, silk, and wool and, increasingly after 1870, foodstuffs (above all, wheat and meat). The second geographical effect was the spread of the new ideas to the continent where, after an appreciable time lag and in suitable areas, especially on coal fields, the present industrial regions began to take shape.

The industrial map of Europe shows a highly populated belt extending from the Pennines and South Wales in Britain to the Ural Mountains and the Donets Basin in the U.S.S.R., where rocks of Hercynian folding are still exposed. These rocks were originally rich in economic minerals, although some of the former lodes are now worked out. With them are associated considerable coal deposits of the Carboniferous period, which helps to explain the location and character of industrial regions engaged mainly in mining, smelting, steel-making, heavy chemicals, and engineering. Within this diagonal belt across the continent lie the British industrial areas, some of which were just mentioned, the Franco-Belgian coal field, the Luxembourg and German Westphalian industrial regions, that of Western Bohemia in Czechoslovakia, the Upper Silesian coal field of Poland, the Donets coal field and industrial region (mainly in Ukrainian S.S.R.), and lastly, the industrial region which bestrides the central and southern Urals. In Iberia, too, where Hercynian structures also occur, a wealth of minerals—tungsten, copper, mercury, and iron, together with some coal in the north—testifies again to the link between geological history and economic geography, although these resources have not as yet become the basis of any considerable industrialization.

Other industrial regions of Europe are explained by considerations which are different from that of the Hercynian coal basins. For example, the extensive lignite deposits of north Germany, which are of the Tertiary period, have provided in recent decades an abundant low-grade fuel for many important industries, including chemicals, as in the middle Elbe region of Saxony. Another distinct category of industrial region includes large seaports such as Hamburg, Rotterdam, Marseille, and Glasgow, well placed for the economical import of raw materials and the distribution of their manufactured products. Shipbuilding, and the many associated industries which it involves, have established themselves at certain estuarine and seacoast sites, near supplies of coal and steel: Clyde-side below Glasgow in Scotland, Tyneside below Newcastle, and Hartlepool on the Wear in Northeast England are outstanding centers. There remain, also, the newer industrial regions which draw their power resources from hydroelectricity.

Hydroelectric power in Europe is derived—to an estimated 86 per cent—from its glaciated lands. Thus metallurgical, chemical, engineering, and other industries of the continent are not confined to areas with accessible supplies of solid fuel. Hydroelectric undertakings, of course, call for a substantial capital investment and usually a considerable engineering effort. The relief features of a landscape eroded by ice, such as steep valley slopes and high-level lake basins, coupled with an abundant supply of running water from rainfall and snow melt, have provided the means for a number of countries deficient in coal to play their part, if modestly, in modern industry. Italy, Sweden, Norway, Finland, Switzerland, Austria, and Spain owe their industrial activity largely to "white coal." In 1950, hydroelectricity indeed amounted to the following proportions of their consumption of electrical energy: Norway, Switzerland, and Sweden virtually 100 per cent; Italy and Finland 90 per cent; Austria and Spain 80 per cent. France is now dependent equally on hydro and thermal power. The Soviet Union, which produces less coal than it needs and imports some from Poland, continues to exploit the very considerable hydroelectric potentialities which exist in its glaciated northern lands, in the Caucasus Mountains, and in its rivers. Nevertheless, only 17 per cent of its electrical energy consumption is derived from hydroelectric power.

Electricity supplies 25 per cent of all the forms of energy consumed in Europe outside the U.S.S.R., and of this three fifths are produced in thermal plants. Even so, the use of "white coal" explains the growth of some of the industrial areas which are aloof from coal fields. It explains, also, the dispersion of industrial undertakings, since electricity can be cheaply distributed over short distances, and the avoidance of the landscape features of the "black country" which disfigure so many industrial areas located on coal fields. Witness as illustrations the semirural location of industries in the Swedish Midlands, the specialized clock- and watchmaking in the Swiss Jura, and the metallurgical industries at Zaporozhe and Dnepropetrovsk on the lower Dnieper in Ukrainian S.S.R. While "white coal" is mainly used in light industries, it is particularly useful in a group of industries which make very heavy demands on electrical power: electro-chemicals, electric smelting and refining, nitrate-making by extraction of nitrogen from the air, and synthetic rubber. Thus Norway has been able to develop the manufacture of nitrates, the refining of copper, and an aluminum industry based on imported bauxite.

While the industries of Europe depend primarily on its generous endowment of coal and lignite, which are widely distributed though often difficult to obtain, to these must be added its hydroelectric capacity, and its petroleum supplies, in large part imported. Outside the U.S.S.R., which has many important fields (Baku, North Caucasus, Volga-Urals ["Second Baku"], Pechora, and others), Europe's oil production—to which Romania contributes most—accounts for only one sixth of its consumption.

Thanks to its wide command of mechanical energy and a long tradition of industrial skill, Europe has achieved a very high place in industrialization. It has more than recovered from the damage and setbacks caused by World War II. Europe outside the Soviet Union had raised its industrial production 26 per cent above the 1938 level by 1950, although, owing to better utilization and economies, its energy consumption had increased by only 12 per cent. Whereas in 1938 Germany and the United Kingdom both led industrially (each accounted for about 30 per cent of the energy consumption of Europe outside the U.S.S.R.), the United Kingdom now leads, with Western Germany second and France third. The Soviet Union, whose available supply of energy is about half that of the rest of Europe, claims a 73 per cent increase above its 1940 level of production in 1950, when its first postwar five-year plan was successfully completed.

Broadly, it is true to say that industrialization has spread eastwards in Europe during the last hundred years and that the most recent developments in basic industries, those of the U.S.S.R. in its Asiatic territories, give the greatest promise of continued expansion. While the U.S.S.R. is largely self-sufficient in metallic and nonmetallic minerals and in many other raw materials—natural rubber, wool, jute, and tin appear to be its chief deficiencies—the rest of Europe is more dependent on seaborne supplies.

Iron ore supplies are as a whole insufficient, although France (from her Lorraine mines), Sweden, Spain, and Britain are big producers. The European countries command large supplies of bauxite (in France and Hungary) and appreciable amounts of copper, zinc, mercury, sulphur, ferro-alloys, and salt, but variously depend on imports for many metals and other industrial raw materials: aluminum, tin, nickel, chrome, lead, copper, manganese, wool, cotton, jute, and natural rubber. Most of the industrialized countries west of the U.S.S.R. and south of Fenno-Scandia need also to import timber. Scientific and technological progress, however, continues to provide new industrial products, of which artificial fibers and plastics are two striking illustrations.

Commerce. Leaving aside a discussion of trade within state-territories, which of course vividly reveals the regional differences of climate, terrain, and economy, we shall glance here at the historical geography of the interregional trade within Europe and at Europe's overseas commerce.

During many centuries—until the Columbian era—Europe's trading activities were confined largely within its own limits. The chief traders of Europe were first to be found in cities of the coastlands of the Mediterranean Basin; Phoenicians, Greeks, and Romans did not venture very much outside this virtually tideless sea. So, during the Middle Ages, the Mediterranean "lake" proved the main trade route of Europe with cities like Constantinople (Istanbul), Venice, Pisa, and Genoa taking the lead through importing by overland and sea routes valuable goods from the monsoon lands of Asia and exporting the high-grade manufactures from their own workshops.

The rise of Northwestern Europe in the centuries which followed the creation of Charlemagne's empire was reflected in the activities of industrial and commercial cities in that area. It made the interconnecting Baltic and North seas another highway for shipping their local produce, i.e., fish, salt, timber, flax, wool, and finished textiles. Between the two parallel maritime axes of trade —the southern and the northern—overland routes carried traders and goods. In 1317, the Venetians, having built sailing ships with oars (galleys) strong and mobile enough to face the troubled tidal waters beyond the Strait of Gibraltar, opened up direct trade by sea to the ports of Southampton, London, and Brugge.

As the limits of the known world expanded during the Age of Discovery, the positional values of the two inland seas of Europe— the Baltic and the Mediterranean—decreased, for in the sixteenth century geographical knowledge, advances in shipbuilding, new navigation aids, and commercial enterprise broadened the theater of trade by use of the ocean highways and created an all-sea route via the Cape to India and the East Indies. The riches of Central and South America and of the Indies were the chief lure. Trade followed the flag, for the power of the state was fundamental for the protection of shipping as well as for the securing of territory, trade depots, and privileges in distant lands. In this oceanic phase, it was the nations fronting the open sea which were the first to exploit the new opportunities, not only in trade, but also in conquest, settlement, and proselytization of the Christian faith; in turn Portuguese, Spaniards, Dutch, English, and French turned to overseas commerce. The first two have long lost the leading position which they earned by their early achievements in sea-borne exploration. The Dutch, as the "waggoners of Europe," had their commercial hey-day in the seventeenth century. Britain, which had played during the Middle Ages a mainly passive role in overseas trade, achieved, thanks to its naval strength and empire-building, a leading position among the commercial states of the world. Others like Norway (with a large merchant tonnage), Germany, and Italy (before World War II) joined much more recently in large-scale maritime commerce.

The interregional trade in Europe naturally arose from the variety of products which were available in different parts of the continent, partly because of climatic contrasts; now it is much reduced by the divergent politico-economic policies of the Soviet Union and the West. It is enough here to recall some of the distinctive products of particular countries and areas: the iron ore of Sweden, Lorraine, and Spain; the timber and timber products, especially of Sweden and Finland; the olive oil, tobacco, citrus and dried fruits of Mediterranean countries; the early vegetables and flowers (*primeurs*) of Italy, Brittany, and Mediterranean France; the wines of France, Spain, Portugal, and Hungary; Swiss watches and watch parts; Swedish electrical equipment; British machinery, transport equipment, tin plate, and textiles; French, Dutch, and Swiss cheeses and the high-class dairy produce of Denmark; and German capital goods and chemicals. On purely geographical ground, it might have been expected that Eastern and Western Europe, since the former is relatively well-wooded and largely agricultural in its economy and the latter is more emphatically industrial, would have engaged as in the past in a profitable trade in complementary products. But Soviet policy, which is now extended to cover its many satellite states in East Central Europe and the occupied areas of Germany and of Austria, aims at diverting the trade of these areas from the West to itself and also at achieving, behind the "Iron Curtain," a high degree of economic self-sufficiency. This policy discourages the interregional East-West trade in Europe, although the latter has not wholly ceased. The attempt to link the trade of the U.S.S.R. and that of its satellites should in some measure succeed, for the former has command of many valuable commodities which it can make available to the latter, as it deems expedient: cotton, flax, and hemp; manganese and chrome ores; apatites for phosphate fertilizers; some petroleum; platinum and gold. In exchange for these products it can hope to obtain, for example, machinery and textiles from Czechoslovakia and coal from Poland.

The overseas trade of Europe, which commands virtually one half of the world's ocean-going merchant tonnage, is largely in the hands of the western countries. One feature of this trade, which is world-wide, derives from the fact that many states, i.e., Britain, France, the Netherlands, Belgium, and Portugal, still have political dependencies overseas which afford sheltered markets for their metropolitan products. Another feature, especially since 1945, has been the increasing volume of trade with the United States. Of the European exports to the United States, Britain supplies more than one third, as compared with one fourth in 1938 when Germany was a substantial exporter. The American market is valuable for countries with various surplus raw materials, ores, and semi-processed goods. Such are wood pulp and furs from the Baltic countries, Greek and Turkish tobacco, and Yugoslavia's copper ore. But it receives, too, some highly reputed and specialized products from the industrial countries of Western Europe. Central and South America also remain an important field for trade, especially for Great Britain, but this particular trade has relatively decreased to the advantage of the United States.

Circulation. In this age of fast travel and speedy communication we are not likely to underrate the importance of routes of all kinds—by land, by sea, by inland waterways, and by air—"as a sustenance without which organized society would be impossible." In the earliest days of human colonization in Europe, it is true, men used the route-ways left open by nature: the inner seas, the river valleys, the unwooded or lightly wooded steppe. Travel by horse or horse-drawn coach and transport by pack horse, by sailing ship, and by river craft long provided the best means of movement until the inventions of the last century brought the steamship and the locomotive. These were supplemented, in turn, through application of the internal combustion engine, by the motor car and the airplane. The student of the human geography of Europe must concern himself with those man-made elements of the countryside which reflect social efforts to promote circulation and at the same time interpenetrate the region. The route patterns of European countries present today features etched on the surface of the land by many past and sometimes remote periods of history. And although the railroads, the motor highways, and the navigable rivers and canals are now the paramount means of travel and of shipment of goods, the prehistoric ridge-way and stretches of Roman road (in some areas still in use) survive to remind us of earlier geographies of circulation.

Trade and travel do not depend merely on routes; they are sensitive to political conditions. Roman roads, built by legionary and auxiliary troops, gave Europe, south of the Danube and west of the Rhine, its first system of engineered roads which, thanks to the efficiency of Roman government, served the needs of soldiers, merchants, officials, and others. These highways, firm and cambered though of course narrow, were less useful after the collapse of centralized imperial government. Even though they suffered from neglect, they largely survived to serve the varied needs of governments and of the two Christian Churches—the one organized from Rome and the other (after 395 A.D.) from Constantinople.

The seaways—and this meant chiefly the Mediterranean—suffered no less from the fall of Rome and the subsequent advance (in the seventh century) of the Arabs into the Mediterranean Basin. Although the East Roman Empire, centered on Constantinople, maintained some show of sea power, it was not until the rise of the Italian trading cities that the Mediterranean came to flourish as a commercial thoroughfare. In the same way it was the political and naval strength of the northern cities of the Hanseatic League which opened the Baltic and North seas to trade. Although Roman trade had spread into parts at least of the Baltic, Ptolemy (second century A.D.) had mapped Scandinavia as an island. The new importance of the Baltic Sea was marked when Adam of Bremen, in the eleventh century, described its maritime entries and the peninsular character of Scandinavia. A few centuries later, such was the stature of the Baltic in European commerce and politics that it was carefully portrayed in a semipictorial map by Olaus Magnus.

Already in the later Middle Ages a system of roads, aligned roughly east-west and north-south, brought into relationship the various parts of the continent and its neighboring seas. Naturally, the contemporaneous distribution of population, cities, ports, and economic activities defined the starting points and goals of routes, the volume of traffic which they carried, and their relative importance. We may note how many Alpine passes carried well-frequented thoroughfares and linked the ports and industrial cities of North Italy (and also Rome, the seat of the Pope) with France, Germany, and the Balkan Peninsula. In the western Alps, the Great St. Bernard and the Mt. Cenis passes, approached via Turin, were preferred. The St. Gotthard Pass, its northern approach facilitated by the building of a bridge and valley road in the thirteenth century, joined Milan to the Rhine at Basel (Basle) and the Danube at Ulm. Farther east, the Brenner Pass became the principal link between the Italian and German lands of the Holy Roman Empire and for traders between North Germany and North Italy. In the eastern Alps, several passes carried roads from Venice toward the Drava and Sava rivers, along which passed roads leading to the Balkan Peninsula. The laden mule and ass afforded the means of transport. Thanks to modern engineering, the railroads, using long tunnels, can now ignore the passways, although they must seek the easiest gradients provided by the valleys.

Another interesting north-south route across the continent, which then served the needs of European commerce and now affords only internal circulation, was based on navigable rivers and portages. It was opened up in the ninth century across Russia from the Gulf of Finland to the Black and Caspian seas. In part, this route was an attempt to find an alternative to sea and land routes in the western basin of the Mediterranean which were obstructed by Moslem power. The importance of the new route lay in the fact that Constantinople was its chief southern terminal and that, as a result, Russia derived therefrom its Orthodox or Greek Christianity, its alphabet, some architectural influences, and perhaps too, some imperialistic notions.

In some parts of the continent the medieval road system was largely that bequeathed by Rome, in others new routes were laid out in the course of conquest and colonization. Thus in the Balkan lands of the Byzantine Empire the major routes which made government possible were still those which linked Constantinople with Salonika and Durrës (Durazzo) on the Adriatic coast and with Belgrade on the Danube via Sofia; another route led from Salonika to Belgrade via Niš. In each case the road was closely related to valley-ways and structural depressions. But in Central and East Central Europe, largely as a result of German conquests, new roads were built to give access from the Rhine and Danube cities. Figure 9, based on an early topographic map made about the year 1570, shows that an effective route system existed in this part of the continent. Among the roads there shown, that which led eastward from Brugge, Antwerp, and Cologne to Leipzig, Breslau (Wroclaw), and Cracow, the medieval capital of Poland, is of special interest. It follows one of the major lines of movement across the continent at all periods, and is aligned below the northern edge of the middle mountain zone.

The lack of west-east roads in the North German Plain, except for the Hamburg-Lübeck-Stettin-Danzig road, reflects the scantier settlement and lower value of these lands of glacial deposition. The route centers, too, arouse interest: Frankfurt and Würzburg (both on the Main), Nuremberg (Nürnberg) and Prague (Praha), Leipzig, Breslau, and Vienna. The principal rivers supplemented the land routes in no small measure: the Rhine, Elbe, Oder, Vistula, and Danube all played a part.

Figure 9 may be compared with Figure 10, which depicts the principal highways of Europe in 1850, at a time when the railroad network was at an early stage of its development. Paris was clearly *the* center of the French road system which had been re-created in the eighteenth century, although in the Roman period Lyon was the route center and Rheims, nearer the Rhine frontier, was the chief route focus of northern Gaul. London occupies a similar position as the chief focus of the routes of England. The closeness of the network of roads in Central Europe is very striking, testifying *inter alia* to its middle position within the continent. No less striking is the paucity and wide spacing of the roads in Southern, Eastern, East Central and Northern Europe—which still obtain.

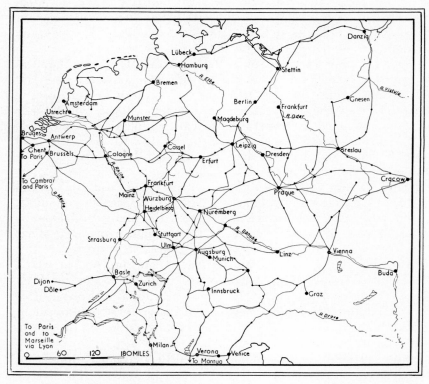

FIGURE 9. Road system of Central Europe about 1570.

Waterways, too, contribute much to the transport geography of the continent. After the improvement of rivers by engineering works, the construction of canals, especially in the eighteenth century, was hailed as a triumph in man's control over Nature. They provided water connections between navigable points on rivers and indeed could be built in watershed areas where no navigable rivers existed at all. Above all, they were designed to carry bulk cargoes—coal, stone, fertilizers, ore, timber—and, until the advent

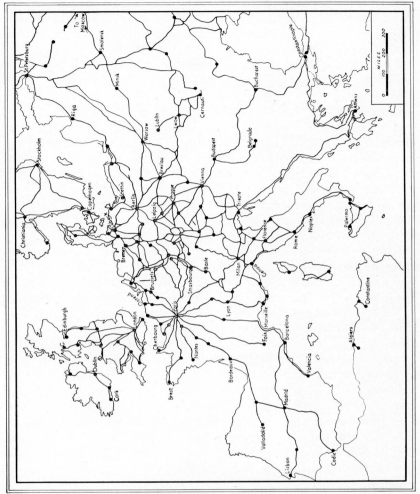

FIGURE 10. Post roads of Europe in 1850.

in turn of railroad and motor transport, proved indispensable, notably in the Netherlands and in Britain.

While the railroad and motor truck could and did efficiently usurp the functions of many canals, these have by no means lost importance. In countries like the Netherlands, canals serve more than one purpose. German canals provide not only routes (as in Westphalia) for ore and coal shipments to the Rhine and Ems, but also the means of internal distribution of goods (in north Germany). Moscow is known as "the Port of Five Seas" thanks to the waterways which link it to the Baltic, White, Black, Azov, and

Caspian seas. In England, the Manchester Ship Canal makes inland Manchester a port for ocean-going shipping, while the commercial and strategical importance attached to the Kiel Canal needs no elaboration here.

Of the great rivers of the continent, the Rhine and Volga carry the largest tonnages of goods. The Rhine, which admits fleets of large barges far upstream, owes its importance primarily to its proximity to the Rhine-Westphalian industrial region and to the Dutch commercial cities near its outlets. The Volga, which lies wholly within one state territory, that of the U.S.S.R., carries upstream heavy cargoes of oil, salt, fish, and grain, which can reach as far as Moscow with the aid of the Moscow Canal. The Danube, "the king of rivers," as Napoleon called it, although its navigation was improved by engineering works at the Iron Gate in 1899, today plays a humble role. Although by a Convention of 1921 it retained the legal status of "an international river" open to the navigation and trade of all nations, access to it is now denied to nonriparian states by the U.S.S.R., which borders one of the channels of the river's delta and, through its satellites, dominates the river from the Black Sea to Linz—except for the Yugoslav section.

Europe, owing to its central position in relation to the land areas of the earth, to its indented coastline, and to modern engineering works, boasts many of the great seaports of the world. One broad geographical contrast may be noted here—that between ports on navigable tidal rivers, such as London, Antwerp, and Hamburg, where docks must be provided with lock-gates because of the tidal range, and those of the almost tideless Mediterranean Sea, where modern docks offer access at all times and lie aloof from the deltaic accretions of the rivers. Note, in particular, Marseille, Trieste, Genoa, Naples, Barcelona, and Salonika. The great international port of Rotterdam, related to the Rhine, has improved access by canalization.

Finally, we may allude to the beginnings of railroad building born of the Industrial Revolution and the need for faster bulk shipment of heavy freight. Figure 11 shows that, by 1850, Great Britain already had a network of railroads, closest in the English Lowlands. Across the English Channel, the Low Countries and northern France had already built many connected lines, but to the north and east of Germany and in Mediterranean Europe, railroad construction had scarcely begun. In Russia, only the line from St. Petersburg (Leningrad) to the Tsar's summer palace at Tsarkoye Selo (opened in 1838) and the first stretch of the St. Petersburg-Moscow railroad had been constructed. Although many

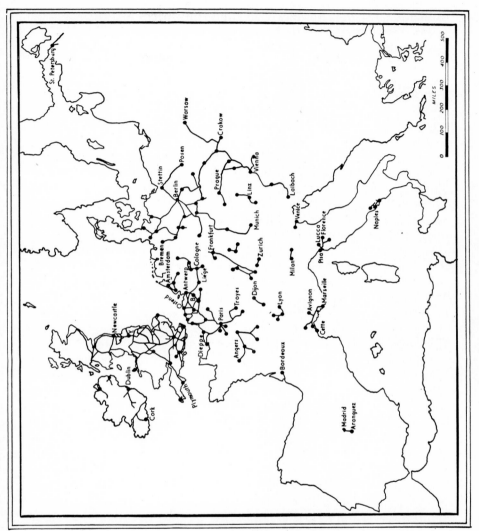

FIGURE 11. The European railway pattern in 1850.

69

railroads must now be drawn on the blank spaces of this map, the network of lines remains relatively open outside Western and Central Europe.

Conclusion

The present is but the past flowing into the future. The geography of Europe has been fashioned during several millenniums. Changes are presently in operation and will continue. This chapter will have achieved its purpose if it has convinced the student that geography, in its concern with place, cannot neglect time. There is no finality in the human value which attaches to the areas of Europe. The value attaching to land changes, as ideas and technology change. While we note the high densities of population and the high degree of industrialization and commerce which characterize the more peninsular and more physically varied western part of the continent, we should not fail to recognize that the larger and physically more uniform eastern part of the continent has developed belatedly and should economically progress further. We should not fail to note, also, that in the east, Europe has only conventional limits and that in Siberia, Kazakhstan, and Central Asia it has projected its culture into Asia in the guise of Soviet Communism and modern technology.

Above all, the study of the history behind geography underlines how little unity, except in the formal sense of territorial continuity, the term "Europe" connotes. We have glanced at some of the past processes which explain the social and territorial divisions of the continent—its many tongues, nations, and states—which clearly reflect the earlier localism of human groups in days of slow and difficult travel and their close attachment to the soil. So far, political unity over large areas of Europe has been achieved only temporarily and by the coercive efforts of would-be master states. Soviet power and Soviet policy have produced, since 1945, some trend towards unity, if only within two opposed eastern and western segments of the continent. The unity of Europe is not yet.

BIBLIOGRAPHY

A. BOOKS IN ENGLISH

CHADWICK, HECTOR MUNRO. *The Nationalities of Europe and the Growth of National Ideologies.* London: Cambridge University Press, 1945.

CHILDE, V. G. *Prehistoric Migrations in Europe.* Cambridge: Harvard University Press, 1951.

CLAPHAM, J. H. *The Economic Development of France and Germany 1815-1914,* 4th ed. London: Cambridge University Press, 1948.

CLAPHAM, J. H., and POWER, EILEEN (eds.). *The Agrarian Life of the Middle Ages*. ("The Cambridge Economic History," Vol. I.) London: Cambridge University Press, 1941.

CLARK, J. G. D. *The Mesolithic Settlement of Northern Europe*. London: Cambridge University Press, 1936.

COON, CARLETON S. *The Races of Europe*. New York: The Macmillan Co., 1939.

DICKINSON, R. E. *The West European City*. London: Routledge & Kegan Paul, Ltd., 1951.

DOMINIAN, L. *The Frontiers of Nationality and Language in Europe*. New York: Henry Holt & Co., Inc., 1917.

DOPSCH, ALFONS. *The Economic and Social Foundations of European Civilization*. Condensed by E. Patzelt and translated by M. G. Beard and N. Marshall. New York: Harcourt Brace & Co., Inc., 1937.

EAST, W. GORDON. *A Historical Geography of Europe*, 4th ed. New York: E. P. Dutton & Co., Inc., 1950.

HUXLEY, J. S., and HADDON, A. C. (eds.). *We Europeans*. London: Jonathan Cape, Ltd., 1935.

MORANT, G. M. *The Races of Central Europe. A Footnote to History*. New York: W. W. Norton & Co., Inc., 1940.

PIRENNE, H. *Economic and Social History of Medieval Europe*. Translated by I. E. Clegg. London: George Routledge & Sons, Ltd., and Kegan Paul, Trench, Trubner & Co., Ltd., 1949.

POSTAN, M. M., and HABAKKUK, H. J. (eds.). *Trade and Industry in the Middle Ages*. ("The Cambridge Economic History," Vol. II, ed. by M. M. Postan and E. E. Rich.) London: Cambridge University Press, 1952.

SAUER, C. O. *Agricultural Origins and Dispersals*. New York: The American Geographical Society, 1952.

WHITTLESEY, DERWENT. *Environmental Foundations of European History*. New York: Appleton-Century-Crofts, Inc., 1949.

WRIGHT, JOHN K. *The Geographical Basis of European History*. New York: Henry Holt & Co., Inc., 1928.

ZEUNER, F. E. *Dating the Past: An Introduction to Geochronology*, 2d ed. London: Methuen & Co., Ltd., 1950.

B. BOOKS IN FOREIGN LANGUAGES

ANCEL, J. *Manuel Géographique de Politique Européenne* (Manual of the Political Geography of Europe). Paris: Librairie Delagrave, 1936-45.

BLOCH, M. *Les Caractères Originaux de l'Histoire Rurale Française* (The Original Character of French Rural History). Cambridge: Harvard University Press, 1931.

DEMANGEON, A. *Problèmes de Géographie Humaine* (Problems of Human Geography), 3d ed. Paris: Librarie Armand Colin, 1947.

DION, R. *Essai sur la Formation du Paysage Rural Français* (Essay on the Formation of the French Countryside). Tours: Arrault et Cie, 1934.

MEILLET, A. *Les Langues dans l'Europe Nouvelle* (The Languages of Modern Europe), 2d ed. rev. Paris: Payot, 1928.

SCHMIDT, P. W. *Die Sprachenfamilien und Sprachenkreise der Erde* (Language Families and Language Regions of the World). Heidelberg: C. Winter's Universitätsbuchhandlung, 1926.

chapter 2

THE PHYSICAL
BACKGROUND

THE TOTAL AREA of continental Europe and its adjacent islands is approximately the same as that of the United States, including Alaska. The size of Europe, however, is in itself not of great significance except for one outstanding fact: the complexity of the political pattern of nations which has developed in this comparatively limited area. This complexity applies to size as well as to types or kinds of political organizations. In size they vary from minute enclaves such as Andorra in the Pyrenees, San Marino on the flanks of the Apennines in Italy, and Liechtenstein in the Alps to the huge area encompassed by the European part of the Soviet Union. In type of government, the countries range from the long-recognized democracy of Switzerland to the totalitarian rule of the Soviet Union.

The Significance of the Size and Shape of Europe

The shape of Europe is of direct geographic significance. Europe is, broadly speaking, a peninsular projection westward of the huge land mass of Asia. This projection, in turn, is characterized by a number of important peninsular appendages among which the Balkan, Italian, Iberian, and Scandinavian are the largest and geographically the most significant. The British Isles are, of course, insular but the narrowness of the Strait of Dover is such that the general effects are those of a great peninsula extending northward from the western mainland of the continent.

The peninsular appendages extending from the main land mass enclose several arms of the sea of such size and depth as to have important climatic effects on the adjoining shores, as well as to bring access to ocean transportation within easy reach of much of the continent. The Mediterranean Sea is an arm of the Atlantic occasioned by the comparatively recent geologic thrust which resulted in the fault or break now known as the Strait of Gibraltar. Thus the Mediterranean is coincidental with the general peninsular form of the European continent. Within the Mediterranean itself, there are three major extensions that occupy depressions coincident with the great peninsulas that project southward from the continental mass. These are of such magnitude as to be also called *seas*, namely the Aegean, the Adriatic, and the Tyrrhenian. Even the Black Sea is, in a true sense, an arm of the Mediterranean.

In western and northwestern Europe, likewise, the arms of the ocean are brought deeply toward the heart of the continent. The largest of these are the Bay of Biscay, the English Channel, the North Sea, and the Baltic Sea. Through this characteristic pattern of peninsulas and coincident arms of the oceans, marine influences have penetrated deeply into the interior of the continent and have provided low-cost access to the markets of all of the extensive coastal areas of Europe. The proximity of the sea has given impetus to the establishment of shipbuilding industries for vessels large and small, and has facilitated the promotion of world-wide trade on a basis of low-cost transportation. In proportion to area and population, no other land mass has been so favored with natural advantages, and thus we can readily appreciate at least a large part of the basic reasons for the long-time position held by the Europeans as seafaring peoples. This holds true particularly of the Greeks, Italians, Spanish, Portuguese, French, British, Dutch, and Norwegians.

Although Europe is outranked in size by all the other continents except Australia, it embraces a diversity of land forms, climatic conditions, natural resources, and density of population, nowhere else exceeded. This diversity constitutes a source of strength that should not be overlooked, nor should it be neglected when we are puzzled by the complexities of problems which have confronted the European peoples throughout history. Coupled with the lack of ready internal transportation and communication facilities during earlier times, this diversity was conducive to the organization of small states and led to the creation of extensive and complicated boundaries which in themselves became obstacles to a ready exchange of goods and ideas. This still holds true for twentieth-century Europe, even with the present opportunities for rapid transit by rail and air, and the advance of telecommunications.

In general, the configuration of the land surface in Europe includes a diversity of forms comparable to that of any other continent. These forms range from the extensive flat plains of the European part of the Soviet Union, some of these depressed below sea level, to the sharp, pyramidal peaks of the Alps and the Caucasus. In between these extremes of topography are the rounded Kjölen Mountains of Scandinavia, the plateau-like Slate Mountains cut through by the Rhine Gorge, the Massif Central of France, and the Spanish Meseta, deeply scarred by steep-sided stream valleys.

In natural resources the same holds true. The granites of Scotland and Scandinavia, the slate of Wales, the ceramic clays of England and France and the marble of Italy have won world renown and fame for their beauty and quality. France, Hungary, and Yugoslavia are well known for their bauxite, the most important of aluminum ores. Iron ore occurs in several regions of Europe with northeastern France, northern Sweden, and the Ukrainian S.S.R. holding front rank as producers. All the common nonferrous metals have long been mined in Europe, while in power resources the coal of Great Britain, the German Ruhr, Polish Silesia, and the Donets Basin in the Soviet Union, as well as the water power of Scandinavia and the Alpine countries have supplied on a grand scale the energy necessary for manufacturing and commerce.

The diversity of climatic conditions is another important characteristic of Europe. Consider the contrasts involved in the shift from the subpolar belt in the north to the subtropical regions in the south, from the marine climate in western Britain to the continental climate in most of European Soviet Union. Coupled with this diversity of climates is an attendant diversity of soils and native flora. European soils range from residual to alluvial, from the leached topsoil in areas of heavy rainfall to the saline flats adjacent to the Caspian Sea, and from the glacial till of Germany and Scandinavia to the loess of the Ukraine. In the far north the treeless tundra is impressive, giving way southward to the conifers which pass gradually to the mixed broad-leafed deciduous forest. Toward the drier margins of the southeast, the short-grass steppe is followed by virtual desert near the Caspian Sea. In the Mediterranean area the distribution of natural vegetation is chiefly based on the available soil moisture and soil content. *Maquis* grows on the more humid sandy or siliceous soils and consists of a fairly continuous ground cover of thorny bush. The *garrique* grows on calcareous limestone soils and forms a discontinuous cover of steppe-like grass and stunted trees. These two forms generally occur at comparatively low altitudes. As the elevation and moisture efficiency increase, broad-leafed trees predominate and at still higher altitudes they are replaced by cedars and other conifers.

From this brief description of the European scene, is it not clear that Europe is a land of contrasts? In order to understand even in small degree the problems which confront the Europeans of today and which are of vital importance to the rest of the world, a very careful study should be made of some of the basic features of European geography.

The Climates of Europe

It is a far cry, indeed, from the barren tundra of northern Finland to the vineyards of southern Spain or the lemon groves of Sicily. In a similar fashion, there is a striking contrast between the damp and rainy coast of northwestern France and the dry and dusty steppes of the Caspian lowland, or between the equable, year-round mild temperatures of Normandy and the distinctly seasonal heat and cold that prevails from Poland to the Urals. When climatic regions are delineated upon maps to show these large-scale differences, each region represents an area wherein, on a basis of averages, the fundamental characteristics of temperature, precipitation, and winds are broadly similar. It seems in order, therefore, first to deal briefly with the causes that give rise to the diversity of climates and then to undertake the outlining of areas within the continent, which are climatically similar.

Among the fundamental causes that must be considered in accounting for the climatic conditions that characterize Europe, the following should be enumerated and briefly discussed:

1. The latitudinal extent from the island of Crete at 35° N. to North Cape, Norway, 71° 10′ N.
2. The peninsular form of Europe as a whole with its numerous peninsular extensions.
3. The west-east trend of the principal mountain ranges of Europe, from the Pyrenees to the Caucasus, with the Kjölen Mountains in Scandinavia as the only major exception.
4. The prevailing westerly winds and cyclonic storm movements in Europe north of the Pyrenees and the Alps.
5. The relative warmth of the surface waters of the North Atlantic Ocean, induced by the drift from the southwest, generally termed the Gulf Stream Drift.

6. The general northeast to southwest direction of the western coast of Europe, which affords opportunity for the Gulf Stream Drift to extend to high northern latitudes.

7. The seasonal atmospheric pressure changes within the immense area of Eurasia, from a well-defined winter high to a pronounced summer low.

A summary discussion of these causative factors is presented below. It must be understood at the outset that local modifications are many, some of them being of high importance; these are dealt with in fuller detail as the various countries are discussed in later chapters.

The north-south extent of Europe is such that temperatures range from subpolar in the north at low altitudes, with ice-cap conditions prevailing in Norway at less than 3,000 feet in parts of the Kjölen Mountains, to subtropical in the Mediterranean countries. Nevertheless, while the extremes given must be recognized, most of Europe is properly known as a middle latitude area.

The peninsular characteristic of Europe has been stated in sufficient detail, but perhaps it is well to recall that the climatic conditions of the extensive peninsular areas are greatly modified by the large bodies of water which practically surround them. The ice-free sea which washes the coast of Norway is the best known example, but marine influences are just as evident in the south of Europe, where their effect upon seasonal warmth and rainfall is considerable.

The highest mountain ranges of Europe trend generally from west to east, quite the opposite of the highest range of North America in the same latitudinal belt. In Europe the influence of the western sea can thus be air-borne far inland without encountering any transverse mountain barrier of great consequence, whereas in North America the lofty western ranges parallel the coast and restrict the major influence of the Pacific to a narrow littoral belt. While it is quite true that the European plain between the Alps and Scandinavia is crossed by several mountain ranges, they are of comparatively minor extent, are of low elevation, and are not continuous for great distances. Only locally do they give rise to climatic consequences of considerable import.

Winds are the carriers whereby weather and climatic conditions are transferred from one area to another. When we speak of the influence of the Atlantic extending deeply into Europe we presuppose an understanding of the action whereby this is accomplished, namely of the mechanism of the prevailing westerlies. The term "westerlies" does not imply continually blowing winds from the west, but rather a general movement of air masses from the south-west, within which are centers of low pressure separated by centers or ridges of higher pressure, thus giving rise to variable local winds. The centers of low pressure are commonly known as cyclones, those of high pressure as anticyclones. The subtropical high in the North Atlantic centers in the general area of the Azores, while the low-pressure center is established more or less permanently near Iceland. The procession of the westerlies dominates much of the climate of Europe from northern Scandinavia to the Alps (Figures 12, 13).

Where the waters from the Gulf of Mexico emerge between Florida and Cuba they constitute a definite measurable current of water that has been fed into the Caribbean Sea and the Gulf of Mexico under the impact of the northeast trade winds. These surface waters, warmed by the continual sunlight of the tropics, flow out as the Gulf Stream through the Straits of Florida. The Gulf Stream retains its distinct identity as it veers northward beyond the coast of North Carolina; and thence it gradually becomes a part of the great North Atlantic Drift, often referred to as the Gulf Stream Drift, which is pushed by the westerlies toward the European shores. Through its warming influence, it continually adds heat energy to the waters of the North Atlantic in such tremendous quantities that it becomes one of the chief factors in giving ice-free coasts to the British Isles and to the coast of Norway, far beyond the Arctic Circle. The importance of the Gulf Stream is universally conceded, although the mathematical ratio of this factor to others likewise recognized may still be a controversial topic.

Another major factor that affects the climate of Europe is that of the large seasonal pressure changes characteristic of the interior of the vast Eurasian land mass. In winter, high pressures are built up over north central Asia that obstruct the cyclonic storms in their passage eastward and thus not only intensify the marine influence along the west coast but also prevent, in a large measure, the penetration of this influence into the plains of Europe beyond eastern Germany. In summer, a pronounced low develops in southern Asia and, coinciding with the weakening of the Icelandic low, facilitates the penetration of the moisture-bearing westerlies as far as and even beyond the Urals. The result of these pressure changes upon precipitation and temperature causes the western part of the extensive central plain of Europe to have a fairly even distribution of rainfall throughout the year, while the eastern part receives most of its precipitation during the summer. Furthermore, the western part of Europe is characterized by relatively mild temper-

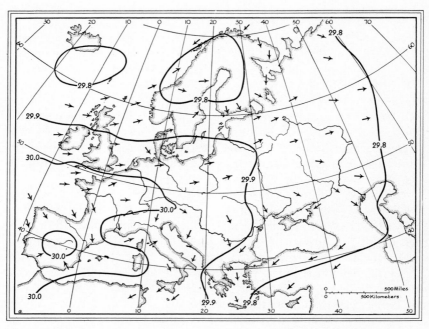

FIGURE 12.   Summer pressures (in inches) and prevalent wind directions.

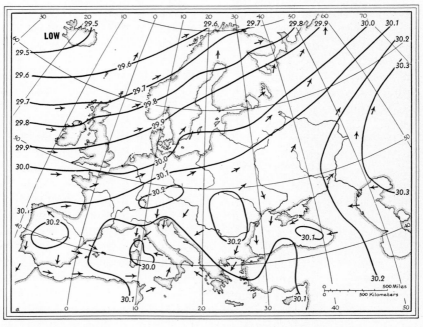

FIGURE 13.   Winter pressures (in inches) and prevalent wind directions.

78

atures during all seasons, while the eastern part has hot summers and intensely cold winters. The transition is, of course, gradual and no sharp line can be drawn between the marine climate of the west and the continental climate of the east, but the difference between the extremes should be stressed.

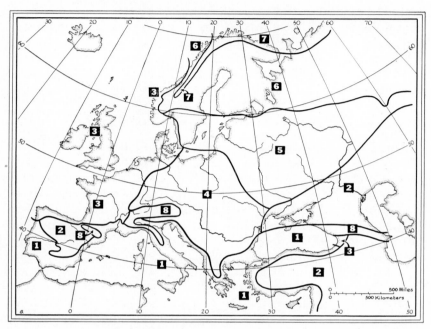

FIGURE 14. The climatic regions of Europe: (1) Mediterranean, (2) Middle-Latitude Steppe and Desert, (3) West Coast Marine, (4) Short Cold-Winter, (5) Long Cold-Winter, (6) Subpolar, (7) Tundra, (8) Mountain.

The seasonal pressure changes over Europe are attended by and in part caused by the intensification of the Iceland low in winter and its weakening in summer; the reverse occurs in the subtropical high centered in the general area of the Azores. It is weak in winter and strong in summer. The general results of these pressure shifts, together with the seasonal shift of the wind belts in the North Atlantic and over Eurasia, cause most of Europe north of the Pyrenees and Caucasus to have rainfall maxima in the warm months of the year, while in the Mediterranean area most of the rainfall occurs during the cool months, with several summer months, particularly June, July, and August virtually rainless.

The causes and consequences thus outlined apply to most of the lower altitudes throughout Europe. There are, however, great differences in climatic conditions between the steppes of southeastern U.S.S.R. and the plains of northern France, or between the lowlands of Italy and those of southern Sweden. These contrasts necessitate the subdivision of Europe into several climatic regions within each of which broadly similar conditions prevail. Although the outline of European climatic regions may differ according to authors, all the classifications have one characteristic in common, namely that nearly all the division lines drawn represent transition belts rather than clear-cut boundaries. The map presented herewith must be interpreted in this fashion, and the names of the regions considered as descriptive of their dominant climatic conditions (Figure 14).

The Major Climatic Regions of Europe

The Mediterranean Region. The coastal lands adjacent to the Mediterranean Sea have a type of climate so distinct and so well known that the term "Mediterranean climate" has been commonly used to describe analogous conditions in California, Chile, Africa, and Australia. The Mediterranean climate is of a marine or littoral type. It is characterized by mild winters of light to moderate rainfall, because of the westerly winds and the traveling cyclones, and by warm to hot summers slightly tempered by sea breezes. Several summer months have little or no rainfall. The mean temperatures of the coldest month are from 45° to 48° F.[1] The mean temperatures of the warmest month range from about 72° F. at Marseille to 80° F. at Athens (Figures 15, 16). There is abundant sunshine during both summer and winter.

The natural vegetation consists of broad-leaved evergreens and drought-tolerant trees and shrubs at low to moderate altitudes, with cedars and other conifers at higher altitudes. As previously stated, the vegetational zonation is largely based on available moisture and soil content, with *garrique* and *maquis* at the lower altitudes where moisture deficiency is most pronounced. This lower zone of thorny bushes and small trees is surmounted by a belt of broad-leaved evergreens, of which the live oak and the cork oak are the best examples. Higher still are the well-known cedars, junipers, and pines.

The Mediterranean region is noted for its specialized agricultural production. Olives, wine grapes, raisins and currants, and durum wheat are the distinctive crops grown here. People early found this part of the world a desirable area in which to live but the prolonged summer drought (Figures 17, 18) induced them to

[1] See the climatic graphs, Appendix II.

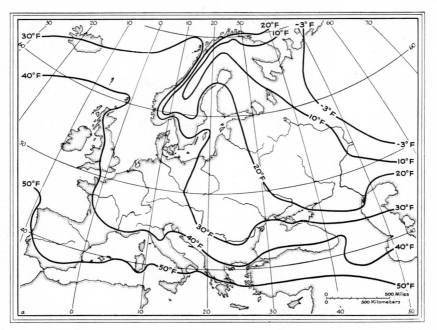

FIGURE 15. Mean temperatures, January. (After Kendrew and Bartholomew.)

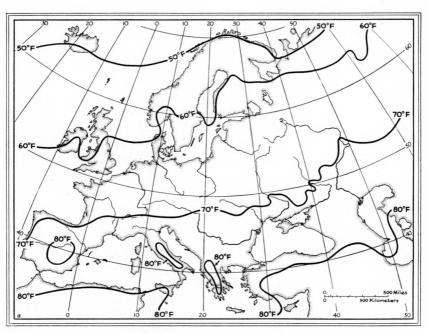

FIGURE 16. Mean temperatures, July. (After Kendrew and Bartholomew.)

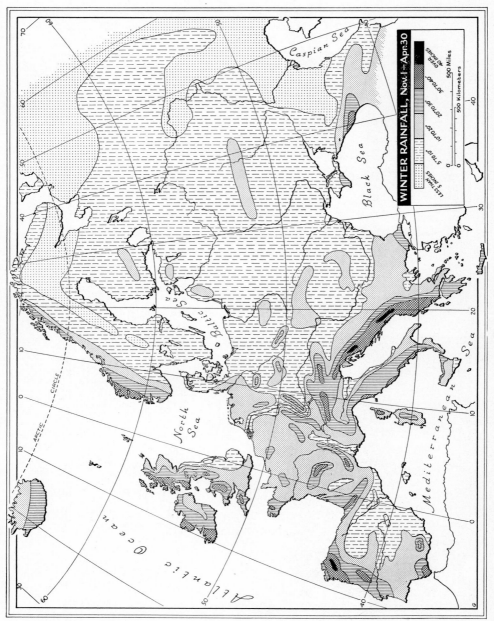

WINTER RAINFALL, Nov.1–Apr.30

LESS THAN
5 INCHES

5 TO 10

10 TO 20

20 TO 30

30 TO 40

OVER
40 INCHES

0   500 Miles

0   500 Kilometers

FIGURE 17

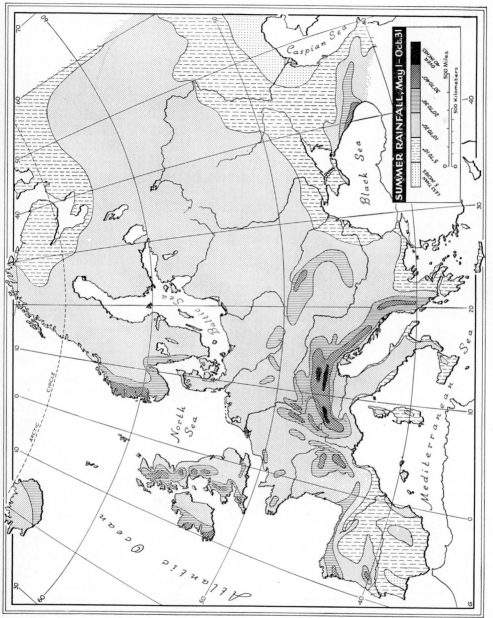

SUMMER RAINFALL, May 1 - Oct. 31

OVER 40
30 TO 40
20 TO 30
10 TO 20
5 TO 10
LESS THAN
5 INCHES

500 Miles
500 Kilometers

FIGURE 18

83

undertake irrigation works in order to provide a dependable food supply. Seasons are conducive to outdoor activities most of the time and the stability of settlement is strongly expressed.

Middle-Latitude Steppes and Desert Region. The southeastern section of Europe is a continuation of the arid and semiarid conditions extensively developed in Asia, beyond the Caspian Sea. It comprises a small area of desert located north and northwest of the Caspian Sea. This is the only dry desert within the European land limits and it constitutes a smaller percentage of the whole continental area than is true of any of the other grand divisions of the world. Near the mouth of the Volga the mean annual rainfall is less than five inches a year.

The Middle-Latitude Steppe region occupies much of the southern part of the Soviet Union, including the well-known Ukraine area noted for its rich black soil and high productivity when rainfall is sufficient. It is a gently undulating plain, treeless except along watercourses, with grasses of short to medium height constituting the native vegetation. At Odessa, on the Black Sea, the mean yearly rainfall is 15.6 inches, the mean annual temperature 49° F., the January mean 25° F., and the July mean 72° F. West of the Dnieper River, the rainfall averages about 15 to 20 inches a year, two thirds of which falls during the growing season. This distribution favors the successful production of wheat, oats, barley, and sugar beets. Large quantities of sunflowers are produced because of the oil content of their seeds. East of the Dnieper River, drier conditions prevail, the average rainfall being between 10 and 15 inches per year. In this region short-grass pastures and herding are important, but considerable farming is carried on because of the drought-tolerant grain crops, notably wheat and millets, that have been developed.

Except for a narrow strip along the Black Sea, where Mediterranean climatic conditions are approximated, the southeastern steppes of Europe are distinctly continental, as is evidenced by the seasonal temperature extremes. In Spain, on the Meseta, is another area of steppes where a rather wide seasonal range of temperature is dominant and the rainfall is comparatively light. Madrid, for example, has a mean annual rainfall of about 16 inches, with July and August as the driest months. Coupled with mean summer (June to August) temperatures of 72° to 73°, this makes for semiarid conditions. Native vegetation tends to be scattered and scrubby, the trees growing to proper stature only where underground water is available in springs, seepages, or along stream courses.

Thus the Spanish Meseta is a steppe region although in many respects it differs sharply from the steppes of the Soviet Union.

The West Coast Marine Climatic Region. The characteristic of a marine climate, which sets it off in sharp contrast to continental climates, is its small annual range of temperatures resulting from mild winters and cool summers. All along the Atlantic coast, from northwestern Spain to western Norway, the mean range of monthly temperatures does not exceed 20° F. Inland, the range sharply increases, chiefly because of higher summer temperatures. Thus, throughout the area mapped as the West Coast Marine climatic region, the winters are warm in relation to the latitude, this climatic anomaly being most pronounced along the west coast of Norway and the British Isles.

The middle-latitude west-coast marine climate is of greater extent in Europe than on any other continent. A combination of causes accounts for this situation, perhaps the most important being the irregular coast line, together with the absence of a high mountain barrier except in Norway. This gives west-east depth to the region. Other causes must also be taken into consideration, for instance, the abnormally warm water in the North Atlantic in winter and westerly winds which prevail throughout the year. In winter, the Iceland Low is well developed and extends from Greenland to the north of Norway. At that season, the subtropical high pressure belt of the North Atlantic is weak. This pressure distribution gives rise to a strong cyclonic circulation which gives western Europe prevailing southwesterly winds that bear warmth and moisture from the Middle Atlantic. These prevailing westerlies are characterized, however, by disturbances. Cyclonic lows travel eastward over the Atlantic attended by northeast winds in their northeast sector and southeast winds in their southeastern sector.

The Iceland Low is relatively weak in summer, but at that time there is a strong high-pressure center in the vicinity of the Azores, a distribution which results in an anticyclonic circulation and in cool west or northwest winds blowing across western Europe. Marine influences are thus carried far inland both in summer and winter, far inland because, as has been stated, there are no high mountain ranges over which the air masses must pass and so lose much of their marine quality.

The general effects of the middle-latitude west-coast marine climate may be summarized in a single expression: equable temperatures and fairly even distribution of rainfall. The sharp contrast between summer heat and winter cold is definitely lacking, and this is likewise true of the seasonal distribution of rainfall. Furthermore, in western Europe the percentage of cloudiness is high. The rains tend to be of the prolonged drizzly kind and less prevalently of the thundershower and cloudburst type so common where continental climates prevail. Droughts and floods sometimes occur, but not so frequently as they do farther east in Europe or in the interior of the United States, where marine characteristics are not so evident.

The significance of the gentler although relatively ample rains to soil erosion should be mentioned in this connection. Slow, drizzly rains give opportunity for a high percentage of percolation into the soil; the percentage of surface runoff is small and its velocity is comparatively low. The net result is a minimum rate of soil erosion in contrast to the erosion brought about by rains of the thunderstorm type, so typical of much of the United States.

The Short Cold-Winter Climatic Region. The middle latitude marine type of climate merges eastward into typically continental conditions in central and east central Europe. This change is gradual but persistent, the continentality increasing with the distance from the Atlantic Ocean. The marine influence is still reflected in a longer growing season and less severe winters in central Europe, while in the east-central plains of European Soviet Union winters are of longer duration and of greater severity than along the Polish Baltic coast or in western Poland. This intensified continentality appears to justify consideration under two headings, namely, the short cold-winter type and the long cold-winter type. Both are characterized by warm to hot summers but have differences in the duration of their growing seasons. Their limits are shown on the accompanying map (Figure 14).

The area of the short cold-winter type extends from the middle Rhone Valley across Germany to the Baltic. To the east it includes most of the drainage basin of the Danube and, farther north, the undulating plain of the Vistula in Poland. This region is characterized by interspersed mountains and enclosed valleys, with great local climatic variations. As a consequence, the uniformity of climate so well marked in the marine region to the west is lacking.

In general, however, at the lower altitudes, the average temperature of the coldest month is below 42° F. but not more than three months have averages below the freezing point and the average of the warmest month is at least 36° F. higher than that of the coldest month. In many places the differences are even greater. These extremes are usually not so severe as to cause serious discomfort, and many claim that the seasonal amplitudes are stimulating to mental and physical activity. The growing season varies from 150 to 240 days. While light frosts may occur during the early and the late weeks of this period, ordinarily they are not damaging to the major crops of the region. In the southern sections, the winters are mild, but along the northeastern borders subzero weather may occur at times during the winter season. The areas remote from the sea, where continentality is most pronounced, are characterized by spells of severe cold in winter and sometimes by devastating heat in summer.

The average annual rainfall on the plains varies from about 20 inches in the drier areas to about 30 inches or above. Low mountain areas have still greater rainfall on their west-facing, windward slopes with summer maxima the rule, but in nearly all instances moderate precipitation occurs in winter as snowfall. This is in contrast to some other regions, classified similarly, where the cold season has little if any precipitation in some years.

Although centuries of intensive cultivation by European peoples have removed virtually all the native vegetation, the evidence clearly indicates that broad-leaved forest was the predominant type. The predominant soils are of the gray-brown podzolic group, in which leaching has not been quite so pronounced as in some rainier areas. Although these soils are distinctly pedalfers, their structures are quite stable and the organic content is comparatively high. On most of the mature soils, however, manure and mineral fertilizers are needed if satisfactory crop yields are to be obtained from the land.

The Long Cold-Winter Climatic Region. While the two humid climatic regions of Europe have many points of similarity, they differ in one important respect, namely, in the length of their growing seasons. In the long cold-winter region, which extends from Poland to the Urals and southward to the steppes of southern Russia, the average monthly temperature drops below freezing more than three months of the year, but during the summer season at least four months have averages above 50° F. As fairly representative of the temperature conditions that prevail in this region of Europe, we may consider the seasonal temperatures of Vilnyus, Moscow, and Kazan, all in nearly the same latitude of about 55°.

	Vilnyus	Moscow	Kazan
Duration of mean daily temperatures below freezing	4 months	5 months	5 months
Mean annual temperature	43.0° F.	38.5° F.	39.0° F.
Mean July temperature	64.0° F.	64.4° F.	67.6° F.
Mean February temperature	21.4° F.	15.6° F.	8.6° F.

The absolute summer maxima in this region may be as high as or even higher than they are in the short cold-winter region, but the hot spells are of shorter duration. The minima of winter are likely to be lower; for example, occasional periods of $-30°$ to $-40°$ F. are not uncommon and these cold spells last longer than in the short cold-winter regions. The major factors which cause these seasonal extremes are distance from the ocean, the great difference between the duration of sunlight in summer and winter, and the occasional masses of intensely cold polar air of winter, and warm tropical air of summer, which flow into the area under varying pressure gradients.

On the average, the annual precipitation is relatively low, 20 inches and less, with some favored areas in the west receiving as much as 25 inches. This comparatively low rainfall is offset by its favorable distribution and efficiency. The major part of the precipitation falls during the warm months, June to August inclusive. The efficiency is high because of the comparatively low summer temperatures, which means less loss of soil moisture by direct evaporation. When exceptions to this general condition prevail, as they do in some years, the resulting droughts become severe and serious damage to crops results.

On the whole, forests constitute the native vegetation with hardy deciduous trees dominant north of the grasslands of the steppes and conifers, mostly pines, established where sandy soils prevail. The southern part of the region is a transition area from steppe to forest, an area of prairie interspersed with forest, mostly oak, and noted for its fertile black soil. Its southern section—the Ukraine—has developed into one of the major wheat-producing regions of the world, long famous as "Russia's breadbasket." Northward, rye assumes premier place as a bread grain with some wheat, oats, and flax also important. Northward still, the deciduous forest is intermixed with conifers which become thoroughly dominant in the taiga [2] of the subpolar zone.

In summation, it is well to review the causes, from a meteorological point of view, that give rise to the conditions just discussed. In Europe the region lies farther north than do the corresponding regions elsewhere because the prevailing winds are westerly from an abnormally warm water surface, and the general flatness of the terrain permits these winds to move far inland, even to the central part of European U.S.S.R., in some measure beyond the Urals.

---

[2] "Taiga" is a Tannu-Tuvan word also used by northern Mongols. It means the bald summit of a forested mountain, but its original meaning has been corrupted by the Russians and accepted by modern English to refer to the forest zone.

In winter the region lies between the western side of the great Siberian high and the eastern side of the Atlantic low, and hence the normal flow of air is from the southwest. In summer the ridge of high pressure from the Azores to the Baltic results in winds that are prevailingly from the northwest. The net effect is to bring in air masses that carry with them moisture from the Atlantic and also the tempering influences that reduce the severity of the cold of winter and the intensity of summer heat.

The Subpolar Climatic Region. Northward from the region of long-cold winters and short-warm summers is a belt dominated by conifers, where even in the warmest months of the year temperatures near the land surface may drop at times below the freezing point. This subpolar climate extends in Sweden and Norway from approximately 60° N. to about 70° N. In Finland and the European part of the Soviet Union, it lies virtually between the 60th parallel and the Arctic Circle. Within this belt, a winter landscape of somber dark green and cold dreary white is predominant for nearly nine months of the year. During a brief summer period nature bursts into life and richly colored flowers carpet the ground wherever the forest is not too dense. Daylight is nearly continuous, and for a few weeks life surges through root and limb into leaf and flower.

During the winter, four or five months have average temperatures below freezing, while in the summer average monthly temperatures of 50° F. are reached less than four months each year. Even during the warmest season, light frosts often occur at night although daytime temperatures may be quite high. The soil and subsoil are generally free of frost during the midsummer period, a factor of great importance in the development of the dense coniferous forest known as the taiga. In the southern part of the region the conifers, chiefly spruce, fir, larch, and pine, are interspersed with stands of mixed deciduous hardwoods, principally linden, birch, and oak. Toward the northern border of the taiga the size of the trees declines, and they become mere shrubs and bushes as the taiga merges northward into the tundra.

The high annual range of temperature is a marked characteristic of the subpolar climatic region. The range is smaller in the western part where marine influences are most marked and increases eastward as the continentality becomes more pronounced, although even in the northern parts of the Soviet Union, west of the Urals, the modifying influence of the northern sea keeps the annual temperature range within closer limits than is true farther east in Siberia.

Nevertheless, in the subpolar zone of Scandinavia and Finland conditions are so severe that agricultural crops are limited to such hardy grains as rye and barley and to quick-maturing vegetables. Extensive experiments in plant breeding have been under way there for some time, in the hope that crops of shorter maturing qualities may be developed so as to increase the food-producing potential of these far-northern lands.

The subpolar region is located along the northern edge of the prevailing westerlies. Its climatic conditions are consequently affected by the same shifts in pressure distribution as those described for the climatic regions of central and east central Europe, but to a lesser degree because of the marginal location of this region.

Forests are the principal natural resource of the subpolar zone. Intensive exploitation is carried on profitably in Norway, Sweden, and Finland where scientific replanting programs have long been in operation. The Soviet Union has vast forest resources within this region but until recently they have not been extensively utilized.

The Tundra Type of Climatic Region. In the far north of Europe, from the northern tip of Scandinavia, and extending eastward in a relatively narrow strip along the Arctic coast of Finland and the European part of the Soviet Union, and in a broader strip across Siberia, is the tundra.[3] This climatic region includes all the areas of Europe where the average temperature of the warmest month is below 50° F. but above the freezing point, 32° F. Due to higher altitudes and moderate slopes, the tundra pushes farther southward in the Kjölen and Ural Mountains than can be shown on the small-scale map (Figure 14). A measure of vegetative cover exists where the mean temperature of the warmest month rises above 43° F. Where the average daily temperature is continuously below 43° F. there is an almost complete absence of macroscopic vegetation and for such places the term "desert tundra" has come into use.

In the tundra regions of Europe the temperature extremes are less than have been recorded in similar regions of Siberia and North America. The adjoining Arctic Ocean, although frozen over during the long winters, serves, nevertheless, as a modifying influence because there is more conduction of heat from the water beneath the ice than there is from the frozen land.

---

[3] The term is Finnish in origin, *tunturi*, which means a flat, barren plateau, but has been broadened in meaning to include land areas where persistent cold precludes the growth of tall trees and where the vegetative cover consists of mosses, scanty grasses, and low shrubs. Therefore, "tundra" has become widely accepted also as a climatic term.

The precipitation is not heavy, only about 8 to 10 inches a year. Most of it becomes soil moisture because of the flatness of the land, the high atmospheric humidity and, hence, a low rate of evaporation. From man's standpoint, the tundra suffers rather from the absence of summer than from the severity of winter.

Few people live in the tundra region. Most of those who do so are attracted by the abundance of fish and animal life that can be caught during the short summer period. The Lapps, for example, come to the coast in summer for fishing and, where conditions are not too marshy, bring their reindeer for grazing on the tundra pastures. They then retreat to the forest, the taiga, where winter shelter can more readily be provided.

The Mountain Climates. It has often been said that mountains make their own climates. This is particularly true of areas where high altitudes exist and deep valleys are characteristic, as in the case of the Pyrenees, Alps, and Caucasus. For these regions local variations from any specific mean weather data obtainable are so wide as to make generalizations of little value. They are, therefore, indicated on the map (Figure 14) as a single type without any other differentiation. Nevertheless, those mountain masses are significant climatologically as well as topographically in that they have direct influence not only within their regions, but also upon climatic conditions within neighboring areas. For example, when moist, cool air masses from Germany pass over the Alps toward Italy, they cause heavy snowfall on the northern slopes of the Alps and then descend into Italy as clear and warm winds known as the *föhn*, giving to the sheltered valleys north of the Po the delightful winter conditions for which they are world famous. Of even greater importance than the north föhn just described is the south föhn which develops when low pressures prevail in eastern France and central Germany with higher pressures south of the Alps and over the Mediterranean. Then the southerly winds cause precipitation on the south slopes of the high Alps and, after crossing the summits, descend the northern slopes into the valleys as comparatively warm and dry winds. These winds temper the winter cold on the Swiss and Bavarian plateaus and extend the growing season in many of the Alpine valleys. Similar general characteristics hold for the other areas of mountain climate.

It should be understood, however, that the numerous mountain ranges of lower altitude and extent may also give rise to climatic conditions that vary from the broad descriptions of the regions in which they are found. This is particularly true of the Asturias in

northwest Spain, where the west-facing slopes are drenched with
40 to 60 inches of rain per year. It is true likewise of the Vosges
and the Black Forest along the upper Rhine, the Slate Mountains
of the middle Rhine, the Bohemian Massif, and the Carpathians.

As a closing summary we might say that climatic conditions in
Europe vary from the sunny Mediterranean coastal lands of Spain,
Italy, and Greece where winters hardly exist to the tundra climate
of the northernmost Soviet Union where summers are virtually
nonexistent. They vary from the marine type along the west coast
to the distinctly continental type of east central Soviet Union and
from the rain-drenched west coast of Scotland to the desert along
the Caspian Sea. In general, however, the changes are gradual with
distances involved. May we repeat, lines drawn on maps mark
transition zones rather than sharp distinctions between the types
on either side of the line. While the differences noted are due
largely to latitudinal extent, nearness to or remoteness from the
sea, pressure distribution and prevailing winds and storm tracks,
the configuration of the surface of the land is also important,
particularly in giving rise to local climatic aspects. Thus the
consideration of the relief of Europe becomes a fitting close of this
chapter.

The Natural Regions of Europe

The term "natural region," as here used, implies a high degree
of similarity, but not uniformity, of structure, topography, soils,
and native vegetation, and usually also of climatic characteristics
within the area so defined. Hence, within a region broadly classified as a plains area there may be low folds that structurally would
be mountains, or there may be worn-down crystalline rocks within
an area of sedimentary deposits. Even so the integrity of the natural region would be undisturbed as long as the dominant features
described are present.

Man's adjustment to the natural environment within such a
region leads to a similarity of human activities, a similarity more
evident in agricultural production than in manufacturing and commerce. Agriculture is limited by the temperature, length of growing season, amount and distribution of rainfall, and to a less generally recognized extent by the intensity of winds and atmospheric
humidity. Man produces crops under conditions which he can
modify but slightly, if at all. Although within each set of conditions he can often choose from several possibilities, to go beyond
the broad limits set by nature spells failure.

The natural regions of Europe correspond roughly to the con-figuration of the surface of the land and so have a general west-east pattern very different from that of North America where the pattern is, broadly speaking, a parallelism of north-south features. As we have seen, this west-east trend in Europe favors the penetration of oceanic climatic influences far into the interior. Trade, likewise, moves readily in response to this topographic arrangement because land transportation systems face no difficulties of construction nor extensive mileages of low population and meager production. In this respect, Europe is a favored continent for the promotion of west-east exchange of goods. Unfortunately, barriers do exist in the form of man-made custom duties and other restrictions by the governments of the various political units.

Europe is fortunate, also, in the fact that the several parts of the continent are readily accessible to other parts by sea. Even by land, the gateways across the southern mountains are numerous enough for trade to move readily from the Mediterranean lands to central and northern Europe. Furthermore, transportation by air makes the transfer of passengers, mail, valuable and perishable goods swift and practicable regardless of mountains and plains, and nearly regardless of winds and storms. Yet, the importance of the terrain continues to be dominant insofar as the exchange of heavy traffic is concerned, and it still holds true that the land is the mother of production.

In order to appreciate the fundamentals underlying the present arrangement and geographic significance of the larger features of the land surface of Europe, it seems advisable to call attention to a few geologic time-scale terms.[4] The geological eras are of unequal length. The earliest era of earth history, the Archeozoic, or Ar-chean, was undoubtedly longer than any of the succeeding ones and probably of longer duration than all of the later divisions added together. During Archeozoic times some forms of lower or cellular life may have existed, but if so, paleontological evidence has thus far not been proved. There are large areas in Canada, northern South America, and in the Scandinavian countries where the sur-face bedrock is classified as of Archeozoic age. During that era, as in all succeeding ones, rock weathering, erosion of surfaces by running water and wind action, and deposition of detritus were continually active. Sedimentation went hand in hand with erosion.

Gradually definite forms of life appeared. Their remains were imbedded in the sediments and thus preserved as fossils. Since

[4] See Appendix I.

these early forms are the most ancient of which we have any knowledge, the era during which the rocks which contain them were laid down has been named the Paleozoic. The time involved was tremendously long and the sediments deposited have been subjected to great pressures and in places to mountain-building processes.

In Europe, two extensive periods of folding are generally recognized and referred to as the *Caledonian* of about mid-Paleozoic times and the *Hercynian* at the close of the Paleozoic. These mountainous folds greatly affected the sediments preserved along their flanks and in many instances metamorphism was pronounced. Since much of the higher-grade coal resulted from organic accumulations of the late Paleozoic, it is important to bear in mind that coal of that age is now being mined on the flanks of and on the plains adjacent to several of the Hercynian uplifts.

Following the Paleozoic are the Mesozoic and Cenozoic eras, each of importance in resulting landforms; here we shall deal only with the Cenozoic, which is usually subdivided into Tertiary and Quaternary periods. The third and latest great mountain-building era in Europe occurred at the close of the Cretaceous and during the Tertiary period, as was also the case in North and South America. Because of its association with the Alps, it is referred to as the *Alpine* mountain-building episode. Following the Tertiary, another long period elapsed during which perhaps the most important earth-sculpturing event was that of the continental glaciation in northern Europe plus extended but local glaciation in the southern mountains. The Ice Age, geologically designated as the Pleistocene, is a comparatively recent event. Its duration probably far exceeded the post-glacial times, even though the latter are conceded to have been begun tens of thousands of years ago.

In discussing the general topographic aspects of Europe, we shall begin with the region of most ancient structure and thence deal with the regions southward toward the geologically younger but more rugged areas bordering the Mediterranean Sea.

The Northwest Highlands. The ancient land of Pre-Cambrian age reached its greatest extent in Europe in Fenno-Scandia (Norway, Sweden and Finland), commonly referred to as the Archean Shield similar to that of eastern Canada but not nearly so extensive. It is not all of Pre-Cambrian rock structure because along part of the coast of Norway steeply tilted layers of early Paleozoic sedimentaries give rise to coastal ruggedness. This same structure dominates the topography of northern Scotland and the nearby part of Ireland. Therefore, the Northwest Highlands, as outlined on the accompanying map (Figure 19), must be defined as being predominantly Pre-Cambrian in age but also including sedimentaries of early Paleozoic times now steeply tilted and generally metamorphosed by the lateral pressures that gave rise to the Caledonian mountain-building period. Thus, while granitoids and associated igneous rocks predominate in Finland and Sweden as well as in the Kjölen Mountains, they constitute only the core of the northern mountains of Scotland.

The abrupt front of the Northwest Highlands faces the northwest and thus gives rise to the world-renowned water power resources, potential and developed, of Norway. These, of course, result from several factors, climatic as well as topographic, but among them the moderately high summit range and the plateaulike surface of the Kjölen Mountains should be given high rank. This same general area was the Fenno-Scandian center of continental glaciation, still represented by the greatly contracted Hardanger and Jöstedals ice sheets of the present. The heavy snows of winter accumulate on the gentle slopes and nearby flat surfaces. Melting in summer, this snow forms lakes in the scoured basins and supplies huge quantities of water for power development throughout the year.

The Fenno-Scandian highlands were the centers of the most extensive glacial ice accumulation in Europe during the Pleistocene period. Other centers were in Scotland and in the mountain areas of central and southern Europe, the most extensive of which was that of the Alps. The Fenno-Scandian center was the only one from which glacial ice spread so extensively as to be termed continental glaciation. At its maximum development, this ice sheet spread over much of the Central Lowlands, and covered portions of the Great Russian Plains, the North Polish, and the North German Lowlands (Figure 20).

Glaciation during the Pleistocene was characterized by several periods of advance followed by retreat, that is, melting back of the ice front. The early advances, of which there appear to have been two or three stages, were more extensive than the later ones. The terminology applied to these advances in Europe are, the Günz stage corresponding to the Nebraskan in the United States, the *Mindel* stage corresponding to the Kansan, the *Riss* stage corresponding to the Illinoian, and the Würm corresponding to the Wisconsin. The earliest and most extensive advances are marked by terminal moraines and the later ones by recessional moraines. The interglacial stages were characterized by ice recession and the deposition of ground morainic material, mostly of sand, silt, and clay. Loess,

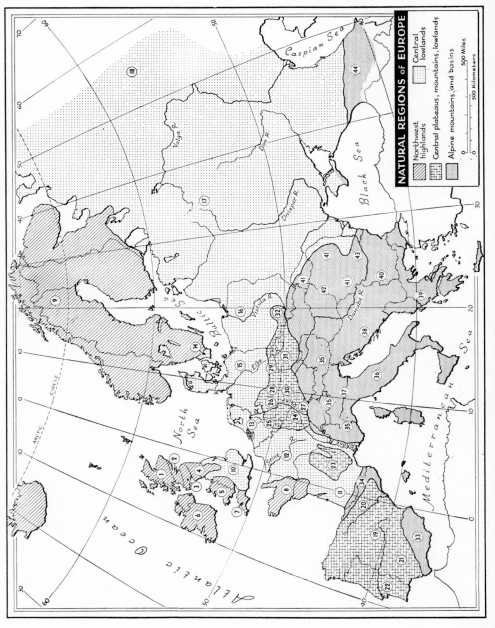

NATURAL REGIONS of EUROPE

Northwest highlands

Central lowlands

Central plateaus, mountains, lowlands

Alpine mountains, and basins

500 Miles

0   500 Kilometers

FIGURE 19

96

Natural regions of Europe (map on opposite page)

NORTHWEST HIGHLANDS

1. Scottish Highlands
2. Central Scottish Lowlands
3. Scottish Southern Uplands
4. Pennine Range
5. Wales
6. Ireland
7. Cornwall
8. Armorican Upland
9. Scandinavian Mountains and Uplands

CENTRAL LOWLANDS

10. Anglican Plains (Lowland England)
11. Aquitaine Basin
12. Paris Basin
13. Low Countries
14. Ground Moraines of southern Scandinavia
15. North German Lowlands
16. North Polish Lowlands
17. Great Russian Plains (East European Plains)
18. Ural Mountains

CENTRAL PLATEAUS, MOUNTAINS, AND BASINS

19. Spanish Meseta, including Cantabrian Cordillera
20. Aragon Basin
21. Andalusian Basin
22. Portuguese Lowlands
23. Massif Central
24. Vosges
25. Ardennes
26. Central German Uplands (Rhenish Slate Mountains)
27. Black Forest
28. Thuringian and Hessian Depression
29. Saxon Uplands
30. Scarplands of Swabia and Franconia
31. Bohemian Massif
32. Lysa Gora

ALPINE MOUNTAINS AND BASINS

33. Baetic Cordillera
34. Pyrenees
35. Alps
36. Apennines
37. North Italian Plains
38. Dinaric Ranges
39. Pindus Ranges
40. Balkan Ranges (Rhodope Massif)
41. Carpathian Arc
42. Carpathian Basin
43. Wallachian Plain
44. Caucasus Mountains

a silty deposit caused by wind action upon a vegetation-bare land-scape, was formed during recessional ice movements and during interglacial intervals. Loess formation appears to have been most active following the Riss stage on the Great Russian Plains, and it is believed that the extensive loess deposits of the Ukraine date from that period. Less extensive loessal areas are also found in various localities in the north central lowlands of Europe.

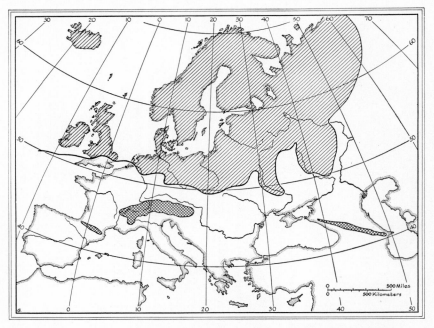

FIGURE 20. Pleistocene glaciation in Europe. The diagonal shading shows the extent of continental glaciation, and the crosshatch shading the approximate extent of alpine glaciation.

Northern Scotland and Ireland are principally associated with the Caledonian mountain-building period. Their structure in-cludes a granitic core and steeply tilted sedimentaries, with evi-dence of much subsequent volcanic intrusives in the world-famous Giant's Causeway of northeastern Ireland. Pronounced faulting occurs in the great rift valley in Scotland known as Glen More and along the southern edge of the Highlands. The Central Scottish Lowlands are located in the great rift between the Highlands and Scottish Southern Uplands. They are characterized by belts of low hills which owe their existence to hard rock outcrops. The Pennine Range, extending from the southern uplands of Scotland through northern England, is hardly of mountain height or ruggedness, but is of major importance structurally because along its eastern and western flanks and its southern front are the coal beds whose exploitation has provided much of the power necessary for the great industrial progress of England. These extensive areas of high quality coking coal were supplemented by the coal preserved by nature in the Central Lowland of Scotland, and by the coal resources in South Wales, where they occur on the flanks of the Welsh mountain uplift.

The older rocks of the Cornwall Peninsula of southwestern England have for centuries been noted for tin production, and for their high quality ceramic clays. In the Armorican Upland of northwestern France (Brittany and Normandy), the ruggedness of the coast line is due in part to the varied resistance to erosion and wave action provided by the complex structure of this Hercynian uplift. This coast has long been famous for its sheltered harbors, large and small.

Thus the region of the Northwest Highlands of Europe exhibits a great structural complexity that must not be overlooked. The most conspicuous features of the land surface are, however, the high and rugged Scottish Highlands and the Kjölen Mountains of the Scandinavian Peninsula. The Northwest Highlands have ample resources, varying from the extensive forests of Finland, Sweden, and Norway, the iron ores of Sweden and Norway, varied ores of silver, copper, building stone, cement materials, water power potentials, to the protected fiords and harbors for the fishing fleet and small but productive areas of profitable agriculture.

The Central Lowlands—Western Section. At the outset we must realize that the area thus indicated is a lowland in the sense that its surface does not reach such altitudes as are reached in the highlands of either northern, central, east central, or southern Europe. The western section of the Central Lowlands includes the English Lowland (Anglican Plain), the extensive plains of France (the Aquitanian and Paris Basin included) and of the Low Countries, and the North German Lowlands, as far eastward as marine climatic influences are highly effective. The Ground Moraines of southern Scandinavia are included in this section.

On the whole, the real lowland is characterized by flatness of surface or by gentle slopes, and the structure is that of flat lying or but gently folded sedimentaries. In general, the upper bedrock is not highly consolidated and is geologically of later age than is the case with the massifs to be discussed later. Much of the plains area is covered with such unconsolidated rock debris as glacial till, alluvium or Tertiary sands and clays. These, together with residuum from weathered bedrock, make up the parent material for the soils of the west Central Lowlands with the quality of the soil at any given place dependent upon the various factors there dominant. Except where too sandy, the lowland soils are capable of high productivity because of their favorable, fairly stable structure and moderately open texture. Fertilizers must be added, however, because the plentiful rains have induced leaching of chemical solubles, and because of long-continued cropping.

The major features of the west Central Lowlands which deserve emphasis are (1) their west-east extension facilitates eastward movement of marine climatic influence far into the interior of Europe; (2) they facilitate swift and low-cost trade between east and west; (3) their comparatively numerous but low-altitude blocks or horsts [5] and folds of older rock masses have been influential in the quality and distribution of mineral resources now of industrial importance; and (4) they lie between the subdued, moderate highlands of Pre-Cambrian and early Paleozoic Age on the north and the high, rugged Alpine mountains on the south, with the Pre-Cambrian rocks also dominant in northwest Iberia. Hercynian uplifts are interspersed within and along the margins of the west Central Lowlands and are of high geographic importance.

The Central Lowlands—Eastern Section. The east Central Lowlands are characterized by continental climatic conditions rather than by any sharp differentiation in relief from the western part. A definite western boundary of this division cannot be drawn, and the line shown on Figure 19 must be considered as quite arbitrary. We deem it justifiably drawn because it divides fairly satisfactorily two distinct surface conditions even though both are plains types; namely, (1) the western part notably interrupted by prominent low mountainous structures, (2) the greatly expanded eastern part marked by almost uniform plains topography but with few structural interruptions visible at the surface.

This eastern section of the Central Lowlands extends to the Ural Mountains and from the Black Sea to the Arctic Ocean, thus embracing nearly one half of the total European area. On the whole, this great plain is due to extensive downfolding of the ancient

[5] A horst is a rock-block of simple or complex structure, but usually of plain-like surface, bounded by faults or sharp flexures and then lifted above its surroundings. Generally speaking, there is structural and topographic similarity between massifs and horsts, but the former are the more extensive while the latter are more restricted in area.

crystalline base of Archeozoic rocks which forms much of the surface bedrock of Finland and is also exposed in places in the Ural
Mountains, and constitutes the core of the high Caucasus. This
downfolding does not, however, constitute a simple, synclinal basin
because the ancient crystallines are exposed in a few places, covered with shallow deposits of sedimentaries in a number of areas,
while deeply buried in others.

The Podolian-Azov block north of the Black Sea, the southwestern part of the Soviet Union, is the best known example of
the first type mentioned. There the rocks have been raised to form
a well-known horst, although the surface is overlaid by Tertiary
formations and by loess. The underlying complex is exposed in
only a few places, mostly west of the Dnieper (Dnepr) River,
where the Podolian plateau has an elevation of 600 to 1,000 feet
and slopes gently to the southeast. Where the Dnieper has cut its
gorge into the hard rocks of the shield, rapids occur, and there has
been constructed the huge dam and hydroelectric plant which furnishes much of the power for the nearby industrial districts of the
Ukraine.

Adjacent to the northeast part of the Podolian-Azov block is a
deep structural basin, the Donets, where later sedimentaries have
been deposited covering coal measures which have been of great
value in developing the iron ore resources of the nearby Krivoi Rog
district. The downfold which produced the Donets Basin is classified as Caledonian and thus represents a feature of long duration
which has withstood several periods of slow, massive uplift and
subsidence without losing its early structural identity. Other and
similar instances of folds and block uplifts (horsts) are well known.

One additional well-known topographic feature within the Great
Russian Plain, namely, the Timan Mountains of northeast European U.S.S.R., should be mentioned. These mountains are not
high and are only moderately rugged but, like the Podolian-Azov
Shield and the Donets Basin, are of Caledonian origin. Thus they,
too, have maintained their structural entity during all the changes
that have occurred since approximately mid-Paleozoic times.

The instances given should suffice to give us a fairly clear view
of the complexity of structure, the folds, basins, and horsts, which
are known to constitute the broadly synclinal platform which supports the sedimentaries that constitute the bedrock of the extensive
North Polish Lowlands and Great Russian Plain. The topography
is monotonous, but the underlying structure is complex. The details are still only partly known despite the geologic investigations
that have long been carried on.

Earlier in this discussion the eastern limits of the Great Russian Plain were defined as the Ural Mountains. Let us now, in summary, merely add that the Urals are generally classified as Hercynian mountains because on their flanks and in some places even on their summits are the gently sloping and folded rock beds of late Paleozoic Age, the youngest being the Permian System, the type locality of which is in the area of the old Russian city of Perm (now Molotov). The Caucasus is younger and much more rugged, and is recognized as Alpine in age as well as in topographic features. The eastern division of the Central Lowlands of Europe is, therefore, a vast area of gentle relief, much more monotonous as to surface features than is the western division, and yet one of great structural complexity.

Central Plateaus, Mountains, and Basins. These comprise a nearly continuous zone from the Iberian Peninsula to Poland, between the Central Lowlands and the Alpine mountains. The Spanish Meseta is separated from the rest by the Aquitaine Basin and by the Pyrenees, which belong to the Alpine mountain system of Europe. The Spanish Meseta and the Andalusian, Aragon, and Portuguese Lowlands are discussed later in this chapter together with the whole Iberian Peninsula.

The Massif Central of France and the Rhone-Saone Lowlands connect with the Central Uplands. The Vosges, Ardennes, the Rhenish Slate Mountains, the Black Forest, the depressions of Thuringia and Hesse, the Saxon Uplands, the Scarplands of Swabia and Franconia and the Bohemian Massif present an irregular mass of hills and low mountains, interspersed by basins and the important thoroughfare of the Rhine. The plateau basin of the Lysa Gora in Poland forms the farthest eastern extension of this region.

The geographic significance of the ancient blocks, such as those of the Massif Central of France, the Slate Mountains, and the Bohemian Massif, needs special emphasis if one would understand in reasonable measure the distribution of natural resources in this part of Europe. Virtually without exception, these blocks remained resistant to the lateral pressures of pre-Hercynian times. When culmination came the Paleozoic rock layers were tilted and upraised by the pressures, and thus they became more readily discovered and exploited for use. This general statement applies to the clays of Limoges and the coal in the faulted central and eastern parts of the Massif Central as well as to the coal along the flanks of the Ardennes and the Slate Mountains, and in Silesia on the flanks of the Sudeten of the Bohemian Massif. The Harz Mountains must also be mentioned because on their steeply pitching flanks are the largest known deposits in the world of readily available potash salts. Let it be made clear, however, that the movements attributed to the Hercynian uplift do not imply absence of either earlier or later orogenic activity. In some cases, earlier movement, classified as Caledonian, has been proved, and in nearly all cases important uplift activity is known to have been nearly contemporaneous with the later (Alpine) revolution which is held responsible for the mighty southern mountains. In a number of instances, for example on the north flank of the Massif Central and of the Bohemian Massif, faulting has preserved coal beds of economic importance. These ancient blocks have in many cases been mantled by later sediments, but through periods of subsidence and uplift have withstood *en masse* the orogenic distortions that pressed against them. Their marginal contacts were more distinctly affected than the internal structure of the block.

The Alpine Mountains and Basins. Extending across Europe from the Pyrenees to the Caucasus is a mountainous terrain, sinuous, virtually unbroken, and characterized by high peaks, steep slopes, and deep canyons. The term "Alpine," which designates their dominant relief features, designates also their geologic sequence in the great mountain structural features of Europe beginning with the Pre-Cambrian, thence the Caledonian, Hercynian, and Alpine. They have in common the ruggedness characteristic of young mountains and their effects are and long have been to give meaning to the term, "Southern Europe," quite apart from the mere directional point of view.

Since it is the purpose here to point out only the broad relationships that characterize these mountain areas, we shall not deal with the details characteristic of the individual ranges because they are adequately treated in connection with the several countries in which the ranges occur. In order to understand how the Alpine mountains came into being, it is necessary to bear in mind that they are predominantly of Tertiary age, of late geologic origin so to speak, and that they were upfolded under tremendous pressures. The sediments which long had been accumulating through the deposition of detritus eroded from pre-existing lands to the north and possibly to the south produced a zone of weakness which gave way to high and extensive upthrusts and folding where it encountered blocks of old land so firmly anchored as to entirely withstand the pressure against them or suffer only faulting. Remnants of such blocks occur to the north in Central Europe. The ones most commonly recognized are the Armorican of northwestern France, the Massif Central of France, the Slate Mountains, the central block of Bohemia, and the Podolian Shield. Against these older blocks, mostly of Hercynian Age, the pressures from the south produced intense and lofty compressed folding even to the point of overturned folds in some cases. During the long millenniums of mountain building, fractures and faults were caused and weathering, erosion by wind, water, and ice were active, as they have been throughout earth history. The mountains as we know them are the products of these forces acting through long periods of time. The consequences, expressed in relation to our human activities, have long been subjects of study and discussion.

The steep slopes and higher crestal altitudes of the Alpine group of mountains, more than of any of the other mountains of Europe, have caused some effects to be so obvious as to impel early recognition. This holds true particularly of the passes across the mountains and the gateways between the several well-known units. For example, the Asiatics could most easily reach Europe through the lowlands north of the Caucasus, the Turks readily crossed the Dardanelles and moved into the Balkans along river valleys that conveniently opened eastward between the Balkan ranges. Along the mighty Danube lie the plains of Wallachia, separated from the Carpathian Basin by the Iron Gate where the river cut its gorge across the crystalline structure of the Transylvanian Alps. Beyond the Carpathian Basin the plateaus of Bohemia and Bavaria were within comparatively easy reach. Therefore, it is little wonder that during the past two thousand years these valleys into and through Alpine heights have been marked by the surging movement of peoples and a resultant mixture of ethnic and linguistic stocks.

To the west the Rhone Valley has served in similar manner as a route for movements of north and south Europeans. The Pyrenees, likewise, with passages along their eastern and western termini, have presented routes of invasion or retreat as the comparative strengths of peoples north and south varied. In general, however, the barrier effects of the mountains have remained most pronounced, this being particularly true of the Caucasus, the Carpathian, the Alps, and the Pyrenees.

A broad generalized grouping of the Alpine mountains would include the Baetic Cordillera of southern Spain, the Pyrenees, the Alps, the Apennines, the Carpathians, the Dinaric Ranges, the Pindus, and Balkan Ranges, and their eastward extensions along the Black Sea below the sea surface until the Crimea is reached, thence continued across the Kerch Peninsula and again reaching rugged grandeur in the Caucasus. To the north of this curved belt are the older shields and horsts of subdued topography, mostly Hercynian in age.

It must be kept in mind, however, that the general similarity of structure of the Alpine belt does not imply similarity of other aspects of geographic importance. Wright has aptly said that "a mountain range is not like a fence, it forms rather a wide zone of country." [6] The mountain ranges classed as of the Alpine group vary greatly in detail, but they are everywhere bold and impressive. Glaciers have sculptured the higher parts into serrated summits and crest lines. In the central and eastern Alps, ice filled all the main valleys during the last glacial epoch and extended far out upon the plains bordering the mountain ranges. Upon the recession of the ice, many lakes were formed in and beyond the mountains, valleys had been broadened, and thus favorable conditions for occupance and transport resulted. Where glaciers were not developed on so grand a scale, as in the Pyrenees and the Caucasus, the valleys are commonly narrower, more difficult to use for transportation routes, and the mountains are less readily accessible.

The width and extent of the mountain ranges are important geographic factors. When we consider that the areas of the ranges are extensive, we can realize that within them are conditions that tend to foster types of living quite different from those that prevail in plains areas. As examples we might note that the Alps north of Italy are from 80 to 150 miles in width, the Carpathians from 60 to 75 miles, the Pyrenees in places 70, and the Caucasus up to 125 miles. The barrier effects of mountain ranges are usually (and rightly) emphasized, but we should not overlook the fact that these large mountainous areas in themselves foster community life, along valleys separated from nearby valleys by mountain spurs that tend to develop and intensify local isolation. Nevertheless, the common factor of mountainous terrain facilitates the development of the independent spirit and the individuality of character which are universally attributed to the mountaineer.

Enclosed within the sweeping semicircle of the Carpathians is the Carpathian Basin, bordered on the west and southwest by the eastern Alps and the Dinaric ranges. The middle Danube enters from the northwest through the gap near Vienna and leaves the lowland on the southeast through its deep and narrow gorge, the Iron Gate, through the Carpathians. The larger part of the basin

[6] John K. Wright, *The Geographical Basis of European History* (New York: Henry Holt & Co., 1928), p. 55.

constitutes the Great Hungarian Lowlands. The Bihor Massif appears to have been largely responsible for the folded sedimentaries of the eastern and southeastern Carpathians, in somewhat the same manner as the block of interior Bohemia caused the surrounding mountain structure of that well-known projection of the southern mountains into the central plains realm of Europe.

The Southern Peninsulas. Projecting southward from the Alpine mountain masses and physically connected with them are the great Iberian, Italian, and Balkan peninsular lands of southern Europe. These peninsulas do not exhibit such general uniformity of structure as do the Alpine mountain ranges nor do their directional axes show any west-east uniform trend.

THE IBERIAN PENINSULA. Much of Portugal and Spain consists of a Paleozoic block, with a small area of Pre-Cambrian crystallines in the northwest, mostly covered in places by younger sedimentaries but which as a whole felt the mountain building forces of Hercynian age and has withstood the great thrusts associated with the later Alpine revolution. This central upland massif, briefly mentioned under Central Plateaus, is known as the Meseta, a broad tableland averaging 2,000-2,500 feet in elevation which overlooks with a bold escarpment the lowland of Aragon on the north. On the southern border is the dissected escarpment, the Sierra Morena, overlooking the lowlands of Andalusia drained by the Guadalquivir River, beyond which are the folded ranges of the Baetic Cordillera (which include the Sierra Nevada), of Alpine type and Tertiary age.

The surface of the Meseta is gently undulating, deeply cut by canyons, and surmounted by the Sierra de Guadarrama with crestal altitudes of 5,000 to 6,000 feet. This central range is often referred to as the Great Dividing Range because to the north is Old Castile and to the south New Castile. In both of these divisions there are rather extensive, fairly productive plains, formed by younger sedimentary deposits, Tertiary to Recent, laid down in broad, shallow depressions on the surface of the Meseta. This high upland is bordered by high mountains north and south and by steep escarpments east and west which serve to shut off much of the marine influences from the interior. On the west, because of the valleys which open in that direction, Portugal is the chief beneficiary of the marine influences and thus is favored by heavier rainfall and more moderate seasonal temperatures than is true of the Meseta. On the northwest, the sharply rising and rugged Asturias give rise to heavy rainfall and moderate temperatures which are restricted to a narrow zone because there are no broad valleys penetrating deeply into the interior.

The complex structure of the Iberian peninsula contains a wide variety of mineral resources. Associated with the older formations are veins and other ore bodies of iron, gold, silver, copper, tin, and mercury, some of which have been worked for centuries. Associated with late Paleozoic and younger strata are coal and various kinds of building stone, as well as clay.

THE ITALIAN PENINSULA. "Peninsular isolation with varied relief is most favorable to the development of marked individuality in a people." [7] Italy exhibits these characteristics in high degree. This peninsular strip is well anchored to the continent in the north by its attachment to the lofty central Alps. The extensive North Italian Plain has an east-west extent of over 350 miles or about one half the length of peninsular Italy proper. At the northwest, the Apennines are tied in without a major break with the Maritime Alps, so it may well be said that peninsular Italy is safely pegged to the roof of the continent. At its southern tip its structural connection with the Atlas Mountains of North Africa is suggested by the large island of Sicily and the smaller islands such as Malta and Pantelleria which project above the shallow waters of the straits between Sicily and Cape Bon.

The western Mediterranean thus appears to represent a great depression of the surface, probably coincident in origin with the great folded uplifts which gave rise to the surrounding mountains. These movements were attended by faulting and along some of the major faults volcanic activity was pronounced as evidenced by crater lakes in the Rome area and by still-active volcanoes. The islands of Corsica and Sardinia appear to be old lands that either remained as uplands when faulting lowered the adjacent basin floor or, more probably, they are upthrusts of horst-like origin in conjunction with the adjacent downthrusts. The net results of this series of crustal movement was (1) to divide the Mediterranean into two major divisions, (2) to give rise to the exceptionally deep portion, the Tyrrhenian Sea, and (3) to give rise to an "island bridge" from North Africa to the tip of the Italian boot. One needs merely to mention Carthage to recall the historical importance of the last-named point.

The Apennines are mountains of rather recent origin and consist of folded sedimentary rocks of Cretaceous and Tertiary age,

[7] Lionel W. Lyde, *The Continent of Europe* (London: Macmillan & Co., Ltd., 1924), p. 86.

the folding having occurred contemporaneously, in a geologic sense, with that of the Baetic Cordillera, the Pyrenees, and the Alps. They are, therefore, classified as members of the Alpine group. Their structure has involved pressures sufficient to transform some of the flanking limestone into marble and some of the shale into slate. Volcanic activities have given rise to deposits of sulphur and of mercury ores. Structure has also been a factor in the relief of the peninsula because steeply inclined beds have been conducive to rapid runoff of the seasonal rainfall and thus have induced severe erosion at the higher levels. In places the resulting relief is rugged in the extreme, canyons of one to two thousand feet being not uncommon. The higher altitudes generally have poor soils, are snow covered in the winter, and are sparsely populated. Thus, along the backbone of the peninsula there is not only a physical divide but a human "divide" as well.

South of the Alps and north of the great bend of the Apennines is the deep depression of the Po Valley, about 350 miles east and west, with an average width, north and south, of about 100 miles. During the latter part of the Alpine mountain building this area was warped down sufficiently to admit oceanic waters, and it was then an arm of the Adriatic Sea extending westward to the present Piedmont in the upper part of the Po Valley. Streams from the adjacent mountains, many of them glacier fed, have ever since been pouring their waters and their sediments into this long, curved arm of the sea and have built up the floor to become the present valley plain. The North Italian Plain drained by the Po is, on the whole, the most productive part of Italy because of the fertility of the soil, the accessibility of mineral raw materials, abundant water power from the mountain streams, and its energizing climate, stimulating because of moderate diurnal changes but protected by its adjacent mountains from undue seasonal extremes.

THE BALKAN PENINSULA. Some geographers and social scientists describe the Balkan Peninsula as including the broad area between the Black Sea and the Adriatic with the arc-like bend of the Carpathians and the southern part of the Great Hungarian Lowlands as its northern limits. Others prefer to consider the Grecian peninsula as the only representative element of this part of Mediterranean Europe. For the purpose of this introductory discussion it seems advisable to follow the structural lines and thus place the Rhodope Massif, and its rugged continuation across the Bosporus into Anatolian Turkey, as part of the Alpine continental mountain area, although the massifs were not due to alpine folding. Thus within its embrace are also the Hungarian Lowlands, the Wallachian Plain, and the ranges and valleys of Bulgaria. Westward from this complex topography are the sharp folds of the Dinaric Alps, coming down as a spur from the eastern or Julian Alps. These continue southward with their steep, escarpment-like slopes, caused by block faulting, facing the Adriatic and their gentler eastern slopes leading toward the Danube. In the southern part of the Dinaric Alps are deep and extensive sink holes known as *dolines*, which have developed upon the limestones and have given rise to the world-renowned karst region, where steep slopes, unproductive tablelands, and the highly productive valley floors of the dolines characterize a region difficult to cross or to conquer.

Beyond the Dinaric karst region southward the Pindus ranges take form and dominate peninsular Greece. These continue with karst characteristics as steep-sided ranges paralleled by valleys, all losing altitude southward with the result that in southern Greece the valleys have subsided below the sea and the highest parts of the ranges form the Aegean Islands, beyond the peninsular mainland. In the eastern part, along the line of contact with the Rhodope Massif, there appears to have been some faulting that has contributed to a line of weakness now marked by the Morava-Vardar valley, which has facilitated a relatively easy overland route between the Carpathian Basin and the eastern Mediterranean. In Greece this same zone of faulting is marked by some evidences of vulcanism as well as by steep-sided ranges extending beyond the mainland as islands separated by deep water straits. On the whole, therefore, the complexity of structure and of relief of southeastern peninsular Europe stand out in sharp contrast to the comparatively simple anticlinal structure of the Italian Peninsula.

For all the peninsulas of southern Europe the surface configuration of the land is of major importance climatically. While, broadly classified, the Mediterranean area is characterized by mild temperatures and moderate precipitation during the northern winter season, and by clear, sunny skies almost rainless during the summer, the diversity of relief and exposure causes sharp variation of local weather conditions. The typical Mediterranean type of climate is characteristic of the lowlands, and everywhere the effects of altitude as well as distance from the sea, and of exposure to prevailing winds must be recognized. The Sierra Nevada range of the Baetic Cordillera in southern Spain was so named because of the snow-mantled winter aspect of its peaks, quite in contrast to sunny Andalusia immediately to the north of them. The higher Apennines have heavy winter snowfall, as was painfully attested by the complaints of American soldiers who during World War II were sent to Italy with light clothing—some even taunted their geography professors back in the United States, who had expounded upon the beauties and the mildness of Mediterranean winters. Even in sunny Greece, famed Mount Olympus is snow-capped during much of the year.

Perhaps in conclusion we should emphasize that the geographic importance of the southern peninsulas can be summarized in their position as but slightly interrupted land bridges with Asia Minor and North Africa. The presence of numerous islands across the narrow gaps facilitated communication and exchange among the peoples concerned. While in many instances the nearness of people of unlike concepts of conduct and ambitions led to wars, we believe that the evil effects of such episodes were offset in large measure, if not entirely, by the long-run effects of ready exchange of goods and ideas. Of the two groups the exchange of ideas was, we believe, by far the more important. This provided the stimulus as well as the incentive to progress and through them developed the classical culture that still is held as an ideal throughout western civilization.

Conclusion. In the preceding pages we have tried to outline briefly and concisely the major natural environmental conditions under which the European people, past and present, have lived and must continue to live. While it is quite true that man himself is a great geographic architect, he must work with the materials at hand as truly as the sculptor or the builders of bridges and cathedrals. The results may be ordinary or mediocre, or they may be masterpieces. Europe has contributed both mediocrity and masterpieces, but it is the latter that constitute the essence of European culture and of progress. The chapters that follow will set forth more fully how this has been accomplished, and what the trends appear to forecast for the years ahead.

BIBLIOGRAPHY FOR THIS CHAPTER

DALY, R. A.   *The Changing World of the Ice Age.*   New Haven: Yale University Press, 1934.

KENDREW, W. G.   *The Climates of the Continents,* 3d ed.   New York: Oxford University Press, 1942.

SCHUCHERT, CHARLES E., and DUNBAR, C. O.   *Historical Geology.*   New York: John Wiley & Sons, Inc., 1933.

GENERAL BIBLIOGRAPHY

A. BOOKS IN ENGLISH

ALNWICK, HERBERT. *Geography of Europe*. London: George G. Harrap & Co., Ltd., 1948.

BLANCHARD, RAOUL, and CRIST, RAYMOND E. *A Geography of Europe*. New York: Henry Holt & Co., Inc., 1935.

BLANCHARD, W. O., and VISHER, S. S. *Economic Geography of Europe*. New York: McGraw-Hill Book Co., Inc., 1931.

BOGARDUS, J. F. *Europe, A Geographical Survey*. New York: Harper & Bros., 1934.

FITZGERALD, WALTER. *The New Europe*. New York: Harper & Bros., 1946.

GOTTMAN, JEAN. *A Geography of Europe*. New York: Henry Holt & Co., Inc., 1950.

HOLBORN, HAJO. *The Political Collapse of Europe*. New York: Alfred A. Knopf, Inc., 1951.

HUBBARD, GEORGE D. *The Geography of Europe*, 2d ed. New York: Appleton-Century-Crofts, Inc., 1952.

MORGAN, ORA S. (ed.) *The Agricultural Systems of Middle Europe*. New York: The Macmillan Co., 1933.

NEWBIGIN, MARION I. *Southern Europe*, 3d ed. London: Methuen & Co., Ltd., 1949.

NOTESTEIN, FRANK W., and others. *The Future Population of Europe and the Soviet Union*. New York: Columbia University Press, 1944.

SHACKLETON, MARGARET R. *Europe, A Regional Geography*, 4th ed. New York: Longmans, Green & Co., Inc., 1950.

VAN VALKENBURG, S., and HELD, C. C. *Europe*, 2d ed. New York: John Wiley & Sons, Inc., 1952.

B. BOOKS IN FOREIGN LANGUAGES

BAUER, L., and HIRSCH, R. *Länderkunde von Mittel-Europa* (Regional Geography of Central Europe). Munich: R. Oldenbourg, 1951.

BLANCHARD, RAOUL. *Géographie de l'Europe*. Paris: F. Alcan, 1936.

DEMANGEON, ALBERT, and PERPILLON, AIMÉ. *Le Monde moins l'Europe* (The World Outside of Europe). Paris: Librairie Hachette, 1948.

KOPPEN, WLADIMIR, and GEIGER, R. (eds.). *Handbuch der Klimatologie* (Handbook of Climatology). Berlin: Gebrüder Borntraeger, 1930-39.

KOSSMANN, O. *Warum ist Europa so?* (Why Is Europe the Way It Is?). Zürich: S. Hirzel, 1950.

MACHATSCHEK, FRITZ. *Europa als Ganzes* (Europe as a Whole). Leipzig: F. Deuticke, 1929.

MAULL, OTTO (ed.). *Länderkunde von Südeuropa* (Regional Geography of Southern Europe). ("Enzyklopädie der Erdkunde," ed. Oskar Kende). Leipzig and Vienna: F. Deuticke, 1929.

PHILIPPSON, ALFRED. *Europa ausser Deutschland* (Europe Except Germany), 3d ed. Leipzig: Bibliographisches Institut, 1928.

REINHARD, R., VOPPEL, K., KRAUSE, K., and others (eds.). E. V. Seydlitz'sche Geographie. *Hundertjahrausgabe: Europa ohne Deutschland* (Centennial edition: Europe Except Germany). Breslau: F. Hirt, 1931, Vol. II.

VIDAL DE LA BLACHE, P., and GALLOIS, L. (eds.). *Géographie Universelle*, 7 vols. Paris: Librairie Armand Colin, 1927-47.

chapter *3*

THE BRITISH ISLES

Two main islands—Great Britain and Ireland—make up the British Isles. Set between the ports of Northern Europe and the trade route to the Americas, these islands have for long exerted a power disproportionate to their tiny size. On their 121,000 square miles there live 53,000,000 people, a population density of almost 440 to the square mile. A vast colonial empire remains within the jurisdiction of the United Kingdom, and Dominions many times her size owe allegiance to either the British Crown or the Commonwealth. The English language has become the most widely spoken *lingua franca* of the civilized world, as well as the mother tongue of millions non-British by birth.

Four peoples, three governments, and two states exist within the British Isles, and the succeeding account will be unintelligible to the student unless he has a clear notion of their political organization and mutual relations. *Great Britain* consists of the three national units of Scotland, Wales, and England, each conscious of its separate identity, but divided today by unmarked boundaries of very limited political significance. The *United Kingdom* includes these three units and the six counties of Northern Ireland —comprising most of the ancient province of Ulster. The Irish people is thus divided, for the remainder of the island is the *Irish Republic*, created as a Free State in 1921, and now by its own vehement wish independent of the British Crown.

The United Kingdom is a parliamentary democracy (based on universal suffrage) with a limited constitutional monarchy. Paramount authority rests with Parliament, over which neither the Crown nor the Judiciary has any power; it has been well said of the British Queen that she reigns but does not rule. Parliament— seated in Westminster, on the bank of the Thames—governs Eng-

land and Wales directly. In certain aspects of government: agriculture, health, planning, education, and home affairs, Scotland
is governed through administrative departments responsible to the
Secretary of State for Scotland; there is, however, no separate Scots
parliament. Northern Ireland elects members to Westminster,
but also has its own parliament in Belfast; this body legislates for
most matters except foreign affairs, income tax, the post office, and
the Judiciary and fiscal policy, including customs and excise.

The Irish Republic is also a parliamentary democracy, with an
elected President of limited constitutional powers not unlike those
of the British monarchy. A long and harsh record of interference
in Irish affairs has earned for the Protestant English the bitter
anger of the Catholic population, a sentiment fanned and exploited
by most political groups. The partition of Ireland into two units
is vociferously denounced by the southern Irish and as stoutly defended by the Protestant Ulstermen, who precipitated the Civil
War by their refusal to accept government, as they put it, from
Rome via Dublin.

English is the first tongue of most members of all four nations.
Three of the old Celtic tongues survive, however: Gaelic (in the
western Scottish Highlands), Welsh (spoken as the first tongue
in parts of Northern and Western Wales), and Irish Gaelic, the
tongue of the densely populated Atlantic shore of Ireland, the
Gaeltacht. Manx (on the Isle of Man) is virtually extinct, as is
Cornish. The Celtic tongues and the ancient traditions with which
they are associated are jealously preserved by nationalist sentiment.
In Wales, this nationalism takes the benevolent form—as a rule—
of a widespread interest in a national literature and in song. In
the Irish Republic, however, efforts are being made to revive Gaelic
as the national tongue, and access to public office is now confined
to those who speak it.

The British Empire, one of the largest world-wide territorial
organizations, is joined to the parent country by ties of widely varying closeness. The self-governing dominions, including Canada,
Australia, South Africa, New Zealand, India, Ceylon, and Pakistan,
are joined only by ties of sympathy and comradeship. Not even
allegiance to the Crown can now be claimed for all of them; India,
for example, is constitutionally a republic, though she accepts the
Queen as the symbol of the free association of the independent
member nations and as the Head of the Commonwealth. All these
self-governing states are politically independent of the United Kingdom and may withdraw from the Commonwealth if they so wish.
The dependent territories (i.e., those lacking complete autonomy

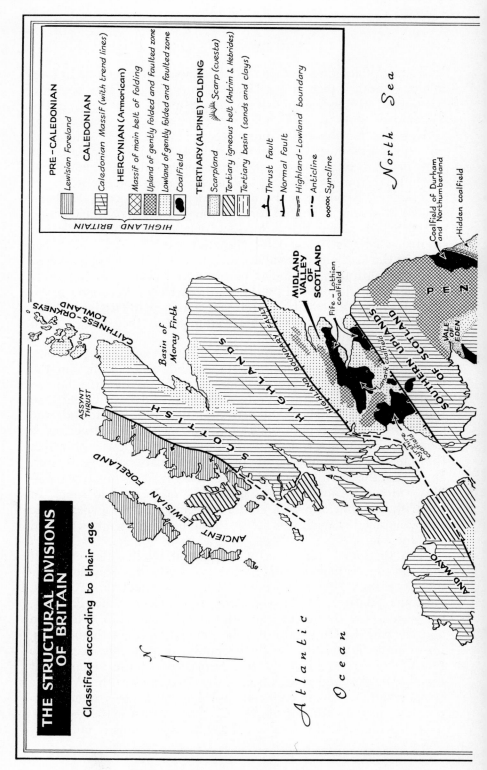

THE STRUCTURAL DIVISIONS OF BRITAIN

Classified according to their age

PRE-CALEDONIAN
- Lewisian Foreland

CALEDONIAN
- Caledonian Massif (with trend lines)

HERCYNIAN (Armorican)
- Massif of main belt of folding
- Upland of gently folded and faulted zone
- Lowland of gently folded and faulted zone
- Coalfield

TERTIARY (ALPINE) FOLDING
- Scarpland   Scarp (cuesta)
- Tertiary igneous belt (Antrim & Hebrides)
- Tertiary basin (sands and clays)

- Thrust Fault
- Normal Fault
- Highland–Lowland boundary
- Anticline
- Syncline

HIGHLAND BRITAIN

North Sea

Atlantic Ocean

N

ANCIENT LEWISIAN FORELAND

CAITHNESS-ORKNEYS LOWLAND

ASSYNT THRUST

Basin of Moray Firth

SCOTTISH HIGHLANDS

HIGHLAND BOUNDARY FAULT

MIDLAND VALLEY OF SCOTLAND

Fife – Lothian coalfield

Ayr coalfield

Ayrshire coalfield

SOUTHERN UPLANDS OF SCOTLAND

VALE OF EDEN

PEN

Coalfield of Durham and Northumberland

Hidden coalfield

AND MAYO

114

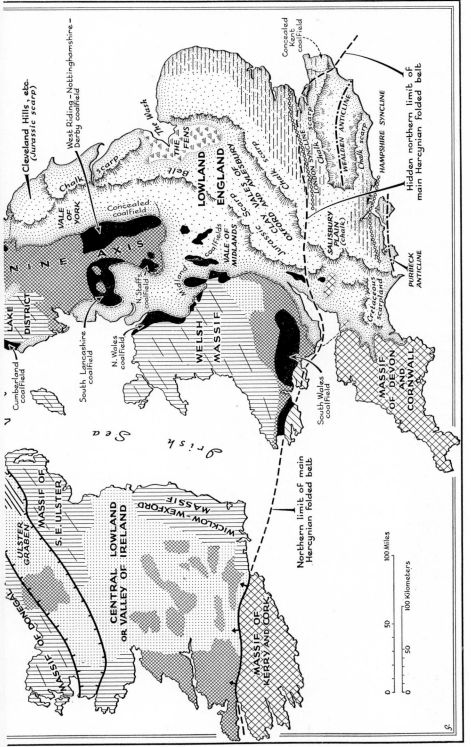

FIGURE 21

115

and the freedom to secede) are governed in several ways: some are colonies, others protectorates, still others federated states like Malaya. Some, like Malta, have achieved complete self-government in home affairs. European territories having the status of British colonies are Malta and Gibraltar, both strategic naval bases vital to the defense of the Mediterranean.

To the parent nation, the colonial territories long ago ceased to serve purely as areas exploitable for raw materials and cheap labor. In all of them, the colonial authorities are committed to programs of education, better social services, improved technology, and scientific research. The aim of the British has been, in general, to raise the level of education, technical skill, and communal responsibility to the point at which each colony can attain self-government. This program has proved costly, and most of the colonies are liabilities rather than assets, in the financial sense. In certain areas, however, these territories produce exportable surpluses of goods having a high value on the world's markets: thus the rubber production of the plantations of Malaya is vital to the dollar earnings of the entire Sterling Area.

The Physical Landscape

The land of the British Isles exhibits two strikingly contrasted aspects. The west and north, confronting the Atlantic, is hilly or mountainous, and has a wet, oceanic climate. The term *Highland Zone* is often applied to it. Southern and eastern England, by contrast, is the gently rolling *Lowland Zone* with a drier climate akin to that of the nearby European lowlands.[1]

The major divisions of the British landscape are structurally determined; each division has its characteristic types of rock and a distinct structural pattern (Figure 21). The landscape also shows many traces of a complex erosional history, upon which we can barely touch in this chapter.[2] It falls readily into three provinces, each of which corresponds to one of the major divisions of the mainland of Europe:

1. *Caledonian Britain*, comprising a series of rugged uplands in the north and west, which continue the structural province of the Kjölen Range in Scandinavia.
2. *Hercynian Britain*, making up the rest of the Highland Zone, and including in addition the chief coal fields. As its name

[1] See, for example, H. J. Mackinder, *Britain and the British Seas* (Oxford: Oxford University Press, 1902). Much of this geographical classic is written around the Highland-Lowland theme.
[2] For geologic terms, see Appendix I.

implies, this province corresponds to the Hercynian belt of the continental mainland.

3. *Lowland Britain,* consisting of the gently folded Mesozoic and Tertiary rocks of the English plain, and very comparable in structure, for example, with the Paris and Münster basins.

Caledonian and Hercynian Britain together make up the Highland Zone already mentioned. They have much in common, and might be considered together but for the vital difference that only the Hercynian structures affect the distribution of coal fields.[3]

The Three Major Provinces

Caledonian Britain. In this province, the surface structures largely date from a mid-Paleozoic disturbance. The belt consists of (a) the Scottish Highlands and the hills of Donegal and Mayo, a unit composed largely of gneisses and schists, with large granite intrusions, (b) the Scottish Southern Uplands and the mountains of southeast Ulster, where the bedrock is chiefly of greywackes, slates, and intrusive granites, and (c) the plateaus of North Wales and Wicklow-Wexford in Eire, where the rocks are similar but contain the giant Wicklow granite. In all these separate uplands, the physiographic trend follows the NE-SW run of the folding, as it does in Norway. All three consist of bleak, rain-swept highlands, broken into Irish and British segments by the Irish Sea and its channels. To them may be added the small, compact mountain region of the English Lake District, with its nucleus of early Paleozoic volcanics. To this upland the later mountain-building episodes have contributed much, but its affinities are Caledonian.

Though the rocks of Caledonian Britain range in age from Silurian to early Pre-Cambrian, and in lithology from fine-grained slates to massive, coarse-grained granites, differentiation between rock-types is not of major geographical significance. Everywhere the land is rolling, considerable in elevation (usually 1,500-3,000 feet), and generally rather impervious. The Caledonian highlands are *par excellence* the scene of that characteristic British landscape, the moorland. Since they are nowhere heavily mineralized and nowhere present extensive lowland areas, they have remained unattractive lands for settlement since the Bronze Age.

---

[3] Valuable additional material is given in Great Britain, Geological Survey, *British Regional Geology* (London: H. M. Stationery Office, various dates), a series of short memoirs covering all parts of Great Britain.

Hercynian Britain. The continuation and structural contemporary of the Hercynian hill country of Central Europe and France, this second province presents a striking contrast to the bleak, thinly populated landscapes of the Caledonian belt. Coming as they did at the close of Carboniferous time, the Hercynian earth movements were able to involve in their structures the precious Coal Measures that were to be the basis of the British Industrial Revolution. The largest concentrations of population now occur in the coal fields along the margin of the Highland Zone.

This second component of Highland Britain is divisible into two broad parts. Southernmost Britain, from southwest Ireland to Kent, lies within the main belt of Hercynian folding (continued in Brittany to the south). The mountains of Kerry, Cork, and Waterford belong to this belt. Here the chief ranges trend roughly east-west, parallel to the folding. The valleys between the ranges have been partially drowned to form the celebrated *ria* coast. The peninsulas of Devon and Cornwall, Pembroke, Gower, and the Vale of Glamorgan in South Wales make up the rest. Most of the rocks of these areas are limestones, sandstones, shales, or slates, but large granite bosses occur in Devon and Cornwall, forming the high ground of Bodmin Moor, Dartmoor, and smaller uplands. This southern division of Hercynian Britain resembles the Caledonian belt in landscapes. Coal-bearing rocks are rarely involved in the principal folded belt.

The second division lies north of the chief folded zone, and consists of an extensive series of gently folded and fractured basins or uplifts. The relief is varied, extensive lowlands alternating with some of the hilliest parts of Britain.

The Midland Valley of Scotland, the northernmost division, separates the Caledonian masses of the Highlands and Southern Uplands, from which it is divided by boundary faults, making it a true graben. Much of the floor of the Valley, the populous heart of Scotland, is underlain by sandstones, but certain areas of volcanic rocks have formed high hills, such as the Ochils and the Campsie Fells. There are three large basins containing coal-bearing sediments, in Ayrshire, Lanarkshire, and Fife-Midlothian. The boundary faults are continued into northern Ireland, where a similar graben (unfortunately coal-less) separates the Donegal-Mayo Caledonian massif from that of southeast Ulster.

The Pennine axis forms the backbone of Northern England, extending from the Southern Uplands of Scotland to the Trent Valley in the Midlands. The upland consists chiefly of an upfaulted block, whose western rim is a high fault-line scarp looking across the lowlands of the Eden Valley and the Lancashire basins (Figure 22). The eastern slope is less abrupt, the Carboniferous sediments that make up the entire upland dipping gently eastward beneath the younger rocks of Yorkshire and Lincolnshire. The upland is floored chiefly by the Millstone Grit, an estuarine deposit whose name suggests its connection with the metallurgical industries of Sheffield. In places, however, limestones form the upland surface, which is then dry and riddled with potholes, caverns, and dry gorges. Most of the Pennines are wet moorlands with summits averaging 1,500 to 2,000 feet.

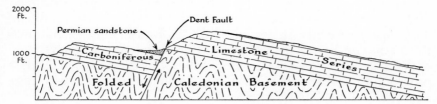

FIGURE 22. Geological cross section of the Northern Pennines, about latitude 54° 30′ north. The Uplift is a tilted block of the Carboniferous Limestone Series (Mississippian Period), bounded along its western margin by a fault-line scarp on the Dent Fault. Elsewhere in the Pennines structure is more akin to a true upfold (anticline), but the western edge is usually faulted as above. (After D. A. Wray.)

On either flank of the Pennines are basins containing Coal Measures, some of which form major coal fields. On the west flank there are three such basins. The northernmost borders the north slope of the Lake District massif. The central basin, the largest, is the South Lancashire coal field, the home of the cotton textile industry. The third is the North Staffordshire coal field, around Stoke-on-Trent, forming the southwestern extremity of the Pennine upland. On the east flank there are two basins only, but both are large and important coal fields. In Durham and Northumberland the Coal Measures outcrop over a wide area of low moorland, and continue eastward beneath the sea and the younger rocks of the Lowland Zone. In West Riding, Nottinghamshire, and Derbyshire there is an even larger coal-bearing region, which is extended eastwards as a "hidden" coal field beneath the younger rocks of the Trent Valley.

There is no Irish equivalent of the Pennine structures. The entire center of the island, the Central Valley, between the Caledonian and Hercynian massifs already discussed, is floored by gently folded sandstones, shales, and limestones, now largely obscured by glacial till and the great peat bogs. Though generally a lowland, central Ireland has several areas of considerable hills.

A large basin makes up much of South Wales and Herefordshire north of the main Hercynian folded belt. In Glamorganshire a large area of Coal Measures forms the South Wales coal field, a hilly country traversed by deep valleys in which the mining towns are clustered. In Herefordshire, by contrast, the Devonian Old Red Sandstone underlies a broad, fertile lowland famous for its brilliant red soils. Between the two contrasted landscapes is a line of formidable moorlands, the Brecon Beacons, Black Mountains, and other hills.

The remaining element in Hercynian Britain is the submerged floor of Lowland England, where the Paleozoic rocks are obscured by the younger cover. In many parts of the Midlands the buried landscape re-emerges; the small South Staffordshire coal field and the basins of Leicestershire are of this type. The entirely concealed East Kent coal field was first deduced by geologists, and then proved (in 1890) by a trial boring put down in connection with the abortive Channel Tunnel project.

Lowland Britain. This third province is a rolling countryside whose highest cuestas barely exceed 1,000 feet. Composed of Mesozoic and Cenozoic rocks much softer than those of Caledonian and Hercynian Britain, the Lowland Zone is essentially a cuesta-form landscape with cuestas (escarpments) on the resistant limestones and sandstones, and broad lowlands (*vales* being the accepted local term) on the intervening clays and marls. Throughout the history and prehistory of human settlement these vales and cuestas have remained strikingly distinct in the opportunities they offered to the settler. Most of them are identified by local names, after the fashion of the French *pays*.[4]

In general, the beds dip gently southeastwards towards the English Channel or southern North Sea. The oldest rocks outcrop in the Midlands, lapping like a sea against the limits of the Highland Zone, and the youngest occur in eastern East Anglia. But the simplicity of this picture is disturbed by the existence of four major east-west folds that dominate the outcrop-pattern of southern England. These are (a) *the London basin or syncline*, roughly coincident with lower and middle Thames basins, (b) *the Wealden anticline*, forming the peninsula of Kent, Surrey and Sussex, (c) *the Hampshire basin or syncline*, and (d) *the Purbeck anticline*, delimiting that basin on the south. Much of the last system is drowned by the English Channel.

---

[4] A very detailed account is given in S. W. Wooldridge and D. L. Linton, *Structure, Surface and Drainage in South-East England* (London: Institute of British Geographers, Publication 10, 1939).

The two basins of London and Hampshire respectively form broad vales floored largely by Tertiary sands and clays (hence the common term "Tertiary basins"). The anticlines, however, bring to the surface the Mesozoic strata, and the cuesta-and-vale landscape of the east Midlands is renewed about their flanks.[5]

The Midlands of England are largely floored by bright red soils developed on the clays and sands of the Triassic outcrop. The Midland plain passes southeastwards into a succession of cuestas and vales that makes up the whole of southeast England. Some of the cuestas are very significant in the life of the country. The Cotswolds, for example, developed on limestones of Jurassic age, have become a rich farming land famous for the beauty of its stone houses and rich villages. Elsewhere in the Jurassic outcrop are the iron-rich deposits of Northamptonshire, Lincolnshire, and the East Riding. Scarcely less significant is the cuesta developed on the Chalk, an upper Cretaceus limestone that provided the dry uplands on which early man preferred to live, as well as the flints from which he fashioned his tools (Figure 23). None of these cuestas much exceeds 1,000 feet (the highest being the Hambleton-Cleveland Hills in the Yorkshire Wolds) and many are much less. The whereabouts of the most significant are shown on Figure 21.

The vales between the cuestas, being developed chiefly on heavy clays, remained for long under heavy forest. Today, however, they are mostly prosperous farmlands devoted to a pastoral husbandry.

The gentle folds that diversify the structure of the Lowland Zone were formed at the time when the great convulsion of the Alpine mountain-building period was in progress. The British Isles were in the groundswell of this disturbance. While the Lowland of England was receiving the imprint of these movements, igneous activity broke out in the north of Ireland and in western Scotland. The islands of Mull and Skye, and the great basalt flows of Antrim were formed at this time. Though these igneous rocks are among the youngest elements of the British structure, the landscapes developed from them are akin to those of Caledonian Britain, to which they properly belong.

The Effects of Glaciation

In common with most of Northern Europe, the British Isles succumbed to several glaciations during Pleistocene times, and the landscapes of both Highland and Lowland zones show many traces of this ordeal. The ultimate advance of the ice covered almost all

[5] Ibid., pp. 52-56, 80-97.

FIGURE 23. The Chalk Cliffs of Dover. Much of England's coast line is "cliffed" by the recent marine submergence. (UKIO Photo.)

122

of Britain north of a line from the Severn estuary to the coast of Essex. The ice sheets were local, deploying onto the plains from dispersal centers over the principal massifs of the Highland Zone. The main Scandinavian glacier did, however, reach east coastal districts during at least one of the glacial episodes.

In the Highland Zone, the erosive effects of the glaciation were considerable. The uplands are typically thin-soiled, and there are many *roches moutonnées*, crag-and-tail phenomena, and the like to confirm the effects of the ice. These are conspicuously absent from the hills of Devon, where deep residual soils are widely developed, and bare rock is chiefly notable in the curious granite caps of the Tors of Dartmoor. Many of the higher summits of the glaciated country also show the effects of local alpine glaciation. Cirques, arêtes, and other characteristic alpine forms are well developed, for example, in the Snowdon and Cader Idris ranges of Wales, the English Lake District, the western Highlands, and the higher hills of Ireland.

The valley systems of the Highland Zone were much modified by the ice. In the highest areas the characteristic features of glacial overdeepening are magnificently displayed, especially in the Scottish Highlands, the Lake District, and Snowdonia. The wider valleys of lower districts are usually heavily drift-plugged, and diversions of drainage are numerous. Perhaps the most spectacular evidence of glaciation in the Highland Zone is the complex of fjords (sea-lochs) in western Scotland.

Ireland owes much of its present-day landscape to the glaciations. The Central Lowland is plastered with drift, much of it yielding soils of high fertility. Charlesworth has estimated that one eighth of the country consists of drumlins, of which there are tens of thousands, averaging in size about 1,350 by 750 feet.[6] Eskers, too, wind across the Irish plains in bewildering profusion, often carrying roads and railways, and offering well-drained land for farm buildings. The drainage is badly disturbed, and there are numerous ponds and lakes. Large areas of peat bog—a characteristic Irish landscape— overlie the till and provide the inhabitants with much of their fuel.

Lowland England contains considerable areas of drift-covered terrain. Much of the east is covered by thin sheets of calcareous till, largely derived from the Chalk or Jurassic oolites over which the ice was forced to pass. The Midland tills are made up chiefly of Triassic débris. The rivers of southern and eastern England are flanked by numerous gravel terraces, associated with the fre-

[6] J. K. Charlesworth, quoted by T. W. Freeman, *Ireland* (London: Methuen & Co., Ltd., 1950), pp. 28-29.

quent shifts of base-level in Pleistocene and recent times. Many of these terraces appear to have attracted Paleolithic and Mesolithic man, whose hand axes and other flint implements abound in the gravels. The most recent movement of base-level has been upward, and most of the rivers reach the sea through drowned estuaries, with wide areas of marshes and saltings. The Wash, with the Fens that surround it, is the best-known example. Drainage and careful containment of the sea, the patient work of English and Dutch engineers for three centuries, has converted the Fens into the richest arable land of England.

Climate

Little need be written of the general character of the British climate beyond what has been said in Chapter 2.[7] The country exhibits in a marked degree the oceanic characteristics typical of the whole northwest coast of Europe. Within Britain itself there are marked differences of climate, chiefly of rainfall and secondarily of temperature. The Highland Zone has in general a high rainfall and a small annual range of temperature, whereas the Lowland Zone is much drier and more extreme in its temperature cycle. Rainfall is lowest in the Thames Estuary and in the Fenlands, but is nowhere so low as to create serious problems for the farmer except in drought years. The wettest parts of the Highland Zone— the Lake District and the Snowdon Massif—have stations with mean annual rainfall over 150 inches. At the opposite end of the scale are falls of less than 20 inches in the Thames estuary.[8]

Winter is mild. Mildest conditions extend along the west coast, and even the Orkney Islands have mean temperatures of 40° F. in January (warmer than Paris). Coolest regions are the east coastal districts of Scotland and East Anglia and, of course, the high hills. Very heavy rainfall deluges the uplands, and severe gales are frequent along the south, west, and north coasts as Atlantic cyclones pass to the north of Scotland. Snowfall is uncommon, and rarely lies long on the west coast or the lowlands. The southwest coast is exceptionally mild, and may escape frost during many winters. Subtropical plants are open-grown in many places along the Cornish Riviera, which is also the place of origin for early vegetables and flowers for the London market.

[7] The standard reference work is E. G. Bilham, *The Climate of the British Isles* (London: Macmillan & Co., Ltd., 1938). Note that temperature maps in this volume are reduced to sea level, a fact which deprives them of all value.

[8] See climatic graphs, Appendix II.

The summer is warm enough for most of the common cereal and root-crops, though corn (maize) cannot be attempted except for silage. Over the southern half of Ireland and Britain, July temperatures slightly exceed 60° F., whereas in the coolest parts of Highland Scotland they barely attain 55° F. Wheat can be grown over most of Ireland, Wales, and England; it is ripened as far north as the Moray Firth. Oats and barley are at home throughout the country.

Sunshine is often deficient in Britain. The south comes off best, and may attain almost Mediterranean durations (because of the long days) in a good summer. Sometimes, however, cool and cloudy weather may persist throughout the summer, and the ripening and reaping of the harvest then presents many problems. In fact, the British climate is prone to prolonged spells of good or bad weather; British meteorologists call this "persistency of type."

Vegetation

The landscape of Neolithic Britain was very densely forested, like that of eastern North America before white settlement. Today, after several millenniums of assaults by man, the forests have all but vanished, and Britain has the poorest forest cover in Europe. The landscape of the lowlands shows few traces of the vanished forests, though hedgerow trees and farm woodlots or game-coverts give the distant prospect a wooded look. Ireland has the least area of forest—if St. Patrick banished the snake from Ireland, his people have been almost as successful in ousting the tree. British forests have vanished under the combined needs of farmers for cleared land, the early navy for ships and their masts, the ironsmith for charcoal, and the populace generally for firewood.[9]

The climax forest appears to be dominated by the pedunculate oak (*Quercus robur*)[10] and the durmast oak (*Quercus sessiliflora*), both of which extend right across peninsular Europe. Oakwoods occur in every part of the British Isles. The durmast oak seems dominant in the woodlands on the thin, acid soils of the wet hill lands of the Highland Zone, whereas the pedunculate oak is dominant in the drier east. The two species hybridize freely. The common ash (*Fraxinus excelsior*) is often a co-dominant, and may form

[9] This section owes much to A. G. Tansley, *The British Islands and Their Vegetation* (Cambridge: Cambridge University Press, 1939). This monumental work also contains long treatments of soil, a topic little regarded in much plowed England, where soil profiles of a mature sort are hard to come by.

[10] Recent opinion suggests that *Quercus robur* may have been introduced by man.

extensive pure stands, especially in limestone country. The beech
(*Fagus sylvatica*) is also common as an associate of the oaks. Like
the ash, it may occur in pure stands, but is largely confined to the
south and southeast of England. Other hardwoods of common
occurrence are the birches (discussed below), certain elms, willows
(*Salix spp.*), alder, aspen (*Populus tremula*), lime (*Tilia cordata*),
and the hornbeam (*Carpinus betulus*).

This deciduous forest climax closely resembles that of Central
Europe and has obvious affinities with the forest of eastern North
America. In fact, each of the above genera has representatives in
the forests of the Ohio Valley, though in no case is the same species
present. The climax has been established in Britain since the climatic optimum some 7,000 years ago. Since it now survives only
in patches, it is impossible to sketch the constitution of the climax
cover in any detail. In particular, one cannot say for sure whether
the cover extended without essential thinning over the lower hills
of the Highland Zone, or over the dry chalk Downs of England,
which may have been grassy.

The forests that covered Britain in the Boreal and pre-Boreal
climatic periods (roughly 9000–5000 B.C.) were very different in
composition. The birches (*Betula pubescens; Betula pendula*)
were the most widespread trees, but their dominance was challenged
by the Scotch pine (*Pinus silvestris*). Today the birches are common all over Britain, especially in open heaths and sandy soils. The
pine forms considerable forests in Highland Scotland, but finds its
ideal home on the sandy soils of southern England, where it forms a
distinctive and handsome landscape. The Bagshot plateaus in the
London Basin and the New Forest in the Hampshire Basin have
the largest stands.

Much of the surviving woodland of Britain is harvested regularly for coppice, i.e., faggots of shrubby species like the hazel (*Corylus avellana*) grown beneath an open canopy of fully developed
trees. There is also much ornamental woodland planted by park-
land designers, usually of hybrids or of exotic conifers. Indeed,
over many parishes in southern England the number of foreign
species probably exceeds considerably the roster of native ones.
There are specimens of Douglas fir (*Pseudotsuga taxifolia*) nearly
200 feet high in Wales, as well as numerous groves of developing
redwoods (*Sequoia sempervirens*). There are probably more Cedars of Lebanon (*Cedrus libani*) in some English counties than in
Lebanon itself.

The hills of the Highland Zone of Britain are characteristically
treeless, and present the landscape known throughout the country

as "moorland." Much of this vegetation is today established on land that would certainly sustain forest, but for the work of domesticated animals, rabbits, and other beasts. The moorland is by no means uniform and presents several contrasted types of cover:

1. Upland heaths or heather moors, dominated by the common heather (*Calluna vulgaris*), occur over huge areas, especially on fairly steep slopes.

2. Grasslands are also common, dominated by bent (*Agrostis tenuis*), purple moor grass (*Molinia caerulea*), and mat grass (*Nardus stricta*), often associated with gorse (*Ulex galeii*) and that spreading scourge of the hill farmer, bracken (*Pteridium aquilenum*).

3. Sedge-moors occur on the wetter ground, dominated by sedges like cotton grass (*Eriophorum spp.*) and deer grass (*Scirpus caespitosus*), as well as rushes (*Juncus spp.*) and a few shrubs.

4. With increasing wetness true bogs are found, in which the vegetation grows on a peat layer, often of considerable thickness. *Sphagnum* moss is the characteristic plant, though sedges, rushes, and certain shrubs, like sweet gale (*Myrica gale*) are also widespread. Huge expanses of bog cover much of Ireland and the hills of western Scotland.

Moorlike vegetation also occurs on sandy common land in the Lowland Zone, often as an early stage in the succession leading to pine forest. Characteristic species are the lowland gorse (*Ulex europaeus*) and various brambles.

The Peopling of Britain

Prehistory. The peopling of the British Isles began at so early a date that its detailed story is forever lost. The earliest inhabitants have left us nothing but primitive flint tools and weapons with which to trace their homes and characteristics. Paleolithic man appears to have been scattered thinly around the coasts and in the hills of southern England, where he practiced in the second and third interglacial periods his crude economy of fruit gathering and hunting. The *Riss* and *Würm* glacial advances may have driven him from Britain, or perhaps into the sea caves and limestone caverns of southern England: we have no means of ascertaining his movements. In any event the early dawn of man's occupance, though it was probably spread over a period a hundred times as great as that which has elapsed since Paleolithic times, has left no trace on the

British landscape, and contributes nothing to present-day geography.[11]

It is all otherwise with the primitive societies that spread across Britain in Neolithic, Bronze Age, and Iron Age times (2500 B.C.–100 A.D.). The peopling of the islands proceeded in these years from both western and eastern sources. Over Ireland and the Highland Zone of Great Britain there arose in Neolithic times a vigorous Megalithic culture, presumably derived from Iberia and the Mediterranean via the western sea route and Brittany (2350–2000 B.C.). It left us a lasting record in the shape of burial cairns, dolmens, long barrows, and other hill-top or headland monuments, which abound throughout western Britain: of these the greatest is Stonehenge (actually of early Bronze Age date) on the Chalk plateau of Salisbury Plain. This Plain—which remained an important focus of early settlement—was the easternmost region settled by the Megalithic peoples in strength. In the rest of the Lowland Zone settlement proceeded chiefly from the Low Countries, Denmark, and the Baltic, partly by sea, partly by the disintegrated land bridge from Artois to Kent. These eastern invaders occupied all the Lowland Zone during the Bronze Age (2000 B.C.–500 B.C.) and the ensuing Iron Age (500 B.C.–100 A.D.). The record they have left us is less impressive than that of the Megalithic people, whose Lowland settlements they absorbed, though it is easily reconstructable by archaeological methods. The final pre-Roman invasion—that of the Belgic peoples—penetrated only to Essex and the southeast Midlands, but each preceding wave tended to occupy the entire Lowland Zone, driving the older cultures before it into the Highlands.

Within the Lowland Zone, pre-Roman settlement appears to have preferred the high limestone plateaus or sandy plains with loamy soils. Here the forest (of beech and ash) was thinner and may have yielded more readily to the primitive axe of the pioneer. Much of the lighter land was brought under the plow, or was used to pasture stock, and the settlements themselves tended to be grouped along spring lines. Salisbury Plain, on which several of the drier ridges converged, continued to be the most thickly and continuously settled area; the fields of the farm on which the author of this chapter was born still bear the impress of this early agricultural civilization. The clay vales, by contrast, resisted for long the efforts of early man to occupy them; the dense oakwood and the

---

[11] A classic in the geographical literature of Britain is C. Fox, *The Personality of Britain: Its Influence on Inhabitant and Invader in Prehistoric and Early Historic Times* (Cardiff: National Museum of Wales, 1933).

abundant surface water were both unwelcome to a people of limited technology. As Sir Cyril Fox has put it,

> This forest was in a sense unbroken, for without emerging from its canopy a squirrel could traverse the country from end to end. . . . [The forests were] haunted by lynx, wolf and boar, bear and fighting ox; and were hostile in themselves to Man, his flocks and herds.[12]

Thus in pre-Roman times both Highland and Lowland zones were thinly occupied by Celtic-speaking Britons. As later, more vigorous settlers invaded from the east, both the ways and the tongues of these primitive folk were banished into Ireland, Highland Scotland, Wales, and Cornubia. Vestiges of the old traditions linger in the ceremonial of the Welsh, the most tenaciously conservative of the Highland people. Such traditions find their expression in modern literature, as in the poetry of Dylan Thomas, and in local ritual (though not in the annual Eisteddfod, whose Druidic rites are charming but apochryphal). They also form the basis of resurgent Irish nationalism, whose disciples are striving doggedly to revive the moribund Gaelic tongue.

The Roman Interlude. Upon this simple culture the Roman Empire imposed four centuries (A.D. 43–400) of Mediterranean civilization and law. The Roman conquerors entirely subjugated the Lowland Zone of Britain, but made little attempt to penetrate the Highlands. Civil administration was established over the Lowlands, and the Celtic peasantry was in considerable measure knit into the structure of a Romanized state. Towns of typical Mediterranean plan were constructed, and trade, already active in Bronze and Iron age times, was substantially increased, both internally and externally. Wales, northern England, and southern Scotland were constituted military zones, whence the Roman legionaries watched the tribesmen of the hills beyond.

The most significant modern legacy of the Roman interlude was the military road system. As in other parts of conquered Western Europe, the Romans built straight, well-metalled highways which have in some areas survived into modern England as major routeways. Thus Watling Street, from Richborough (now defunct as a port: near modern Sandwich) to London (already the largest trading center) and across the Midlands to Wroxeter, today forms highways A2 and A5. Ermine Street (London-Lincoln-Humber) is still in several stretches a major north-south route-way. On the other hand Fosse Way, a route following roughly the belt of Juras-

[12] *Ibid.*, p. 82.

sic scarps from Lincoln to Cirencester and Exeter, has for considerable distances lapsed to the status of a footpath (Figure 24).

Of the cities that flourished under Roman rule, some (like Sil-
chester—*Calleva Atrebatum*) have vanished as such, others have
flourished. Since the Roman interlude London, for example, has
remained the largest commercial center of the kingdom. The root
"-chester" is a corruption of the Latin *castra*, a camp, and its
abundance in English place-names is proof enough of the capacity
of the Roman overlords to select sites that would stand the test
of time.

FIGURE 24. The Fosse Way, near Tetbury, on the Cotswold back slope. The
large arable fields and the abundance of hedgerow trees should be noted. (Aero
Pictorial, Ltd.)

The Anglo-Saxon, Norse, and Danish Invasions. In the fifth
century A.D. the Romanized Celtic civilization of Lowland England
was eclipsed by renewed barbarian invasions from the east—the
Angles, Jutes and Saxons, whose Teutonic tongues and warlike
philosophy swept the civilized culture of the Britons from the Lowlands into the Highland refuges of the west. In the Britain of the
Dark Ages we lose sight of the progress of settlement and cannot
regain our perspective until the Norman invasion. It is clear, however, that the Anglo-Saxons completely occupied the Lowland Zone

and in several places penetrated deeply into the Highlands, as in southeast Scotland and Devon. They showed a marked preference for well-drained, loamy soils, though they did not shun the oak-woods of the clay vales as thoroughly as did their Celtic predecessors.[13]

In the eighth and ninth centuries A.D. the young English kingdoms so established were themselves overrun by the second wave of "Nordic" invaders, the Danish and Norse Vikings. The Norwegians followed the outer-sea route round Cape Wrath and established scattered settlements all along the western seaboard; Caithness, Galloway, much of Ireland, the Isle of Man, the Lake District, and parts of South Wales were invaded. The Danes, in contrast, landed in great numbers in eastern England, establishing a broad belt of Danish settlement in the *Danelaw*, essentially the Lowland Zone east of Watling Street. They also established a kingdom in Normandy, from which, two centuries later, the final invasion and conquest of Britain were to come.

Despite war and bloody rapine, the ordinary events of pre-Norman Britain, it is clear that the Lowland Zone was fairly fully occupied at this time. Even the clay vales, with their damp oakwoods, had begun slowly to yield. We can attempt to reconstruct the process of settlement by the study of place-names, a fascinating field of geographical research. Names in -ingas (now -ing) and -ingaham (now -ingham) are of early Anglo-Saxon origin, and -ton is of a later Saxon period. In the Danelaw, names in -by (Old Scandinavian -byr, i.e., village, town), -thorp (Danish, hamlet) and those containing Danish proper names abound. Place-name research is an intricate and highly developed technique for which little space can be found here.[14]

The Norman Conquest. The Norman Conquest was the final episode in the peopling of Britain from without her shores. The Normans were few in numbers, but they extended their autocratic rule over most of Britain and introduced a Latin element into the English language. The English feudal system was largely their creation, and the rural settlement of both England and Ireland bear many traces of their rule. Once again it was in the English

[13] S. W. Wooldridge, "The Anglo-Saxon Settlement," chap. iii of H. C. Darby (ed.), *Historical Geography of England before 1800* (Cambridge: Cambridge University Press, 1936), p. 91. See also S. W. Wooldridge and D. L. Linton, "The Loam-Terrains of Southeast England in their Relation to Its Early History," *Antiquity*, VII (September, 1933), 297-303.

[14] The method is explained in E. Ekwall, *The Oxford Dictionary of English Place-Names* (Oxford: Clarendon Press, 1936), pp. vii-xxxiv.

lowlands that Norman feudalism was most readily established; beneath its heel the English peasantry and its manorial overlords occupied all but the most intractable soils. The Norman castle on its mound survives in many places to remind us of this vital phase in the taking up of the land. Over all England there spread the Norman conception of statehood, of authoritarian government, of codified and enforceable law. In the cities arose the great cathedrals, Romanesque at first, derived from France, but expressing later a rising English genius in Gothic architecture. Through the teaching of Norman, French, and Italian clergy the mainstream of European civilization resumed its flow into Britain.

The Highland Zone was less tractable. Wales was subjected to conquest, but could not be assimilated into the English kingdom until the Tudors—a Welsh family—ascended to the Throne. Scotland, a poor, lightly settled land in which Saxons and Celtic clansmen intermingled, was nevertheless united with the British crown only in 1707, and separation still exists as a political aspiration. Ireland was conquered by part-Welsh earls who established Norman feudalism only to see it absorbed by Irish tribalism.

Nevertheless, the Norman period marked the final stage in the emergence of the English state and in the initial occupance of the soil. By the time the Normans themselves had been absorbed into the English people, and the English tongue was once again the language of power and government, England and Wales had become a consolidated kingdom that has never since bowed to invasion. Scotland was as yet independent, but her days were numbered. Only Ireland stood beyond the pale, as she still stands. The peopling of Britain was thus complete, and the identity of her four subsidiary nations—Welsh, Scottish, Irish, and English—established.

Medieval Britain was a land of cities and trade on the one hand, and an entrenched, landed feudal aristocracy on the other; town and country were distinct in the landscape at least to the Highland border.[15] They have remained distinct into modern Britain, whose geography can best be discussed in terms of the urban and rural landscapes.

The Rural Landscape

The British Isles as a whole are blessed with a climate that permits a varied and productive agriculture. Almost all the tillable land has been under the plow or improved grassland for generations and, in some areas, since Neolithic times. Today, the acute finan-

[15] H. C. Darby, "The Economic Geography of England, A.D. 1000-1250," chap. v of Darby, *op. cit.*, pp. 165-229.

cial crisis that hovers over Great Britain (and over the Irish Republic in equal measure) has made the land an irreplaceable asset whose use has been brought to a high pitch of efficiency.

In the United Kingdom, 48,000,000 acres (about 80 per cent of the whole country) is in agricultural use, and about 6 per cent of the working population is employed upon it. In the Irish Republic, by contrast, no less than 48 per cent of the labor force is engaged in agriculture. In highly industrialized Britain the gross agricultural output amounts to only about 6 per cent by value of the gross output of goods and services. In contrast, agricultural production and that of associated industries is the kernel of the national economy of the Irish Republic. Notwithstanding the apparently small contribution it makes to the national income, British agriculture is highly organized and productive. Agricultural labor is better paid and has a higher living standard than that of most other European countries, though less fortunate than that of the United States.

The 12,000,000 acres of British land not in agricultural production is largely inaccessible mountain or moorland, much of it peatbog, of which most is in the Scottish Highlands. The Land Utilisation Survey of Britain reported that in Britain itself (excluding Northern Ireland) about 3,000,000 acres are occupied by houses with gardens, cities, industrial or mining sites, and other agriculturally unproductive uses. In short, Britain's urban economy, which contributes at least 90 per cent of the national income, and which has made her one of the world's largest industrial powers, is prosecuted on only 6 per cent of her land, which remains overwhelmingly rural.

British farming is highly mechanized. On her 350,000 farms there were 332,100 tractors in January 1950, a six-fold increase since 1939. Similar advances have occurred in the use of electrical dairy equipment and combine-harvesters. She now ranks among the world's most mechanized countries.

The account that follows immediately excludes Ireland, whose problems are quite distinct from those of Great Britain; they receive attention in a later section.

The Medieval Landscape and Its Legacy. The modern British countryside is largely the creation of the past two centuries, when most of the enclosed fields, compact farms, and ornamental parklands that personify it were created. Until the seventeenth century most of the land was occupied under a husbandry derived from the medieval manorial system, or the more primitive organization of Celtic Britain. Though the Agricultural Revolution has effaced the older landscape effectively, it has not fundamentally changed the distribution of settlement. Certain villages have been abandoned, and much secondary dispersal of settlement has followed the enclosures; nevertheless, enough of the older pattern survives to make it necessary for us to glance at the husbandry of medieval times.

The Lowland Zone was cultivated under variants of the open-field system, in which the tenantry (largely in a condition of serfdom in earlier days) plowed intermingled strips of from a quarter to a whole acre in extent, within two or three arable fields. Each field was sown to a single crop—usually rye, wheat, oats, barley, peas, or some other "green" crop. One field was left under fallow. Beyond the arable fields was a common pasture on which a small head of cattle or sheep was tended. There was also much-treasured hay-meadow along the stream courses. A woodlot for communal grazing, timber, and firewood made up the rest of the land. None of the fields was enclosed, though growing crops and hay were protected by hurdles. The village's inhabitants were thus communally concerned with the management of all the land; the individual farm was a thing of the future.[16, 17]

The two-field and three-field systems were widely distributed in the Midlands and Southwest. In East Anglia, the eastern London Basin, and Kent, however, the open-field system in its pure form never existed, and some measure of enclosure seems to have prevailed very early.

The Highland Zone was thinly settled, but was nevertheless agriculturally organized. The most widespread system of land use was the infield-outfield system. Here from two to fifteen tenant families operated (also communally) a looser form of husbandry. The infield was close to the settlement: it was plowed continuously, and upon it was spread all the available dung. The larger outfield was used for poor pasture, but strips of it were also plowed from time to time in a shifting fashion, so that in time all of it was cultivated and prevented from relapsing to rough grazing or moorland. This so-called "Celtic" system—a bad misnomer—was widespread in Scotland, the Pennines, Wales, and Cornwall, but also occurred on poor soils and uplands in Lowland Britain.[18]

[16] Ibid., pp. 189-207.
[17] A good summary of field systems is given in W. Smith, An Economic Geography of Great Britain (London: Methuen & Co., Ltd., 1949), pp. 3-23.
[18] The crofting system of modern Highland Scotland has certain affinities with the older Celtic husbandry. See I. F. Grant, "The Highland Openfield System," Geographical Teacher, XIII (1926), 480-82.

The older husbandry, all over Britain, was close to a subsistence economy. Regional differentiation of farming practice was kept to a minimum because the necessities of life had to be produced locally. Nevertheless, upon the richer lands of the Lowland Zone and the outer fringe of the Highlands there arose a considerable surplus which was ultimately to color Britain's modern economy. The first and foremost was wool, for which medieval Britain was famous. It made her, first, a large exporter of raw wool and, later, the home of a prosperous woolen and worsted textile industry which remains one of her industrial staples. The second was grain —rye and wheat for the larger cities, of which London was pre-eminent, and barley—the "drink-corn" of the countryman. At times the country even exported grain.

FIGURE 25. Traditional village architecture of southernmost England, Wherwell, Hampshire. Note the thatched roofs, the half-timbered walls, and the carefully tended hedges. (Central Office of Information, London.)

All over the Lowland Zone, the old economy tended to create nucleated settlement: each village, a little world in itself (Figure 25), was located at or near a source of drinking water, usually a spring. The dry tablelands of limestone or sandstone, and the wet, marshy clays were avoided. Favorite sites were along the spring lines flanking the cuestas (Figure 26).

The breakdown of the medieval system was slow. It was marked by enclosure of the old common pastures, as well as of the arable.

At first the enclosure movement derived from the desire to create vast sheep-runs, when wool was the most precious raw material in Europe. Later, however, enclosure became the preliminary to improvement in farming, for the new techniques of the eighteenth and nineteenth centuries could not be applied to open fields. By 1820, only six English counties had more than 3 per cent of open field and, by 1830, most of this had vanished.[19] The culmination

FIGURE 26. The cuesta of the South Downs (Chalk) at Poynings, Sussex. The beds dip toward the left, where the chalk forms a bold face about 600 feet high, largely supporting poor, dry pasture land. At the foot of the scarp is a wide shelf covered by fertile downwash; the shelf is under arable cultivation in large fields. Poynings is on the spring line and is a typical nucleated village clustered around its church. (Central Office of Information, London.)

of the movement came with the General Enclosure Act of 1845. Henceforward Britain was a land, not of communal manors, but of farms and farmers, each with his distinct plot of ground. The villages remained, but to them was added a disseminated farming population. The enclosure movement also established a four-fold division of the rural population which persists to the present day in the Lowland Zone:

    1. *Landed gentry,* owning much land, and deriving income chiefly from agricultural rents.

[19] W. G. East, "England in the Eighteenth Century," chap. xiii of Darby, *op. cit.,* p. 471.

2. *Owner-farmers,* owning their own farms and land, and living off the sale of produce, or off the produce itself.
3. *Tenant farmers,* renting their farms from the gentry, and making up the largest group in modern Britain.
4. *Laborers,* owning and renting no land, but working for wages for the farmers. The farm laborer is the descendant of the villager displaced from his land by enclosure.

The tenant farmer is the characteristic countryman of modern Britain. Protected by legislation from arbitrary displacement, he no longer occupies a hazardous position. In 1941-43, the National Farm Survey showed that about 67 per cent of the farmland was farmed by tenants in England, and 61 per cent in Wales. Over most of northern England the figures exceeds 75 per cent.[20]

The farm laborer is essentially an inhabitant of eastern and southern England. In Highland Britain, enclosure of the old "Celtic" townships did not displace so many landsmen, nor did it provide a market for agricultural hired labor. In Wales, Highland Scotland, the Pennines, and Ulster the typical unit is the family farm in which the farmer, his wife, and his family can work the land without assistance. Even the itinerant shepherd is vanishing.

The Modern Farming System. Present-day land use in Great Britain is well known through the nation-wide studies of the Land Utilisation Survey (directed by L. Dudley Stamp), whose maps of land use on a scale of 1:63,360 cover the whole country, and whose nine-volume report, *The Land of Britain,* is unique in geographical literature.[21] Stamp's own *Land of Britain—Its Use and Misuse* is an appraisal of the results [22] and renders all other studies of the subject obsolete or incomplete. A similar survey exists for Northern Ireland (directed by D. A. Hills), though its reports are as yet incomplete. These land-use studies have been supplemented by the publication of maps showing types of farming and land classification in terms of fertility. They show a complexity that makes nonsense of most attempts at a regional division of British rural life. The striking difference from the old patterns is the existence of local specialization and differentiation, in which the farming

[20] Great Britain, Ministry of Agriculture and Fisheries, *National Farm Survey of England and Wales* (London: H. M. Stationery Office, 1946), p. 20.
[21] L. Dudley Stamp (ed.), *The Land of Britain* (9 vols.; London: Geographical Publications, Ltd., 1943-46).
[22] L. Dudley Stamp, *The Land of Britain, Its Use and Misuse* (London: Geographical Publications, Ltd., and Longmans, Green & Co., Ltd., 1948).

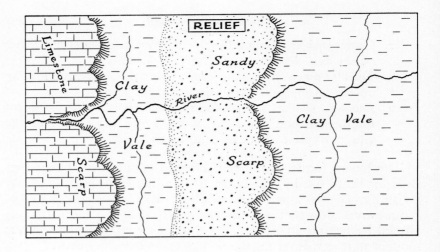

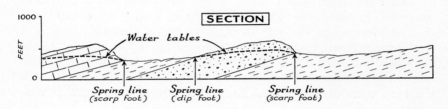

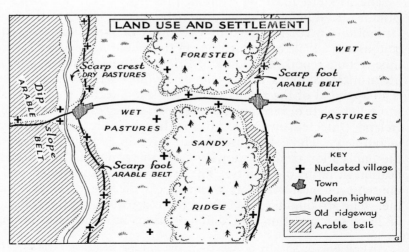

FIGURE 27. Cuestaform relief, nucleation of settlement, and differentiated land use in Lowland England. The upper diagram shows a typical example of the relief and the diagram below shows the location of spring lines. Upon these many villages are sited. Larger settlements tend to occur near the mouths of wind- or water-gaps at old bridging points.

practice shows a high and increasing correlation with soil-type and climate (Figure 27).

Significant differences exist between Scotland and the rest of Britain in agricultural practice, and it has been necessary to adopt a slightly different classification of farming types for that country.

England and Wales: Farming Types. In general it may be said that Anglo-Welsh farming tends towards two extremes:

1. An arable economy, in which most of the land is plowed regularly on an established rotation. Such land is largely confined to the drier east and is most widespread in East Anglia, the Fenlands, and much of Yorkshire. The plain of southwest Lancashire is the only significant western area with a truly arable economy.
2. A pastoral economy, in which the land is left unplowed. There are two distinct subtypes, the rough hill-grazing of the moorlands of the Highland Zone and the richer pastures widespread on the heavier soils of the Midlands of England.

Between these extremes there is a broad range of intermediate economies, in which arable and permanent improved grass intermingle. The three types are mapped in Figure 28.

Such a classification gives no adequate idea of the complexity of the economic basis of farming. Stamp recognizes eight distinct categories, which form the basis of the following description.

Hill sheep farming is typical of the higher moorlands of the Highland Zone, both in Wales, Devon, and Cornwall, and in northern England. The farms are large, partially enclosed tracts of heather and grassy upland on which flocks of hardy mountain breeds are maintained. The flocks are of ewes, and the economy depends on the sale of the annual lamb-crop, either for fattening on the lower ground or for butcher's sales. The highest ground is remote and sustains only a low density of ewes (Figure 29).

Stock rearing is localized on the lower hill country of the three main parts of the Highland Zone: Devon-Cornwall (Figure 30), Wales, and northern England. The land may either be improved pasture or arable. If the latter, however, it is usually under the specialized form of husbandry known as ley-farming, in which the land is sown out to grass for two, three, or four years after each phase of cropping. The crops themselves are usually oats, turnips, swedes, or other animal foodstuffs. The economy turns on the rearing of young cattle (or sheep in some cases) for sale to the rich fattening lands to the south and east. In most cases the cattle are of famous

beef breeds like the Hereford and Devon (which are now world-
wide in distribution) or dual-purpose animals like the Shorthorn.
The greater part of the world's beef production today comes from
breeds fixed on these British hill farms.

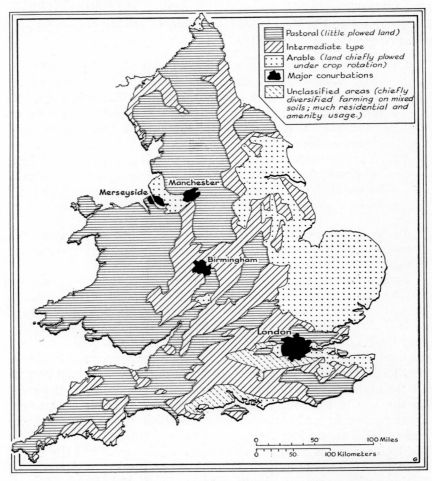

FIGURE 28. Pastoral and intermediate farming economies of England and Wales.
Note the concentration of pastoral types on western moors, and on the clay vales of
the Midlands; intermediate types are most widespread on limestone soils and in
the Midland Vale.

Stock fattening, the complement of stock rearing, is widely dispersed among the Lowland pastoral and intermediate economies,
but is especially noteworthy on the permanent grass of the clay
plains of the English Midlands, particularly in Leicestershire.

FIGURE 29. A typical farm of the more rugged parts of the Highland Zone, Langdale Valley, Lake District Caledonian Massif. Oats are being harvested for winter fodder. Sheep moors in the background. (Fox Photos, London.)

FIGURE 30. Stock-rearing country on a more tractable part of the Highland Zone (Vale of Widecombe, Devon). Note the small fields on the lower ground and the rough moors above the small village of St. Pancras. The farms are widely disseminated. (UKIO Photo.)

141

Dairying is now the most widespread farming type of Lowland Britain, where it attains its highest form on the permanent grass of the clay vales of the south and east. It also occurs, however, on some of the wetter hill country of the west of England and Wales, where it is usually associated, as is stock rearing, with ley-farming, i.e., with arable and rotation grass. Concentration upon dairying was determined originally by the nearness of great local markets. Nowadays, however, improved access by road, the marketing services of the Milk Marketing Board, and the increased demands of the large creameries have made dairying profitable in most areas where soils are not excessively light. The small dairy farm is hence the commonest English farm-type. The characteristic breeds are the Dairy Shorthorn and the Holstein, with the Jersey and Guernsey in the south. Dairying is also a subsidiary element in the farming types that follow.

Mixed farming is a collective term for the varied economies typical chiefly of the lighter soils of the Lowlands. Barley and wheat are common crops, and sheep are usually numerous, especially in the limestone belts. Much of this land now has an increasing interest in dairying.

Arable (crop) farming, in which the production of crops for sale off the farm is the preoccupation, is mainly an eastern type, being found on medium soils in the drier belts. The till-covered plains of East Anglia, the rich, organic or silty soils of the Fens and the Vale of York are the largest areas. Wheat and barley are the major cereals, sugar beets and potatoes the chief root crops. In the Fens crop farming is the only significant activity: the richest soils in England are here farmed in drained areas reminiscent of the Dutch polders. Elsewhere, however, the crop economy is added to by extensive sheep flocks, by dairying and stock fattening. The plain of southwest Lancashire, the only western representative of this type, is a region concentrating largely on poultry, potatoes, and green vegetables.

Market gardening in which arable specialization reaches its ultimate form, is not extensive, but raises much of the needs of the large cities in small-fruit, fresh vegetables, and flowers. The largest areas are: (a) the brickearth belt of the Thames terraces east and west of London, (b) a part of the clay vale of Evesham, and (c) areas of sandy soil in Bedfordshire and Cambridgeshire. Regions (a) and (c) serve the London market.

Fruit farming is of limited significance in cool, cloudy England. Two areas, however, stand out—the west Midlands (Worcestershire, Herefordshire, Gloucestershire, Somersetshire), and Kent.

The latter county has been aptly named the garden of England. The Kentish orchards, nurseries, and hop gardens occur in two principal belts, the loam-soil belt of north Kent, along the foot of the back-slope of the North Downs, and the similar belt to the south along the back-slope of a cuesta of calcareous sandstone. Apples, cherries, plums, and hops are the characteristic products (Figure 31).

FIGURE 31. Apple and cherry orchards, fruit belt of north Kent, near Sittingbourne. Note the oast houses around the farm.

Scotland: Farming Types. Scotland has less good land than England and has a shorter, cooler summer. Nevertheless its farming is technically superior, and follows in several ways a distinctive tradition.

As in England, one can distinguish arable, pastoral, and intermediate economies, but the distinction loses some of its force. Much of the arable land is farmed on the ley principle—with several years of unplowed rotation grass following each period of cropping. On the other hand, purely pastoral economies are rare on the improved land; there is no Scottish equivalent for the great Lowland permanent pastures of England. Only the moorlands present large areas of unplowed, but productive land. Four distinct farming types can be distinguished, and are outlined on Figure 32.

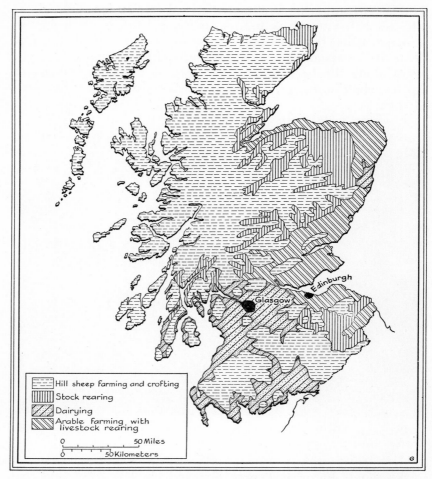

FIGURE 32. Predominant farming types of Scotland. (After L. D. Stamp.)

Arable farming with livestock farming occurs on areas of level ground and loamy soils along the drier east coast. The chief crops in the arable rotation are oats, barley, wheat (chiefly south of Aberdeen), potatoes, turnips, and other root crops designed for use as winter feed for livestock. There is also much rotation grass, the timothy-hay crop being especially valuable. A considerable volume of off-the-farm sales of crops is characteristic. Throughout the belt, however, there is a specialization in the feeding and fattening of livestock. In the Tweed Valley, sheep outnumber beef cattle; Cheviot, Border-Leicester and their cross, the Half-Bred, are the characteristic breeds of this spacious country. In the rest of the belt the fattening of store cattle from the nearby rearing lands is commoner than sheep farming. The eastern half of the Midland Valley has such an economy, and dairying is also considerable. The significance of cattle fattening rises northwards, and along the shores of the Moray Firth vastly exceeds the sale of cash crops in the income of the farmer.

Stock rearing, as in England, is localized on the hilly margins of the main uplands, namely the Southern Uplands and the more accessible Highlands. Almost always the rearing is carried out on arable farms using long leys of rotation grass, and producing oats and turnips as the only significant crops. Famous beef breeds have characterized this country, the Aberdeen Angus in the northeast, the Highland in the west, and the Galloway in the western Southern Uplands. Sheep rearing, though widespread, is dominant only around the Tweed Valley.

Dairying is widespread, and is the dominant farming type in two principal regions, the western half of the Midland Valley (where it supplies the large markets of Clydeside), and around the western flanks of the Southern Uplands in Ayrshire, Wigtown, Kirkcudbright, and Dumfries, where the milk is sold wholesale to creameries or the Scottish Milk Marketing Board. In Renfrewshire permanent pastures support the industry, but elsewhere the land is mainly under the long-ley arable system, producing oats and root crops, with much rotation grass. The Ayrshire cow is the characteristic dairy animal.

Hill sheep farming extends over the moorlands of the Southern Uplands and the Highlands; the Blackface ewes roam the bleak heather-moors in thousands, with Cheviots on the grassy slopes.

Crofting is a vanishing farming type, thinly scattered through the Highlands, and seen at its purest in the Hebrides and Shetland Islands. It involves the inherited tenure of tiny patches of cultivated lands on the raised beaches and coastal platforms or valley floors, with limited grazing rights on the nearby hillsides. The holdings are tiny and the land poor. As a rule the crofters eke out their living by fishing or spinning and weaving; Harris tweed, the best-known local cloth, commands a high price in the United States market.

Planning. One of the most striking developments of the last ten years in the United Kingdom has been the emergence of town and country planning as a national policy and interest. The acute pressure on land, the necessity of protecting the food supply, the problems of rebuilding war-damaged cities, and the widespread de-

sire to protect Great Britain's lovely countryside have combined to
awaken the nation to the need for land-use planning. All parties
agree on the need, though there is some difference between them
on the emphasis laid upon specific problems. Space is lacking to re-
count here the immense body of work undertaken in this field.
The most remarkable visible result of the planning movement is
the construction of new towns, which are intended to rehouse the
overcrowded population of the large cities, and to achieve some
measure of decentralization of light industry away from strategically
vulnerable areas.

The Rural Life of Ireland. The Irish landscape in no way
resembles that of Britain to the east. Behind the apparent peace
of the white farmhouses and the emerald green pastures there lies
a troubled history of passions, of famine, and of cultural traditions
tenaciously held against foreign influences. It has already been
said that 48 per cent of Ireland's working population lives off the
land, and that even her industry is largely concerned with agricultural produce. The mild climate, with its cool, cloudy summers
and largely frost-free winters, has encouraged the development of a
pastoral economy that allows a large scale export of farm produce.
Nevertheless, the social and economic problems of rural Ireland,
though they have receded since the tragic days of the middle nineteenth century, are acute, and call for ceaseless labor on the part
of government to bring them under control.[23, 24]

In the early nineteenth century Ireland was a densely populated
land of tenant farmers, occupying tiny farms rented, without security of tenure, from a land-owning class whose political and
economic ambitions were best served by a minute subdivision of
the land. Much of the land was arable, producing potatoes as the
staple of the local diet and wheat for export to England. A progressive increase in population taxed the resources of the land beyond its limit, and in 1845 there began a famine that let 750,000
country folk die of starvation before they could escape to the ports.
There ensued a drastic revolution in population and land-tenure,
of which three elements can be distinguished here:

1. Large-scale emigration to Britain, the Dominions, and America
   has reduced the population from 8,175,000 in 1841 to 4,204,000
   in 1936-37, since when population has slightly increased. Ire-

[23] The best reference on the geography of Ireland is Freeman, *op. cit.*

[24] E. Estyn Evans, *Irish Heritage* (Dundalk: Dundalgan Press, 1942) and S.
O'Faolain, *The Irish* (London: Penguin Books, Ltd., 1947) give excellent accounts
of the cultural and traditional background of modern Irish life.

land is unique in Europe in showing a large decline in population over this period. There has also been—especially in Ulster —a migration from the country to the towns, notably to Londonderry, Belfast, Dublin, and Cork.[25]

2. The land has been transferred by governmental action from the landlord class to the farmers, who now largely own the land they farm in both Northern Ireland and the Irish Republic. In the latter, especially, attention has been given to the congested lands of the western *Gaeltacht*.

3. The economy has become mainly pastoral, devoting the land to the rearing or fattening of cattle (largely for the British market), or to dairying and poultry farming.

Acute land hunger still exists, and farms remain remarkably small. Population pressure in some areas continues severe. Forty-one per cent of the surface of the Republic is in farms of 50 acres or less, and upon this minutely divided land dwells the greater part of the farming population: the smaller the farm size, the greater the rural population density. The record of individual holdings is even more striking; in 1946, for example, 63 per cent of all farm-holdings in Northern Ireland were of less than 30 acres, and the equivalent figure (in 1936) for the Republic was 57 per cent.

The greatest concentration of small farms—and hence of high population density—extends up the west coast from the Shannon through the hilly Caledonian country of Galway, Mayo, Sligo, and Donegal. This area contains a high proportion of those able to speak Gaelic; its farmers eke out a humble living from their tiny crofts—like those of western Scotland—by planting a few acres of oats or potatoes and keeping a few cows, together with poultry. In northwest Donegal the system attains its ultimate form, with an average farm size of only eight acres, often including poor land.

Ulster is also a land of minute farms, but here there is a higher level of prosperity. The traditional crop is flax, grown for the production of linen, a famous specialization of the province. The acreage of flax sown fluctuates widely, and the remaining energies of the people are devoted to the raising (in the higher regions) or fattening of beef and young dairy cattle, of which there is some export to Britain. Dairying is also practiced, especially in Fermanagh.

The southern and eastern parts of the Republic present a happier picture than does the congested Gaeltacht. Farms are larger,

[25] Cork is unique among the group in that its population has not markedly increased. Emigration from the town has offset the influx from rural districts.

and population densities lower. The land is mainly pastoral. Dairying predominates in the southwest, stock fattening in the eastern Central Plain. Sheep rearing and fattening is common in the Hercynian and Caledonian massifs. There is, however, a wide variety of local products, and specialization is nowhere excessive.

Ireland's agricultural surplus goes almost wholly to Britain, on whom she is dependent for imports of coal and many industrial products. The trade relations between the Republic and Britain have been prejudiced on numerous occasions since 1921 by political differences, whereas Northern Ireland has derived much benefit from her status within the United Kingdom.

The Urban Landscape: Industrialization

Britain has been an industrialized nation since medieval times, when her woolen textiles began to figure largely in international and domestic trade. The Industrial Revolution began in Britain, a country rich in coal and mechanical skills. Well ahead of her nearest rivals, Britain became in the mid-nineteenth century the workshop of the world. She pioneered in the development of the locomotive, textile machinery, the iron ship, and the Bessemer and open-hearth steel processes. In a brief century, Britain had changed from the peaceful, agrarian aristocracy depicted in the pages of Addison and Steele, into an arrogant, industrial empire whose ships carried the world's commerce, whose capital city was the financial center of the earth, and whose exports of manufactured goods poured forth in a steady stream to all the world's markets.

She remains a modern, industrialized society. Her early start, however, has had unfortunate repercussions. The men who captained the nineteenth-century industrial expansion had little thought for the well-being of the vast new proletariat that flocked into the cities. The latter became squalid, overcrowded, and gloomy, and today present abundant problems to the city planner. Much of her industrial plant is old or obsolescent and an endless program of modernization lies before her industrialists. Her markets have dwindled as manufacturing industries sprang up overseas. Two wars have also disrupted her economy.

Nevertheless the United Kingdom remains a great industrial power, second only to the United States in the western world's commerce. The Irish Republic, in contrast, has virtually no heavy industry and only one industrial center of any size—Dublin. The

Republic's poverty is traceable mainly to her shortage of power. She has practically no coal and too little hydroelectric power.

Coal. Coal lies at the root of Britain's industrial eminence. Her reserves and present fields lie distributed in several large and many smaller basins on the flanks of the Highland Zone in England and Wales, and in the Midland Valley of Scotland. Reserves of workable seams are estimated at 44,000 million metric tons, enough to last some 200 years at present rates of consumption. The coal is mostly bituminous, though there is some anthracite in south Wales. Steam and coking coals are both available in quantity. The disposition of the individual basins has been indicated on Figure 21.

In 1950, production was 226,000,000 metric tons, the largest in Europe itself, though the Soviet Union as a whole slightly exceeded this figure. The coal was raised by about 300,000 miners and 400,000 other colliery workers employed by the National Coal Board, the publicly owned monopoly established since World War II to operate the mines. In recent years much difficulty has been found in maintaining adequate levels of production. In 1938, 231,000,000 metric tons were raised, of which 47,000,000 metric tons were exported or used in foreign ships; the prewar economy was in fact adjusted to a large export of coal, chiefly to France, Eire, Argentina, and the Scandinavian countries. Production during the war declined seriously due to a variety of factors, of which the most significant are (a) an aging and diminishing labor force— it being difficult to persuade young men to enter the collieries; (b) the rapid exhaustion of the more accessible seams, especially of good coking coal, in great demand today; (c) poor techniques of extraction, including a low degree of mechanization; (d) poor pit-head conditions, wages, and housing for the miners; and (e) embittered labor relations. These and other factors, notably the folded or faulted character of the coal seams, which rendered mechanization difficult, had reduced productivity to a very low ebb. In 1947, during an unprecedented cold spell which disrupted transport, reserves were exhausted, and industry was paralyzed for two weeks.[26]

Successive investigating committees had recommended national ownership as the only solution of these difficulties, and in 1945 this advice was put into effect, when the policy was no longer politically controversial. Despite much-publicized differences and labor disputes, the industry has recovered remarkably, the 1950 produc-

[26] For statistical tables, see Appendix III.

tion being 14 per cent greater than that of 1946. Exports have been resumed, amounting to over 17,000,000 metric tons in 1950. These results are being achieved by a tremendous program of rehabilitation that has very far still to go. Mechanization, recruitment of a larger labor force, better pithead conditions, and better pay for the miners are some of the devices employed. Efforts are also being made to close old, uneconomic shafts and shift production to newer fields, like the concealed part of the Yorks-Derby-Nottingham field and the Fife and Lothian fields in Scotland. There has also been a large-scale development of open-pit mining, 12,000,000 metric tons being raised in this fashion in 1950.

The largest producing field is that of Yorks-Derby and Nottingham, on which is located the large concentration of industrial population associated with the textile industries of the West Riding, the heavy metallurgical industries of Sheffield and Rotherham, and many smaller activities. The concealed coal field east of the older area of mining is the most active area of recent development; deep shafts sunk through the overlying Mesozoic sediments reach the coal seams. The pitheads of many of these collieries are surrounded by the oaks of Sherwood Forest, famed as the home of Robin Hood.

South Wales and the Northumberland-Durham fields have much in common. Both are very near the coast, and both have contributed much in the past to the export trade. Each is famous for special types of coal—South Wales for steam coal and anthracite, Durham for coking coal. Heavy metallurgical industries and a large industrial population characterize both areas.

The remaining fields are smaller, though several are associated with major concentrations of industry. Thus the Lanarkshire and Ayrshire fields (the latter being largely worked out) have for long supplied Glasgow and Clydeside, the world's greatest center of the shipbuilding industry; south Lancashire has begotten Manchester and the cotton-textile industry; the North Staffordshire field is the site of Stoke-on-Trent, which concentrates 80 per cent of the British pottery industry, including the celebrated Wedgwood plant; the multifarious metallurgical and engineering works of Birmingham lie near the Black Country field of South Staffordshire. It becomes clear, therefore, that the great bulk of British industry and nearly all the major centers of population lie on or near the coal fields. London, the national capital and greatest seaport, is the only striking exception in England, though in Ireland neither Belfast nor Dublin has nearby coal.

Coal, apart from imported oil and gasoline, is the only important fuel in Britain. Electricity, the demand for which is increasing rapidly, is 97 per cent coal-generated; hydroelectric installations (in Wales and Scotland) contribute only about 2½ per cent. In 1950, about a seventh of the national output was converted to electricity, and more than a fifth was consumed in coal gas plants or coke ovens. Domestic consumers receive 65 per cent of the present output of coal gas.

Steel. If coal is the motivating force of British industry, steel is its indispensable raw material. Iron manufacture has a long history in Britain; the local ores have been smelted since pre-Roman times, and the modern techniques of steelmaking had their origin here. Though she has since been eclipsed by the United States, prewar Germany, and the Soviet Union, Britain has remained a major producer and is at present expanding her output rapidly. High quality alloy-steels and special finishes are a specialization. Until recently, production was largely in the hands of large, vertically integrated companies. Under the Iron and Steel Act of 1949 the industry passed into public ownership in 1951, and is administered by a public corporation. The Conservative government elected in October, 1951, is committed, however, to the return of the industry to private hands.

The raw materials of the industry—coal, ore, and limestone—are bulky, and their producing areas are highly localized. British ores are largely of low iron content, and of the bedded type. Most of them are extracted from the Jurassic cuestas of Yorkshire, Lincolnshire, and Northamptonshire. Much of the needed ore is imported, by far the largest port of entry being Middlesbrough. Most of the steel industry now operates with basic open-hearth converters.

The producing areas are mostly on or near coal fields, the cost of coal transportation being the determining factor. In many instances, the smelting of pig iron was originally based on Coal-Measure iron ores (as in South Wales, the Black Country, and Clydeside). These are largely worked out, and nearly all blast furnaces use Jurassic or imported ores. The largest producing centers are Clydeside (Glasgow, Coatbridge, Motherwell, etc.), supplying the local shipbuilding and engineering industries, Teeside (Middlesbrough), south Yorkshire and Derbyshire (Rotherham, Sheffield, and Chesterfield), South Staffordshire and South Wales (the Swansea area, Cardiff, and Ebbw Vale). The Scunthorpe (Lincolnshire) and Northamptonshire plants are unusual in being located on the ore-body rather than on the coal field.

High cost, high quality, and local specialization characterize the industry. Thus the Swansea district is largely concerned with the needs of the local tinplate industry, now undergoing expansion. Sheffield—a famous name among steelmen—is a steelmaking town, having no blast furnaces. For centuries, it has specialized in quality work and has become the home, among other types, of high-grade alloy steels, Sheffield stainless being an example, based in part on imported pure iron. The nearby Coal Measure grit allowed a grinding industry, and the valleys behind Sheffield have long specialized in cutlery.

The Nonferrous Metals. The nonferrous metals, though less bulky and less central to the economy, are essential to the steel and engineering industries. Aluminum, copper, lead, tin, zinc, nickel and many less common metals are produced largely from imported semirefined concentrates rather than the crude ore. Birmingham is the chief center, concentrating especially on brass and aluminum ware; over 40 per cent of the labor engaged in these industries work in this city and the surrounding satellite towns. Birmingham is unique among the world's great cities (it has over 1,000,000 inhabitants) in being built on a drainage divide (which accounts, incidentally, for the early date on which it was served by canals). No one geographical factor can account for this specialization at Birmingham. Today the district has one of Britain's greatest concentrations of the engineering industries, and a ready market for semifinished and finished nonferrous articles is close at hand.

Other major centers of this complex group of industries are the London district (where again there is an immense local market and an accessible port), south Lancashire, the West Riding of Yorkshire, and South Wales.

The Engineering Industries. The engineering industries represent the other end of the scale of heavy industry. Here again there is a long tradition of skill, and British engineers—especially the Scots—have penetrated every corner of the earth, as have their products. In recent years technical precedence and the greater part of the world's market have passed into American hands, but the British engineer was never busier than he is today. A very wide variety of finished metal goods is produced, and the industry is widely distributed. Nevertheless, certain marked concentrations are visible:

1. Shipbuilding is concentrated on a number of estuaries. Since 1945 Britain has launched about half the world's new shipping; in 1949 alone 441,000 gross metric tons were launched on Clydeside (the Glasgow region), which in prewar days launched the "Queens" and many other liners. The Tyne (with 221,000 tons), the Wear

(184,000), and the Tees (106,000) were the next group, launching chiefly colliers and tankers. Belfast (99,000) has long specialized in the smaller liners, motor ships, and refrigerated vessels. There are smaller yards on Merseyside and at Barrow-in-Furness. A large marine-engineering industry supports each of these regions, especially in the Glasgow district (Figure 33).

FIGURE 33. A 19,000-ton tanker being built in the Clydebank yards of John Brown and Co., Ltd., near Glasgow, the world's leading center of the shipbuilding industry.

2. Textile machinery is a marked specialization of the south Lancashire and West Riding coal fields, where it feeds the large local textile industry.

3. The heavy constructional and automotive industry—bridges, locomotives, armaments, automobiles, etc.—is typical of the Scottish lowlands (especially near the great Firths), Manchester and South Lancashire, Birmingham and the Black Country, and the Yorks-Derby-Nottingham coal field. Britain is now the largest exporter of automobiles, most of which come from Birmingham, Coventry, and Oxford. Bicycles, popular in Europe, come chiefly from the Midland area.

4. Specialized light engineering, though widely disseminated, is increasingly concentrated in the London district, which is also the center of the new "luxury" industries; London is surrounded by hundreds of new plants producing a thousand-and-one small products which reach the country's largest market with ease.

Textiles. These industries, the last for which we can offer details, are among Britain's oldest skills. Using her traditional and home-produced raw material, wool, her craftsmen had created for themselves a high reputation before the Industrial Revolution. It was in the textile industries that this Revolution really began, when successive inventions in the late eighteenth century made possible the use of power, first from water mills and then from James Watt's steam engine. The traditional industries were widely dispersed, in the southern Pennine valleys, in East Anglia (the early home of worsteds), in the Cotswolds, and in southwest England. With the advent of steam power and factory manufacture, however, the districts remote from coal either expired or specialized, and today production is concentrated overwhelmingly on South Lancashire (cottons) and the West Riding of Yorkshire (woolens and worsteds). Smaller areas of production are the Glasgow district (cottons) and Belfast (cottons, poplins, and linen). All the raw cotton and most of the wool required are imported.

The specialization on cotton in South Lancashire dates from the early eighteenth century. Here, there is soft water, a naturally high humidity, abundant coal for power (and, in earlier times, waterpower), and the largest concentration of the country's chemical industries, on the salt deposits of nearby Cheshire. From this center British cottons grew to great significance in the national economy, and were the largest export (by value) from the late nineteenth century until World War II. In recent years, however, stiff competition in the Asiatic markets from cheaper Japanese and Indian cottons has severely restricted this trade, and the industry has been chronically depressed. The plants are usually old and mechanically inefficient by comparison with those, for example, of the United States Piedmont. A large-scale program of rehabilitation is now proceeding, much of it concerned with the installation of automatic looms. Exports doubled between 1947 and 1950, but are still far below prewar levels.

There are three distinct areas of specialization. Spinning of yarn from raw cotton is concentrated in the headwaters of the Mersey tributaries, north of Manchester, in and around the towns of Bolton and Oldham. Weaving of cloth takes place in the Colne and Ribble valleys further north, the largest centers being Burnley, Blackburn, Preston, Nelson, and Colne. Finishing—largely a chemical process—takes place in and around Manchester-Salford, the commercial and technological capital of the industry.

The concentration of woolen and worsted manufactures on the West Riding of Yorkshire is equally emphatic; the Aire and Calder valleys are the scene of the largest production, which was originally based on local wool and an abundance of waterpower. More recently, soft water (from the outcrop of the Millstone Grit on the Pennines) and the local supply of coal have been the significant localizing influence; the inheritance of traditional skills and the absence of a competing metallurgical industry (which excludes the industry from the Sheffield-Rotherham district, equally suitable on most other counts) have also assisted. The largest producing center is Bradford, in many ways the Manchester of the wool trade. Halifax, Huddersfield, Dewsbury, Keighley, and Wakefield are other large centers. Leeds is in some degree the commercial capital of the West Riding, but plays little role in the woolen and worsted trades at the weaving stage; the city concentrates, however, a large fraction of the clothing trade.[27]

Like cottons, woolen goods have for long figured very large in the British export trade. Stiff overseas competition has been experienced in recent years, but the high quality of British cloth has maintained her position. Stress is laid upon exclusive lines of pattern and color, but the range of types is wide, extending from tweeds—of which the Harris tweed is a well-known example—to tropical worsteds. In 1950, 127,000,000 square yards (106 million square meters) of woven piece goods were exported, a figure much larger than that for 1938, the last prewar year. Considerable modernization of plant is in progress, and efforts are being made to compete vigorously in the cheap-cloth field.

Linen—the raw material of which is the field crop, flax—is another textile in which the United Kingdom has long dominated the world market. Spinning and weaving of linen was formerly widespread in Britain, and some production is still active in the eastern part of the Midland Valley of Scotland. The industry has become concentrated, however, in Ulster and especially in Belfast. Flax grown locally normally supplies about 10 per cent of the demand, and the rest is imported. In a typical year linen amounts to about a quarter of Northern Ireland's exports by value. Londonderry has

[27] The West Riding landscape in many ways exemplifies industrial Britain. See S. H. Beaver, "The West Riding," part 46 of L. D. Stamp (ed.), *The Land of Britain, op. cit.*

a large production of finished linen and cotton goods, especially shirts.

It remains to be added that Great Britain, like most other countries, has witnessed the development in the past twenty years of large scale artificial-fiber manufactures such as rayon and nylon. The largest producing areas tend to lie within the older textile provinces, notably for example, the North Lancashire district.

Communications

Overseas Shipping and the Ports. The British mercantile marine is the world's largest, comprising about a fifth of the world's shipping. A large fraction of the nation's overseas earnings has come during the past century from carrying the commerce of other nations; the British tramp steamer carrying anything to and from anywhere is an indispensable element in world transportation. The importance and heavy bulk of Britain's own overseas trade is a further guarantee of her maritime activity. Her losses in shipping during World War II amounted to no less than 12,000,000 metric tons, yet her merchant fleet today exceeds 18,000,000 metric tons, largely the result of rapid launching of new vessels.

Britain has numerous ports, as befits a trading nation. Many of them suffered considerable damage during the war from air raids, though in few cases was the damage serious enough to render the port inoperative even for a few days. Much-needed programs of renovation, especially of warehouse and transshipment facilities, are now proceeding. Six ports—London, Liverpool, Hull, Manchester, Southampton, and Glasgow—do more than three quarters of the maritime business.

London, discussed as a city below, is much the largest port, concentrating about a third of the overseas trade. The Thames estuary provides a deep, easy approach. The outer docks (for large shipping) are at Tilbury, in Essex, but most of the shipping comes right into the East End of the city. Though there are numerous wharves, much of the unloading is carried out by lighters and barges, which transfer the imported goods into warehouses that line the Thames for miles below Tower Bridge (and even above). The commerce of the port is extremely varied, but especially noteworthy are the imports of perishable foodstuffs for which London, with its warehouses and cold-storage facilities, is much the biggest port (Figure 34).

Liverpool, the second port, handles at least a fifth of the overseas trade, and is the principal transatlantic port. It is above all the Atlantic port of the industrialized north of England and the Midlands. The port is built at the mouth of the Mersey estuary (which has completely replaced Chester on the Dee as the main Irish Sea harbor); on the Lancashire shore is Liverpool itself, but there are also docks on the Cheshire shore in the large urban areas of Birkenhead and Wallasey.

FIGURE 34. The Royal Victoria, Royal Albert, and King George docks. The barges and lighters that form so pronounced a feature of London's method of handling cargoes are much in evidence.

Hull is the third port of the country. It stands on the north shore of the Humber estuary and has easy communications with the industrial north, especially the West Riding of Yorkshire. It has varied interests. Much of its connection has been with northern Europe, but it also has a large coastwise trade and an immense trawling fleet. The wool for the West Riding textile belt is largely landed at Hull, though surprisingly enough the greater part is transshipped coastwise from London, the main port of entry.

Manchester, the fourth port of the country, is an inland city linked to the Mersey estuary by the 35-mile long privately owned Ship Canal, completed in 1894. The canal has 28 feet of water over the lock sills and allows ordinary cargo vessels to reach the port.

Southampton, fifth in the value of commerce, is the chief passenger port and the normal starting point of passenger ships to all western and southern destinations, including the important trans-Atlantic traffic. Southampton Water is reached from the English Channel from either east or west by the Solent, a drowned river valley sheltered on the south by the Isle of Wight. The double entry is enhanced by a double high tide, a valuable adjunct in the handling of large ships, though even at low tide there is 35 feet of water.

Glasgow, the remaining large port, is approached by the beautiful Firth of Clyde. It is the great port of Lowland Scotland and has an active export trade in heavy engineering goods. Other chief ports are Bristol, Newcastle, and Harwich.

Inland Communications. Land transportation in Great Britain is now under the administration of the British Transport Commission, set up on January 1st, 1948, to integrate road, rail, and canal services. In Northern Ireland the Ulster Transport Authority, also established in 1948, has similar powers. In the Irish Republic however, inland transportation has been under the merged *Coras Iompair Eireann* for a longer period.

Rail and road penetrate every corner of inhabited Britain, and traffic densities are very high. There is scarcely a point in the settled area of the country more than five miles from a railway. The railway system is now nationally owned and is known as "British Railways"; administration is carried on within regions that resemble both in name and extent the old independent systems. Nearly all the main-line trackage is two-, three-, or four-tracked, and both speeds and traffic densities are high. Most passenger movement is by rail for long hauls, and there is also an extraordinarily dense suburban traffic, especially in the London area. The motive power is largely steam, though diesel power is being used on some lines. There is a large mileage of electric propulsion, chiefly in the south; London is linked to the coast at Portsmouth, Brighton, and Eastbourne by frequent electric services that have brought many of the beach resorts within commuter-range, though they are 50 to 60 miles from London.

The Irish railways present a less satisfactory picture. Northern Ireland is well served from Belfast and Londonderry by the old

Northern Counties Committee lines, which were owned and operated by the L.M.S.R., a British company. The Great Northern links Belfast and Dublin, and has a large mileage on both sides of the border. Formerly privately owned, it passed (in 1952) into the joint ownership of the two Irish governments. Main-line services in the rest of the Republic are over the tracks of the Great Southern, Midland Great Western, and other former lines; there is also a considerable mileage of light railways. Inland transportation, however, is in a state of near-crisis because of gasoline and coal shortages, as well as declining revenues from most of the light railways.

Roads throughout Great Britain are hard surfaced, and the network is astonishingly dense. Much the same is true of Ireland, though some western districts are less accessible. In both islands truck and bus transportation have made considerable headway, and have created serious competition for the railways.

The British canal systems (except for the Manchester Ship Canal) are old, narrow, and shallow. Though they carried over 10,000,000 metric tons in 1950, most of them are little used, and many have been allowed to fall into disrepair.

The Four Capitals

It is fitting that we should glance finally at the four capital cities of the British Isles: London, Edinburgh, Belfast, and Dublin. Wales is remarkable in having no true capital and no focal point in its communications system; it has been truly said that a future Welsh parliament, if one is ever convened, would have to meet in some border town like Wrexham or Shrewsbury if the legislators were to get there with a minimum of fatigue! The grain of the country renders any internal site difficult of access; good Welsh route-ways lead to England.

London, home of the Crown, seat of the United Kingdom government, and center of the Sterling bloc, the colonial empire and a host of other organizations, is perhaps the world's greatest city. Today it is challenged by New York, both in function and in population, but it has no other peers. It is a vast, sprawling but attractive city lacking any formal plan—unlike Paris and Berlin— but possessing an appeal that some others lack. Its status as a city arises not merely from its governmental functions, but from its role as the nation's leading port; from the commercial, financial, and legal power of the City's institutions; from the vast new industries that have sprung up in its outskirts; and from the intangible appeal of its cultural and intellectual eminence, to say nothing of the power to entertain in theaters, cinemas, restaurants, and bars.

The old core of the town, on a gravel terrace which provided the lowest feasible bridging point over the Thames, is still identifiable as the "City," in whose half a square mile are concentrated most of the banks, the insurance houses—including Lloyds—the Royal Exchange, and St. Paul's Cathedral, as well as the headquarters of a large part of Britain's commercial and industrial empire. The shopping and entertainment districts lie two miles or more to the west, around Charing Cross, Trafalgar Square, Piccadilly Circus, and Oxford Street. Westminster, a mile upstream from Charing Cross, is the home of government. Around this differentiated center sprawls a densely populated ring of boroughs, residential and industrial, and still further out a forest of new houses served by the electrified lines of London Transport and the southern lines of British Railways. Every year the city expands still further. Much damage was done by enemy bombardment in 1940-41 and again in 1944-45.

Edinburgh is the traditional capital of Scotland; today it houses many of the administrative branches of Scottish government, as well as the official seat of the Crown in Scotland. It is a handsome town on a striking site overlooking the Firth of Forth. The Castle and much of the old town lie on a steep, volcanic hill, whereas the chief shopping districts—of which Princes Street is renowned—lie on another ridge to the north. Between them is a deep valley unfortunately occupied by the partially concealed main line of the old London and North-Eastern Railway, and its Waverley Station. In spite of everything that the twentieth century has done to ruin it, the heart of Edinburgh remains one of the sights of Europe. In recent years, the town has been the site of an annual festival of music and drama that bids fair to outdo Salzburg.

Belfast is not so much a traditional capital as a modern industrial city. Nevertheless, it is the site of the Northern Ireland government and is closely identified with the Orange movement and the cause of Protestant Ireland. It is also the site of Queen's University.

Dublin dominates the life of the Irish Republic as Vienna does that of Austria. There are no competitors among the smaller towns of this rural country. Its harbor affords the natural gateway to the Central Lowland and was recognized as such by the Norsemen, who established the town, and by Normans who captured it in the twelfth century. Thenceforward it was the English capital of Ireland. They established its cathedrals, its old University (Trinity

College), and the great castle that still dominates the city. In the eighteenth and nineteenth centuries the modern city was laid out by Georgian architects, whose broad streets, terraced houses, and formal squares gave the city an air of spacious dignity that it has never lost. Today it is the seat of the president and government of the Republic, and of the administrative machinery both of government and finance. No city in Europe has more claim to the geographer's attention, for its site and its functions are admirably blended. The large industrialization it has undergone during the past century has created behind the Georgian terraces a welter of slums, and overcrowding is a perennial problem. Nevertheless, the city retains a real beauty and fascination.

The Economic Crisis

The picture we have just drawn portrays a rich, varied, and predominantly industrial economy. The author has repeatedly found himself comparing British production with that of the world as a whole, and quite often he has been able to round off his review with a broad fractional proportion, like the "fifth of the world's shipping" on British registry. Yet Britain is in the grip of an acute economic crisis for which no ultimate solution is in view. The Irish Republic, too, is in a like state, for her economy is indissolubly linked with Britain, however much she may strive for political independence.

In a century, then, Britain has fallen from undisputed primacy in the world's commerce to a nation fighting for survival. By comparison with this struggle, her social and political difficulties are trivial—and are largely the product of economic factors. The crisis has arisen slowly, but was brought to a peak by World War II and the subsequent reconversion. The contributing factors can be summed up quite briefly:

1. In the nineteenth century the technical superiority of British industry, together with less tangible advantages, enabled her to assume a dominating position in world trade. Britain bought freely the raw materials produced by less developed countries, and in return sold manufactured products. Her navy dominated the seas, and a large overseas empire was built up. Her population grew enormously, and large imports of foodstuffs became necessary.

2. To an increasing extent, however, she paid for her imports, not by the sale of exported goods, but by rendering services: her ships carried much of the world's trade, her banks and insurance

companies extended their activities to the remotest country. By such means she built up an enormous overseas investment, the interest on which became a large part of her income.

3. As other countries developed, the markets for her manufactured products declined, for many competitors arose; Japan, the United States, and Germany were her special opponents. Her share of the world's shipping also declined—from about 45 per cent in 1913 to one quarter at the beginning of World War II. Nevertheless, her overseas investment income, the proceeds of her financial "services," and the sale of gold more or less maintained her balance of payments.

4. World War II precipitated the present crisis. First, Britain was compelled to liquidate her foreign investments, especially those in dollar countries, to buy armaments from North America. Little of this former wealth remains. Second, her industry, already showing many signs of wear and tear, suffered five years during which no replacements or repairs could be effected; there was, furthermore, widespread bomb damage, especially to housing. Third, she lost 12,000,000 tons of shipping and had to replace all of it, and even expand her fleet. Finally, the cost of agricultural imports rose more rapidly than did the selling price of her industrial exports.

Since the war ended, Britain's difficulties have been severe. World trade has been disrupted, and as a trading nation she has suffered accordingly. She has been faced with the problem of the so-called "dollar gap." This gap arises from the fact that she has to purchase much of her needed food from Canada and the United States, which do not reciprocate, however, by needing to buy British goods in such quantities. Britain is the banker for the Sterling Area, a voluntary association of the Dominions (excluding Canada), the colonial empire, the Irish Republic, and certain other states. In spite of all difficulties, however, substantial recovery has been made.

The cardinal point in the recovery program has been an increase in productivity, both in industry and in agriculture. In 1950, for example, British agriculture was producing 40 per cent more than in 1938, and the proportion of home-grown food had risen from 31 to 39 per cent. Industrial production was at a record level, though productivity was still well below that of the United States. Over-all production nevertheless increased no less than 40 per cent between 1946 and 1949. This increased production has enabled Britain to build up her exports to something like 50 per cent above prewar levels. A gigantic program of capital investment has been necessary to achieve the result; about 20 per cent of the national income is being invested annually in new housing, new plants, better agricultural methods, and in a host of other fields.

Such results have been possible only because of two things, the restriction of home living standards, and dollar aid. "Austerity" has become a byword in modern Britain. Rigorous controls of consumer spending have continued: severe rationing of foodstuffs (especially meat), high taxation, and temporary wage freezes have kept inflationary pressure under reasonable control. In particular, every effort is being made to divert the economy from imports from the dollar-countries to those from the Sterling Area.

The Marshall Plan, initiated in 1947, provided the support necessary for recovery, together with generous aid from Canada.

> Of all United Kingdom imports in 1949, over 13 per cent were financed by Marshall Aid, representing two and a half per cent of total resources available. Large items paid for in this way included one-third of all wheat and flour, including home production, one-third of sugar, one-fifth of cheese, one-tenth of bacon, one-quarter of petroleum, just over one-quarter of copper, one-third of zinc, four-fifths of virgin aluminum, one-sixth of lead, two-fifths of raw cotton and one-half of tobacco.[28]

Such was the voice of the Chancellor of the Exchequer in March, 1950. Marshall Aid was terminated early in 1951, for the dollar earnings of the Sterling Area had increased so greatly that Britain's dollar reserves were back to reasonable levels. No words of praise could be too high for the farsightedness of Secretary of State Marshall's plan.

So, for a moment, a balance had been achieved, and Britain was solvent. But over her were gathering the clouds of European unrest. Within six months of this temporary balance, the drain upon dollar resources had been renewed. A large new defense program has become necessary and will hinder her ultimate recovery. In Britain, as in every part of Europe, full prosperity can only come when peace, stability, and justice can be guaranteed without the maintenance of military power.

BIBLIOGRAPHY

BILHAM, E. G. *The Climate of the British Isles*. London: Macmillan & Co., Ltd., 1938.

DARBY, H. C. (ed.). *Historical Geography of England Before 1800*. London: Cambridge University Press, 1936.

[28] Great Britain, *Economic Survey for 1950* (London: H. M. Stationery Office, 1950), p. 9.

DEMANGEON, A. *The British Isles.* Translated by E. D. Laborde. London: William Heinemann, Ltd., 1939 (original French edition 1927).

EKWALL, E. *The Concise Oxford Dictionary of English Place-Names,* 3d ed. New York: Oxford University Press, 1947.

FOX, C. *The Personality of Britain: Its Influence on Inhabitant and Invader in Prehistoric and Early Historic Times.* Cardiff: Natural Museum of Wales, 1933.

FREEMAN, T. W. *Ireland.* London: Methuen & Co., Ltd., 1950.

GREAT BRITAIN. *Monthly Digest and Annual Abstracts of Statistics.* London: H. M. Stationery Office.

GREAT BRITAIN, CHANCELLOR OF THE EXCHEQUER. *Economic Survey.* Published annually. London: H. M. Stationery Office.

GREAT BRITAIN, DEPARTMENT OF SCIENTIFIC AND INDUSTRIAL RESEARCH, GEOLOGICAL SURVEY. *British Regional Geology,* 2d ed. Eighteen regional monographs on British rocks and structure. London: H. M. Stationery Office, 1948.

GREAT BRITAIN, MINISTRY OF AGRICULTURE AND FISHERIES. *National Farm Survey of England and Wales.* London: H. M. Stationery Office, 1946.

JONES, LL. RODWELL. *The Geography of London River.* London: Methuen & Co., Ltd., 1931.

MACKINDER, H. J. *Britain and the British Seas.* New York: D. Appleton & Co., Inc., 1902.

OGILVIE, A. G. (ed.). *Great Britain, Essays in Regional Geography.* London: Cambridge University Press, 1930.

STAMP, L. DUDLEY. *The Land of Britain, Its Use and Misuse.* London: Longmans, Green & Co., Ltd., 1948.

——— (ed.). *The Land of Britain.* Report of the Land Utilisation Survey of Britain. London: Geographical Publications, Ltd., 1943-46.

STAMP, L. DUDLEY, and BEAVER, S. H. *The British Isles.* London: Longmans, Green & Co., Ltd., 1933.

TANSLEY, A. G. *The British Islands and Their Vegetation.* London: Cambridge University Press, 1939.

WOOLDRIDGE, S. W., and LINTON, D. L. *Structure, Surface, and Drainage in South East England.* London: George Philip & Son, Ltd., The London Geographical Inst., 1939.

chapter 4

NORTHERN EUROPE

$\mathbf{I}$F ASKED TO DEFINE "Northern Europe" as a region, many persons would have only the haziest notion as to which countries should be included. Most of them would certainly begin by naming the Scandinavian countries, that is, Norway, Sweden, and Denmark, but which other nations to include (if any) would be a point of serious debate. In the following chapter, therefore, the author has chosen to define Northern Europe in terms of an areal concept which long has been an integral part of Scandinavian geographic thought: the so-called "Norden" concept.

The term itself means simply "the North," but in this connection is specifically intended to designate five nations in Northern Europe which are more closely related to one another than they are to any of the countries surrounding them. They are the three Scandinavian countries, together with Iceland and Finland. A sixth area, the Faeroes, while constituting an administrative part of Denmark, is usually regarded as a distinct geographic unit within the region.

The "Norden" concept derives its validity not so much from the facts of physical geography as it does from those of cultural and historical geography. To demonstrate this point one need only cite a few of the characteristics which distinguish the countries of Northern Europe as a regional group. They are, for example, all nations of relatively small populations, the ethnic and linguistic compositions of which are both simple and uniform. In fact, the same ethnic and linguistic stock finds representation in all five countries, though in one of them it exists only as a minority. Moreover, the overwhelming majority of the peoples profess the same religious faith.

In each of these nations illiteracy has long since been abolished and the regional standards of education, health, and sanitation can scarcely be equalled elsewhere on the continent. Though their resources are neither varied nor abundant, the nations of Northern Europe have achieved a level of economic well-being which is among the highest in the world. Because there are no great discrepancies in the distribution of their national wealth, these countries are often regarded as working models of economic democracy. In the field of social legislation the nations of Northern Europe are outstanding pioneers, having long set the pace for the rest of the world. Though three of them retain a monarchial form of government, they all have well-established traditions of political freedom and democracy. Also, despite an earlier history marked by bloodshed and violence, the nations of Northern Europe have demonstrated such exemplary harmony and cooperation in the conduct of international affairs for the last century, that the region as a whole has come to be called "Europe's quiet corner." When seen in the light of such considerations, Northern Europe will be appreciated as a distinct geographic region with a character and qualities of its own.

Physiographic Basis of Cultural Forms

Location, Size, and Configuration. The region of Northern Europe occupies a position in the Old World which is almost directly comparable to that of Alaska in the New World. Its southern border, the Danish-West German boundary, is situated in the same latitude as the southern tip of the Alaskan Panhandle (55° N.), while the North Cape of Norway, the northernmost point of continental Europe, is located on the same parallel as Point Barrow (71° N.). Longitudinally these two regions show a similar correspondence, for the distance is just as great from the eastern boundary of Finland to the western extremity of Iceland as it is from the Alaskan Panhandle to the outermost islands of the Aleutian chain. When the Norwegian islands of Spitsbergen (Svalbard) are included, however, the plane of reference must be altered, for the only regions in the New World which are located at a corresponding latitude (namely 74°-81° N.) are the northernmost islands of the Canadian Archipelago and the northern quarter of Greenland.

In point of size, Northern Europe is about seven eighths as large as Alaska. With an area of nearly 500,000 square miles, it constitutes just over one eighth of the European land mass and has close to 19 million people. Unlike Alaska, however, Northern Europe is not a single, relatively unbroken expanse of land (Figure 35). Instead, it is a region of peninsulas and islands, each separated from the other by varying widths of open sea. By far the largest continuous land mass in Northern Europe is what we may call the Fenno-Scandinavian Peninsula. Joined to the subcontinent along a front extending from the Gulf of Finland to the White Sea, this compound neck of land stretches northward between the Gulf of Bothnia and the White Sea and then mushrooms out into the Scandinavian Peninsula (which extends 1,200 miles to the southwest) and the Kola Peninsula (which extends some 300 miles to the east). The fact that this appendage is divided politically among Finland, the Soviet Union, Norway, and Sweden in no way detracts from either the physical continuity or the essentially peninsular character of the area as a whole. Northern Europe's only other land contact with the subcontinent is the Peninsula of Jutland in Denmark. Owing to its location, this peninsula has been infinitely more important as a link between the Northern countries and the remainder of Europe than the broader but less accessible Fenno-Scandinavian Peninsula.

Apart from these two peninsulas, however, Northern Europe has no physical continuity, for its remaining areas are composed of islands. Among these are Iceland and the Faeroes in the Atlantic; Spitsbergen and Jan Mayen in the Arctic; the Danish Archipelago and the Swedish islands of Gotland and Öland in the Baltic; and the Åland Archipelago at the entrance to the Gulf of Bothnia. As a consequence of this peninsular and insular configuration, Northern Europe stands somewhat apart from the rest of the subcontinent. This relative isolation has in turn played an important role in the historical and cultural development of the region and in large part explains the sense of community which exists between these nations today. A brief introductory description of the individual countries follows.

Norway. The Kingdom of Norway occupies the western and northern sides of the Scandinavian Peninsula, extending through 13° of latitude and 26° of longitude. Lindesnes, its most southerly point, is located in the same latitude as Juneau, Alaska, while its northernmost extremity, North Cape, is situated on the same parallel as Point Barrow. The country has an extremely attenuated shape, stretching some 1100 miles from north to south. From a maximum width of 280 miles near 61° latitude, it constricts to less than four miles near 68° (measured from the Swedish border to

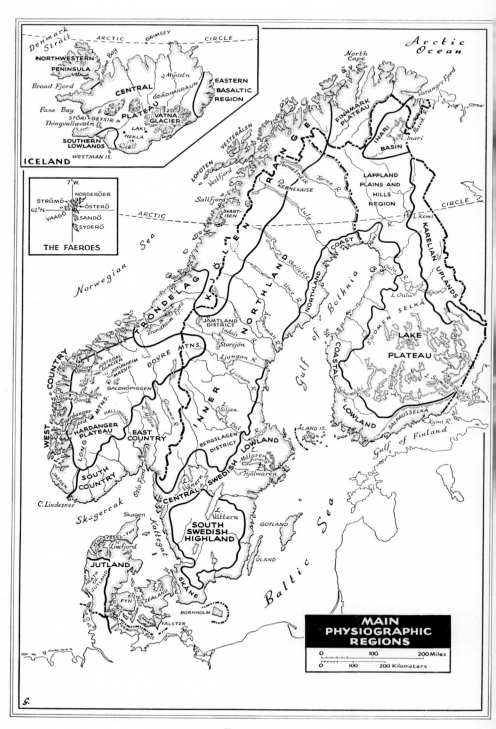

FIGURE 35
168

the head of Tys Fjord) and then broadens out again to 160 miles in the Finnmark Plateau in the far north. If embayments are not included, its coast line measures about 2,100 miles, but if they are reckoned in, this figure rises to 12,500 miles, or roughly half the circumference of the earth. On its landward sides Norway is bounded by Sweden in the east (1,025 miles) and by Finland and the Soviet Union in the northeast (452 and 125 miles respectively). Its total area is 124,556 square miles (slightly larger than the state of New Mexico), of which almost 10,000 square miles are made up by the 150,000 islands and skerries which line its coasts. In addition to its continental area, Norway has sovereignty over Spitsbergen and Jan Mayen in Arctic waters and Peter I and Bouvet islands in the South Atlantic. Norway also claims a portion of the Antarctic continent under the name of Queen Maud Land.

Sweden. The Kingdom of Sweden is situated on the eastern side of the Scandinavian Peninsula. Its shores face the Gulf of Bothnia in the north, the Baltic Sea on the southeast, the Skagerrak and Kattegat on the southwest and the Sound (Öresund) separates it from Denmark. Like Norway, it has an elongated shape, extending 975 miles from north to south and 310 miles from west to east at its widest point. Its coast line measures about 1,600 miles in length, embayments excluded. On its landward sides it is bordered by Norway in the west (1,025 miles) and Finland in the northeast (332 miles). With a total area of 173,035 square miles, of which 158,450 are land, Sweden is the fourth largest country in Europe and is slightly larger than the state of California.

Finland. The Republic of Finland is situated east of the Gulf of Bothnia and north of the Gulf of Finland. The total length of its coast line along these bodies of water is about 680 miles, embayments not included. On its landward sides Finland is bounded by Sweden in the northwest (332 miles), Norway in the north (452 miles), and the Soviet Union in the east (787 miles). Like both Norway and Sweden, Finland has an elongated shape, measuring over 700 miles between its northern and southern extremities. Except for the northernmost tip of Lappland and the Hangö (Hanko) Peninsula in the southwest, the entire country lies between 60° and 70° north latitude. With a total area of 130,125 square miles, of which 117,935 are land (somewhat larger than the combined areas of Michigan and Wisconsin), Finland is the sixth largest country in Europe (Figure 35).

Denmark. The Kingdom of Denmark is located between the North and Baltic seas and is composed of the Peninsula of Jutland

(Jylland) and the islands lying to the east of it. At one and the same time it commands the sea approaches to the Baltic and the southern land approaches to the Scandinavian Peninsula. In such a key position, Denmark can truly be called the "Crossroads of Northern Europe."

The largest continuous land area in the country is the Peninsula of Jutland, which totals 9,186 square miles. Lying just north of it across the Lim Fjord is the island of Vendsyssel-Thy, which for all intents and purposes can be considered a part of the peninsula itself. Together, their combined areas total 11,410 square miles, or roughly two thirds that of the entire country. On the west they face the North Sea, on the north the Skagerrak and on the east the Kattegat. Near the base of the peninsula Denmark shares a 42-mile land boundary with Western Germany.

The Danish Archipelago consists of some 480 islands, of which about 100 are inhabited. Most of them are very small but together their areas come to 5,166 square miles. For the sake of convenience, we can consider them under three principal headings: (1) the Fyn group, (2) the Zealand group, and (3) Bornholm. The group centered on the island of Fyn is separated from the Peninsula of Jutland by the Little Belt, a strait which is about a half-mile wide at its narrowest point. On the east it is separated from the Zealand group by the Great Belt which averages 10 miles in width. This group in turn is separated from Sweden by the Sound, which constricts to a width of less than four miles near Helsingör. On the south both groups are separated from the German coast by the Fehmarn Belt. The most distant of the Danish home islands is Bornholm, about 90 miles east of Zealand and 25 miles off the coast of Sweden. Together the archipelago and the peninsula have an area of 16,576 square miles, or slightly less than the combined areas of Massachusetts and New Hampshire. The country's overall coast line is 4,612 miles in length. Denmark also has sovereignty over the Faeroes and Greenland in the North Atlantic.

Iceland. The most remote member of the European family of nations is the Republic of Iceland, lying just south of the Arctic Circle between 13° and 25° west longitude. Its nearest neighbor is Greenland, 200 miles to the west across the Denmark Strait, but it lies some 500 miles from the coast of Scotland and over 600 miles from the mainland of Norway. Despite this off-side position with respect to the main currents of European life, Iceland served as a steppingstone to the West in the days of the Vikings and occupies a similar strategic position in the Air Age of today.

Roughly rectangular in shape, the island has a total area of 39,709 square miles (slightly less than the state of Virginia). Its coast line, about 3,600 miles in length, is broken in the west by three large peninsulas and on the north and east by numerous fjords. Only the south coast is relatively unindented.

Faeroes. Situated some 400 miles west of Norway and 250 miles southeast of Iceland are the Faeroes (Föroyar), located at 62° north latitude and 7° west longitude. Composed of 18 larger islands and numerous skerries, the archipelago has a total area of 540 square miles, or roughly half that of Rhode Island.

Geologic Structure

Within the limits of Northern Europe, rocks of both the most ancient and most recent geologic ages are found. Over most of Finland and Sweden, the eastern portions of Norway, and the northern coast of the Danish island of Bornholm one finds resistant granites, gneisses, and schists which date from Pre-Cambrian times.[1] These outcrops are remnants of the so-called "Fenno-Scandian Shield," an ancient land block which not only underlaid these areas but also once extended for a considerable distance west of the present Norwegian coast, north into the Arctic and southeastward into the European part of the Soviet Union. Though the surface of this region was originally warped into several extensive mountain systems, by the beginning of the Cambrian period these had all but been eroded away and reduced to a peneplain. From Cambrian to Silurian times large sections of this plain were invaded by epeiric seas (shallow seas of temporary duration) and vast areas were covered with fossil-bearing sediments. By far the greatest accumulation of sediments took place in the west, where a geo-syncline, or trough, had developed. About the end of the Silurian period, the sediments in this trough were compressed, folded, and faulted into a vast mountain range which extended from Scotland northward through Norway and Spitsbergen to the northeastern coast of Greenland. After this mountain-building process (the so-called Caledonian Revolution) has subsided, the entire shield area was once more subjected to a prolonged period of erosion. Only in Spitsbergen and the region of southernmost Sweden and Denmark did any noteworthy deposition take place. In Spitsbergen all geologic ages from the Cambrian to the Tertiary are represented but of greatest importance are the coal-bearing deposits of the Car-

[1] For geologic terms see Appendix I.

boniferous period. In southern Sweden and Denmark, beginning in the Mesozoic Age and continuing into the Cenozoic, thick layers of limestone and chalk were laid down.

During the Tertiary period, the North Atlantic area was convulsed by a great diastrophic upheaval in which the relative land and sea levels were considerably altered. In the west, great outpourings of lava built up an island which embraced large parts of present-day Iceland and central Greenland and may have extended from Jan Mayen in the north to the Faeroes in the south. Concurrent with the appearance of "Greater Iceland," as this island was known, was the faulting and sinking of the western and northern portions of the Fenno-Scandian Shield. As the land west of the present Norwegian coast sank into the sea, the land to the east was elevated once more, with the greatest rise taking place along the newly formed coast. This caused a rejuvenation of all the watercourses in the vicinity and particularly intensified the erosion on the western slope, which now fell abruptly into the sea. Here the steep gradient and copious moisture allowed the streams to cut into the peneplained plateau with such vigor as to capture several drainage basins from the less active southeastward flowing rivers.

Scarcely had Greater Iceland appeared and the Scandinavian Peninsula been re-elevated when vast snow fields began to accumulate in the higher districts of both regions, eventually consolidating into great ice sheets. In Iceland the advancing ice met strong opposition in the flame and fury of the continuing vulcanism. Further tectonic disturbances had already reduced the island to more nearly its present proportions, however, for there is evidence that the ice sheet which covered the Faeroes was purely local in nature. Here, what was originally a single basaltic block that was slightly tilted to the south and east was progressively cut along old fault lines, by the combined forces of ice and sea, into a number of smaller islands.

Over the remainder of Northern Europe the ice sheets alternately expanded and contracted several times, rounding off the resistant uplands and broadening the existing valleys and depressions. In Finland, Sweden, and Norway most of the surface mantle was carried away, while Denmark became the resting place for much of this glacial material. During the final glaciation, the edge of the ice remained stationary over central and southern Jutland for some time, building up an extensive terminal moraine. In Finland too, one finds evidence of a stationary ice lobe in the two great recessional moraines which parallel the south coast—the so-called *Salpausselkä* (ridge). As the glaciers finally melted back for the last time, the lower lying areas were inundated by postglacial seas (forerunners of the modern Baltic and its appendages), while numerous lakes formed in the ice-scoured fissures of the interior. At the same time the areas which had been depressed so long by the great weight of the ice began rising back into isostatic balance. This process is still in operation over much of Scandinavia and can be noted most effectively on the Bothnian coasts of Finland and Sweden. Here, near the cities of Vaasa and Umeå respectively, the rise amounts to about one foot in thirty years. Though the Pleistocene ice sheets have long since disappeared from most of Northern Europe, their scattered and contracting remnants are still found in the mountains of Scandinavia and Iceland.

The region of Northern Europe as we know it today is the direct product of this long and colorful geologic past. In the Scandinavian Peninsula we find an extensive mountain range which falls abruptly into the sea in the west (Norway) and slopes gently down to sea level in the east (Sweden). Denmark and Finland are both largely lowland countries with little variation in relief, while the Faeroes represent the dissected remnants of an old plateau. In Iceland the struggle between fire and ice even now goes on shaping the land forms of that rugged island.

Main Physiographic Divisions

Norway. Using the mountains which comprise its backbone as a basis, we can divide Norway into five distinct physiographic regions. (Figure 35). The mountain ridge itself has the general name of Kjölen (the Keel), though in its various portions it has other local designations. The southern part of the ridge is called the Long Mountains (Langfjellene) and separates the country into (1) the East Country (Östlandet) on the east facing slopes and (2) the West Country (Vestlandet) on the western side. In the Jotunheim massif, where the highest peaks are located (Galdhöpiggen—8,097 feet), the ridge turns in a more east-west direction and bears the name of Dovre Mountains (Dovrefjell), separating the East Country in the south from (3) Tröndelag in the north. Here the main ridge is broken by the Tröndelag-Jämtland gap, but is resumed once again to the north as the (4) Kjölen Range. Associated with this range is the mountain bulwark which makes up the Lofoten Islands and the coast of Finnmark. The final region is

(5) the Finnmark Plateau which forms a continuation of the Lappland Plains and Hills region and Inari Basin of northern Finland.

The East Country is characterized by its relatively broad, open valleys which tend to converge in the region of the Oslo Fjord. In the southern portion of the area (the South Country), Sörlandet, the valleys are narrower and their axes are more nearly north-south. The region as a whole is a continuation of the Swedish Northland, and as such has Norway's longest rivers (Glomma—365 miles) and largest lakes (Mjösa—140 square miles). The easily eroded Cambro-Silurian deposits which covered part of this area have contributed not only to its essentially lowland character but also to its distinction as Norway's most extensive region of tillable soils. The East Country is linked to Tröndelag by two natural pass routes through the Dovre Mountains, namely Gudbrandsdal and the valley of the Glomma River, while the main route to the West Country is by way of Hallingdal.

The West Country is separated from the East Country by the Long Mountains, which in their southern half broaden out to form the Hardanger Plateau. The most distinctive feature of the West Country is its narrow, steep-sided valleys which in many instances have been scoured by the ice far below the level of the sea, producing deep fjords. The greatest of these is Sogne Fjord which measures some 125 miles in length and is over 4,000 feet deep near its outer end. Hardanger Fjord to the south is 105 miles long and over 2,900 feet in depth at its deepest point. Tributary streams have been left far up the fjord sides in hanging valleys; as a consequence, waterfalls are numerous. Places of habitation are limited either to the more sheltered of the islands which line the coast or to the strandflats at the head of the fjords. The Jaeren district south of Stavanger affords a noteworthy exception, for here the coastal lowland is covered with moraine deposits and constitutes one of Norway's best agricultural areas.

North of the Dovre Mountains, centered on the Trondheim Fjord, is the region of Tröndelag. Thanks to its easily eroded Cambro-Silurian deposits, this region is Norway's second most extensive lowland area and agricultural district. On the east the ridges of the Kjölen Range dip down over a thousand feet, forming a natural pass route into the Jämtland District of Sweden. (See Figure 35.)

Northward from Tröndelag, Norway is squeezed onto the lower western slopes of the Kjölen Range. Its varying geologic character gives it a very broken relief, ranging from the sharp Alpine peaks of the Lofotens to the relatively broad interior valleys which extend from the Trondheim Fjord to Salt Fjord.

Eastward from the northernmost spurs of the Kjölen is the Finnmark Plateau, a gently rolling upland averaging 650 feet in elevation and covered with moraine deposits. In the east it grades down into the Inari Basin of Finland and in the south it slopes up to the watershed of the Lappland Plains and Hills region.

Sweden. Sweden lends itself to division into seven physiographic regions: (1) the Kjölen Range, (2) Inner Northland, (3) the Northland Coast, (4) the Central Swedish Lowland, (5) the South Swedish Highland, (6) the Skåne (Scania) Lowland, and (7) Insular Sweden. Near the northwestern border of the country the main ridge of the Kjölen Range runs through Swedish territory, reaching its highest point in Kebnekaise, 6,965 feet. Lying above the tree line (about 3,000 feet in elevation), the region is characterized by its relatively great local relief and the presence of several small valley glaciers.

The region of Inner Northland constitutes the gently sloping eastern declivity of the Kjölen Range. Though its lower limit is about 300 feet elevation, the greater part of the region lies between 700 and 1,500 feet. Large lakes are common in the upper valleys, often occurring in step-like series. The valleys themselves tend to be broad and open but the surface of the interfluves is highly irregular, long drumlin-like moraines being interspersed with resistant monadnocks and swampy plains. In the far north the region grades into the Lappland Plains and Hills region of Finland. In central Northland, centered on Storsjön (lake) is the Jämtland District. This area is underlain by Cambro-Silurian deposits and averages 1,000 to 1,200 feet in elevation, with individual hills rising to 1,600 feet. Opening into Norwegian Tröndelag on the west, it forms a natural pass route across the central portion of the Scandinavian Peninsula.

The Northland Coast is a continuation of the Coastal Lowland of Finland and comprises the area lying between sea level and 300 feet elevation. Averaging 20 to 30 miles in width, this plain is pinched out to the south of Umeå by the hills of Inner Northland.

The Central Swedish Lowland extends from sea level to 300 feet elevation except in its central portion, where hills rising from 400 to 600 feet form the watershed. Having served as a strait between the Baltic and the ocean for the postglacial seas, this region is characterized by its relatively extensive flat plains and large lakes. Vänern, the largest of Sweden's lakes, has an area of 2,140 square miles and owes its existence partly to faulting and partly to inundation of the low plain. Vättern to the east occupies an ancient fault valley and, with an area of 735 square miles, is Sweden's second largest lake. Rising above the general surface of the plain are numerous remnants of the Fenno-Scandian Shield. Off the east coast similar remnants make up the Stockholm skerryguard of some 25,000 rocks and islets. A narrow strip of coastal lowland extends northward to Sundsvall where the hills of Inner Northland come down to the sea.

South of the Central Swedish Lowland is an upland region of ancient crystalline rocks and gravel hills—the South Swedish Highland. Everywhere over 300 feet elevation, it reaches its highest point (1,237 feet) about 20 miles south of Lake Vättern. Traversed by numerous fault lines running in a roughly north-south direction, the region's uneven surface is accounted for by the alternation of horsts and grabens. Small lakes and swamps are especially common in the southern half of the area. On either coast the region slopes down to a narrow coastal lowland.

The Skåne Lowland is geologically associated with the Danish island of Zealand (Sjaelland). This undulating plain is composed of lime-rich moraine deposits and clays lying on a bedrock of sandstone, limestone, and chalk. Running diagonally from northwest to south-east across its northerly portion are a series of horsts which rise to between 500 and 600 feet elevation. Otherwise its elevation averages less than 300 feet. Due to the fertility of its soils and the mildness of its climate, Skåne is Sweden's most productive agricultural region.

Insular Sweden is made up of the two Baltic islands of Gotland (1,160 sq. miles) and Öland (519 square miles). Both of them are composed of tabular limestones of Cambro-Silurian age which dip slightly to the south-southeast. On southern Gotland sandstones from the same period are found. Owing to their generally level surface there are no true valleys anywhere on the islands.

Finland. Though Finland is essentially a lowland country with little over-all variation in relief, it can be divided into five rather distinct physiographic regions: (1) the Coastal Lowland and skerryguard, (2) the Lake Plateau, (3) the Karelian Uplands, (4) the Lappland Plains and Hills region, and (5) the Inari Basin. The Coastal Lowland is a gently sloping plain varying in width from 20 to 80 miles and extends from the seacoast to about 300 feet elevation. Here and there its surface is broken by crystalline hills which stood as islands in the postglacial seas. Off the present-day coast many similar crystalline blocks stand as skerries, their roughly

parallel distribution testifying to their formation along old fault
lines. The largest such archipelago is that of the Åland skerryguard off the southwest coast. Of the nearly 40,000 islands strewn
along the coasts of Finland, this one group contains well over half.

The Lake Plateau, occupying the interior of the country and
averaging from 300 to 500 feet in elevation, is Finland's most distinctive landscape. Delimited on the south by the Salpausselkä
(two great moraines which run roughly parallel to the Gulf of
Finland) and on the north by the Suomen Selkä (a secondary
watershed), the Lake Plateau merges into the Karelian Uplands
in the east and is even less well defined in the west. Its distinctive
character, however, is its great profusion of lakes interspersed with
eskers, drumlins and low crystalline hills.

The Karelian Uplands constitute the watershed between the
Gulf of Bothnia and the White Sea and average between 500 and
700 feet in elevation. In the southern half of the region, individual
points top 1,000 to 1,200 feet, while in the north a number of summits range from 1,400 to 2,100 feet. The Soviet-Finnish boundary
is drawn through this region but does not coincide with the watershed in all areas.

The Lappland Plains and Hills Region occupies the interior of
the country north of Lake Oulu and averages between 300 and
1,000 feet in elevation. Its surface is largely that of a gently sloping
plain but ridges of hills rising 200 to 800 feet above the general
level are not uncommon. In the northwest it is bordered by the
Kjölen Range and it is here that the highest point in Finland is located (4,439 feet). On the north the region merges into a range
of hills which form the watershed between the Gulf of Bothnia
and the Arctic Ocean.

The Inari Basin is a region of Arctic drainage in the far north of
the country and centers on Inari, Finland's largest lake. It averages from 500 to 600 feet in the vicinity of the lake and rises to
over 2,000 feet in the west.

The drainage of the Lake Plateau is effected chiefly through the
Vuoksi River in the east, the Kymi in the south, and the Kokemäki
in the west. The Oulu River drains the southern half of the
Karelian Uplands while the Kemi taps its northern half and much
of the Lappland Plains and Hills region. The Pasvik (Paats) is the
most important outlet of the Inari Basin.

Denmark. The surface of Denmark has the general character
of a gently to moderately rolling plain. Running through central
and southern Jutland is a chain of hills which marks the terminal

moraine of the last glaciation. To the west of the moraine, glacial streams built up extensive outwash plains of sand and gravel, an area which today constitutes Denmark's least productive region—the so-called Heath of Jutland. By contrast, the country to the east of the moraine was covered to a large extent by glacial till derived from the limestone bedrock formations and accordingly it is among the most productive farm land in all of Northern Europe. The highest point in Denmark is Yding Skovhöj (567 feet in elevation), located in east central Jutland.

Iceland. Using its geologic structure as a basis, we can divide Iceland into four physiographic regions. Of Tertiary age are (1) the Northwestern Peninsula and (2) the Eastern Basaltic Region, both areas of tabular basalt which have been dissected by local glaciation into a number of narrow, steep-sided fjords. Of Quaternary age are (3) the Central Plateau and (4) the Southern Lowlands. Constituting the greater part of the island, the Central Plateau averages 1,000 to 2,000 feet in elevation and is covered by extensive lava flows, the largest of these being the Ódádhahraun. The surface of the plateau is far from even, however, for numerous isolated mountains rise above the general level of the land. Some of these are horsts (up-faulted blocks), others are young volcanic cones, and still others are old volcanic necks which have remained after the volcano itself has been eroded away. These range from 3,000 to 6,000 feet in elevation, and, inasmuch as the snow line averages about 3,000 feet, glaciers are common on their upper slopes. The Southern Lowlands constitute the major portion of Iceland's lowland area and were formed essentially through the deposition of clay, sand, and gravel by glacial melt-water streams flowing out from the Central Plateau.

Iceland is one of the most intensively volcanic regions in the world. Best known of its volcanoes perhaps is Hekla which has had 23 eruptions within historic times, the most recent occurring in 1947-48. In addition, hot springs are found in virtually every part of the island, totaling several thousand in all. Many of them boil over periodically, sending great columns of superheated water and steam into the air. The most famous of these springs is the Stóri Geysir in Haukadalur, from which our word "geyser" has been derived. Over 5,000 square miles of the island are covered by glaciers, with Vatna Glacier, the largest, totaling some 3,200 square miles in itself. When volcanic activity takes place beneath these glaciers, it often produces a spectacular phenomenon known as a "glacier burst."

Climate and Vegetation

The climate of Northern Europe is unique, for nowhere else in the world do such high positive temperature anomalies occur so near the poles. The most striking example is found in the outer Lofoten Islands of Norway, where the winter temperatures may range as high as 43° F. above the average for that latitude. Here, of course, the moderating influences of the North Atlantic Drift and the prevailing westerlies have their most direct effect, but even Finland, the most continental country in Northern Europe, experiences a climate which is far less severe than its latitude might suggest.

In the winter, temperatures average above freezing in the Faeroes, along the Norwegian coast south of the Lofotens and over most of Denmark. Along the south and west coasts of Iceland the coldest month averages 30°, thanks to the influence of the Irminger Current, a branch of the North Atlantic Drift. In the interior and along the north and east coasts, the effects of the cold East Greenland Current make themselves felt, and winter temperatures here average some 5° to 10° lower. During the late winter and spring, drift ice frequently blockades the coasts in this region, materially reducing the temperature. Extremes in the northern zone range to −10° as compared to 5° in the south. In the southern mountains of the Scandinavian Peninsula and in the interior of Lappland (the region where Norway, Sweden, and Finland meet in the north) the temperature of the coldest month averages 15° and 5° respectively, with minima as low as −40° occasionally being recorded in the latter area. Southern Sweden normally experiences averages of 25° and above, while the more densely settled coastal districts of southern and western Finland all have winter averages above 15° F. It is interesting to note in passing that both the North Cape of Norway (71° N.) and the city of Chicago (42° N.) have an average January temperature of just under 26° F.!

In July, temperatures average between 60° and 65° over most of Denmark and the southern portions of Norway, Sweden, and Finland. Averages below 50° F. are experienced only along the northernmost coast of Norway and in the higher mountain districts of the Scandinavian Peninsula. In the Faeroes and along the south and west coasts of Iceland July temperatures average between 50° and 52°, while in the northern zone the mean is 50°. Maxima range as high as 75° in the north of Iceland and 65° in the south. Over most of the remainder of Northern Europe maxima range in the 70's and temperatures above 80° are exceptional. The summer season over most of Northern Europe can therefore be directly compared to that of New England or the northern Great Lakes states.

The amount of precipitation received varies widely from region to region in Northern Europe. In Iceland three distinct zones can be delimited: the southern, where more than 40 inches of moisture (rainfall, and snowfall equated as rain) fall each year; the western, which receives between 20 and 40 inches; and the northern and interior zone, where the annual precipitation amounts to less than 20 inches. In the Faeroes about 60 inches of moisture are recorded each year. The west coast of Norway everywhere receives from 40 to 80 inches a year and in the southern portions the annual average rises to from 80 to 120 inches. On the higher mountain slopes in this region as much as 230 inches is not uncommon. In contrast, the regions to the east of the mountains everywhere receive less than 40 inches a year, while in some sheltered valleys and in the far north an annual total of less than 20 inches is the rule. Most of Sweden, Finland, and Denmark receive between 20 and 30 inches a year, though near the west coast of Sweden the annual average is between 40 and 50 inches. In Iceland, the Faeroes and the coastal districts of Norway the maximum precipitation falls in the winter season, while over the remainder of Northern Europe the heaviest moisture is received during the summer months. In southern Iceland, the Faeroes, the coastal districts of Norway and over most of Denmark the snow cover is light and transitory, but in northern Iceland, the mountains and eastern districts of Norway, and over most of Sweden and Finland it is deep and stable. Sea ice rarely forms along the coasts of Iceland, the Faeroes, Norway, or Denmark, but the Baltic and its appendages are normally blocked by ice for a considerable period each year. With the exception of the island of Gotland, the Baltic coast of Sweden is blocked on an average of two months each year. The Gulf of Bothnia is closed to traffic for about three months in its southern reaches and the port of Luleå at its northern end is icebound for nearly seven months out of the year. Though the Gulf of Finland is usually blocked from two to five months by ice, the Finnish port of Hanko is held open the year around with the aid of icebreakers.[2]

Owing to its location in the high latitudes, Northern Europe experiences a marked seasonal variation in solar insolation. At midsummer the sun does not set at all north of the Arctic Circle and in the latitude of the North Cape it remains constantly above the horizon from the middle of May until the end of July. In Spits-

[2] For climatic data. see climatic graphs, Appendix II.

bergen this period of continual sunlight is two months longer, extending from the middle of April until the end of August. Over the more southerly portions of Northern Europe the days are lengthened by long periods of twilight and at 60° N. (the parallel of Oslo, Uppsala, and Helsinki) there is just over one hour of complete darkness at midsummer. In contrast, at the winter solstice (December 22), the regions north of the Arctic Circle receive no sunlight whatsoever and at 60° N. there is only about six hours of daylight and two hours of twilight. During the winter half year the North Cape is in perpetual darkness from mid-November to the end of January, and in Spitsbergen the sun does not rise from the end of October until the middle of February. Such wide fluctuations in sunlight from season to season have a direct influence not only upon the plant life of the region but also upon the activities of the human beings who live there.

In Northern Europe as elsewhere, the climate is closely reflected in the vegetation of the region. In Iceland, grass today covers the greater part of the lowland areas, though before the coming of man these regions supported rather extensive birch forests (*Betula odorata*). Small birch groves are now found only in isolated or sheltered valleys, where they are protected by law. The greater part of the island, however, is covered with a sparse mountain vegetation consisting of mosses and lichens, together with grasses, heather (*Calluna vulgaris*), and dwarf birches (*Betula nana*).

The Faeroes have had no forests within historic times and for the most part are covered with grass. In Denmark deciduous forests in which the beech tree was particularly common originally covered most of the country, though the barren Heath of Jutland may have been an exception. As more and more of the land was taken under cultivation, however, the forests gradually disappeared until today only 9 per cent of the country remains in woods. Owing to man's long exploitation even these remaining groves have a parklike character and they can in no way be compared with the forests which are found in Norway, Sweden, and Finland. But if man has left his mark on the forests of Denmark, so has he altered the Heath of Jutland, for there numerous plantations of spruce (*Picea abies*) and pine have been made and considerable cultivation taken place.

In southern Sweden and along the south coasts of Norway and Finland one finds a mixed-forest type where both deciduous and coniferous species occur, but by far the greater part of these countries falls into the zone of northern coniferous forests where spruce and pine are dominant. In Norway almost a quarter of the land area is in forest and the principal producing areas are the eastern slopes of the mountains in the south, the basin of Tröndelag farther north, and the valley of the Pasvik River along the Soviet border. In Sweden more than half (52 per cent) of the land area is in productive forest, though the percentage varies from five in the far south to over 80 in some northern districts. Finland has 64 per cent of its land area in forest and accordingly it has more productive woodland per capita than any other nation in Europe, almost 11 acres per inhabitant. In the higher districts of Fenno-Scandinavia the conifers give way to the birch, but even this hardy species cannot withstand the cold of the highest mountain districts and the northern coast. Here, instead, we find tundra vegetation consisting of mosses and lichens, together with grasses and small flowering plants.

Historical Geography

Prehistoric Settlement

Although Northern Europe was the last major region of the subcontinent to be inhabited by man, owing to its long immersion in ice, Germanic tribes established themselves on the peninsula and islands of Denmark at an early date and later spread northward into Sweden and Norway. The earliest settlements in Finland appear to have been made on the southwest coast and these too may have been Germanic in origin. About the beginning of the Christian era, however, the second and last major ethnic group to settle in Northern Europe began moving into southern and central Finland—these were Finno-Ugrian tribes. Apart from these two peoples, however (i.e., the Germans and the Finno-Ugrians), no other ethnic group of importance is today represented in Northern Europe.

For some time, the chief forms of economic activity in Northern Europe continued to be hunting and fishing, though in those areas where easily cleared deciduous forests coincided with patches of good, easily worked soil, hunting and fishing were gradually replaced by agriculture. The greater part of Denmark early became the home of a relatively dense agricultural settlement, though this was much less true in Sweden, Norway, and Finland. In these countries, deciduous forests were formerly much more widespread than they are today, and while this served as an inducement to the primitive farmer, the paucity of good soils served as a strong deterrent. Early cultivation in these countries was largely restricted to easily tilled soils derived from Cambro-Silurian and/or marine deposits, as it is even to this day. When iron came into more general use, it not only allowed agriculture to spread into the coniferous forest areas but also made possible the construction of better boats, a factor which greatly improved the communications of the time, particularly in Norway. A simultaneous deterioration of the climate soon nullified the gains made in farming, however, and in some areas, notably Norwegian Tröndelag, it is probable that all previous cultivation had to be abandoned. In the regions remaining, animal husbandry became the dominant form of agriculture and shelters had to be provided for the animals, which up until then had been pastured out-of-doors the year around.

The major lineaments of the present-day settlement pattern of Northern Europe appear to have already been well established in prehistoric times. Both agglomerated villages and dispersed farmsteads, found in Denmark today, were common at an early date. The oldest of the villages tended to be located in plains regions, the rolling hill regions being still largely in forest. In the wooded areas a more dispersed settlement was the rule. Main roads ran along water divides and villages were located on watercourses only where fords had to be made. A much more important determinant of village locations was access to ground water in the form of ponds where animals could be watered. The Danish villages tended to take two general forms—a round village comprised of farms situated roughly in a ring around some central nucleus such as a pond or common pasture, and a linear village, usually comprised of two rows of farms strung out along a roadway. Round-village types were common on Zealand and on Jutland south of Limfjord and east of the Heath; the linear type was more prevalent on Fyn and in southern Jutland. Danish farm buildings were commonly made of bricks which were plastered over and whitewashed and the roofs were often of thatch.

Although much of Sweden was early characterized by a settlement pattern of dispersed farms, villages have also been common since prehistoric times. The farms themselves fall into a half-dozen separate types, each distinguished from the other by the varying location of the animal shelters with respect to the dwelling house. The villages fall into three main groups—the linear village, the round village, and the family village, the later being created through the subdivision of the original farms into smaller units. The linear village type is most prevalent in east-central and southeastern Sweden and on the island of Öland. The round village type is limited to those regions of the country where the Danish influence was the strongest, namely Skåne and the adjacent west and south coasts. The family village was most common in the South Swedish Highland, west-central Sweden and in the southern parts of Swedish Northland. Though most construction was of wood, the form in which it was used varied from planks in Skåne to notched logs in Swedish Northland.

In Norway the settlement pattern was conditioned by the country's physical relief almost as strongly as it was by access to good soil. Apart from the lowland regions near the coast, early agricultural settlements were made on the sides of the more open valleys in the southeast. Such locations combined the advantages of soil (in this case, lateral moraines) and exposure to the sun, advantages which locations either higher up or lower down the valley sides did not possess. From these *midtligårder* (literally, "farms on the middle of the slope"), settlement spread up into the high mountain pastures where the women would usually spend the summer in small huts (*seter*) tending the animals. The farms themselves were widely scattered and true agricultural villages did not exist. Unlike Danish farms, which might be centralized in one or two large buildings, those in Norway were composed of often as many as 20 to 30 smaller buildings, each with its specific use. Along the coasts the location of fishing settlements was determined not only by proximity to good fishing banks but also by suitable harbors and access to small patches of land where subsidiary agriculture might be carried on. As early as the ninth century Norwegian fishermen from the western and northern coastal districts made annual expeditions to the Lofoten fisheries. Thus, with transhumance being practiced in the farming regions and seasonal migrations taking place along the coast to fish or into the mountains to hunt, the population of prehistoric Norway can hardly be thought of as permanently situated.

The rural settlement pattern of Finland was likewise characterized by small, dispersed farms, and agricultural villages in the central European sense are quite unknown even today. In so far as possible, the farms were located on river terraces or on small knolls or eskers so that they would not only have better exposure to the sun but also some degree of protection from the frost. Finnish farm buildings were then and are today customarily built of wood and besides the dwelling house there may be from a dozen to 30 separate out-buildings, each with its own specific purposes. Almost invariably one of these will be a *sauna* (steam bathhouse), usually located somewhat apart from the rest of the buildings and in close proximity to a lake or stream. In the Åland islands, small, protected harbors early gave rise to little fishing villages.

Of the five Northern European countries, only Denmark and Sweden can be said to have towns which date back to prehistoric times. These originally grew up around heathen centers of worship or at tribal meeting places, but somewhat later advantageous trading sites were also selected. Among the earliest Danish towns were Aarhus, Viborg, and Ribe on Jutland, Odense on Fyn, Ringsted and Roskilde on Zealand, and Lund in present-day Swedish Skåne. The earliest Swedish towns grew up in the vicinity of the Mälaren, among them Uppsala and Birka, though the latter has since become extinct.

Originally, all the German tribes spoke the same language, though by the beginning of historic times this had already evolved into three principal dialectal variants. Two of these were spoken in Northern Europe, namely Gothic (now extinct) in the Baltic area and Old Norse (or North German) in Denmark, Sweden, and Norway. Both dialects used the runic characters of the Gothic alphabet in their written language. Among the Finno-Ugrian tribes there also were several spoken dialects but no written language at this time.

The Viking Period (800-1100 A.D.)

About the close of the eighth century the story of the Scandinavian peoples suddenly emerges from the realms of legend into the pages of written history. For the next three hundred years these northern peoples demonstrated such a tremendous surge of activity that scarcely any part of Europe escaped their impact. Norwegians ranged from Spitsbergen and the White Sea in the north to the Mediterranean in the south, and likewise pushed westward to Iceland, Greenland, and the coasts of North America. In the east the Swedes coursed up and down the river systems of European Russia and ultimately reached Byzantium and the lands of the Caspian. The Danes were no less active, for they turned their attention to the lands bordering the North Sea and most particularly concentrated on the British Isles. Begun as voyages of exploration and trade, in many areas these expeditions took on the character of sporadic pirate raids and later developed into organized campaigns of conquest and settlement. Named for the audacious seamen who led these expeditions, this dynamic chapter of Scandinavian history has come to be called the "Viking period."

What the causes for this outburst of peoples may have been is not known with certainty, though they have variously been attributed to overpopulation with respect to the level of technology, to large-scale political dissatisfaction (particularly in Norway), to the attractive realization that the countries of Western Europe were too weak to defend the wealth they were accumulating, and to a sheer love of adventure. Indeed, all of these factors may have played a part, but far better known are the effects of this dispersal. In Northern Europe there was not only a northward movement of peoples in the Scandinavian Peninsula itself but also the beginning of a large-scale Swedish movement into Finland. It was during this same period that the Faeroes and Iceland were permanently settled, though both of these areas had probably been visited somewhat earlier by the Irish. Norwegians landed in the Faeroes sometime during the eighth century and the first permanent settlement was made in Iceland in 874, near present-day Reykjavík. Once begun, the tide of emigrants from Scandinavia (particularly Norway) and from the Viking possessions in the British Isles swelled rapidly, and by 930 there were some 60,000 to 70,000 people on the island. This original period of settlement in Iceland, the so-called *Landnám*, saw all of the coastal areas populated while the interior remained virtually uninhabited, a pattern of distribution which has continued unchanged to this day. The story of this settlement has been preserved in one of the most complete works of historical geography in existence, the so-called *Landnámabók*.[3]

It did not take long for the settlers in Iceland to realize that their new environment offered them fewer opportunities (and greater obstacles) for making a living than had the lands they had left. As a consequence, various aspects of their culture had to be modified to conform to this more exacting milieu. The construction of wooden buildings, for example, was a virtual impossibility, for there was little suitable timber on the island. Instead the settlers were forced to build their homes of stone, earth, or peat. As the birch forests disappeared, the problem of fuel became more pressing and the people had to resort to burning driftwood and sheep dung. Furthermore, only the hardiest of the grains they had brought with them would ripen in the short cool summers of Iceland and during the fifteenth century, possibly because of the deterioration of the climate, even this cultivation had to largely be abandoned. With local exceptions, agriculture in Iceland came to mean harvesting hay during the summer to carry the livestock through the winter.

[3] Written during the twelfth and thirteenth centuries, the *Landnámabók* contains the names of 417 of the earliest colonists and describes in detail how the land was apportioned. About a third of the persons so mentioned appear to have come from the British Isles.

The Viking period saw the introduction of Christianity into Northern Europe and the respective unification of the three Scandinavian countries. In Sweden both the Swedes and the Goths had been brought under one king and the country's borders had been pushed westward against the Norwegians and southward against the Danes. During this same period, the island of Gotland rose to prominence as a trading center, its chief town being Visby on the west coast. Though Christianity was introduced into the country early in the ninth century, its triumph was not complete until the middle of the thirteenth century, making Sweden the last great nation in Europe to bow to the authority of Rome.

In Norway the settlement pattern became more fixed as trade increased and as Christianity gained a foothold. The country's first trading center was founded near Larvik in the ninth century and shortly afterwards Tönsberg became Norway's first town. In the next two centuries a number of other towns came into being— Bergen, Nidaros (present-day Trondheim), Oslo, Stavanger, Borg (now Sarpsborg) and Hamar. When Christianity came in about the year 1000, these embryonic trading towns were selected as sites for its churches and from then on the growth of both church and town was reciprocal. In 1153 Norway became a separate ecclesiastical province, with an archbishopric established at Nidaros.

It was likewise during the Viking period that the Danish trading town of Hedeby (now the West German city of Schleswig) grew into importance. Also dating from this period are the *Dannevirke*, an extensive earthenwork defense line built across the narrows of Jutland just south of Hedeby, and several large, circular Viking encampments on Jutland and Zealand. As Christianity gained ground in Denmark during the tenth century, churches were established in the more important administrative and trading towns and in 1104 a Danish archbishopric was created at Lund. First mention is made of Copenhagen (Köbenhavn) about 1043 when it was referred to as a fishing and trading village, but after 1167 when a castle was established there, the town grew in importance. In Iceland the first *Althing*, or legislative assembly convened at Thingvellir in 930, and it is from this date that the republic reckons its birth.

During the Viking period, a further step in the evolution of the language pattern of Northern Europe took place. Old Norse, which up until then had been the language common to all three Scandinavian countries, split into two parts—an East Norse spoken in Denmark and Sweden and a West Norse spoken in Norway, the Faeroes and Iceland.

The Middle Ages

Soon after the close of the Viking period, the countries of Northern Europe began turning their energies to a more intensive development of their own resources and trade began to develop with Western and Central Europe. From Tönsberg in Norway timber was early exported to the Low Countries and Bergen likewise became an early center for the marketing of fish. In fact, by the thirteenth century Bergen had managed to gain control of all Norwegian fish exports from the mouth of Hardanger Fjord to Finnmark and in order to maintain this dominant position foreign merchants were forbidden to sail north of that city. In Sweden the mining of iron had probably begun during Viking times and the production of so-called "Osmund iron" in Central Sweden (particularly the Bergslagen district at the southern edge of Swedish Northland) soon led to an appreciable export due to its relatively high quality for the period. Stockholm grew up as an important iron-shipping port, as did Göteborg sometime later, when iron exports from the Vänern district began. In the thirteenth century copper was also being mined in the Bergslagen and together these two metals dominated Swedish exports for several centuries. Whereas Birka had been superseded by Stockholm, the ancient town of Visby was continuing to grow and prosper. In the south of Sweden the salting and marketing of Baltic herring was already a thriving business.

It was not long before the commerical league of the North German cities (the so-called *Hansa*) began casting covetous eyes on this growing trade of Northern Europe. Through a combination of shrewd business tactics, economic sanctions, and the threats or actual use of force, the Hanseatic merchants soon managed to gain control of the greater part of the region's commerce. When the Hansa established its factory in Bergen in 1343, it secured control of virtually the entire Norwegian coast, thanks to the fact that this vast region was dependent upon imported bread grains, which the Hanseatic League was in a position to monopolize. Though the exchange of dried fish and butter for grain, meal, and salt soon made Bergen the leading trading center in all of Northern Europe, the general effect on the Norwegian economy was detrimental. When the Hansa's privileges were finally revoked in the sixteenth century, Bergen nevertheless continued its domination of northern Norway and it was not until the middle of the nineteenth century that this region began to enjoy a measure of economic independence, thanks largely to improved communications.

In Sweden, the Hansa early monopolized the salting and marketing of fish in the south and its influence was likewise strongly felt
in mining and in the local government of the many new towns
which came into existence at this time in the central portion of
the country. Though a German settlement had been made in
Visby as early as the twelfth century, that city gained its greatest
prominence about the end of the thirteenth century, when it became the chief trading center of the Hanseatic League in the Baltic.
Near the height of its power, however, it was sacked by the Danes
(1361) and never regained its former importance. In 1370, after
long opposition, Denmark was likewise obliged to grant trade
privileges to the Hansa.

During the Middle Ages several political changes took place in
Northern Europe which have had a considerable influence on the
subsequent development of the region. About the middle of the
thirteenth century Norway reached the height of its power when
all of its far-flung colonies recognized the Norwegian king as their
sovereign. Within a century, however, the country's fortunes had
been seriously reversed, for with the extinction of her royal line
in 1380, Norway and its possessions were joined to Denmark, first
as an equal kingdom but then as a dependent area in 1536.

Throughout the medieval period Sweden continued to focus
her attention on the east, turning her energies first to the Christian-
ization and conquest of Finland, a task which she largely completed
by the defeat of the Russians in 1323. This conquest was followed
by such an influx of Swedish immigrants to East Bothnia that from
1362 on that region was recognized as an integral part of the Swedish
realm. Though this political status was later altered by the course
of events, the Swedish conquest of Finland had other consequences
which were more enduring. In addition to bringing the country
under the jurisdiction of the Western church, the Swedes considerably altered the Finnish settlement pattern. Not only were
many Finns pushed north and eastward into the interior of the
country, in turn dislodging the seminomadic Lapps, but the urban
development of Finland was also initiated. The oldest Finnish
town is Turku (Swedish, Åbo) which was founded in 1229 and
became the country's first capital. Rauma and Pori were founded
in 1365 and Viipuri (Swedish Viborg, Soviet Vyborg) was established in 1403. While the locations of these towns were largely
determined by reason of their harbors and their opportunities for
trade, the towns of the interior tended to grow up around fortresses.
Savonlinna, Hämeenlinna, and Kajaani are examples of such towns.
Helsinki was not founded until 1550. Furthermore, by introducing

their own language, the Swedes had a profound influence on the linguistic character of the country. Not only is there a considerable Swedish-speaking minority in Finland today, but the Finnish language itself has incorporated many words of Swedish origin. It was during this period too, that the dialect of Turku became the national standard for the written language, having been used in the Finnish translation of the Bible.

After Norway was joined to Denmark in 1380, the Danes attempted to complete the union of Scandinavian countries by attacking and conquering Sweden. In 1389 the Swedes were forced to join the Danish-sponsored Kalmar Union, but after a long series of bloody wars broke out of this alliance in 1523. From then until the middle of the eighteenth century Denmark and Sweden were almost constantly at war with one another as they both struggled for mastery of the Baltic. By the middle of the seventeenth century it appeared that Sweden would ultimately be triumphant, for she had not only driven the Danes off the Swedish mainland in the south and annexed the Norwegian territories of Bohuslän (on the west coast of Sweden north of Göteborg) and Jämtland, but she had also turned the Baltic into virtually a Swedish lake by consolidating her hold on Finland and annexing Estonia, Latvia, the region around present-day Leningrad, and portions of the North German coast at the mouths of the Oder and Weser rivers. Her dominance in the Baltic was short lived, however, for with the rise of Russia under Peter the Great Sweden was forced to yield or cede all of her overseas possessions except Finland. Thus, by 1750 the countries of Northern Europe had already passed the peak of their political greatness and were in a state of decline.

During the Middle Ages there was a further development of the urban settlement pattern of the Scandinavian countries as well as a further evolution of the language pattern. In Denmark there were 50 towns by the year 1300, most of which were situated on the coast at the shortest crossings between the islands, on fjords, or at river crossings. Several towns grew up at road junctions, near castles, and at the sites of monasteries. In 1416, when the Danish king chose Copenhagen as his capital, he further spurred the town's growth and it became the country's leading center of learning when a university was established there in 1479. In Sweden, whereas there had been some 30 towns previous to 1600, a like number arose during its period of greatness. Among them was Eskilstuna, which has ever since been renowned for its fine-quality steel products. In Norway the seventeenth century saw the rise of several mining settlements, among them Kongsberg, Röros, and Lökken.

The influence of King Christian IV of Denmark is witnessed in such place names as Kristiania (since renamed Oslo), and Kristiansand on the south coast. The Norwegian language also bears the imprint of the country's long association with Denmark, for throughout this period Danish was the official literary and commercial language of Norway and as such made its strongest inroads in the towns of the southeast. In the less accessible rural and mountain districts, however, old West Norse dialects continued to be spoken throughout the Danish period. In Sweden the strong influence of the Hansa is evidenced by the many German words which entered the Swedish language at that time.

No discussion of the Middle Ages in Northern Europe would be complete without some mention of the untold hardships which the people of Iceland were forced to bear during this period. In the centuries following the Landnám, it is reasonable to assume that the population grew gradually to something over 80,000 persons, but about the beginning of the fifteenth century, a series of natural calamities struck the island, carrying away a great number of inhabitants. The Black Death is said to have wiped out nearly two thirds of the population, while several volcanic eruptions and the deterioration of the climate, with its attendant starvation, also took a heavy toll. In 1602 the Danes imposed a trade monopoly on the island which only further aggravated the people's suffering. When the first census was taken in 1703, there were only about 50,000 inhabitants remaining. This number was further reduced by nearly one fifth as a consequence of the catastrophic eruption of Laki Volcano in 1783. In the Faeroes, the Black Death is believed to have killed virtually everyone, with a resettlement of the islands taking place from western Norway somewhat later. This is believed to account for the fact that the present Faeroese population speaks a medieval Norwegian dialect rather than Old Norse, as in Iceland.

The Modern Period

Since 1750 the countries of Northern Europe have abandoned all dreams of political expansion and greatness and instead have devoted their energies to the improvement of their economic and social conditions at home. Beginning about the end of the eighteenth century, land reforms were initiated in both Denmark and Sweden to correct the continually worsening situation which was created by repeatedly subdividing farm properties into ever-smaller units. In both countries a more scattered settlement pattern has resulted and new areas have been taken under cultivation. In Finland, land reforms were also begun after the country gained its independence and since that time an area as large as Swedish Skåne has been opened to new agricultural settlement. During the modern period, the strongest influence on the urban settlement pattern of Northern Europe has been the Industrial Revolution. Because it came rather late, in most instances after the middle of the nineteenth century, it was not attended by the overcrowding and congestion which has plagued much of industrialized Western and Central Europe. Instead, owing to the nature of its raw materials and sources of energy, industry in Northern Europe has tended to be rather evenly divided between rural and urban locations. Where towns already existed, it has spurred their growth, but where they did not exist, industry has given birth to them. Because many of its raw materials and most of its fuel must be imported, industry has found it of particular advantage to locate in port cities.

The past two centuries have seen a steady rise in the standard of living in Northern Europe and with it the transition from aristocratic monarchy to social democracy. During this same period, great numbers of Northern Europeans emigrated to North America and the release of this population pressure on the land undoubtedly did much to promote the rapid economic advances which have since taken place. Throughout the modern period, the political destinies of the Northern European countries have rested largely in the hands of the Great Powers which surround them. In 1808-9 Sweden was expelled from Finland by Russia and Finland became a Grand Duchy of the Russian Empire. During the Napoleonic Wars Denmark reacted against British pressure by joining the French. As a result of this mistake, Norway was taken from her and joined to Sweden, though she still maintained sovereignty over Iceland, Greenland, and the Faeroes. The duchies of Schleswig and Holstein (on the southern frontier of Jutland) had always been a bone of contention between the Germans and Danes and when Denmark attempted to extend her constitution of 1849 to cover the Duchy of Schleswig, Prussia used this as an excuse to attack her in 1864 and take both territories from her. In 1905 Norway chose to end its union with Sweden and the two countries parted in peace. Throughout the First World War the Scandinavian countries successfully maintained a policy of neutrality, though the war nevertheless had several important repercussions within the region. In 1917 Finland declared its independence from Russia, in 1919 she drew up a democratic constitution, and in 1920 she was recognized as an independent republic. In 1918

Iceland became a sovereign state in personal union with the King of Denmark and in 1920, on the basis of a plebiscite, north Schleswig was returned to Denmark. In 1925, pursuant to a treaty signed in 1920, the Spitsbergen islands became a constitutional part of the Kingdom of Norway, followed by the annexation of Jan Mayen and the Antarctic islands of Bouvet, in 1930, and Peter I, in 1931. In 1939 Norway laid claim to a portion of the Antarctic continent under the name of Queen Maud Land.

When World War II broke out, the countries of Northern Europe announced their intention to remain neutral, but this hope was shattered in November, 1939, when the Soviet Union launched the so-called "Winter War" against Finland. In the peace of March, 1940, Finland was forced to cede the city of Viipuri and the Karelian Isthmus, as well as a border region in the central Karelian Uplands. In addition, the Hanko peninsula was to be leased to the Soviet Union for a thirty-year period. Then in April, 1940, Nazi Germany invaded and occupied both Denmark and Norway, and in order to forestall a similar move in the Faeroes and Iceland, these latter areas were occupied by the British. In 1941 the Americans took over the defense of Iceland. In June of the same year, three days after the Nazis attacked the Soviet Union, the Finns entered the war on their side but were forced to sign a separate peace in September, 1944. Likewise in 1944, the people of Iceland voted to sever their ties with Denmark and become an independent republic. In May, 1945, with the end of the war in Europe, Denmark and Norway were liberated. In the peace treaty signed in September, 1947, Finland lost Viipuri and the Karelian Isthmus in the south once more, and the region in the central Karelian Uplands. In addition, the Petsamo (now Pechenga) region was taken from her, the Porkkala peninsula was leased to the Soviet Union for 50 years and $300 million in reparations were levied against her, payable over an eight-year period ending in 1952. Of the Northern European countries, therefore, only Sweden escaped the direct effects of the war, though her neutrality was strained and precarious throughout. In the postwar period, Denmark, Norway, and Iceland have joined the North Atlantic Treaty Organization, while Sweden has elected to refrain from joining any alliance outside of the Scandinavian area which might precipitate an invasion of Finland.

Each of the Northern European countries is divided into several administrative subdivisions, and though they have a different name in each country, they correspond most closely to the American county. In Norway the unit is called a *fylke* and they number 20 in all, including one each for the cities of Oslo and Bergen. In Sweden the unit is a *län*, of which there are a total of 25 including one for the city of Stockholm. The Finnish unit is a *lääni*, of which there are nine including the Åland Islands which enjoy a large measure of self-government. In Denmark the administrative subdivision is called an *amt* and the country has 23 in all, including one for the Faeroes which has the right to use its own language and flag and is to a large extent self-governing. The Icelandic unit is a *sýsla*, of which there are a total of 21.

The modern language pattern of Northern Europe is a direct product of the region's historical development. In Iceland, the language is the direct descendant of the Old Norse which was introduced during the Viking period. Due to its isolation, Icelandic has preserved its old grammatical system virtually unchanged since the days of the Sagas, in contrast to the more simplified Scandinavian languages. In a further effort to preserve this purity, original Icelandic terms have been coined to take the place of foreign words. This attempt to correlate a medieval language with modern technology and items of culture which are not native to Iceland has produced some rather imaginative compounds. Electricity, for example, is literally translated as "amber-power" while a banana is called a "sausage-fruit." Many of the younger people speak English and many of the older generation know Danish. The Faeroese language has likewise retained its medieval grammar and is accordingly very difficult for most Scandinavians to understand. Both Danish and Faeroese are recognized as official languages in the archipelago, however. In Denmark itself, Danish is the only official language, though there is a small German-speaking minority in Schleswig. Norway has two official languages, both of which are Norwegian but which differ in their historical development. They are *bokmål* (literally, book-language) and *nynorsk* (new Norwegian). Bokmål is a derivation of Dano-Norwegian, the official language of Norway during its long association with Denmark. Nynorsk is a composite of the rural dialects which continued to be spoken throughout the Danish period in the more isolated regions of the country and was first given written expression about the middle of the nineteenth century. In Sweden there is only one official language, namely Swedish, though there are small Lapp and Finnish minorities in the northern part of the country. In north Norway the Lapps number about 20,000 and in north Finland about 3,000. In the latter country both Finnish and Swedish are recognized as official languages. In their written forms, the three Scandinavian languages are mutually intelligible in all three countries, although this is considerably less true of certain of the spoken languages, particularly Danish and Norwegian nynorsk.

In addition to their language ties, the countries of Northern Europe have several other cultural bonds of an enduring nature. In all of these countries the Evangelical Lutheran church has been the state church ever since the Reformation, though there is almost complete freedom of worship in the region today. In the fields of education, labor relations, customs, travel, and humanitarianism the nations of Northern Europe have demonstrated a strong sense of regional unity. Each year an inter-Nordic parliament with advisory powers is held in an attempt to correlate the foreign policies of the region. Many of these advances in regional cooperation have come about as the result of efforts of an organization known as the "Nordic Union" which was founded in 1919. Of a less official nature but no less important in strengthening the bonds of friendship between these northern countries is the vast tide of tourists which flows between these nations every summer. With a uniformly high standard of living, a great variety of scenic and cultural attractions to visit and travel restrictions reduced to a minimum, the peoples of Northern Europe are perhaps the most tourist-minded of any region on the continent. In all but a political sense, "Norden" is a symbol of the unity of Northern Europe.

Norway

Population

In 1950 Norway had a population of over 3¼ millions, of whom about half lived in cities, suburbs, or rural agglomerations. Over two thirds of the total live along the coasts and another one seventh is scattered over some 2,000 offshore islands. The region of the East Country has about 54 per cent of the population, the West Country 25 per cent, and Tröndelag 9 per cent. The counties north of Tröndelag have only 12 per cent of the country's inhabitants. The largest city is Oslo, the capital, with about 435,000 inhabitants (in 1950). The west coast port of Bergen was second with 111,000, followed by Trondheim with 57,000, Stavanger with 51,000, Drammen with 27,000, and Kristiansand with 26,000 (Figure 36). In the period from 1820 to 1940 about 800,000 Norwegians emigrated to the United States.

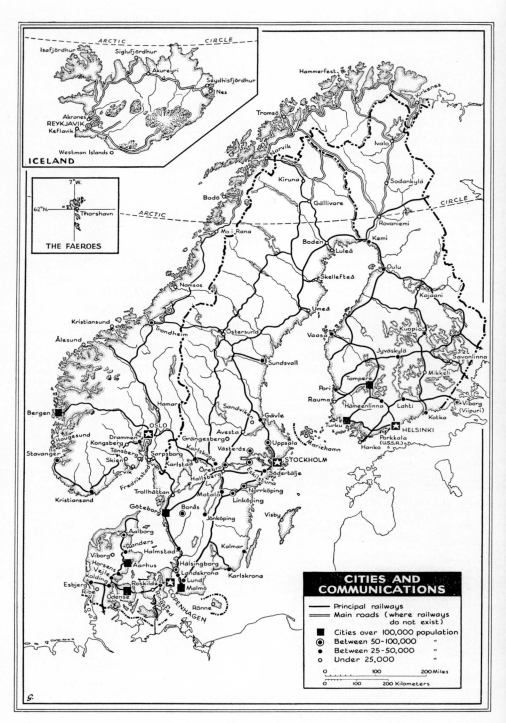

FIGURE 36

196

Present Economic Life of Norway

Agriculture and Fishing. For reasons of topography and climate, less than 3 per cent of Norway's land area has been brought under cultivation (Figure 37). The country's most fertile agricultural regions are those lowland areas which are underlain by Cambro-Silurian deposits and/or covered with postglacial marine sediments. Such regions are found in three sections of the country, namely in the lower valleys of the East Country, the district of Jaeren in the West Country and central Tröndelag. Together these three districts comprise only 8 per cent of Norway's total area, yet they contain almost one half of her total land under cultivation. In the lower valleys of the East Country both animal husbandry and an intense cultivation of field crops are carried on, with grain, especially wheat, being grown on the better soils and potatoes in the sandier tracts. In Jaeren main attention is given to the production of animal products, based both on locally grown fodder crops and imported fodder concentrates. In the central Tröndelag district, due to its shorter growing season and lower summer temperatures, hay and fodder crops are dominant, with wheat giving way to barley as the principal grain. Elsewhere Norwegian agriculture is limited to small plots on the valley sides of the East Country, in the valley bottoms or on the strandflat of the West Country, and to the high pastures in the mountain districts.[4]

With the exception of a few large farms in the lower valleys of the East Country, Norway is essentially a country of small, family farms. More than half of all Norwegian farms are smaller than five acres in size and 98 per cent of them have less than 50 acres. Over nine tenths of all farm properties are owned by their operators and about 80 per cent of all farm labor is supplied by the individual farmer's family, with women comprising over half of the total labor force. Due to the small size of the farms, their often prohibitively steep slopes and scattered distribution, the use of machinery is limited and, even when operated on a cooperative basis, rather inefficient (Figure 38).

Hay is by far the most important crop, normally constituting from two thirds to three fourths of the total acreage under cultivation. Next in order come oats, potatoes, barley, and wheat. With four fifths of its cultivated area in fodder crops, Norway must import the greater part of her bread grains, but by concentrating on the production of animal products she can generally cover her

---

[4] See the statistical summation, Appendix III.

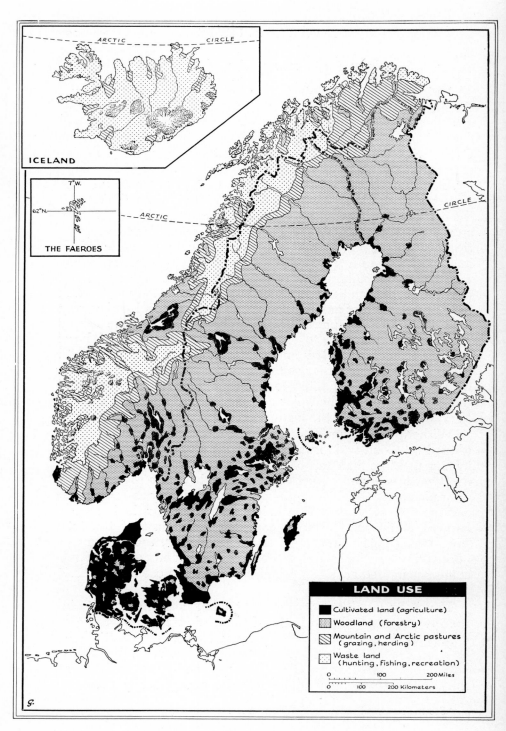

ARCTIC   CIRCLE

ICELAND

7°W.

62°N.

ARCTIC

THE FAEROES

CIRCLE

LAND USE

■ Cultivated land (agriculture)

▓ Woodland (forestry)

▨ Mountain and Arctic pastures
   (grazing, herding)

⸬ Waste land
   (hunting, fishing, recreation)

0   100   200 Miles
0   100   200 Kilometers

G.

FIGURE 37
198

domestic needs of dairy products, meat, and eggs. In order to do even this, however, a considerable quantity of fodder concentrates must be imported each year and margarine must be made to meet the nation's fat requirements. Sheep and goats make up a sizable part of the country's livestock herds, and in recent years fur farming has become an important adjunct to agriculture. In the coastal districts farming is often found in combination with fishing and in the wooded regions a joint farm-forest economy is common. In all, about 25 to 30 per cent of the Norwegian population earns its living from agriculture.

FIGURE 38. A farm in Gausdal in the Norwegian East Country. A typical *midtligård*, it is located in the middle of the slope where the soils and exposure are best. Compare the wooded areas with those shown in Figure 41.

Though Norwegian fishermen normally catch a larger volume of fish each year than do the fishermen of any other European nation, the average value per ton of the catch is lower than that of any country in Europe save Iceland. This is explained in part by the varieties of fish caught, in part by the seasonal nature of the occupation making preservation of the catch a serious problem, and in part by the form in which the catch is sold. Herring makes up about two thirds of the volume of the catch each year but just over one third of its total value. This species is taken off the west coast from Lindesnes to Trondheim Fjord from December to March, and whether it is marketed fresh or salted, it does not command a very high price. The problem of processing such huge quantities of fish in a short time is so acute that much of the herring has to be reduced to fish meal for fertilizer or to oil for margarine if it is to have any value at all. Cod, on the other hand, accounts for about one fourth of the volume and another one third of the value. This species spawns along the north coast from January to April, with the largest concentration being found in the Lofoten Islands. Because of the long distance even to Norwegian markets, the bulk of the cod catch must either be dried or salted to prevent spoilage in transit; as a consequence, it commands a much lower price when it does reach the market. Brisling, a small variety of herring, is taken off the coast of the West Country from July to September and forms the basis of the Norwegian sardine industry.

FIGURE 39. The floating factory "Kosmos III" tied up at her home port of Sandefjord. The ship has 1,100,000 cubic feet of storage-tank capacity. Whales are pulled onto the ship through the slipway, which can be seen in the stern.

In all, less than 10 per cent of the Norwegian population is directly concerned with fishing in some degree. About 3 per cent of the population lives solely from fishing, 3 per cent have some other occupation as a subsidiary livelihood, and 3 per cent have fishing as a subsidiary livelihood.

Whaling has been an important Norwegian livelihood for several centuries, but the modern period began in the 1860's with the invention of the explosive harpoon. From then until 1904 Norwewegian whaling was carried on in the Arctic Ocean from a series of coastal stations in Finnmark, Iceland, and Spitsbergen. The number of whales was so reduced, however, that the center of operations shifted to the Antarctic, with land stations being established in the South Shetland and South Georgia islands. In 1925 the first floating factory began operations in the Antarctic, inaugurating the start of pelagic whaling, for land stations were no longer required. Since that time whales have been towed by small catching ships to the floating factory, where they are hauled on board through a slip-way in the stern (Figure 39). Norwegian whalers normally account for over one third of the world's annual production of whale oil, the bulk of which is used for the production of margarine. The principal ports of the Norwegian whaling fleet are Sandefjord, Larvik, and Tönsberg, all near the mouth of the Oslo Fjord.

Industry and Raw Materials. The industrialization of Norway began about the middle of the last century when steam power was introduced into saw milling and a number of small industries were begun using imported coal as fuel. The greatest industrial expansion has taken place since the turn of the century, however, thanks to the development of part of the country's vast hydroelectric resources. Now about one third of the Norwegian population earn their living in industry and almost three fourths of the country's exports are derived from it.

With the greatest waterpower reserves of any country in Europe, Norway has been generously compensated for its otherwise serious lack of energy sources. Estimated at 9,200,000 kilowatts when operated at 75 per cent efficiency, these reserves have as yet been only 25 per cent developed, yet Norway is already producing over 17,000 million kilowatt-hours annually. About 80 per cent of the reserves are advantageously located in the more densely populated southern half of the country (i.e., in the East and West Countries). Of the total production of electrical energy about three fourths is used in industry with the largest single consumer being the chemical and electro-chemical industry.

The raw materials for Norway's industries come principally from her forests, mines, and fisheries. After an early start in the timber trade, Norway has given her main attention to the production of pulp and paper ever since Sweden, Finland and Russia, with their vaster stands of saw timber, came into competition with her. In contrast to both Sweden and Finland, which export much greater quantities of better-grade chemical pulp than they do of the lower-grade mechanical pulp, Norway normally exports roughly equal quantities of each type. On the other hand, Norway exports finished paper to a greater degree than do either Sweden or Finland. The country's largest pulp and paper mills are located near the

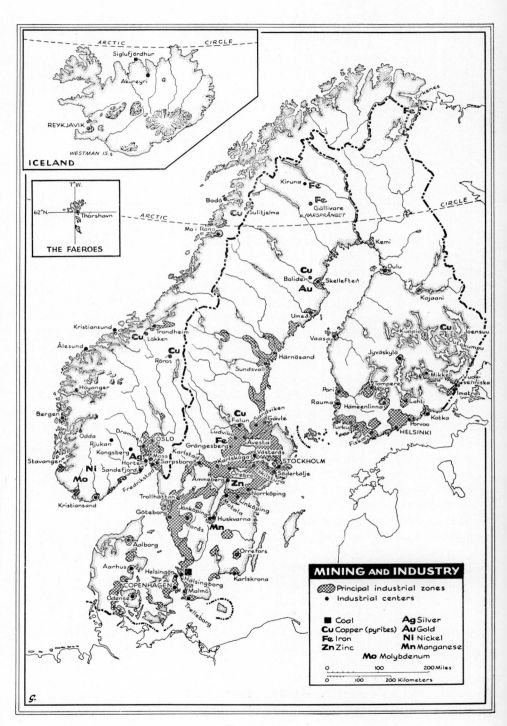

MINING AND INDUSTRY

[legend]
Principal industrial zones
• Industrial centers

■ Coal
Cu Copper (pyrites)
Fe Iron
Zn Zinc

Ag Silver
Au Gold
Ni Nickel
Mn Manganese

Mo Molybdenum

0   100   200 Miles
0   100   200 Kilometers

ICELAND

THE FAEROES

FIGURE 40

mouths of the larger rivers, for reasons of floating and shipping convenience. The chief centers of the industry are Sarpsborg, Drammen, and Skien—all in the East Country, but there is also some pulp production in Tröndelag. Norway's export of pulp and paper generally make up more than one quarter of her total export trade.

Norway has a variety of mineral deposits but like those of Finland, they are for the most part of low metallic content (Figure 40). The largest mining operation in the country is open-pit iron mining in the Syd-Varanger district near Kirkenes. The ore here contains about 33 per cent iron in a natural state but it is beneficiated and shipped in briquets of 65 per cent purity. Norway's next most important mineral resource is copper pyrite, with more important centers of operation being Sulitjelma in the Kjölen Range and Lökken, southwest of Trondheim. Apart from the production of metallic copper, sulphur is extracted for use in the cellulose and chemical industries. Limestone is quarried in the southern portions of the East Country and plays an important role in the production of artificial fertilizers as well as being used in the making of cement.

Norway's vast resources of hydroelectric energy have enabled her to build up a considerable electro-metallurgical industry based on imported raw materials which often come from great distances. This industry is largely localized in the West Country, for there Nature has concentrated bountiful supplies of electrical energy in close proximity to sheltered, deepwater harbors. Ocean-going freighters unload their raw ore directly at the factory where it is processed with cheap power and then exported as finished metal. A typical example is the large aluminum factory at Höyanger in Sognefjord, which uses bauxite from France, Italy, and Yugoslavia (Figure 41). A large refinery at Kristiansand on the south coast processes semifinished nickel shipped in from Canada. Other plants along the coast process manganese, zinc and chromium ores. Pig iron is produced in electric smelters at Stavanger and Bremanger at the entrance to Nordfjord. The country's largest electric steel mill will soon come into operation at Mo i Rana, just south of the Arctic Circle.

Another Norwegian industry which is based on hydroelectric power is the electro-chemical industry, and foremost among such enterprises is the famous Norsk Hydro Corporation which produces saltpeter from air, water, and limestone. Based on a Norwegian process requiring tremendous amounts of electrical energy, the corporation built three large power stations near Rjukan and began production there. Switching later to an improved German process, the company transferred about half of its operations to a plant located on the coast near Skien, although the Rjukan power stations still supply the energy for both installations. Another branch of the electro-chemical industry is the production of carbide and cyanamide, the largest of such plants being located at Odda on Hardanger Fjord.

FIGURE 41. The industrial town of Höyanger, located on an arm of Sogne-fjord. This view not only gives a good impression of the Norwegian West Country but likewise testifies to the dispersed nature of the Norwegian settlement pattern. In the foreground is the factory of the Norwegian Aluminum Corporation, which gave rise to the town in 1916.

Metal working is Norway's largest industry in terms of the number of persons employed, but its production is almost entirely limited to the home market. Shipbuilding alone employs about one third of all metal workers, though most of this work is repair rather than the construction of new ships. Also producing chiefly for the home market are the country's textile and clothing and food-products industries. One branch of the latter, however, is strongly oriented toward export and this is fish canning, which is centered in Stavanger. Tinned sardines and fish balls normally make up about 5 per cent of Norway's total exports by value.

Transportation and Foreign Trade. Transport in Norway has always been confronted with tremendous topographic and climatic obstacles, as well as by great distances between widely scattered settlements. It is not surprising, therefore, that the sea has been the dominant theme in Norwegian transport all through the country's history; even today, it continues to play a decisive role in Norway's communications. In 1893 the so-called *hurtigruten* (express route) was begun between Bergen and Finnmark and this still remains the only dependable year-round connection between northern and southern Norway. Daily sailings are maintained between Bergen and Kirkenes and the entire distance can be covered in 5½ days.

Begun in 1854, Norway's rail net now totals about 2,750 miles in length, of which all but 25 miles belong to the state. By 1950 only 20 per cent of the mileage had been electrified but, on the completion of an eight-year plan in 1953, this figure will total 30 per cent of the mileage and account for about 60 per cent of the country's traffic. Under construction at the present time is a rail link to Bodö in northern Norway, but it is later hoped to continue the line to Narvik and possibly to Kirkenes. In the wintertime, service on some lines may be halted a week or more owing to heavy snows or snowslides.

Norway's road system totals about 27,300 miles in length, of which nearly 10,000 miles are maintained by the national government. For the most part, Norwegian roads are narrow and surfaced with gravel, but they have opened many regions of the country which had no previous land communications. Even so, some sections of the country remain isolated from October until late May because of the snow.

The greater part of the domestic air transport in Norway is carried on by a private company which is under partial state control. Year-round service is maintained between Oslo-Kristiansand and Oslo-Stavanger, and this company also flies the longest internal route in Europe, linking Oslo with Trondheim, Bodö, Harstad, Tromsö, Hammerfest, and Kirkenes during the summer. A second company, likewise operating with state subsidies, maintains a service that connects the coastal cities from Stavanger to Trondheim in the summer. For international flying, Norway has joined with Denmark and Sweden to form a joint corporation in which Norway holds two sevenths of the stock.

Norway's merchant marine has often been called her "floating empire," for without it the country could not maintain its high standard of living. Profits accruing from her overseas shipping make up the discrepancy in her foreign trade, allowing Norway consistently to import a greater value of goods than that which she herself is able to export. Before the war her merchant navy was the fourth largest in the world, totaling 4.8 million gross tons, two thirds of which were motorships and 40 per cent oil tankers. During the war the vessels outside of Germany's grasp (about 85 per cent of the fleet) were organized into the so-called "Nortraship" administration. This corporation not only earned funds enough to pay for the Norwegian government's entire conduct of the war but also made a valuable contribution to the country's postwar recovery. By 1950 Norway had replaced all the tonnage lost during the war and occupied third place in the world's merchant navies. Reckoned on a per-capita basis, however, with 1.6 gross tons per inhabitant, Norway dwarfs all other nations. Some 80 per cent of the activities of her overseas fleet is carried on exclusively between foreign ports and only 20 per cent ever touches Norway itself.

Norway is dependent on many imported goods for maintaining her standard of living, and most of these must be in finished or semifinished form, for with her small population and lack of capital Norway is unable to support a diversified industry of her own. Among her chief imports are ships, machinery and automobiles, metal products, textile goods, fuel, and grains. In return for such goods Norway exports pulp and paper, fish products and whale oil, ores and metals. In the prewar period her best customers, both for imports and exports, were Great Britain, Germany, Sweden, and the United States. Since the war the German trade has been largely supplanted by the United States but it is questionable if such a pattern will prove to be a lasting arrangement.

Norway's Arctic Possessions. In the European Arctic Norway has two territorial possessions—Jan Mayen and Spitsbergen. The former is a single volcanic island located at 71° N. latitude and 8° W. longitude. Earlier used as a base for whaling and sealing operations, its principal importance today is as a weather station. The territory of Spitsbergen is composed of the island of West Spitsbergen and the archipelago lying to the east of it, as well as Bear Island situated halfway between Spitsbergen and the north coast of Norway. With the exception of Bear Island, the archipelago is largely covered by inland ice sheets. Formerly important as whaling and sealing bases, Spitsbergen has more recently served as a "jumping-off place" for Arctic expeditions and the site of three Norwegian weather stations. Since 1900, coal mining has been carried on in West Spitsbergen, first by a United States firm but now by the Norwegians and Russians. The Norwegian population numbers about 1,100 persons, most of whom reside in the mining camps at Longyear City and New Ålesund. The Soviets number about 2,000 and are concentrated in the settlements of Barentsburg and Grumant City. The annual production of the Norwegian mines averages about 300,000 tons, of which the greater part is used in North Norway or by the state railways. The Soviet-mined coal is shipped to Murmansk. All export must take place during the short summer season when the coasts are not blocked by ice.

Sweden

Population

In 1950 the population of Sweden totaled slightly more than seven million persons, of whom almost half lived in cities and towns. From two millions in 1767 the Swedish population grew to three millions in 1835, four millions in 1864, five millions in 1898, and six millions in 1924. In the period from 1820 to 1940 about 1.2 million Swedes emigrated to the United States. The most densely populated region in the country is the Skåne Lowland which has only 2 per cent of Sweden's area but some 12 per cent of her population. The Central Swedish Lowland is next in density with about 13 per cent of the area and 45 per cent of the population. Then come the South Swedish Highland with 13 per cent of the people, Insular Sweden with 2 per cent, and the Northland Coast with 8 per cent. Although Inner Northland and the Kjölen Range together comprise about 60 per cent of the country's area, they have only 20 per cent of the nation's population. Stockholm, the capital, is the country's largest city with nearly 750,000 inhabitants (Figure 42). When its suburbs are included it totals almost one million. Göteborg is Sweden's second largest city with over 350,000 inhabitants, followed by Malmö with nearly 200,000, Norrköping with 85,000, and Hälsingborg with 72,000. Örebro, Uppsala, and Västerås all have more than 60,000 inhabitants and Borås, Linköping, and Eskilstuna all have more than 50,000 (Figure 36).

Present Economic Life of Sweden

Agriculture and Forestry. About 9 per cent of Sweden's land area is under cultivation, though the percentage varies widely from one region to the next (Figure 37). In the Skåne Lowland, for example, over 70 per cent of the land has been brought under the plow, in the Central Swedish Lowland from 40-50 per cent and in the South Swedish Highland about 10 to 20 per cent. Inner Northland, on the other hand, has less than 0.5 per cent of its land under cultivation, while the Northland Coast averages from 3 to 8 per cent and the Jämtland district, 3 per cent. More than three fourths of all Swedish farms have less than 25 acres of tilled land each, though two thirds of the country's total land under cultivation is in farms with larger averages. As might be expected, the larger farms are located in the lowland regions of Skåne, Central

FIGURE 42. The *Gamla Staden*, or medieval center of Stockholm. Originally founded on the islands in the foreground, the Swedish capital has gradually embraced a number of neighboring islands and spilled over onto the mainland on both sides of the Mälaren. Because of Stockholm's many waterways, it is often called the "Venice of the North."

Sweden, and Insular Sweden, while small farm units are the rule in the South Swedish Highland and in Northland (Figure 43). About one out of every five Swedish farms is tenant-operated and over one fourth of all cultivated land in Sweden belongs to such farms. In 1945 less than one fourth of the Swedish population was employed in agriculture.

In terms of the total acreage devoted to its cultivation, hay leads all other Swedish field crops, for almost 45 per cent of the nation's cultivated land is dedicated to this commodity. Oats are second in importance, followed by mixed seed, wheat, rye, and potatoes. When grain prices fell in the 1880's, Sweden, like Denmark, turned its attention more strongly toward animal husbandry, but, unlike Denmark, also maintained its production of bread grains for domestic consumption. Before the outbreak of World War II, Sweden was nearly 99 per cent self-sufficient in wheat, despite the fact that the domestic level of consumption had sextupled since 1870. Moreover she was almost 96 per cent self-

FIGURE 43. View of the Central Swedish Lowland near the inner end of the Mälaren. Once covered by postglacial seas, this region is now one of Sweden's most fertile agricultural areas. At the right is a wheat field. Forests are found on the crystalline outcrops, one of which shows in the foreground. At the left is a *linbana*, or cableway, which transports limestone from a quarry to a large cement factory in Köping.

sufficient in rye, the consumption of this grain having fallen as the standard of living rose. Barley and oats, which were formerly exported to some degree, are now all used domestically and small additional amounts are imported. The export surplus of butter has risen greatly even though the Swedes continue to consume more butter than they do margarine. Export surpluses of eggs and pork have also increased and though the country maintains a small import of meat, this need could also conceivably be filled by curtailing the small export of livestock which now takes place. In all, the country's production of vegetable products rose by 77 per cent from 1870 to 1940, while the volume of animal products increased by no less than 218 per cent in the same period. With a level of self-sufficiency in food approaching 90 per cent, the Swedes suffered no more than a 12 per cent drop in their caloric intake during the worst war year, 1942.

Wheat finds its greatest acreage in the Skåne Lowland, the Central Swedish Lowland (particularly the Plain of Östergötland east of Lake Vättern) and in Insular Sweden. The cultivation of rye is rather evenly distributed over the country south of the Dal River, though in the better agricultural regions it has lost considerable ground to wheat. Oats take up a large part of the cultivated land in the western Central Swedish Lowland (especially around Lake Vänern) and in the South Swedish Highland. Barley is grown over most of the country, though in Skåne and in Insular Sweden it is the finer two-row variety used for malt and in Inner Northland it is the more tolerant six-row variety used for bread grain. The cultivation of potatoes is uniformly distributed over all of Sweden with the exception of the mountain districts, but sugar beets are limited to the Skåne Lowland and Insular Sweden. Cattle are rather evenly distributed over the country, while swine are almost entirely confined to Skåne.

In addition to her soils, Sweden has an extremely valuable resource in her forests. It was not fully appreciated, however, until the middle of the nineteenth century, when the industrial nations of northwestern Europe demanded more timber. From that time on, the forest regions of Sweden (especially Northland) took on the character of a new Swedish frontier and sawmills sprang up rapidly. During the next half century there was a tremendous expansion in the production of sawn timber, culminating about 1900. In the last decades of the nineteenth century the pulp industry also started production, and thanks to the continually growing demand for newsprint and wrapping paper, the pulp industry now ranks as Sweden's most important forest industry in terms of the value of its production. Of lesser importance are a number of other forest industries engaged in making paper, mill goods such as finished window frames and doors, furniture, plywood, wallboard, and prefabricated houses.

Though the forest regions of southern Sweden have likewise benefited by this expansion of the wood-using industries, it has been of especial importance to Northland, where other means of economic livelihood are considerably more limited. Regrowth is slower there, but the quality of the wood is better. Moreover, the region is admirably suited for the transport of timber, for the heavy winter snow cover facilitates the movement of logs by sled during this season. In the spring the logs are then floated down the larger rivers (among them the Ångerman, Indals, Ljungan, Ljusnan, and Dal) to the sawmills and pulp factories situated at their mouths. One disadvantage, however, is the long period during the winter when the ports are blocked by ice, making necessary the concentration of exports during the summer season.

The country's largest sawmills are found along the Northland coast, with particular concentrations near the mouths of the Indals, Ångerman and Ume rivers. There are numerous smaller mills in the southern portion of Inner Northland and in the eastern half of the South Swedish Highland. It is in this latter area that the greatest concentrations of woodworking shops and furniture factories are also found. The distribution of pulp mills largely parallels that of the sawmills, though the two greatest concentrations are along the Northland coast (particularly between the mouths of the Dal and Ume rivers) and in the Lake Vänern area. Those along the Northland coast account for over half of the country's chemical pulp production as well as nearly all of Sweden's pulp exports. The production of the southern pulp mills goes largely into domestic paper making, hence most of the country's paper factories are located in central and southern Sweden, especially around Lake Vänern and in the South Swedish Highland.

A century ago, wood products made up about 10 per cent of Sweden's exports by value, though this percentage rose rapidly as an increasing demand spurred production. In 1897 an export peak of 1.2 million standards of timber was reached and not until 1929 was this figure surpassed. During the '30s a considerable diversification of the sawmill industry took place and the production of plywood, wallboard and prefabricated houses began to assume a more important position. Just before World War I the pulp and paper industry had supplied 20 per cent of Sweden's total exports by value but by 1937 this percentage had risen to 30 per cent. Although Sweden's own paper requirements are fulfilled by domestic production and small quantities are exported, about 90 per cent of the pulp produced is exported to be made into paper elsewhere. The same thing is true with artificial fibers, the bulk of which is processed in other countries.

The wood industries of Sweden have now reached a transitional period, for the age of virgin forests is past and exploitation of second-growth forests has become the order of the day. Even be-

fore the last war, the shortage of raw materials was so acute that
the forest products industries were operating at only 85 per cent
of capacity. During the war the forest reserves were further reduced when it became necessary to use a considerable amount of
wood for fuel. The labor supply in the Swedish forests is largely
derived from farmers who work in the woods during the winter and
tend their farms during the summer. Even so there are about
150,000 full-time employees in the Swedish forest industries.
About one fourth of Sweden's forests are owned by the state, another one fourth by corporations and one half by private individuals.

Mining and Manufacturing. The subsoil of Sweden is the most
richly endowed of any nation in Northern Europe. Metal-bearing
ores are found in three principal districts of the country, namely the
Bergslagen district near the southern edge of Inner Northland, the
Skellefte district centered on the river system of that name in northern Sweden, and the Lappland district in the far north of Northland.

In the early Middle Ages the mining of iron and copper was
already of importance in the Bergslagen district and by the middle
of the fourteenth century these two metals made up almost 40 per
cent of all Swedish exports by value. Two centuries later these
metals constituted over three quarters of the country's total exports.
However, as Sweden's copper reserves gradually became exhausted,
as the foreign competition of coke-smelted ores began to be felt,
and as new domestic industries came into being, the relative importance of iron and copper in the country's economy declined.
Without good coal reserves of her own, Sweden has met the challenge of foreign competition by continuing the production of high
quality charcoal-smelted pigiron, a commodity for which she has
had a leading reputation ever since the production of "osmund
iron" began about the close of Viking times. About 40 per cent
of the total Swedish pigiron production is made up of such high
quality pigiron, its principal raw material being the relatively
phosphorus-free iron ores of the Bergslagen. This production not
only forms the basis of the Swedish domestic steel industry (discussed below) but also provides an important export of quality
steels. Though methods for smelting ores which have a high phosphoric content were developed in the late 1800's, the bulk of these
goes into export (chief mining center: Grängesberg). Copper production at Falun has now all but ceased, though the mining of a
number of other metals has become of increasing importance in
recent years. Among them are pyrites, lead, zinc, manganese, tungsten, and molybdenum.

The mineral resources of the Skellefte district are for the most part covered by a heavy overburden and their discovery and exploration have largely been dependent on geophysical prospecting done with special electrical equipment. Composed chiefly of pyrites, the metal-bearing ores contain a great variety of minerals, among them gold, silver, copper, lead, zinc, and nickel. The chief center of operations in the Skellefte district is Boliden.

Sweden's greatest mineral deposits by far are the vast iron reserves in the Lappland district in the far north. Averaging between 60 and 70 per cent pure iron, these ores have a relatively high phosphorus content and the greatest part of their production is exported. During the summer season, shipments go by electric railway to the port of Luleå at the head of the Gulf of Bothnia and to the Norwegian port of Narvik, but during the winter, when the Gulf is blocked by ice, all ore is shipped via ice-free Narvik. The two principal centers of production are Kiruna (Figure 44) and Gällivare, with most of the mining taking place in open pits.

FIGURE 44. The city of Kiruna, situated between two great iron-ore mountains (Luossavaara and Kirunavaara). Because of Kiruna's high latitude, the variations in sunlight from summer to winter are extreme. Here we see the city as it looks about noon in midwinter.

Among the nonmetallic resources of Sweden mention should be made of coal, peat, building stone, lime, and quartz. Coal of rather low quality is found in northwestern Skåne near Hälsingborg and though production was increased to 600,000 tons a year during the last war, it normally averages about 400,000 tons annually. Most of the production is used by local industries and railways. Peat is found in virtually all parts of Sweden and it is estimated that the country has the fuel equivalent of nearly 4,000 million tons of coal in this resource. Before the outbreak of World War II the average production for fuel was 25,000 tons a year but with the serious shortage of imported fuel during the war, production rose to a maximum of 1.25 million tons in 1945. In the west coast province of Bohuslän the quarrying of granite building stone is an important industry and most of its production is exported. Lime and limestone are found in Skåne, Insular Sweden, and in the Central Swedish Lowland and it is in these regions that the country's cement industry is localized. The production of tiles is concentrated in Skåne and in the Mälar valley of the Central Swedish Lowland. The Swedish glass industry is centered in the southeastern part of the South Swedish Highland around Orrefors, and has long enjoyed a reputation for fine quality.

In the middle of the seventeenth century Sweden was the world's leading producer of iron, annually turning out an amount equal to one third of the world's total consumption. She owed her foremost position not only to her rich iron ore deposits but also to her extensive forests which supplied charcoal for fuel. As iron smelted with coke became increasingly important however, she gradually lost ground to the coal-rich nations of the earth and today Sweden accounts for only about one per cent of the world's total production of iron and steel. Though she is now far down the list in terms of quantity production, Sweden still remains one of the world's foremost producers of quality iron and steel. In the years preceding the outbreak of World War II, about 37 per cent of her total production was exported, though on the other hand an appreciable amount of lower grade iron and steel was imported each year. The main concentration of iron and steel mills is found in and near the Bergslagen district, one of the largest mills being located at Sandviken. Gold, silver, and copper are smelted at a plant near the mouth of the Skellefte River. Aluminum is produced near Avesta in the Bergslagen from imported Norwegian aluminum oxide, though a large part of Sweden's aluminum requirements are filled by imports, especially from Canada. Of the nearly 35,000 persons engaged in metal production in Sweden, about 30,000 are employed in iron and steel mills.

The manufacturing of iron and metal products is spread over a number of localities in the central and southern parts of the country, though the two largest concentrations of such industry are located in Eskilstuna and Stockholm. In the seventeenth century the groundwork for Eskilstuna's diversified production of high-quality goods had already been laid, and since then this Swedish city has become world famous for the matchless quality of its knives, scissors, carpenter tools, surgical instruments, locks, keys, machine tools, hardware, precision instruments, and silverware.

The Swedish manufacturing industries are the most diversified of any nation in Northern Europe and many other products besides steel and glass have attracted world attention. Swedish trade-names in cream separators, refrigerators, vacuum cleaners, calculating machines, and various types of precision and electrical equipment are known the world over. The Swedish Ball-bearing Company (SKF) with headquarters in Göteborg is the world's largest exporter of ball bearings. The L. M. Ericsson Company centered in Stockholm supplies a large part of the world with its telephone equipment, and the name of Bofors is recognized as a world leader in armaments production, particularly of antiaircraft artillery. In addition, Sweden has a number of other mechanical industries whose markets are less embracing. Motor vehicles, for example, are produced in Göteborg, Södertälje, and Stockholm. The country's largest shipyards are located at Göteborg, Malmö, Karlskrona, and Stockholm and much of their work is done under foreign contract. Among the other centers of the mechanical industry are Linköping (aircraft and steam locomotives), Malmö (milling equipment), Trollhättan (aircraft engines, diesel motors and turbines), Huskvarna (bicycles, sewing machines, and firearms), and Västerås (high-tension electrical equipment including electric locomotives). In all, about 110,000 persons are employed in Swedish mechanical industries.

Though most of its raw materials must be imported, the Swedish textile and clothing industry normally supplies 90 per cent of the country's needs for cloth and wearing apparel. Norrköping is Sweden's largest center for the production of woolen goods and also has an important production of cotton products. The Borås-Göteborg district is the country's chief cotton spinning center, however, with a center of secondary importance in Malmö. The linen and jute industries are also concentrated near Sweden's west coast. Rayon and artificial wool are made in Borås and Norrköping. The chief clothing centers are Stockholm, Borås, Göteborg, and Malmö and the production of shoes is concentrated in and near Örebro. The country's largest rubber factories are located in Skåne at Hälsingborg and Trälleborg.

The Swedish chemical industry engages in the production of a number of things, among them being superphosphate fertilizers, explosives, matches, and various wood distillates. Bofors holds the lead in explosives production while Jönköping is a leading producer of matches. Once a virtual world monopoly, the Swedish match industry largely collapsed in 1932 and now employs only one fourth as many persons as it did previously. In 1945 over 40 per cent of all Swedish industrial workers were employed in enterprises of 100 workers or less and one fourth worked in concerns with over 500 employees.

Though she has no petroleum and only small, poor-quality coal reserves, Sweden is bountifully supplied with hydroelectric energy. Of her total water power resources, about 80 per cent are situated in Inner Northland, north of the Dal River. The remaining one fifth south of the Dal has already largely been utilized, so Sweden's future needs must be fulfilled from Northland. In fact, about half of her total hydroelectric energy now comes from this region, the power being made available to the more densely settled and industrialized regions of Central and Southern Sweden through five great high-tension systems, each carrying 200,000 volts. A sixth transmission line carrying 380,000 volts from the Harsprånget power station on the Lule River (Sweden's largest hydroelectric installation) over 590 miles to Hallsberg in the Central Swedish Lowland will be the world's longest and most heavily charged high tension system. The total hydroelectric potential which Sweden might feasibly develop is estimated at between 40,000 and 45,000 million kw-hr annually. In 1950 the country's production of electrical energy topped 18,000 million kw-hr, the bulk of which was produced by water power. To cover her fuel requirements, Sweden is normally dependent on imported coal and coke from Poland, Germany, and Great Britain, though in periods of emergency she is afforded some measure of substitution from her forests and from her peat and oil-shale deposits.

Fishing. Fishing plays a relatively minor role in the Swedish national economy, yet the largest part of the domestic demand for fish products is satisfied by Swedish fishermen. Centered chiefly in the west coast province of Bohuslän, most Swedish fishing takes place in the Kattegat and Skagerrak, with herring, cod, and mackerel representing the most important varieties caught.

Transportation and Foreign Trade. Until the early nineteenth century, most transport in Sweden was by lakes and streams during the summer and by "winter roads" during the winter. In the first half of the last century, however, Sweden, like most of the other nations in Europe, was seized with a canal-building fever and the most important project of this period was the so-called Göta Canal joining Göteborg with the east coast of Sweden through Lakes

Vänern and Vättern. In the 1860's railway construction began in earnest in Sweden and today the country has over 10,000 miles of railroad, of which over 90 per cent are state owned and some 38 per cent are electrified. Of the country's total rail traffic, however, nearly 80 per cent is carried on the electrified lines.

In 1950 Sweden had 59,000 miles of roads of which some 2,750 miles were maintained by the national government and 3,250 miles were hard-surfaced. In the same year Sweden had one automobile for every 25 inhabitants.

Domestic air transport is carried on in Sweden by a state-controlled airline with regular service being maintained between Stockholm-Göteborg, Stockholm-Malmö, and Stockholm-Luleå. During the summer months service is also carried on between Stockholm and Visby, both direct and by way of Norrköping. To conduct international flying, Sweden has joined with Denmark and Norway to form a corporation in which Sweden hold three sevenths of the stock.

In 1950 Sweden had a merchant marine which totaled over two million gross tons. The country's largest port in terms of tonnage handled is Göteborg, which is also Sweden's largest export port. Other export ports, in the order of their importance, are Hälsingborg, Malmö, Stockholm, and Luleå. Stockholm is the country's largest import port, followed by Göteborg, Malmö, Gävle, and Norrköping. Before the war (1938) Sweden's chief sources of imports were Germany, Great Britain, and the United States. In the same year her greatest exports went to Great Britain, Germany, and the United States. In 1949, Great Britain, the United States, and Belgium led the list of import sources, while Great Britain, the United States and Norway were the most important recipients of Swedish exports. Paper pulp, machinery (including ships), metals, and wood products were her most important exports in 1949, while fuel, food products, machinery, textile materials, and cloth constituted her chief imports.

Finland

Population

Finland had just over four million inhabitants in 1950, or ten times as many as it had in 1750. The population topped one million in 1815, grew to two million by 1880 and reached three million by 1912. Some Finnish migration took place to the neighboring countries of Northern Europe before 1890, but since that time almost 350,000 persons have emigrated, chiefly to the United States and Canada. Almost half of this total has come from the province of Vaasa on the west coast. Of the present population, about one third lives in urban areas (Figure 36). Helsinki, the capital, is the country's largest city and has about 370,000 inhabitants. Both Turku and Tampere have about 100,000 persons and Lahti and Pori each have more than 40,000. Oulu, Vaasa, Kuopio, and Jyväskylä all have more than 30,000 inhabitants. Viipuri, which had been the country's fourth largest city (66,000 inhabitants in 1940), was lost to the Soviet Union after World War II. By the end of 1950 virtually all of the 480,000 Karelians who chose to move at the close of the war rather than become Soviet citizens had been resettled, almost half of them on their own farms.

About half of the present Finnish population lives in the Coastal Lowland and skerry-guards, another 40 per cent lives in the Lake Plateau region, and the remainder is spread over the other regions of the country. About 9 per cent of the population is Swedish-speaking, though there are particular concentrations in the Åland Islands (96 per cent), Uusimaa province on the south coast (30 per cent) and Vaasa province on the west coast (21 per cent). Although they have increased in absolute numbers, the relative percentage of Swedish-speaking citizens has steadily declined since 1880, due to greater emigration and a lower birth rate. There is also a marked difference in the rural-urban distribution of the two language groups in Finland, for in 1940 about 40 per cent of the Swedish-speaking group resided in cities while in the same year just over half that proportion of the Finnish-speaking group lived in urban areas.

Present Economic Life of Finland

Agriculture and Fishing. About 7 per cent of Finland's land area is under cultivation, the percentage varying from nearly 25 per cent along the south coast to less than one per cent in Lappland. The average size of Finnish farms is small, about seven eighths of them having less than 40 acres of tilled land each. The remaining farms, those larger than 40 acres in size, comprise about half of the country's cultivated land. These larger farms are concentrated in the southern and western portions of the country, especially on the Coastal Lowland, while small farm units are the rule in the interior, to the north and east. In these latter areas particularly, farming is combined with hunting, fishing, and forestry and is at best a part-time occupation. Formerly a very large proportion of Finnish farms were tenant operated, but a series of land reforms begun about 1920 has reduced this proportion to less than 5 per cent. At the present time about half of the Finnish population gains its livelihood from agriculture.

Like Norway and Swedish Northland, Finland has a climate which is best suited to the growing of fodder crops, and hence animal husbandry has become the dominant theme in Finnish farming. Over three fourths of the country's cultivated land is in fodder crops and of the total, over half is in hay alone. In terms of acreage under cultivation, oats is second in importance, followed by rye, wheat, and barley. Hay is the principal crop in all regions of the country, but oats as a second crop gives way to wheat in the more fertile soils of the Åland Islands and to barley in the far north. Though the Finnish yields per acre were the lowest of any country in Northern Europe before the war, they nevertheless were better on the average than those of countries, like France, whose climates are considerably more favorable for agriculture.

The aim of Finnish agriculture has been to make the country as self-sufficient as possible with respect to its food supply. Before World War II this goal had largely been achieved in such commodities as milk, butter, meat, eggs, and potatoes but had not yet been reached in bread grains. Even in bread grains, however, a tremendous advance in this direction had been made, for whereas Finland produced only 40 per cent of its requirements of bread grains before the First World War, it was almost 90 per cent self-sufficient in this commodity by 1938, thanks both to increased acreages under cultivation and higher yields per acre. Unfortunately, the Second World War and its subsequent cessions of territory have largely nullified these remarkable gains and it undoubtedly will be some time before Finland can again achieve her 1938 level of self-sufficiency. Moreover, to maintain what self-sufficiency she does have, Finland must continue to import considerable quantities of fodder concentrates and artificial fertilizers.

Fishing plays a smaller part in the economy of Finland than in that of any of the other countries of Northern Europe. This is due of course, to the fact that Finland lacks access to the open sea which the other nations possess. Of the annual catch, about three fourths is Baltic herring and over half of these are taken in the skerries off the southwest coast. Sealing has also been carried on since ancient times off the west coast and seals are likewise found in Lake Saimaa in eastern Finland. Only about 10,000 persons live by hunting and fishing in Finland, including the Lapps who tend their reindeer herds in the far north.

Forest Industries. Though less than one fourth of Finland's population derives its living from industry, this branch of the country's economy is steadily growing in importance. Aside from her agricultural land, Finland's greatest single resource is her forests (Figure 45) and in normal times over 80 per cent of her exports are wood products of one sort or another. Of the country's total number of industrial employees, nearly one third work in forestry and in the elaboration of forest products.

FIGURE 45. Part of Lake Saimaa in eastern Finland. Such a landscape is characteristic of the Lake Plateau—Finland's most distinctive natural region. Settled within relatively recent historical times, the region is sparsely populated and shows few evidences of human occupance. Note the small clearings in the middle background. (Finnish Tourist Association.)

Sawmilling in Finland began in the sixteenth century, with the eastern districts of the country around Viipuri taking an initial lead. The greatest impetus to growth, however, came about the middle of the nineteenth century, when Great Britain adopted a free-trade policy and steam power was introduced. Though the earliest mills were located at water-power sites, since the advent of steam the newer mills have grown up at the mouths of the larger rivers. Using their own waste for fuel, these plants are ideally located with respect to both floating and shipping possibilities. Since the loss of Viipuri, Kotka has become the country's largest timber port, handling over one fourth of the export trade. Among

the other large timber ports are Pori, Oulu, Kemi, and Rauma.
Though Finland had nearly 30,000 miles of floatable waterways before the war, the loss of Viipuri and the outlet of the Saimaa Canal
have seriously complicated the movement of timber from eastern
Finland. The postwar cessions likewise cost Finland about 12 per
cent of her sawmill capacity.

In addition to sawn timber, box wood, and planed timber, the
Finnish wood industry also produces spools, plywood veneer, and
prefabricated houses for export. Once the world's leading producer
of spools, Finland has steadily lost ground since World War I,
because of the loss of the Russian market and competition elsewhere. Also using birch as a raw material, the Finnish plywood
industry has grown rapidly since its founding in 1912, and before
the outbreak of the Second World War Finland had risen to first
place in the world's export of plywood, supplying nearly one third
of the total entering foreign trade. A more recent development
in the wood-products industry is the production of prefabricated
houses, most of which are exported to the Soviet Union.

Side by side with her sawmills there have grown up pulp and
paper mills, using the sawmill waste both for fuel and raw materials. In addition to the production of cellulose (both mechanical
and chemical), the Finnish pulp and paper industry has a number
of by-products which have given rise to further branches of industrial activity. Among them are rayon, fodder cellulose, turpentine,
pine oil for soap and varnish, distilled spirits, and during the war
at least, motor fuel and lubricants. While the by-products go
chiefly to the home market, pulp and paper are among Finland's
foremost exports, with Great Britain as the country's best customer.
In the postwar cessions to the Soviet Union, Finland lost about
one fifth of the productive capacity of her cellulose industry and
one tenth that of her paper industry.

More than half of Finland's forests are owned by private individuals, while another one third belongs to the state. The state
exercises a strong influence in the Finnish forest industry and engages in considerable production itself. The motives for its entry
into such production have been varied, ranging from acquiring fuel
for the state railways to opening up less accessible forests in the
north and preventing foreign capital from getting control of the
forests. Corporations own only 8 per cent of the total forest area.

Manufacturing. Producing principally for the home market
are a number of other industries. The largest of these is metal
working, which since the war has become the country's largest

single industry in terms of the number of persons employed. This has largely come about as the result of Soviet reparation demands which have forced the industry to expand in order to meet delivery deadlines. Pig iron is produced by a coke oven in Turku and by an electric furnace near Imatra (Vuoksenniska), using scrap and some ore. Malleable iron production is carried on in Martin ovens and electric furnaces on the southwest coast (Dalsbruk and Fiskars) and also at Vuoksenniska, where steel rails are rolled. Locomotives are built in Tampere and the country's largest shipyards are located at Turku and Helsinki. The Finnish metal industry also produces farm implements, machinery, structural steel, boilers, and turbines. Important as this industry is to her domestic economy, however, Finland must continue to import most of the metal she uses in semifinished form.

Though most of its raw materials are likewise imported, the Finnish textile industry is centered about 90 miles inland, in the city of Tampere. This choice of location was originally due to Tampere's abundant water power, though the later construction of the railway network has also tended to give Tampere an added distributional advantage. Secondary centers of production are located in Helsinki and Turku. Because the production of the Finnish textile industry is neither adequate nor sufficiently diversified to meet domestic requirements, textile goods still constitute a considerable item of import.

Like Sweden's industry, that of Finland is rather evenly divided between rural and urban locations. Though its principal concentration is in the more densely settled Coastal Lowland of the south, access to forest resources and relatively good water and rail transport have encouraged an increasing industrialization of the Lake Plateau and the northern Coastal Lowland. The Åland Islands, due to their offside position, are the least industrialized province of the entire country. A particular feature of Finnish industry as a whole is its large proportion of women employees, amounting to almost 40 per cent of the total. Indeed, an important factor in the growth of Finland's home-market industries has been her supply of cheap labor.

Minerals and Power. Finland's bedrock contains a great variety of minerals, but their metal contents are so low for the most part that mining is not profitable. At the present time Finland's most important mining operation is the copper mine at Outokumpu in Karelia. Discovered in 1910, this deposit of copper pyrite annually yields about 15,000 tons of metallic copper from some 500,000 tons of raw ore, as well as sulphur concentrates which are used in the cellulose industry and iron residues which go into the making of steel. The Petsamo nickel mines, which were just coming into production before World War II, were lost to the Soviet Union in 1947.

Without coal, Finland's industry was originally very closely tied to her water-power sources. The introduction of steam changed this situation somewhat but the advent of hydroelectric power once more shifted the center of concentration back to waterfalls. Because of the nature of her topography, Finland's waterfalls generally have low heads of water, averaging 20 to 30 feet. Of advantage, however, is the fact that almost half of her water-power reserves are located in the southern part of the country, where the large lakes also serve as natural regulators of the water level. With reserves estimated at 10,000 million kw-hr, Finland was producing between 2,500 and 3,000 million kw-hr before the war, but the cessions of 1947 cost her one third of her developed water power and one quarter of her total reserves. Recent construction of generating plants on the Oulu and Kemi rivers (as well as elsewhere) will largely compensate for this loss and should double the present level of production. The country's largest hydroelectric plant to date is located at Imatra on the Vuoksi River, with a capacity of 120,000 kw. Its power is distributed by high-tension lines as far west as Helsinki and Turku. About 90 per cent of all Finnish hydroelectric power is used by industry.

Transportation and Foreign Trade. Finland's earliest communications were by her lakes and rivers during the summer and by winter roads over the snow and ice through the rest of the year. The country now has about 21,700 miles of roads, most of which have been built since the coming of the automobile. Only those in the vicinity of the larger cities are hard surfaced. In 1950 there was one automobile for every 81 persons in Finland.

As early as 1500 discussions began about the feasibility of joining Lake Saimaa and the eastern lake district with the Gulf of Finland by a canal, but nothing was done until the first half of the nineteenth century. Once completed, the Saimaa Canal became Finland's busiest inland waterway. In the 1930's, the tonnage passing through the canal averaged 3.5 million tons a year, though much of the north-bound traffic was empty bottoms. During the war it was within the fighting zone and accordingly unusable and after the war it was lost to the Soviet Union by the territorial concessions. Whether it will be practical to link the

Saimaa district with the Kymi River by a new canal is still being debated.

Begun in 1862, when a line connecting Helsinki and Hämeen-linna (Tavastehus) was completed, the Finnish railway system now has about 3,100 miles in operation, of which all but 160 miles belong to the state (Figure 36). Finland's railways have played an important role in the economic development of the country by opening up new forest and farm lands, expanding the hinterlands of several timber ports, and by providing a trade link with the Soviet Union. Inasmuch as most of the lines were built during the Russian period, the tracks are of broad gauge and despite the railway bridge across the Tornio River to Sweden, Finland has direct rail traffic only with the Soviet Union. The Finnish rail net has not yet been completed, however, and several additional lines are under construction or being planned.

Domestic air transport is carried on by a state-operated corpora-tion. Regular service is maintained on the following routes: Hel-sinki-Turku-Mariehamn, Helsinki-Turku-Pori, Helsinki-Vaasa-Kemi, Helsinki-Tampere-Jyväskylä, and Helsinki-Kuopio. The Finnish capital is also linked to Stockholm by a number of airlines.

Sea transport is the decisive factor in Finland's foreign trade, for only her rail connections with the Soviet Union permit through shipments by land. Because of the nature of her exports, Finland's foreign trade experiences wide seasonal fluctuations compared to that of Denmark, for instance. The export of wood products, which comprise over 80 per cent of the total, is concentrated in the sum-mer and early autumn, with the result that the efficient year-around use of domestic shipping in home waters is impossible. Moreover, because her exports are more bulky on the whole than her imports, almost half of the freighters arriving in Finnish ports are in ballast while only ten per cent of the ships depart in ballast. Winter ice conditions likewise mean a decrease in traffic since only specially constructed ships or limited ports (Hanko and Turku) can be used. Helsinki is the country's largest import port, followed by Turku, Hanko, and Kotka. Kotka leads in export, with Helsinki second and Pori third. The war caused a catastrophic drop in the Finnish merchant marine, the total gross tonnage falling from 649,000 tons in 1939 to 269,000 tons in 1945. By the middle of 1950, how-ever, it had risen to about 515,000 tons.

Until she won her independence in 1917, about 40 per cent of Finland's trade was with Russia. Germany was her second best customer and Great Britain took third place. After Finland's in-dependence, however, Great Britain climbed into first place where

—with the exception of a few years—she has remained ever since. Germany held second place until the close of World War II, when the trade with the Soviet Union once more became important. Finland's principal exports are timber products, paper pulp, newsprint, and plywood. Chief among her imports are fuels, iron and steel, bread grains, and textiles.

Denmark

Population

In 1950, the population of Denmark totaled 4.267 millions, having more than quadrupled since 1800. From one million in 1810 it grew to two million in 1882, three million in 1918, and by 1944 it had passed the four million mark. From 1820 to 1940, about 300,000 Danes emigrated to the United States, though this is considerably less in proportion to the emigration from the other Scandinavian countries during the same period. Of the present population, about half live in urban areas and almost two thirds live in agglomerations of 500 people or more. Largest of the cities is the capital, Copenhagen, which together with its suburbs totals about 1,200,000. The capital so dominates the country as a whole that no other city even remotely approaches it in size. It likewise so overshadows Zealand that no other city over 30,000 inhabitants is found anywhere on the island. Only as far distant as Fyn has another large city, Odense, been able to develop (Figure 36). On the Peninsula of Jutland, however, there are a number of medium-sized cities besides the regional center of Aarhus. After Copenhagen, Aarhus is Denmark's largest city with about 155,000 persons, suburbs included, followed by Odense with 105,000, Aalborg with 85,000, Randers with 50,000, and Esbjerg with 45,000.

Present Economic Life of Denmark

Agriculture and Fishing. Although agriculture has always played an important role in the economic life of Denmark, the specialized export nature which characterizes this occupation today dates back only to the latter part of the nineteenth century. When it became clear to Denmark that she could no longer compete with America and Russia in growing cheap bread grains for the industrial nations of Western Europe, the little nation turned to a concentrated production of livestock products, placing chief emphasis on the growing of fodder crops. Thanks largely to the high level of scientific instruction given to the farmers, to the adoption of the cooperative principle of organization, to a self-imposed regulation of quality, and more recently to the widespread mechanization which has taken place, Danish agriculture has become a model of rational management whose products can command the highest prices in the world markets.

In proportion to its area Denmark has more land under cultivation than any other country in Europe—64 per cent. Even on the relatively infertile western plains of Jutland over half of the land is under cultivation. In general, the percentage of land devoted to the various crops is relatively uniform from one section of the country to the next, though this is the least true in the Heath of Jutland. The greatest proportions of land in wheat are found on Bornholm, Zealand, and Fyn where about 10 per cent of the cultivated area is devoted to this crop. Malt barley likewise finds its greatest concentrations east of the terminal moraine, and on the islands of Laaland and Falster it constitutes over one third of the acreage. Sugar beets are also confined to the better soils and particularly to Laaland and Falster, where they make up another 20 per cent of the cultivated area. Oats, hay, green fodder and root crops are quite uniformly distributed over the entire country, and in the sandy districts of western and northern Jutland crops of rye, potatoes, and mixed seed (barley and rye) reach their greatest extent.

About 64 per cent of the Danish farms are under 40 acres in size and an additional 34 per cent have areas between 40 and 150 acres. When the total acreage of cultivated land is broken down into the same categories, we find that only 29 per cent belongs to the farms with less than 40 acres but that 56 per cent belongs to the farms in the 40- to 150-acre group. Accordingly, against the background of Europe as a whole, it would not be erroneous to think of Denmark as a nation of middle-sized farms (Figure 46). Despite its tremendous importance to Danish economic life, agriculture employed only about one fourth of the population in 1950.

Denmark's specialized production of livestock products has had a number of interesting, and occasionally serious, consequences. Before the last war she was the world's foremost exporter of butter, bacon, and eggs, but because she cannot produce all of her own fodder requirements, Denmark has also become one of the world's leading importers of fodder concentrates. To fatten her swine she has had to maintain a considerable import of corn, and to maintain the fertility of her soils she has become a leading importer of artificial fertilizers. Despite her foremost position as an agricultural nation, Denmark has to import almost one third of the bread grains used for domestic consumption and in order to release as much butter for export as possible, vegetable oils are imported in large quantities to make margarine. Hence we have the apparent inconsistency that in a nation which is one of the world's largest producers of dairy products, the domestic consumption of margarine per capita is two to three times that of butter. With her economy so utterly dependent on such exports and imports it is easily understood why, among the nations of Europe, Denmark's foreign trade is second only to that of Iceland in value per capita.

FIGURE 46. Looking eastward from the lighthouse near the southeastern tip of Bornholm. In the foreground is a typical Danish farmstead. Built around three sides of a central courtyard are whitewashed, half-timbered barns and implement sheds, while a brick dwelling house occupies the fourth side.

Though Denmark's revolution in agriculture has been largely responsible for the high standard of living which the Danes now enjoy, it has also made the country's economy extremely vulnerable to international economic crises, such as that of the 1930's.

Though Danish fisheries employ only about 30,000 persons, the industry has an importance out of proportion to its size. In 1948 for example, Denmark's catch was only 15 per cent that of Norway's in volume, yet its total value was about 60 per cent that of its northern neighbor. This is due, first of all, to a greater abundance of more valuable species in Danish waters, principally the plaice and the eel. Secondly, Denmark's proximity to the consuming markets allows a greater proportion of the fish to be sold fresh rather than dried or salted. The chief ports of the fishing fleet are Esbjerg on the west coast of Jutland and Skagen on its northern tip.

Industry. The industrialization of Denmark has paralleled the shift of Danish agriculture into its specialized production for export, and food-processing has quite naturally become the most important industrial activity. With the exception of the dairies which handle fluid milk, the food-processing industry has tended to locate in advantageous shipping ports rather than in the rural districts near the source of supply. Despite the fact that Denmark has no resources of coal, iron, wood, petroleum or water power, a number of other industries have grown up within the country, most of them designed to produce for the home market but some of them also producing for export. Among the latter are shipbuilding and the construction of marine engines, automobile manufacturing, and vegetable fats. In 1898 a Danish firm acquired the patent of the diesel engine from its inventor and in 1912 the first diesel-powered ocean-going ship sailed from Denmark. Since that time the country has been a foremost builder of motorships. Also, because several American automobile companies have established assembly plants here, Denmark has become a distributing center for motor vehicles in Northern Europe. The vegetable fats industry was originally intended to supply the margarine requirements of the Danish people, but the demand for its by-products (oil cakes for fodder) has so outstripped the domestic consumption of edible oils that a large part of the production of vegetable fats must be exported. Even so, the demand for oil cakes has not been met. Any further expansion of the vegetable fats industry, however, may entail the serious problem of finding new markets for the edible oils.

Denmark is essentially a country of small industries, for almost three fourths of the persons employed in industry work in concerns of 100 employees or less. About one third of the Danish population is engaged in industry and nearly 40 per cent of this industrial population is concentrated in the city of Copenhagen.

Transportation and Foreign Trade. Transport in Denmark is encumbered by the country's lack of physical continuity. In 1950 Denmark had 3,100 miles of railway, of which nearly half were privately owned (Figure 36). Included in this total were 115 miles of ferry routes joining the various islands and linking Denmark's rail net to that of Sweden and Germany. In the same year Denmark had over 5,000 miles of highways, of which 1,360 miles were

Iceland

In 1950 the population of Iceland totaled 144,000 persons, of whom some 72 per cent lived in towns of 300 or more inhabitants. Reykjavík, the capital and largest city, had 56,096 inhabitants, while Akureyri, the regional center of the north, was second in size, with a population of 7,143. In the decade since 1940 the island's population increased by 19 per cent while that of Reykjavík grew by 47 per cent.

As recently as 1880 almost three-quarters of the people of Iceland gained their living through agriculture, but since that time a great

FIGURE 48. Part of Mödhrudalur in the interior of northeastern Iceland. Agriculture in an interior district like this is the exception rather than the rule, but vividly illustrates how every available area has been utilized. In the middle foreground, beyond the small haystacks, are low sod houses of the type which were formerly very common in Iceland, and on the horizon is a row of volcanic cones.

expansion has taken place in both fishing and industry. Today only about 30 per cent of the population is engaged in agriculture, with animal husbandry still constituting its central theme. Less than one per cent of the island's area is under cultivation and the chief crops are hay, potatoes, and turnips (Figure 48). Another 10 per cent of the island is covered by grass which affords pasturage for numerous sheep, cattle, and horses. Large numbers of poultry are also kept but there are few goats and swine. On the Northwestern Peninsula and along the north coast the collection of eider down forms an important adjunct to agriculture. In recent years water from hot springs has been used to heat greenhouses and forcing-gardens, and Reykjavík now derives much of its fruits and vegetables from such sources.

The backbone of Iceland's modern economic life is fishing, for although less than 20 per cent of her population is engaged in this occupation, over 90 per cent of her exports are derived from it. Cod and herring constitute the principal species caught, cod being taken off all coasts and herring more especially along the north coast. The Westman Islands (Vestmanna Eyjar) and Reykjavík are the chief ports of the cod fleet, while Siglufjördhur is the center of operations of the herring fleet. Fishermen from several other European countries likewise fish along the coasts of Iceland, among them the British, French, Norwegians, Russians, and Faeroese.

Industry now supports over 20 per cent of the population and because most of its raw materials come from fishing and agriculture, its most important branch is food processing. Formerly the bulk of the fish catch was marketed after being dried and salted but now a large part of the fish is sold iced or frozen. A considerably smaller proportion of fish is tinned for export, as well as some mutton, shrimp, and lobster. In the last decade a number of subsidiary industries have grown up, among them the preparation of fish meal for fertilizer, herring oil for margarine, and cod-liver oil for medicinal purposes.

Save for a poor quality peat, Iceland largely lacks fossil fuel resources. It is, however, bountifully supplied with hydroelectric power, the reserves being estimated at between three and four million kilowatts, of which half might feasibly be utilized. To date only about 40,000 kilowatts have been developed, but even this rather limited development has largely been responsible for the country's recent strides in industrialization. In 1943 another economic advance of great importance was made when an installation was completed for the heating of most of the city of Reykjavík by water piped from hot springs 11 miles to the east. As a consequence, more than one third of the island's population is no longer dependent on imported fuel for domestic purposes. Since most of the buildings in Iceland are now being made of concrete, the new cement factory at Akranes will be of the utmost importance to the country's economy. A projected nitrate fertilizer plant is expected not only to meet the island's requirements for fertilizer but also to provide another item for export.

Until relatively recent times, all transport in Iceland was either by ship along the coasts or by overland horse caravan. While shipping still is of great significance, the automobile has completely revolutionized the country's land transport. During the Second World War the island's highway net was expanded by the occupation forces and today there are over 2,700 miles of motorable roads. Though it has no railroads whatsoever, Iceland now has more motor vehicles per capita than any other nation in Europe. Air transport is also growing in importance and two companies link Reykjavík with the other main towns of the island. Keflavík airport, about 30 miles west of the capital, was built by the Americans during the war and now is a regular stop for some airlines operating between Europe and North America.

With its small population dependent on imports for most of the essentials of life, Iceland has the highest per capita trade of any nation in Europe. To pay for its required imports, Iceland exports food products (mainly iced or frozen fish), marine oils and fats, and hides and skins. Great Britain was her best customer before the war, normally taking one fifth of her total exports and supplying one fourth of her total imports. During the war the bulk of Iceland's trade shifted to the United States and Canada but in the postwar period it has largely returned to its earlier European markets. In most prewar years Iceland had a favorable trade balance, but during and since the war imports have consistently exceeded exports. In order of their value, the chief imports are machinery and vehicles, food products, fuel and lubricants, metals, and textiles. In gross tonnage per capita, Iceland's merchant marine ranks second only to Norway's.

The Most Urgent Problems
Facing the Nations of Northern Europe

Despite their many basic similarities, the countries of Northern Europe all have their own distinct problems, the most immediate of which (as with most of the rest of Europe) are those associated with the individual country's postwar recovery. In Norway, not only were the occupation costs the highest per capita of any nation in Europe during World War II, but an area of Finnmark nearly as large as that of the Benelux countries was also completely scorched by the Germans. In addition to the reconstruction of Finnmark, top priority has been given to the replacement of the losses which the war brought to her merchant fleet, on which Norway depends so heavily to counter her trade deficit. In the future, as in the past, Norway seeks a free and competitive market in shipping. In whaling she must strive to hold her leading position, for this industry likewise makes an important contribution to her balance of payments. The problem of improved domestic transport is a continuing one, for isolation is still a reality in many sections of the country, especially during the winter. The problem posed by the seasonal nature of her fisheries is also difficult of solution, but if an answer can be found this industry will undoubtedly play a much greater part in the country's economy than it does even now. As a nation which does not live from its land but rather from the seas which adjoin it, Norway will always be sensitive to international maritime competition of any kind.

Finland's chief postwar problem was the settlement of some 230,000 agricultural refugees from the ceded areas of Karelia, a task which was largely accomplished by the end of 1950. To have further subdivided the remaining farm properties would definitely have been a step in the wrong direction, for most of them are already too small to permit the efficient use of horses, much less tractors. Instead, new farm land has been acquired through the voluntary sale of state, corporative, and church holdings, as well as through the compulsory sale of mismanaged farms and lands held by speculators and real estate owners whose chief occupation was not agriculture. Having lost 10 per cent of its agricultural land to the Soviet Union as a result of the war (an area which accounted for one sixth of the country's annual harvest of bread grains), Finland is faced with the task of feeding a greater population from less land. Without continued markets for its goods after the cessation of Soviet reparations, Finnish industry may find itself overexpanded and lopsided in development. It is likely that the Finnish trade pattern in the future will be more strongly oriented toward the east than it was in the period between the two wars, so Finland is confronted with the problem of expanding her commercial relations with her eastern neighbor without jeopardizing her own economic and political independence.

As a small nation with no resources save its soil, Denmark is faced with a number of complicated and far-reaching problems. Economically, its prosperity is directly linked with that of the countries on whom it depends for imported raw materials and for export markets, particularly Great Britain and Germany. Though Denmark had a considerable dollar deficit before World War II, this situation has been further aggravated in the postwar period by the inconvertibility of sterling and by devaluation. As a consequence, Denmark must seek to increase its production and exports on the one hand while simultaneously reducing her imports on the other. She is particularly desirous of reducing trade barriers, especially in dollar areas, for without a fuller measure of free trade it will be some time before Denmark can achieve a suitable balance of payments. Politically, Denmark's strategic position makes it imperative that she maintain satisfactory relations not only with Germany to the south but also with any power that dominates the Baltic.

If Iceland has faced many knotty problems in the past, she is likewise confronted by several difficult issues today. Foremost among them is the necessity of broadening her economic base. Her overwhelming dependence on fishing makes her entire economy unstable, for the fortunes of the catch can fluctuate widely from year to year. Secondly, she must find some way of counteracting the unfavorable trade balance and inflation which have come as a result of the war and the occupation by foreign troops. Without such action, many or most of the material advances gained during the war may have to be relinquished. Thirdly, having had the influence of the modern world so recently and brusquely thrust upon her, she is faced with a serious re-evaluation and adjustment of her age-old culture patterns. And finally, because of her strategic location and the fact that she has no defense establishment of her own, she must reluctantly yield herself to occupation by foreign powers in the event of war or an imminent threat thereof. Whether the Republic of Iceland can overcome these challenges successfully will largely determine her continued existence as an up-to-date, prosperous, and independent member of the European family of nations.

Having largely escaped the consequence of two world wars, Sweden is faced by problems which are more distinctly those which have arisen in the course of her own economic evolution. In Swedish agriculture, for example, there is a growing shortage of labor, for more and more persons, particularly women, are leaving the farms and moving into the larger urban agglomerations. In many agricultural districts the shortage of women is so serious that the farm population is not replacing itself. In Northland, Sweden has a "problem area" whose economic base must be broadened and differentiated if the region is not always to remain a frontier. The establishment of a state-owned iron and steel mill at Luleå has been a step in this direction, but there must also be an expansion of smaller, scattered industries. Agriculture must be intensified and the small farm units welded into larger, more efficiently operated properties. Adding further complications to this problem are the effects of the long, dark winters, the existing shortage of raw materials in the forest industries, the Lapp and Finnish minority groups, and an increasing tendency to migrate to the industrial centers of central and southern Sweden. In the political sphere, as Sweden endeavors to walk the tightrope of neutrality, she must be prepared to pursue an independent policy which oftentimes may not only be misunderstood but also occasionally unpopular in the eyes of other countries.

Thus, while each of the countries of Northern Europe has its own particular problems, to all of them the challenge is the same: how to make a living in an environment which offers many obstacles and provides few resources. That they have largely suceeded in meeting this challenge in the past is witnessed by the high standard of living found in these countries today. How well they will succeed in meeting this challenge in the future will in large part depend on (a) their ability to work together in ever-closer and more harmonious cooperation, and (b) their ability to avoid involvement in the intrigues of the Great Powers which surround them. Northern Europe, like all other regions of the world, can prosper only in an atmosphere of peace.

BIBLIOGRAPHY

A. Books in English

BURNHAM, R. E. *Who Are the Finns?* London: Faber & Faber, Ltd., 1946.
Denmark. Published by the Royal Danish Ministry for Foreign Affairs and the Danish Statistical Department. Copenhagen: Bianco Luno, 1947.
Finland Year Book. Urho Toivola (ed.). Helsinki: Mercatorin Kirjapaino ja Kustannus Oy, 1947.
Iceland 1946. A Handbook Published on the Sixtieth Anniversary of the National Bank of Iceland. Reykjavík: Rikisprentsmidhjan Gutenberg, 1946.
Norway Year Book. Oslo: Johan Grundt Tanum, 1950.
The Northern Countries. Published by the Foreign Ministries of Denmark, Finland, Iceland, Norway, and Sweden. Uppsala: Almqvist & Wiksells Boktryckeri AB, 1951.

B. Books and Articles in Foreign Languages

AHLMANN, HANS W:SON. *Norge: Natur och näringsliv* (Norway: Nature and Economic Life). Stockholm: Kooperativa förbundets bokförlag, 1943.
AHLMANN, HANS W:SON (editor-in-chief). *Sverige Nu: AVC:s Atlas över Sveriges folk, land och näringar* (Sweden Now: AVC's Atlas of Sweden's People, Land and Economy). Stockholm: A. V. Carlsons Bokförlags AB, 1949.
EVERS, W. *Suomi-Finland. Land und Volk im Hohen Norden* (Suomi-Finland. Land and People in High North). Stuttgart: Franckh'sche Verlagshandlung, 1950.
FRISTRUP, BORGE. *Island* (Iceland). Copenhagen: Det Danske Forlag, 1948.
————. "Finlands Krigstab og efterkrigstidsproblemer" (Geographical Aspects of War Losses and Postwar Problems in Finland), *Geografisk Tidskrift*, XLIX (1948-49), 105-38.
HÖIJER, ERNST. *Sveriges jordbruk* (Sweden's Agriculture). Stockholm: Kooperativa förbundets bokförlag, 1924.
KAMP, AA. H. *Lidt om Faeröernes: natur, folk og Erhverv* (The Faeroes: Nature, People, and Economy). Copenhagen: Folkeuniversitetsudvalget, i kommission hos Munkgaard, 1949.

Norrland: Natur, Befolkning och Näringar (Northland: Nature, People, and Economy), Utgiven av Geografiska Förbundet i Stockholm och Industriens Utredningsinstitut. *Ymer*, 1942.

PIPPING, HUGO E. *Finlands Näringsliv* (Finland's Economic Life). Stockholm: Kooperativa förbundets bokförlag, 1946.

SILVERSTOLPE, G. WESTIN. *Svenskt näringsliv i tjugonde seklet* (The Swedish Economy in the Twentieth Century). Stockholm: Kooperativa förbundets bokförlag, 1950.

Sveriges Industri (Sweden's Industry), Översikt utgiven år 1948 av Sveriges Industriförbund. Stockholm: Esselte Aktiebolag, 1948.

SWEDBERG, SVEN. *Våra grannländers näringsliv* (The Economic Life of Our Neighbors: Denmark, Finland, Norway). Stockholm: Kooperativa förbundets bokförlag, 1948.

chapter 5

WESTERN EUROPE

F<small>RANCE</small>, B<small>ELGIUM</small>, the Netherlands, and Luxembourg form the Western "façade" of Europe. Located at the western end of Eurasia, like the British Isles and the two nations of the Iberian peninsula, these four countries are closely bound to the rest of the continent and yet are not cut off from it by seas or mountain barriers. A long shore line, extending from the mouth of the Ems River to the western end of the Pyrenees, gives them the essential characteristic of being oceanic countries whose national outlook is both maritime and continental. On their eastern frontiers they meet Central Europe.

The countries of Western Europe are just as maritime as they are continental. France has 1,925 miles of coastal boundaries out of a grand total of 3,230. No part of the country is more than 300 miles distant from the sea. On the other hand it is only 400 miles from Strasbourg to Vienna, and 360 miles to Berlin. Soviet-dominated Eastern Germany is only 125 miles from the frontier of France.

Besides being the main western gates to the continent, France, Belgium, and the Netherlands form the narrowest isthmus between Northern and Southern Europe. There are but 600 miles of land travel across France, from the North Sea to the Mediterranean, and less than 250 miles between the Mediterranean and the Atlantic Ocean. No high mountains, like the Alps of northern Italy, or vast plains, as in Soviet Russia, intervene. Thus, by their position, these countries of Western Europe were predestined to be cross-roads where all the characteristic features of Europe—physical as well as human—were to meet and merge. No other area in the world could present such a variety, for Western Europe possesses all that others have only in part. Their location between the Atlantic coast, and the center of the continent, and between the 42nd and 54th degrees of latitude, is perfectly central in all respects. From this they derive the benefits of one of the most temperate climates on the earth. Their topography is extremely diversified, ranging in elevation from the highest peaks of Europe in the Alps to the below-sea-level deltaic plain of the Netherlands.

These countries form two distinct groups. On the one hand are the Benelux nations (Belgium, Netherlands, Luxembourg), located at the western end of the great North German Plain, where contacts and conflicts between Western and Central Europe are easiest. The Benelux countries are very small and have access to one sea only, the North Sea. Their relief is generally low and monotonous. On the other hand France is almost completely encased in a mountain frame, but is sufficiently open through gaps and corridors to the south, the north, and the east. It is the largest European nation (the U.S.S.R. excepted). It opens on four different seas and has a wide range of natural features.

Physiographic Basis of Cultural Forms

France

Area and Shape. The total area of France, 212,600 square miles, is about one fourteenth of the area of the United States (less than the State of Texas), or one fortieth of the area of the U.S.S.R. Yet we may emphasize once more that France is the second largest European country, twice as large as the United Kingdom. She is, therefore, large enough to present a great diversity. She combines in her territory all the major aspects of European geography.

Her very regular shape well conveys her central position and the variety of her contacts. France could be exactly included in an almost regular hexagon. From west to east, from north to south, her dimensions are the same, that is, a little more than 600 miles, whether counted from Dunkerque (Dunkirk) on the North Sea to Perpignan at the western end of the Pyrenees, or from Brest at the tip of Brittany to Strasbourg on the Rhine (Figure 49). This distance is similar to that from St. Louis to New Orleans. Transverse lines are about equal and meet almost in the center of the country.

This regularity of shape corresponds with a harmonious disposition of the great masses of relief, as in the architecture of a classical building. France has her portion of all the types of European relief: the Central Lowlands ending in Flanders, the low mountains and sedimentary basins of the Hercynian belt,[1] and the high mountains of the Alpine arc. The old Caledonian mountains alone are missing (Figure 50).

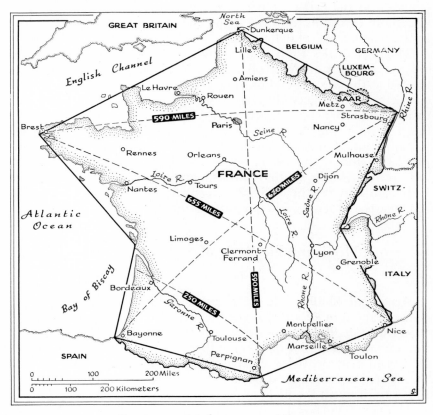

FIGURE 49. Orientation map of France.

Landforms. The diverse landforms are very well disposed. The Alpine arc curves down to the south, sinks into the Mediterranean, thus giving a low seacoast to much of southern France, and reappears in the Pyrenees. These high Alpine mountains cover but a small part of the country, and elevations above 6,000 feet do not comprise more than 11 per cent of the total area.

Within this framework are set the Hercynian elements: The Hercynian belt, widening progressively from southern Poland, covers more than four fifths of France. It is oriented from northeast to southwest in the eastern half of the country, roughly east of the

[1] For geologic terms, see Appendix I.

Paris meridian. Then, turning in a sharp angle, the Hercynian belt takes a northwest-to-southeast direction, forming a typical V. This Hercynian V is particularly well marked in the most important of all Hercynian mountain groups, the Massif Central. The axis of the V is marked by a continuous fault line, along which are preserved some coal measures.

The Hercynian belt of France is not limited to Archaean and Paleozoic rocks, for two very wide depressions were formed within it at the beginning of the Mesozoic period, long after the actual folding. These large basins, the Paris Basin and the Basin of Aquitaine, have been covered with layer upon layer of sedimentary limestone, chalk, clays, etc. of Mesozoic and Cenozoic age. The basins regularly sank down in their center and lowered the old Paleozoic platform to great depths, beneath the present topography. A low gap, the *seuil* (threshold) of Poitou, has, however, maintained a permanent communication open between the two basins, west of the Massif Central and east of the Armorican hill land.

The Massif Central itself is not directly set against the Pyrenees and the Alps: the wide Carcassonne Gap intervenes between the southwest edge and the Pyrenees and links the Basin of Aquitaine and the low Mediterranean plain of Languedoc (Figure 51). On the eastern side, too, the irregular valley of the Rhone River forms a narrow corridor between the Massif and the Alps and ends in the Mediterranean plains. Between the Massif Central and the low Hercynian mountains of the Ardennes and the Vosges to the northeast, there are wide plateaus which allow a free communication between the Paris Basin and the valley of the Saône River, which joins the Rhone corridor. Thus the bulky Massif Central may be bypassed on all sides, a fact of no small importance.

The Hercynian Massifs and the Sedimentary Basins. The Armorican Massif, the Massif Central, the Vosges, and the Ardennes are the important remains of huge mountains erected at the end of the Paleozoic period. The basins consist of Mesozoic and Cenozoic strata. Nothing, probably, would have been left over from the old massifs which were leveled off to a peneplain at the end of the Carboniferous era, had they not been rejuvenated by the Alpine movements in the Tertiary period. As the southeastern part of the Massif Central was nearest to the young mountains, it was much uplifted (it rises now to 5,600 feet), whereas the tectonic effects of the orogenic shock gradually lost their strength westward and northward. The Armorican Massif, for instance, (culminating at 1,314 feet) is no more than 300 feet high on the

PHYSIOGRAPHIC SKETCH OF FRANCE

Strait of Dover

FLANDERS

Schelde

English Channel

Somme R.

PICARDY

Seine R.

Aisne R.

PARIS

Oise R.

Marne R.

NORMANDY

Paris

BRIE

BASIN

BEAUCE

Seine R.

BRITTANY

ARMORICAN

Sarthe R.

MASSIF

Loir R.

Sologne

Loire R.

Cher R.

BERRY

MO

TOURAINE

Loire R.

Limagne

Atlantic

VENDÉE

Ocean

POITOU

LIMOUSIN

Allier R.

Bay of Biscay

Charente R.

MASSIF

AUVERGNE

CENTRAL

Dordogne R.

Quercy

Garonne R.

AQUITAINE BASIN

Landes

Causses

Adour R.

Carcassonne Gap

LANGUE

BASQUE
COUNTRY

Garonne R.

Pyrenees

Hercynian massif

Sedimentary basin

Alpine mountain

Extinct volcano
and lava flow

Very dry
limestone plateau

Sandy plain

Main scarps (cuestas)

242

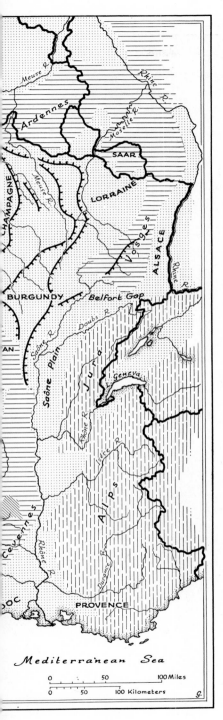

FIGURE 50
Physiographic
sketch of France.

243

FIGURE 51. Carcassonne, in the Carcassonne Gap. The old medieval town is seen on the right bank of the Aude River.

average, and is the lowest of the main physiographic regions in France; even the Paris Basin has an elevation of about 800 feet. The Vosges, being closer to the Jura, the branching arm of the Alps, were cut off from the German Black Forest, thus creating the wide and low plain of the Upper Rhine. The highest summits in the Vosges are located in the southeast and reach a maximum of 4,667 feet. These mountains were high enough to have been partially covered with glaciers during the Great Ice Age, which left its imprint in the form of cirques, wide U-shaped valleys and a series of moraines.

The Massif Central, which overlooks the Mediterranean plains from high and strongly faulted mountains, was repeatedly broken up by Alpine upheaval. The visible after-effects of the thrust are graben plains such as the Limagne in the north, parallel southwest-northeast valleys on the eastern side, and impressive volcanoes (Puy de Sancy 6,185 feet; Plomb du Cantal 6,093 feet), now extinct and dismantled by river and ancient glacial erosion, but still towering in blackish crags, rounded slopes, or chaotic expanses over the tilted Hercynian and Tertiary peneplains. Wide Jurassic limestone expanses were lifted as a whole with the southern part of the massif, and form the desolate karstic plateaus of the Causses, deeply cut by narrow canyons. The northwestern quarter (Limousin), the farthest from the Alps and the Pyrenees, has kept the monotony of worn-down, regular plateaus.

The sedimentary basins also felt, but to a lesser degree, the great Alpine upheaval. The sediments, tilted up toward the ancient Hercynian hills, have been dissected by erosion and appear as a series of curved, outward-facing cuestas, best represented by the famous *Côtes de Meuse* and *Côtes de Moselle*. Some ancient and buried Hercynian folds were reawakened, and corrugated the sedimentary strata lying above them. Thus the Boulonnais near the Straits of Dover and the Pays de Bray in northern Normandy are anticlines aligned along Hercynian axes. In many cases the drainage pattern has followed the same direction: it runs northwest to southeast in the western half of the Paris Basin and southwest to northeast in the eastern part. Although these Alpine transformations were important, flat and regular or slightly rolling plains and plateaus still constitute the greatest area of the Paris Basin (Picardy, Beauce, Brie, Champagne, Lorraine, Loire River countries, and others).

The Basin of Aquitaine, north of the Garonne River, looks much like the Paris Basin, but south of the river valley the basin has been buried under thick masses of debris from the Pyrenees, which form either considerable piedmont fans or huge sandy piedmont plains (the Landes).

The wide valley of the Saône River is deeply sunken between the Massif Central, the Paris Basin, the Vosges, and the Jura. It was for a long time the site of a lake which emptied into the valley of the Rhone. This latter valley is a complex series of basins and defiles.

Later erosion has emphasized structural details. In the Hercynian hills and plateaus, the rivers have eroded deep narrow valleys; the most resistant rocks, whether in anticlinal or in synclinal positions, have been disengaged and have re-created the ancient directions of relief. In the basins, the present river pattern has been progressively shaped by many captures. The Loire River, for instance, flowed for a time from Orléans to the Seine, in the Paris area, before it was diverted into a late Tertiary depression in the region of its present estuary. The Meuse River lost part of its waters when the upper Moselle, once its tributary, was captured by a tributary of the Rhine. The Rhine itself for a time sent its waters towards the depression of the Saône.

Glacial erosion in the Vosges and on the highest volcanic summits of the Massif Central, the spreading of fertile loam upon most of the Paris Basin (except on some areas in the eastern and southern parts which are but barren chalk plateaus, such as Champagne), the slow creeping of slope deposits along many of the valleys—all these are the marks of the changes brought about by the Great Ice Age.

The Alpine Mountains. The structure and morphological history of the high mountains is, of course, complex. The Pyrenees, a rectilinear barrier, preceded by solidly welded ridges on a narrow piedmont, include whole fragments of old Hercynian mountains which, even on the highest summits, retain their massive topography. Powerful but short glaciers have left majestic cirques and very deep transverse valleys. High peaks are numerous, but passes are high and infrequent.

The Jura Mountains, a forward element of the Alps, from which they break off south of Lake Geneva, form a bow-shaped series of limestone ranges folded above the Swiss plateau, as well as several high plateaus above the plain of the Saône.

The northern half of the French Alps may be divided longitudinally into several sections, as follows:

   1. The Pre-Alps, towering limestone fortresses separated by wide gaps or *cluses*. At Annecy and Chambéry the gaps are occu-

pied by beautiful elongated lakes, and at Grenoble by the Isère River valley.

2. The Alpine furrow, a long and wide north-south depression followed by the Isère and Drac rivers.

3. The high crystalline Alps, the highest parts of which probably also of Hercynian origin, have been uplifted to impressive heights (Mount Blanc 15,781 feet).

4. The folded internal Alps, very disturbed by big overthrusts.

Transverse valleys cut through these two last divisions and lead to important passes on the way to Italy. Quaternary glaciation has been intense here, scouring numberless cirques, U-shaped valleys, and spreading morainic deposits as far as the vicinity of Lyon. There are still quite a number of important glaciers, covering some 200 square miles in extent, the longest of which is the Mer de Glace (12 miles long).[2]

The southern half of the French Alps is larger, lower, and more complicated. The crystalline section almost disappears, and the internal core extends farther west, where it forms masses of seemingly contorted mountains. There is no furrow in between them and the Pre-Alps, which become disproportionately wide and make up most of the mountain chain. The folds begin to take a west-to-east direction, which is Pyrenean, and in this jumble there are no major valleys or transverse openings except for the valley of the Durance River. Impressive canyons such as that of the Verdon River had not even been explored until recently. The Mediterranean climate, with its long dry period followed by torrential rainstorms, has great power of erosion, resulting in landslides, wide terraces, stony valley bottoms, deep ravines, and bare mountain slopes.

The small massifs of Estérel and Maures, of picturesque reddish porphyry, are the remnants of ancient Mediterranean lands which emerge again in Corsica. The western part of Corsica is high (9,000 feet), made ragged by glacial and stream erosion, whereas the eastern part is dissected hill land.

The various land features of France are fairly well arranged from the standpoint of communications. With the exception of the high plateaus and hills of the Massif Central, which are fairly difficult to cross, transportation is everywhere easy. Two thirds of France consists of low plains, plateaus, and hills. The steeper slope is outwards and the gentler slope inwards. The higher elevations are located on the periphery, east and south; the western half of

[2] For a detailed discussion of the Alps, see Chapters 6 and 7.

the country, west of a line drawn from the Meuse Valley in the Ardennes to the western end of the Pyrenees, has no elevation over 1,600 feet. Thus the physical landscape does not forbid easy communication between France and Central Europe, and yet, except in the north, protects her against invaders.

Rivers. France has but four major rivers: The Seine, the Loire, the Garonne, and the Rhone. The longest one, the Loire, is only 620 miles long. A great deal of their waters come from the Massif Central, which plays an important part as a source of head-waters.

The Seine, flowing entirely in the Paris Basin, has a rich fan of tributaries (Marne, Oise) coming from the eastern plateaus; it crosses the quiet landscapes of the Paris region as a peaceful and graceful river. Its regular oceanic regime and the rarity of disastrous floods make it most suitable for navigation. Medium-size ocean-going freighters may come up to Rouen, and Le Havre, at the mouth, is the great transatlantic port of France. There has been no difficulty in connecting the Seine by canals with other fluvial basins.

The Loire, born in the southeastern part of the Massif Central from which it receives almost all its tributaries, has wide fluctuations of regime with nasty and unpredictable floods. It is poorly contained by levees and its bed is encumbered with sand bars, uncovered during summer low water. Its deep estuary allows ocean shipping to come to Nantes, 55 miles from the sea, although some ships stop at St. Nazaire, at the entrance.

The Garonne is a torrential stream when it flows down from the Pyrenees to Toulouse, and in its progress across the Basin of Aquitaine it receives important tributaries from the Massif Central. Its flow is rapid and its floods violent. The port of Bordeaux is located at the head of its estuary, the 60-mile-wide Gironde.

The Rhone, surrounded on every side by mountains and having its source in a glacier in Switzerland, keeps a swift and tumultuous flow all along its course. Alpine tributaries (Isère, Durance) and short Mediterranean streams from the Cevennes give it a complex and fairly irregular regime. Its steep gradient and frequent whirlpools make it almost useless for navigation, but great water works capture this energy and use it for the production of hydroelectric power. The Rhone ends in a wide delta in the south, where lie the marshy plains of Camargue.

The Rhine flows in France for only 120 miles, in Alsace. Down to Strasbourg, it is still a mountain stream, glacier-fed, poor in volume in winter, rich in spring and summertime. In spite of

efforts made by the French and the Swiss between Basle and Strasbourg, it is not as useful upstream as it is below Strasbourg, which
is the real terminus of large-scale navigation on the Rhine.

The Benelux Countries

The northern border of France is plainly artificial. Unrelated
to important relief features and constantly shifting according to
the dictates of war and European diplomacy, it acquired its present
position in 1815. Nor does the boundary of Germany with Belgium and the Netherlands coincide with relief features; it crosses
huge boglands. The modern boundary between Belgium and the
Netherlands resulted from the sixteenth century Dutch rebellion
against Spain and was confirmed at the time of the separation of
Belgium from the Netherlands, in 1830. It is just as artificial as
the other Benelux boundaries, and there is a queer appendix of the
Netherlands in the southern province of Limburg that reaches the
outskirts of the German town of Aachen.

The total area of Belgium, the Netherlands, and Luxembourg
is less than 27,000 square miles; that is less than that of Scotland
or Ireland and less than the combined areas of New Hampshire,
Vermont, and Massachusetts. No physiographic unity exists between the Benelux countries. There is not a single major river
and not a single natural region that they do not share with France
or Germany, between which they are inserted like a wedge.

Main Physiographic Divisions. Considerable variety should not
be expected on such a small territory. But, strangely enough, all
major features of the northern half of Europe are here present
(Figure 52). These include (1) a Hercynian massif, the Ardennes;
(2) loam-covered limestone plains (in the Brabant and Hesbaye
in Belgium) similar to those of the Paris Basin, with which they
merge across the Artois backbone; (3) sand and clay plains, a direct
prolongation of the North German Plain. In inner Flanders the
ground is made of sands and clays deposited by Cenozoic seas, and
some sand buttes capped with sandstone are the only relief. In
Campine and Dutch Brabant stretches a wide and sandy alluvial
cone formed by an ancient course of the Maas (Meuse). North of
the Maas and the Rhine, the Quaternary glaciers have accumulated
sand and clay hills as incurved terminal moraines; (4) marshy lowlands, behind a dune wall, formed by the triangular deltas of the
Schelde (Escaut), the Rhine, and the Maas (Meuse). These lowlands are generally below sea level and have been extended by man

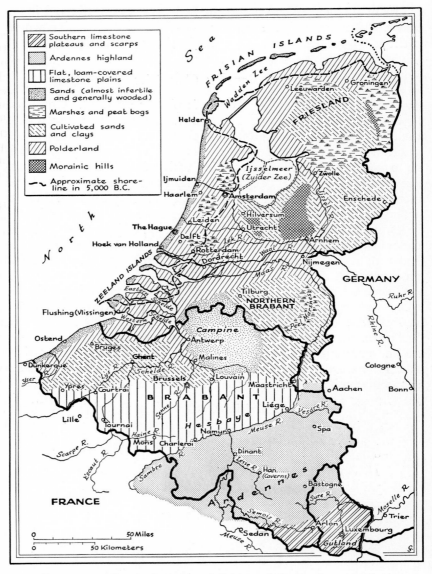

Legend:

- Southern limestone plateaus and scarps
- Ardennes highland
- Flat, loam-covered limestone plains
- Sands (almost infertile and generally wooded)
- Marshes and peat bogs
- Cultivated sands and clays
- Polderland
- Morainic hills
- Approximate shoreline in 5,000 B.C.

FRISIAN ISLANDS

Sea

Wadden Zee

Leeuwarden

FRIESLAND

Groningen

Helder

Ijmuiden

Ijsselmeer (Zuider Zee)

Zwolle

Haarlem

Amsterdam

Enschede

North

Hilversum

Leiden

Utrecht

The Hague

Delft

Lek R.

Arnhem

Hoek van Holland

Rotterdam

Dordrecht

Waal R.

Nijmegen

ZEELAND ISLANDS

Eastern Schelde

Maas R.

GERMANY

Tilburg

NORTHERN BRABANT

Ruhr R.

Flushing (Vlissingen)

Western Schelde

Campine

Peel Marshes

Rhine R.

Ostend

Bruges

Antwerp

Dunkerque

Ghent

Malines

Cologne

Yser

Lys R.

Schelde R.

Brussels

Louvain

Maastricht

Aachen

Bonn

Ypres

Courtrai

B R A B A N T

Liège

Vesdre R.

Spa

Lille

Tournai

H e s b a y e

Namur

Meuse R.

Haine R.

Mons

Charleroi

Scarpe R.

Dinant

Lesse R.

Han (caverns)

Bastogne

Sure R.

FRANCE

Escaut R.

Sambre R.

A r d e n n e s

Moselle R.

Trier

Semois R.

Arlon

Luxembourg

Sedan

Meuse R.

Gutland

0 — 50 Miles
0 — 50 Kilometers

G.

FIGURE 52. The physiographic subdivisions of the Benelux countries.

at the expense of the sea by the ingenious system of polders. Such polders are found from Maritime Flanders in France as far east and north as Friesland.

Three fourths of Belgium has an elevation above 60 feet, but more than one third of the Netherlands lies below sea level. The inhabitants are therefore constantly forced to contend with the threat of the sea. The rock bed has been sinking since the Tertiary period, but the rivers have done much to compensate for this sinking by bringing down huge quantities of alluvium. When this process is slightly slowed, or when the sea level slightly rises, the sea invades the land. This has occurred several times. For instance, the chain of the Frisian Islands off the coast of Friesland is all that remains of an ancient coast line broken down by a penetration of the sea. The changing postglacial sea level provoked several sea invasions. Between the fourth and sixth centuries A.D., an ancient lake, which the Romans called Lake Flevo, was transformed into a gulf, the Zuider Zee ("Southern Sea"). In 1431, a fairly large and fertile area at the mouth of the Rhine and the Meuse was drowned and later became a poor marshland, the Biesbosch. Dams, canals, sluices, and the vast expanses of reclaimed land or polders make up this man-created landscape.

The higher plains of the Low Countries are almost as flat. There are but a few low limestone hills, marking the shape of worn-down cuestas, and sandy hillocks in Flanders, to break the great monotony of the region. The Ardennes section is the only exception to this general rule, for it has some marked features. The upper plateaus have long been eroded into peneplains and the highest elevations are now around 2,300 feet. Most of the area has only 1,000 to 1,500 feet of altitude. The rivers are deeply entrenched and have often cut picturesque gorges, like that of the Meuse betwen Dinant and Namur.

Maritime Features of Western Europe

The Western Sea Front. The North Sea, the English Channel, and the Atlantic Ocean off the coast of the Western European countries are all shallow. Depths of only 60 feet may occur locally as far as 12 miles from the shores of the North Sea. The average depth of the Channel is 180 feet. In the North Sea and the English Channel, in fact, are drowned valleys of the Rhine and the Seine, and of their former tributaries. All the short streams of northern Brittany and southern England were once branches of a much longer Seine River. Under the Atlantic Ocean, in the Bay of Biscay, there is a wide continental shelf and sea depths of 600 feet are attained only at a distance of 250 miles from the coast. This shelf becomes narrower at the western end of the Pyrenees, and a very deep submarine canyon, near the mouth of the Adour River, plunges quickly down to 12,000 feet.

Powerful tidal currents and violent storms blown by the westerly winds constantly stir the waters of these seas. As the major rivers bring huge quantities of silt, they are rarely clear. They look greyish in bad weather, and in fair weather the abundance of plankton gives them a green hue.

The tepid waters of the North Atlantic Drift penetrate the Channel and the North Sea. They raise the temperature of the air, allow a rich fish life where they meet the boreal waters on shallow bottoms, and also cause fogs. The frequency of these increases to the north: there are 42 days of fog per year at Brest, 77 days at Le Havre, and 82 days at the Strait of Dover.

The shape of the coast line is largely determined by the structure and landforms of the mainland. The coasts are low and straight along the plains, while cliffs and ragged rocks mark the plateau edges or the fringes of the hill lands. On the other hand, the marine transgression after the Great Ice Age drowned what had been a continental relief and entered the river valleys. The several oscillations of the sea level have left narrow terraces, sand bars, and other morphological features.

In the Netherlands, Belgium, and French Flanders the shore is low and linear. At low tide more than 2 miles of foreshore are often exposed, and the westerly winds shift the sands to build up dunes on the shore, as high as 60 to 120 feet. North of the IJsselmeer, the sea transgression mentioned above has broken an ancient coast line and left many islands, separated from the mainland by shallow, open lagoons (Wadden Zee).

The coast of the Paris Basin is also fairly regular, being made of two ample curves, the Bay of the Somme and that of the Seine, and two headlands, the Boulonnais and the Pays de Caux. This coast is more linear now than it was when the postglacial sea invaded the rim of the continent. The Bay of the Somme is filled with sediment. "Dead" sea cliffs, now several miles inland, have wide marshy or reclaimed lowlands on their seaward margins. Convex offshore bars stretch northward, constantly carried along by the tidal currents. This movement is responsible for the displacement of the mouths of some rivers, such as the Somme. The Bay of the Seine, scoured by continental waters and the tide, has not been so modified. The onslaught of the sea breaks on the outlying rocks of Calvados, and the bay is filled with tidal marshes and sand beaches (used in the Allied landing of 1944).

The Boulonnais headland, on the other hand, is under constant marine attack and the two small capes—Gris Nez and Blanc Nez—are ever crumbling. The Pays de Caux presents magnificent, straight chalk cliffs, sometimes 300 feet high, the duplicate of the "White Cliffs of Dover."

The aspects of the Armorican littoral are infinitely varied, due to the complex and diverse nature of the old rocks. On the two peninsulas, Cotentin and Brittany, the youth of the coast line is striking. The lower valleys of the streams have been transformed into deep estuaries, the Breton *abers*, similar to the rias of north-western Spain, at the head of which cuddle picturesque fishing towns. Few bays have been sedimented. The central part of the Cotentin Peninsula has been enlarged by wide marshes. The Bay of Mont-Saint-Michel is famous: the beautiful old Benedictine abbey, built on a rocky island between Brittany and Normandy, is now almost attached to the marshy shore by extensive mud and sand flats.

The western coast of Brittany, that of Finistère, offers a succession of towering capes and indented bays. There the strength of the sea is greatest, and powerful waves lash the rocks amidst great clouds of salty spray. The deep Rade de Brest is used as a base by the French Navy.

The southern shoreline of Brittany is not so rugged as the northern. Inland, relief is low, for the highest hills of Brittany are located in the northern part, and the plateaus slope gently to the sea. Hence, the estuaries are larger, encompassed by low shores, and are being rapidly silted. The largest is the Morbihan, where numerous islets offer in summer a quiet landscape of pine-surrounded, white-washed cottages under blue skies.

From the estuary of the Loire to the Gironde (the estuary of the Garonne), there are mainly low shores, with few rock spurs and capes. Sediments, mostly brought by northbound currents, have created sand bars. These have caused extensive marshlands, and have straightened the shore line. Former deep bays are now reclaimed land: the Vendée and Poitou marshes. Very few parts of the European shore line have been so greatly transformed since the stabilization of the sea level after the last postglacial transgression.

One hundred and fifty miles of a straight, monotonous, and uninhabited coast line stretch from the Gironde almost to the Pyrenees. High dunes and small closed lagoons border pine-covered, sandy lands. The sand was brought down from the Pyrenees. Sometimes the landscape recalls the low coast of the eastern United States. The short Basque coast at the western end of the Pyrenees is, by contrast, rugged and wild.

Good harbor locations on the Western European coast are found only in Brittany and around the major river estuaries. In Brittany, most of the sites are too small for more than fishing ports, and the major estuaries have to be dredged to allow larger ships to come up to the ports of Rotterdam, Antwerp, Rouen, Nantes, and Bordeaux. However, the local factors are secondary to those of geographical location. There is a marked concentration of traffic in a few ports, even in some artificial ones such as Dunkerque on the sandy coast of French Flanders, and the harbors located in the estuaries have been complemented by others directly located upon the sea. Examples are Rouen and Le Havre, Nantes and St. Nazaire, Bordeaux, and Le Verdon.

The Mediterranean Coast. The Mediterranean coast of France presents two different landscapes. On the Alpine coast, the mountains trend north-south towards the sea. This is the famous "Côte d'Azur" (known as the French Riviera), where the blue skies and the deep blue sea, the mountain backdrop, and the few rocky islands offshore form a truly enchanting scene. There are almost no estuaries, but very small coves. The lack of tide is a factor in the freshness of the coast. West of the Rhone River there is a total contrast, as the one hundred miles of the Languedoc shores are low and enclose wide lagoons opening to the sea through narrow inlets. The sediments from the Rhone are pushed along this coast. The shifting river channels, shallow lakes, and marshes of the Rhone Delta form a small counterpart of the Mississippi Delta. Marseille, the major port of France, is located several miles east of the Rhone Delta, at the foot of a low mountain range.

At the eastern end of the Pyrenees, the shore is either high and rugged, or very low. Here is located the plain of Roussillon, embraced by arms of the mountains.

Climate and Vegetation of Western Europe

Climatic Factors. Four main climatic factors influence the climate of Western Europe:

1. NORTH ATLANTIC DRIFT. The movement of warm tropical waters northward, far into the North Sea, brings unusually mild

winters and cool summers to the parts of the continent adjacent to the Atlantic Ocean. At the same latitude, the climatic contrast between eastern Canada or the United States and Western Europe is complete.

2. LOCATION. The location of Western Europe halfway between the source regions of the polar and tropical airmasses and between the maritime and Eurasian airmasses is decisive. The polar front gives birth to depressions which move eastward across northwestern Europe. Barometric pressure is ever changing, and there is a permanent instability of weather. In summer, the polar front shifts northward, and southern France is invaded by masses of tropical air which obstruct the path of cyclones. But north of the Loire River, weather conditions remain unpredictable in summer as well as in winter. One thing is certain, rain falls in every season and winds mostly blow from the west.

3. CONTINENTAL INFLUENCE. From the Eurasian landmass come the anticyclonic airmasses, bringing rigorous cold in winter and hot, stifling temperatures in summer. A good deal of rain falls in summer through thunderstorms. Of course, the continental climate is at its strongest in East Central Europe, but its limits move westward, either north or south of the path of the east-moving depressions. The continental effect is slight along the western coast of France, which seldom has cold winter spells or heat waves, but in the Netherlands and eastern France weather conditions are often similar to those in Germany.

4. LATITUDINAL EXTENT. Southeastern France, surrounded by mountains and opening upon a warm sea, the Mediterranean, has in common with the Southern European countries very dry summers and relatively high winter temperatures. Within the oceanic climatic area there is also some variety with delicate transitions from the Aquitanian climate, to the Breton climate, which is particularly regular throughout the year, always cool and wet, and to the Flemish climate, already harsh, with grey overcast skies, cold wet winters, and cool summers.

These four principal factors are of course modified by local relief and altitude. Mountain climates usually vary with elevation, exposure to western winds, width of the valleys, etc. The eastern part of the Massif Central, the northern Alps and the western Pyrenees receive abundant precipitation, whereas the basin shaped Paris area has a particularly low total rainfall. The Loire valley which opens upon the Atlantic, but is protected by the hills of

Vendée and the Massif Central, has been noted for a delightful southern-tinged climate, the mellowness of which so enchanted the kings of France, that in the sixteenth century they built a series of famed chateaux along the river and its tributaries.

Regional Climates. As a result of these factors, seven main regional climatic zones may be distinguished on a map of Western Europe. Except for the first, these zones do not have precise boundaries, and changes are gradual (Figure 53).

1. MEDITERRANEAN CLIMATE. This climate is an exception in France. The vivid light streaming from blue, mistless skies; the warm winters; the parching summers; the brutal northern winds as the Mistral which comes with a devastating strength, channelled along the valley of the Rhone; the wide, dry, boulder-strewn valleys—all these are contained within a very strict climatic boundary which runs along the mountain walls of the Pyrenees, the Massif Central, and the Alps. Only some subtle Mediterranean influences are felt across the corridors of the Rhone Valley and the Carcassonne Gap. The limit of the olive tree is generally considered to be the true limit of the Mediterranean climate in France.

In summer, the subtropical anticyclone is spread all over the area and bars the way to any rain-bearing winds. The Mediterranean area then presents African-like characteristics. The mean July temperature in Marseille is 71.8° F., with a maximum of 100° F.[3] But in winter the continental cold airmass replaces the subtropical anticyclone, after rainy, oceanic depressions have made their way, in the fall, along the front of the retreating subtropical airmass. Winters are as cool as in Brittany, cooler than in most other Mediterranean countries, and the Mistral blows in shivering gusts. The mean January temperature in Marseille is only 44.5° F., and there is an average of 28 days of frost per year. Spring is very mild, often rainy. Fall and spring rains bring, all told, an average of 23 inches of precipitation, falling in 95 days.

The vegetation which grows on the reddish earth is found nowhere else in France: the *garrigue*, the *maquis* (similar to the Californian chaparral), the olive tree, cork oak, and Aleppo pine. There are few natural meadows and green colors are generally missing from the landscape.

2. THE AQUITANIAN OCEANIC CLIMATE. The Aquitanian area, widely open to the ocean, but framed north and south by the Massif Central and the Pyrenees, is sheltered most of the time from

[3] For climatic graphs, see Appendix II.

the continental airmass. Fine summer days, often marred by sudden thunderstorms on the edge of the subtropical anticyclone, rainy winter depressions, early but wet springs, characterize a medial climatic area which is neither definitely oceanic nor definitely Mediterranean.

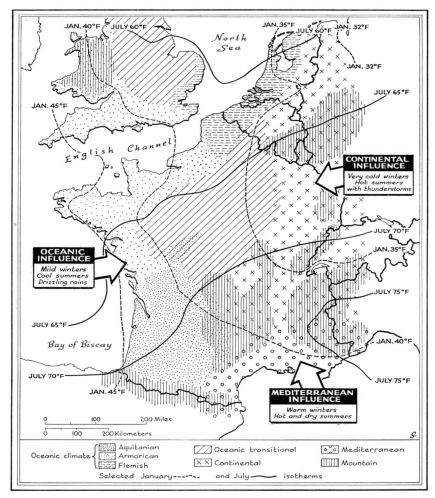

FIGURE 53. The climates of Western Europe.

Toulouse, 150 miles inland, has a mean January temperature of 41° F. and gets an average of 26 inches of rain in 121 days. Bordeaux, on the Atlantic coast, has about the same mean temperature, but is rainier: 32 inches in 201 days.

The western and southeastern parts of the Massif Central also lie within the Aquitanian climatic zone which, through the Poitou gap, extends as far north as the Loire. Some elements of the Mediterranean vegetation have progressed into the Basin of Aquitaine along the foothills of the Pyrenees and across the limestone plateaus which lie against the Massif Central. Corn and vines are everywhere present in the area and thrive under this mild, sunny climate, propitious to a great diversity of crops.

3. THE ARMORICAN OCEANIC CLIMATE. A very small variation between extreme temperatures; heavy rains in every season, with a slight maximum in the fall; westerly winds, often strong on the coast, frequent cyclonic depressions and overcast skies—such are the main points in this ever-changing climate, though constant on the average. Brest, which is typical, has a mean January temperature of 44.9° F., more than Bordeaux or Marseille, and 63° F. in July; 185 rainy days with a total precipitation of 32.5 inches. The rain falls in light and lasting showers and humidity is considerable. Snow is almost unknown.

These characteristics are not so marked inland and along the Channel coast; winters there are slightly colder and summers are warmer. There is more rain on even the slightest elevations (40 to 50 inches), but less in the sheltered areas (less than 20 inches near Le Mans), and snow falls for a few days almost every year. But, on the whole, conditions are about the same. Even at Dunkerque on the North Sea, the mean temperatures in January and July are 38° F. and 63° F. respectively.

The French vineyards stop at the mouth of the Loire. Brittany and Normandy are lands of lush meadows, innumerable apple trees planted in the fields, and heaths or moorlands on the wind-beaten and rain-drenched craggy hills. The purple hue of heather and the glowing yellow of gorse and broom, the lichen-covered walls of a quaint old chapel, and low straggling farmhouses often contrive to paint beautiful landscapes.

4. THE FLEMISH OCEANIC CLIMATE. North of the Artois hills and up to Friesland conditions are harsher, but still really oceanic. In winter the continental air sometimes sends forays to the coast, resulting in frosts and snowfalls, but the number of frost-days is still very small, 31 days at Flushing (Vlissingen). Even in summer there are many showers and as a result of low evaporation the clayey soil remains wet. Peat bogs are extensive on the flat, badly drained plains. However, except for these details, the Flemish Oceanic climate differs little from the Armorican climate.

5. THE OCEANIC TRANSITIONAL CLIMATES. East of a line drawn from Brussels to Nantes and west of another line crossing the Ardennes and the plateaus of Champagne and Burgundy, stretch areas of mixed climatic conditions, both oceanic and continental (Figure 53). Winters are cooler and summers warmer (Paris has a mean January temperature of 36° F., and in July, 65° F.). There are more thunderstorms. From one year to the other fairly wide differences may occur between the climatic averages, according to the relative positions of the dominant airmasses. But in these areas of uncharacterized, fairly mixed climates, local conditions of elevation, latitude, and exposure do make for some differentiation. The Loire country is the most favored and the Belgian and eastern Netherlands plains have the most severe climate (Winterswijk in southeastern Netherlands, for example, has an average of 79 frost days).

6. THE CONTINENTAL CLIMATE. Southern Belgium (the Ardennes), Luxembourg, Lorraine, Alsace, and the Saône-Rhone corridor have a continental climate. At Strasbourg the mean January temperature is 30° F. There are more than 80 days of frost, 20 days of snowfall, penetrating mists, cool springs, thunderstorms in summer, stifling days in July and August. Alsace, sheltered by the Vosges mountains, is the most characteristic. In the Ardennes and in Lorraine, the climate is unpleasant. Summers are warm enough, however, for the vine to grow in the valley of the Moselle River. There are many beautiful beech forests. The soils are podsolized and chestnut colored.

7. MOUNTAIN CLIMATES. In the Vosges, the eastern Massif Central, the Jura, and the lower parts of the Alps and the Pyrenees, temperatures are generally lower. Frost occurs daily for three months, snow lies on the ground for three to four months, and rainfall is heavy (45 inches). Higher up, there are almost Arctic conditions, bare rocks and perennial snow. The southern part of the Alps is penetrated by Mediterranean influences and has but few forests (probably due to overcutting and subsequent soil erosion). Elsewhere there are beautiful mixed forests and mountain pastures on the slopes.

Conclusion. All in all, these climates are very favorable to human occupation. The areas of extreme climatic phenomena are few and there is quite a good deal of pleasant uniformity. Agriculture is nowhere hampered by climate, and owes this privilege to the presence of warm seas along the coasts.

Historical Geography

The general location of the countries of Western Europe has put them in a position to take and to give, to receive and to spread, all the major elements of the various European civilizations. Because they are open to all influences and because they look both toward the ocean and toward the continent, their existence, their shape, and their geographic personality have indeed been modeled not only by their natural background, but in even greater degree by the many contacts they have had in the complex interplay of history.

The Oceanic Outlook

The unity and length of the Western European coasts have been most influential in determining the reactions of their inhabitants towards world relationships. As a fact, the first known elements of civilization in the Neolithic times, around 2000 B.C., whose origin and significance are still partly mysterious, certainly came from the sea, for the main remnants of the megalithic stone monuments are impressively scattered along the Western European coasts. Words like "dolmen" or "menhir" have been borrowed from the Celtic language of Brittany, the seaward-jutting peninsula midway along the coast line.

Looking West. With the Iberian peninsula and the British Isles, the western European countries share the privilege of facing the New World.

The Low Countries have contributed to the settlement and colonization of the Western World. New York was a Dutch city up to 1674. Much more important has been the role of France which, up to 1763, was mistress of the great valleys of the St. Lawrence and Mississippi rivers. In spite of the disintegration of this empire, completed in 1803 by the sale of Louisiana to the young United States, French place names are scattered widely over Canada and the United States, and there are important French-speaking population groups, the vigorous and evergrowing French Canadians, and numerous "Creoles" and "Cajuns" of Louisiana. Every year, French fishermen visit the rich fishing banks off Newfoundland and Greenland, and anchor at the small French islands of St. Pierre and Miquelon. Interchanges between France and North America are many and continuing. Most of the time they have been friendly. Indeed, for America, these Western European countries are the gateway of Europe—in peace as well as in war.

Looking North. Through the North Sea, the Western European countries early came into contact with the maritime and mercantile northern civilizations of the early Middle Ages. Of course, the Vikings first plundered the rich shores of France before they settled in the Bay of Normandy [4] which lay across the path of their southbound navigation. There, in time, they were transformed by their contact with Carolingian France. Their descendants later brought to England and thence to America the benefits of this early Romance civilization.

The Hanseatic merchants created an extraordinary material civilization in the North Sea area. Thanks to these mercantile efforts, industry, mainly wool weaving, was early developed and, to sustain the increasing population, a more intensive agricultural production became necessary. From Flanders, these new techniques were communicated to France; wool weaving thrived in Picardy and Normandy for many centuries, as well as improved agriculture. The knowledge of crop rotation and marshland drainage slowly made its way to the south. Dutch engineers were called to reclaim most of the marshes on the south Atlantic coast of France.

Today the North Sea is the meeting ground of French, Belgian, and Dutch fishermen, all members of this numerous and active community which lives off the richest sea of the world. Constant relations are also maintained between fishermen from Scandinavia and the Low Countries.

Looking South. After the great Spanish and Portuguese discoveries opened the tropical seas to the activities of Western Europe, France and the Netherlands were in a much better position than the Mediterranean or Central European countries to benefit from them. Thanks to the sea, the Dutch and French peoples, and even the Belgians have acquired empires and world-wide interests. They have gained a world outlook which has no equivalent in Central or East Central Europe. Since the sixteenth century, they have outstripped the Mediterranean nations in trade and industry.

Looking to the British Isles. The British Isles are culturally an integral part of Europe. But the English Channel, shallow and narrow as it is, has throughout the years proved to be both a link and a barrier between Britain and the Continent. Not since 1066 has the Channel been crossed by invaders. From Great Britain came those Celts who, driven first to the mountains of Wales and

[4] "Bay of the Seine" is the morphological name for the bay between Cotentin and Pays de Caux, but in human studies the term "Bay of Normandy" has much more significance.

Cornwall by the Angles and Saxons, crossed the Channel in the sixth and seventh centuries and created a new Brittany in the old Armorica. More than one million Breton people still speak a language akin to Welsh. On the other hand, in the eleventh century, the victorious invasion by the Normans brought the benefits of Romance civilization to England.

In the Middle Ages the wool weavers of Flanders depended exclusively on British wool and the cutting off of the wool supply in 1336 by Edward III was one of the main reasons that brought the Flemish to side with England during the Hundred Years' War. For a long time Britain was even a continental power through royal inheritance and since 1259 she has owned a cluster of small islands off the coasts of Brittany and Normandy, the Channel Islands. French and British fishermen share the same fishing grounds at the meeting of the Channel and the Irish Sea. From Great Britain in 1944 came the armies of liberation to the shores of Normandy.

The Continental Outlook

The continent is the second element in the life of France, Belgium, and the Netherlands. From the continent came the Gallic Celts who, previously settled in the south of Germany, arrived in Western Europe around 500 B.C. They amalgamated with the Neolithic peoples already numerous and quite good farmers. The Roman conquest did not alter this solid basis of population, though the Roman legions did impose the Latin language on the greater part of the conquered territory. The Roman influence stopped at the *limes* along the Rhine, built against the threatening Germans.

Looking to Germany. Then began the continuing and dramatic struggle between the Germanic and Latin worlds, fought along a constantly shifting frontier. Following the Barbarian invasions, Frankish kingdoms were created all over Western Europe. Their language did not replace Low Latin, except in the Low Countries, but Germans ruled everywhere, and France is indebted to the Franks for her name.

The Verdun treaty of 843, which divided the huge empire of Charlemagne into three north-south parts, returned the western part to its Celto-Latin tradition and cut off German Europe behind a long border zone, Lotharingia, running from the marshes of Friesland to the olive groves of Italy. But the contest was not settled. This March was to be perpetually fought over up to the present century. The linguistic, religious, and political boundaries were but slowly and spasmodically drawn. The northern part of the Netherlands is Protestant, but Belgium and France are Roman Catholic in tradition, though there is quite an important Protestant minority. Lorraine and Alsace have gravely suffered from the Franco-German disputes, and have acquired a particular provincial character, neither completely French nor German. The creation of Belgium in 1830, between "Francia" and "Germania," well symbolizes this perpetual antagonism. The repeated violations of her neutrality by the Germans and some intermittent French ambitions could not undermine the stability of this new state, smaller than Sicily. The formation of Luxembourg as a tiny, neutral and independent nation in 1866 still reveals the same problem. These are the most typical buffer states ever made.

Fortunately, the boundary between France and Germany is not always a fighting front. An eastern mountain barrier, stretching from the Ardennes to the Alps, somewhat isolates France, but there are enough natural gates in Lorraine, Burgundy, and Flanders to have fostered many contacts. During her history France has, in fact, been more preoccupied with the continent than with the sea, mainly to fight for her own security, but also, time and again, to intervene in Central European politics (for instance, under Louis XIV and Napoleon I). The progressive shift of the western limits of the Holy Roman Empire from the Rhone and the Meuse rivers to the Rhine and the Alps has been called a deliberate French policy of natural boundaries, but was in fact the result of a permanent desire not to be cut off from the rich civilization of the Rhine countries. The acquisition of Savoy in 1860 and a few changes in the Franco-Italian border in 1945 have pushed deeper into Europe the limits of French continental interests (Figure 54).

For Belgium and the Netherlands, the continent plays a major part. The plains of Flanders continue uninterrupted across the Low Countries towards the immense northern plain of Germany. An important traffic has developed along this SW to NE plain, conducive to the circulation of men and merchandise. Through this plain cuts the great south-to-north route of the Rhine, the major river valley of Central Europe. An original Rhenish civilization began to flourish in the early Middle Ages, enriched by the trade between the Mediterranean and Slavic countries and Northern Europe. The rich urban and industrial landscapes of the Rhine provinces are part of this great economic whole, which begins in Belgium and the Netherlands and continues into Switzerland and

THE TERRITORIAL FORMATION OF FRANCE

THE MEDIEVAL FORMATION
(10th to 14th Centuries)

- Limit of Charles the Bald's kingdom after the Treaty of Verdun, 843
- The Capetian kings' possessions in 1030
- The Plantagenet "dominion" in 1154
- English possessions in 1314
- Limits of the kingdom in 1314

THE BIG CRISIS
STRUGGLE AGAINST ENGLAND AND BURGUNDY
(14th and 15th Centuries)

- Limit of France in 1328
- Possessions of Charles VII in 1429
- Possessions of Charles Le Temeraire in 1467
- Limits of France at end of 15th century

THE SPANISH AND AUSTRIAN DANGER
(17th and 18th Centuries)

- Territories acquired by France, 1552-1601
- Spanish and Austrian possessions, 17th C.
- Limits of France in 1789

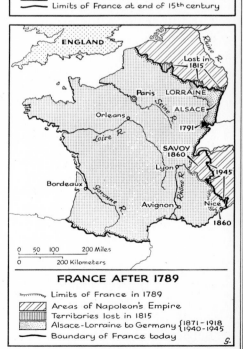

FRANCE AFTER 1789

- Limits of France in 1789
- Areas of Napoleon's Empire
- Territories lost in 1815
- Alsace-Lorraine to Germany {1871-1918 / 1940-1945}
- Boundary of France today

FIGURE 54

Austria. The division of the rich Alsace-Baden plain between France and Germany broke down a neat unity of civilization but did not destroy this intense conjunction of material interests. A great deal of the Swiss and Austrian trade, and a goodly part of the German trade is through the ports of the Rhine delta. Even eastern France uses these ports through the busy fluvial city of Strasbourg.

Looking to the Mediterranean Countries. Western Europe's continental outlook is not solely upon Germanic Europe. In fact, Western Europe cannot be fully understood if one does not consider its important outlook upon the Mediterranean and its civilization. We have already mentioned the fact that France constitutes the shortest link between the two cultural foci of Southern and Northern Europe. Easy corridors and wide plains have allowed a permanent contact and intermixture.

In the Middle Ages, the trade routes from the Mediterranean to Flanders were for a time more important than the Rhine route. Through the Rhone valley the Italian merchants traveled to the fairs of Champagne and to the busy and free cities of Flanders. To Italy France traces its predominantly Latin characteristics. The Roman soldiers brought civilization to Gaul and left their language. During the Renaissance Italy held supreme mastership in all arts and crafts. New ideas and techniques were brought home by French soldiers during the fifteenth and sixteenth centuries. The luxury silk industry of Lyon is, in fact, of Italian origin. In economics as well as in art and spirit, France and her Latin sisters have much in common.

For almost a century France was occupied with wars in Italy. The year after Corsica was annexed by France, in 1769, Napoleon Bonaparte not only gave to Europe the ideas of liberty, equality, and unity of the French Revolution but also drew the main lines of France's present-day administrative and legal institutions. By reopening the port of Antwerp in 1803 he paved the way for the independence and prosperity of Belgium.

Finally, since 1830, France has become a major Mediterranean power by reason of her possessions in North Africa. This huge "island" surrounded by sea and desert, constitutes not only a physiographic contact between Europe and Africa, but also the human contact between Christendom and Islam, between Occident and Orient. North Africa plays a most important part in the economic and human life of France.

Unity and Diversity

To summarize, the oceanic countries of Western Europe occupy a very special position. This position and this common history and civilization have given unity to the countries of Western Europe. It should not obscure their differences. By widening their horizons, they have considerably enriched and enhanced their own characteristics. It is impossible to consider them without thinking of their many relationships with the rest of Europe and with the world.

But it is also a dangerous position. For several periods of her history France has followed a rather unhappy policy of securing prestige and political supremacy over Germany and Italy. More recently, a unified and militarized Germany has brought catastrophe to France. To recover, France has expended a great deal of energy which could have been used for creative developments. Today, the expanding Slavic world has come less than 125 miles from the eastern frontiers of France.

The Benelux Countries. The Benelux countries have much in common. Opening onto the North Sea and facing England, they have much in common with the other countries of northwestern Europe, located on the shores of the Baltic and North Sea. They are densely populated, heavily industrialized, very enterprising countries, but deficient in food production. They have fogs and cloudy skies, comfortable brick houses in rows, and numerous cities. Fair-haired and blue-eyed people are numerous, and two of their three languages are akin to German. To the French, these countries seem more like Great Britain and Scandinavia than France.

France. France is characterized by diversity. Its unity was achieved only through a strong policy of centralization. Now the Alsatian and the Gascon, the vine-grower from Provence and the coal miner from Flanders, the Breton fisherman and the Savoyard mountaineer feel that they belong to a national community even though they may differ widely one from the other and be somewhat foreign to the queer ways of the Parisian. The low population density, the importance of agriculture, the limited degree of industrialization, and many mental characteristics make it impossible to join France completely with any group of European nations. She has her own special place, just like Great Britain, in a regional study of Europe.

But what is France? Located at the crossroads of the many currents of civilization mentioned above, France is the melting pot of Europe, and draws its originality from the harmonious mixture of borrowed elements. When they are in France, other Europeans and even Americans, feel that, in spite of important differences, this country is somewhat their own. In France, everyone finds a part of himself.

How much is Northern and how much is Mediterranean in France? How much is oceanic and how much is continental? These are difficult questions to answer. Surely the extreme south is definitely Mediterranean by its location, its climate and vegetation, and the mental dispositions of its people (Figure 55). The

FIGURE 55. Menton on the French Mediterranean coast. In the distance are the Maritime Alps.

luminous Côte d'Azur, the cosmopolitan city of Marseille could be in Spain or in Italy without sensible differences. Surely too, French Flanders and Picardy do not differ much from the plains of Belgium and the Netherlands. Alsace and Lorraine could be in Germany. Brittany could be a peninsula of Ireland. But in between, how subtle is the interplay of shades and colors! Who could tell where the southern landscapes and folkways really begin? Coming from the north, one feels them already in the valley of the Loire. And do not all Frenchmen have a lightness of wit, a passion for politics, and a need for expansiveness in words and gestures?

Do they not drink wine? But on the other hand, there is little difference between the steady Dutch and the quiet farmers of Central France, and many a French city has a look of austerity and bourgeois decency which is certainly more northern than southern.

And yet there is a strong French personality. It comes from a long common history, from the prestige of Paris, from the beautiful harmony of the natural and rural landscapes, which allow a fusion of the most diversified elements.

The Human Landscapes

There are very few landscapes in Western Europe which do not owe something to the work of man. Natural scenery is rare and almost everywhere there are fields, villages, towns and farms, roads and country lanes to testify the passing of many civilizations. There is not even a direct correlation between the natural divisions of the land as indicated by relief or climate and the real, man-made patterns of the landscapes. History is as necessary as physiography to understand the geography of these countries. Unfortunately, economic and social history does not always have ready answers to the whys of many forms of cities and countrysides. Such origins have rarely been recorded. Furthermore, much is still left undeciphered, for traditions handed down from generation to generation for several thousands of years go back to mist-shrouded prehistory.

The Rural Landscapes. A quick journey across Western Europe, an album of pictures, or, better, an airplane flight, reveal first the utmost utilization of the land. So much work, so much care seem to have been given to every acre of arable land. The division of the land into many very small fields and meadows is striking. Larger than the Far Eastern rice paddies, the plots are yet many times smaller than farm fields in America, and the puzzle offered by the field pattern and the hues of the crops is extremely intricate (Figure 56).

Almost all of France north of a line drawn from Geneva to Besançon, Dijon, Orléans, Blois, Chartres, and Rouen, and most of Belgium is open-field country. There are no trees, except in the forests, no hedges, no earthbanks, no isolated or scattered farmhouses. It is a clean, smooth, simple, and very open countryside. The farmers live in villages, huddled around the church, and the fields stretch all around, generally no larger than a few furrows and forming a crossed ribbon pattern.

In contrast, western France is, as the British Arthur Young said in the eighteenth century, "a somber inclosed country." This the French call *bocage*; small, rather irregular fields and meadows, surrounded on every side by high hedgerows or tree-planted earthbanks, deep sunken twisting cart lanes, scattered farms or small hamlets, unimportant villages. From a hilltop the country looks like a forest, yet real forests and woods are rare (Figure 57). Such is the landscape of the Armorican Massif and the southwestern part of the Paris Basin. Many parts of the Massif Central are similarly enclosed and wooded.

The rest of France, mainly southern France, has not such strong peculiarities. Except in a few places, there are no wide open field areas, nor do hedgerows crowd the landscape. There are coppices, single trees, light enclosures, and small irregular fields. Some landscapes of the Virginia Piedmont remind one of those of south central France.

A fourth type of rural landscape is that of Flanders and the western Netherlands. Canals, rows of poplars, green wet meadows, rectangular plots and large isolated farmhouses make up the *polder* landscape, or reclaimed marsh land wrested from the sea or from lakes. Toward the east and southeast the land becomes higher, plots more irregular, and small forests are interspersed with pasture land.

These are the four main types of rural landscapes. Intermediate forms are numerous and here and there are islands of *bocage* in the open-field area, and of open fields in the hedgerow country.

The Flemish and Dutch *polder* landscape is fairly recent, traceable through history, and is dominated by the reasoned, thorough needs of the land-reclaiming techniques.

There is no mystery about the origins of the southern landscape. It may be explained by a few good reasons. The main one is the diversity of the crops, which requires a thorough and irregular division of the land. If meadows are absent from the Mediterranean area, they occupy quite a large acreage everywhere else. The sunny, mild climate allows many cultures: wheat, of course, comes first, according to the old Mediterranean and French tradition, but there are many other cereals, such as corn which ripens in Aquitaine and the Saône Valley, many kinds of grass and fodder, many species of vegetables and fruit trees. And vineyards are seen almost everywhere except on the roughest, wettest hills of the Massif Central and the high mountains. These vineyards produce fine vintage drinks, as do those around Bordeaux or along the limestone scarps of Burgundy, in the Loire and Rhone valleys, or on the

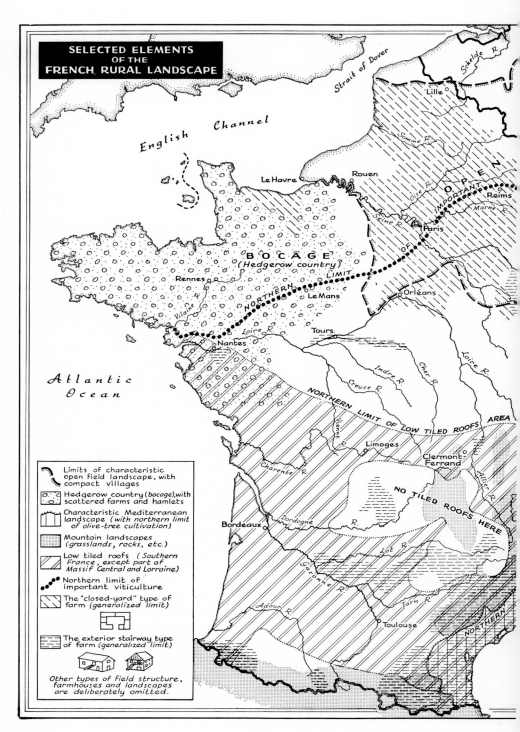

SELECTED ELEMENTS
OF THE
FRENCH RURAL LANDSCAPE

Limits of characteristic open field landscape, with compact villages

Hedgerow country (bocage), with scattered farms and hamlets

Characteristic Mediterranean landscape (with northern limit of olive-tree cultivation)

Mountain landscapes (grasslands, rocks, etc.)

Low tiled roofs (Southern France, except part of Massif Central and Lorraine)

Northern limit of important viticulture

The "closed-yard" type of farm (generalized limit)

The exterior stairway type of farm (generalized limit)

Other types of field structure, farmhouses and landscapes are deliberately omitted.

270

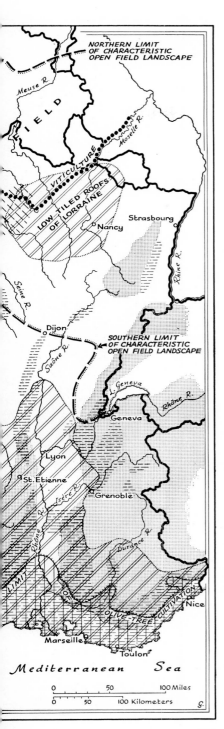

FIGURE 56
Selected elements of
the French rural
landscape.

hill slopes of Beaujolais. They may be for mass production, as are those on the plain of Languedoc, all covered by a green sea of vines. Or they may be to satisfy the domestic needs of the farmer, as in most of the non-vintage areas. The selection of the best locations and the best soils for each particular crop results in an extreme irregularity in shape and dimension of the plots, and in the lack of a definite system of enclosure.

FIGURE 57. Bocage landscape at the tip of the Cherbourg peninsula. Note the many small fields, each divided by hedgerows.

On the other hand, the open field and *bocage* landscapes are too extreme in their forms to be quickly understood. As a matter of fact, the farmers have no good reasons to explain them. It is necessary to dig into the past.

Up to the nineteenth century open-field cultivation was a community affair. The cultivated area of the parish was divided into three parts: one was for winter cereals (wheat, rye), one for spring cereals (barley, oats), and the third was left fallow. Each year there was a rotation and thus, since there were no chemical fertilizers, every third year one third of the land had to rest from the exhaustion of crop bearing. The cattle and sheep of the village were pastured in the fallow area and also grazed the stubble of the cropped fields. Each farmer had his own tiny plots but had to work them at the same time and on exactly the same conditions as his neighbors. Time for ploughing, sowing, and harvesting was given on particular Sundays at church. All plots had to be left unenclosed to respect the rotation system and permit the cattle and sheep free movement on the common pastures.

In the nineteenth century, the cultivation of new fodder plants and the white beet, the use of fertilizers, and the growing individualism of the farmers suppressed the fallows and dispensed with the necessity of a common three-year rotation.

But why this community system? Some said first that it was just a racial habit. A German professor believed it was a Germanic custom brought from central Germany into France by the barbarian invasions. But western Germany, west of the Weser, does not have an open-field landscape and other areas in Europe that have it, such as Sardinia in the Mediterranean, never underwent a German invasion. Others said that it was on account of water. The limestone plains and plateaus of the Paris Basin are dry, and to get water one has to drill deep wells. It was so costly, they said, that the farmers had to make it a cooperative enterprise and share the expenses. All farms were clustered around the parish well. But there are many springs at the foot of the limestone scarps and they did not attract scattered farms. Many parts of the Basin of Aquitaine are just as dry as the Paris Basin and do have scattered farms and hamlets. And the Causses, the driest plateau in Western Europe, have scattered hamlets too, for people use cisterns and ponds to store the rainwater.

One of the main reasons for the community system seems to have been the need for pastures. The climate is fairly dry and the semicontinental winters are not very propitious for the growth of grass. To raise their cattle the farmers had to have fallows and collective herds. It could also be that this strong community system was a defense measure, a binding together of the sedentary farmers on the margins of the weakening Roman Empire. In Germany the open-field system, well described by Tacitus, might have been created by the southern farmers against the nomads of the Northern Lowlands.

The mystery is not quite solved yet. The farmers had a reason for creating this kind of landscape and we have lost this reason. But there still remains the bare monotony of the open fields and the comfortable charm of the agglomerated farming villages.

There should also be a reason for the massive uniformity of the *bocage*, a solidly founded tradition. The peasants still enclose their fields and meadows, and they want thus to give evidence of their ownership of the land. They are extremely individualistic. But this is just a tradition. When did it originate?

Old documents of the early Middle Ages prove that the country-side was then more open than today. There certainly were large areas of semi-open fields. On the coastal plateaus of Brittany there are, here and there, spots of open field landscape and it is probable that they were wider in the past. Is the *bocage*, then, recent? Aerial photography has revealed that the Neolithic farmers had small enclosed fields, similar to those of the hedgerow country of western France. About ten years ago it was discovered that the hedges and the lanes were not disposed in a haphazard fashion. Most of the fields are rectangular rather than square and their greater length points to a few precise directions. These directions are the same as those of the main alignments of megalithic monuments. These directions, particularly studied at Carnac on the southern coast of Brittany, correspond to the positions of the sun at sunrise and sunset on certain days of the year, such as the solstices. Faced with such an astounding fact, it seems legitimate to think that the main lines of the field pattern were drawn in Neolithic times by a numerous, sun-worshipping people. These directions were instinctively followed up to our day, when woods and heathlands were cleared and cultivated.

The disposition and aspect of farmhouses also present a great variety. Local resources in building material, traditions, and types of rural economy account for the many local and provincial types encountered.

There are practically no frame houses in Western Europe, except on the high mountains of the Alps, where a fair number of cottages are built of wood. Shingles are used in some regions, as in Alsace, to cover the roofs. Wooden beams, however, often appear on the walls and half-timbered, picturesque farmhouses are numerous in Normandy, the Basque country, and Alsace.

Where there is little stone available, the walls are built with pressed and dried mud, often strengthened with straw. In northern France and the alluvial plains of Belgium and the Netherlands farmhouses are built of bricks. But stone is what most satisfies the French farmer's desire for solidity and durability. It seems that the tradition of using stone for buildings was brought by the Romans. In any case the tradition is deeply rooted and not to be regretted, for the warm colors and the great diversity of the local stones is a great element in the artistic aspect of many farms. The granite walls of farms of Brittany and Limousin, the white, soft, and easily carved chalk of the Loire country, and the black volcanic blocks of Auvergne are inseparable from the landscape.

Tradition is still more important in the slope and the material of the roofs. Most of southern France is, as in Italy, roofed with Roman, half-cylindrical tiles, which do not need sharply slanting roofs. A curious "island" of tile roofs in Lorraine could be explained by the importance of Roman colonization around Metz. Almost everywhere else slate is the most commonly used material and it needs high sloping frames. In some areas of the Paris Basin farmers use small flat tiles set in a scale-like fashion on the roof.

A long study would be necessary to list the innumerable local varieties of architecture and exterior decoration. There are so many differences, for instance, between the low, whitewashed fisherman's cottage of Brittany, the high, asymmetric Basque house, the thatch-covered, Danish-like Norman house, the rough stone Auvergne house, often with an outside stairway, and the ochre-colored *mas* of Provence.

The best classification of house types is based on the plan of the house, for the plan is the most direct effect of the economic needs of rural life. There are two main types. The first type, which French geographers call *maison-bloc*, groups the buildings which are found under the same roof: the house proper, the stables, and the barns. The buildings may be set on a line along the road or a lane. This is the most frequent type in western, central and eastern France, the Belgian Campine, and the Dutch Brabant. They may also be superposed: the occupants live above the ground floor and use an inside or, more often, an outside stairway. This high house is common in the vine-growing regions, where the cellar is on the ground floor, and in the Mediterranean area, where the farmer has almost no cattle. It is the most frequent type in southern France.

The second main type groups the farms which have a yard. The home, the stable, the barn, the carriage house and the other buildings are set around an open space, in which is located the well or the pond and where lies the dung heap. Sometimes the various buildings are close together and the yard is surrounded by them. Such farms are characteristic of the intensive-cultivation areas of northern France, of central Belgium, and the Netherlands Limburg. Elsewhere the buildings are set apart one from the other, as in many areas of Great Britain and North America, and the yard may be entered from many sides. Such an open-yard type is found in the main cattle-raising areas of western France (Normandy) and of western Belgium (Maritime Flanders) and western Netherlands.

This last type seems to be gaining ground with the modernization of the countryside, which leads to the building of new sheds and stables. There are many transitions.

The Urban Landscapes. In Belgium and the Netherlands industry has been a powerful factor in urbanization and has created two distinct generations of cities. The first are medieval, dating from the time when Flanders and the western Netherlands already had a thriving industry and their cities were numerous, rich, and independent. Evidences of civic liberty and enterprise are still to be seen vividly in their wide city squares surrounded by the high, indented gables of the corporation houses, the city halls decorated and wrought as cathedrals, and the belfries from which bells are always chiming (but not at night in the comfort-loving Netherlands). The second generation of cities are the recent, nineteenth-century developments of modern industry and commerce, either on the coal fields or on the estuaries, or in old handicraft areas. The Netherlands may even boast of a mushroom city, Eindhoven, the seat of big electric apparatus factories. The nineteenth and twentieth centuries have also added to the magnificent medieval city cores endless rows of individual brick-built houses which almost join one city to the other, making new conurbations and giving the whole country a true suburban look.

Few French towns and cities are recent and most of them date back to very ancient times. The study of place names shows that most of the main French cities were already the capitals of Gallic tribes. There are but few towns which were established only a few centuries ago, for instance Le Havre, built on the order of King Henry IV, or Lorient which was the port of the East Indies company of France. The Industrial Revolution has not greatly changed the relative importance of French cities. Modern industries have either been established in mineralized areas or have simply been added to already thriving centers. But on the whole, even non-industrial centers such as Rennes in eastern Brittany, have been steadily growing. There are, indeed, few large cities in France, and Paris alone exceeds one million inhabitants. Most of the cities function as regional centers, fairly regularly spaced on the map and well served by railroads. In this characteristic France strongly contrasts with the industrial countries of Europe, such as Germany or Great Britain, and even with her northern neighbors, Belgium and the Netherlands.

Each city has a kind of individual personality, the outgrowth of its history. This personality is visible in its street plan, its contrasting districts, its monuments, its people, and its functions. There is, however, a certain uniformity. The central core with its narrow, twisting, and busy streets has a few medieval houses, perhaps a cathedral, old ramparts (or a ring of boulevards occupying their former site), and a fairly large number of seventeenth and eighteenth century houses. These old houses are particularly evident in those cities which were active ports (Nantes, Bordeaux), parliamentary centers or courtly residences (Nancy). The old section is still the main shopping center and is badly congested. Beyond are the more recently built areas. There are no high buildings because a French law forbids the building of houses higher than twice the width of the street. Likewise, there are few isolated houses, most being built one against the other, and sidewalks free from flights of steps. Still farther out are the monotonous and often ugly suburbs.

Among all the cities of Western Europe, one is outstanding: Paris. This true center of French civilization has fulfilled its role as a capital since the early Middle Ages and has been enriched by the grandiose buildings and avenues of the monarchies and empires. The Republics have contributed more to the development of its practical facilities. Paris is a strange and fascinating city. Cosmopolitan, artistic, and active, it spreads around a magnificent center along the Seine, from the Arc de Triomphe to the Hotel de Ville. In the middle of the Seine, as it flows through this center, is the island of the Cité, the original city site, where stands Notre Dame (Figure 58). But Paris also has picturesque but ugly quarters where workers live. Paris combines the best and the worst.

Regionalism. All aspects of the human landscape point not only to a great diversity but also to a very old past. Except for the lowlands of the Netherlands and Flanders, and some marshes of the Atlantic coast, almost all the territory of Western Europe was settled long before Julius Caesar captured Vercingetorix (52 B.C.). Such continuity and such stability contrast with the changeful history of the Germanic and Slavic parts of Europe. From such a permanence in the setting of the distinctive traits of each region came durable combinations, and it is easy to understand why French geographers have paid so much attention to regional geography.

The basis for regional divisions is, however, very diverse. Sometimes it may be the natural elements which are considered. Inside the major physiographic divisions there are many well-defined regional unities. The many small *pays* of France and Belgium are distinctive, limited regional unities, often based on the agricultural

FIGURE 58. The center of Paris. In the foreground is the Ile de la Cité, the original site of Paris. The cathedral of Notre Dame dominates the island. Ile St. Louis is in the background and the Louvre in the left foreground.

qualities of the land. Many descend from the Gallo-Roman *pagi*, then the smaller territorial divisions.

Much attention has been given to the old provinces, famous for their history, their folklore, and their popular name. Their limits are sometimes unclear or arbitrary, their originality is not everywhere developed to the same degree. Brittany, for instance, is really Brittany only in its western half. Its eastern part does not differ from other areas of west central France.

In Belgium and the Netherlands, the ancient provinces are still the official administrative divisions of the country. In France the Revolution of 1789 suppressed the ancient provincial boundaries and replaced them by much smaller divisions, the *départements* (there are now 90 of them), of such a size that the administrative center could be reached in less than one day's horse ride. These are now outmoded and most Frenchmen still prefer to talk about Normandy, Picardy, Berry, Auvergne, or Brittany.

It seems likely that more and more modern economic relationships will become prominent in the human regionalism of Western Europe. Natural or historic regions are already less important than economic regions. Relations between country and town, between town and city, between city and national capital, and between the whole nation and the world itself are redrawing the picture left by historical geography.

France

The Land and the People

France, the largest of the Western European nations, and one of the best endowed by nature and the gifts of many civilizations, appears today as one of the less densely peopled. The population density is much below that of all her neighbors, Spain excepted. With only 199 inhabitants per square mile, she ranks but twelfth in Europe.

There are relatively few large cities or wide industrial areas, as in Germany or Belgium, and no overpopulated rural regions, as in Italy. The rural population is fairly evenly distributed and there are but a few districts whose rural density is below 100 per square mile. Such are the high and often bare mountains of the southern Alps and Pyrenees, the dry limestone plateaus of the Causses, the sandy and useless lands of Gascony, and the wide loamless chalk plateaus of the eastern Paris Basin between the Ardennes and Dijon, Reims, and Nancy. In contrast, the coasts of Brittany, the rich loamy plateaus of Picardy, the fertile plain of Alsace, the wide sheltered valley bottoms of the Loire and the Garonne have the highest rural densities, around 250 per square mile. The local unevenness of population density is often very great and corresponds to the agricultural qualities of the soils.

There are only a few large, densely populated industrial or urban areas. The main ones are the northern industrial region, Lorraine, and the cities of Lyon, Marseille, Bordeaux, Nantes, and Rouen—all of which are important economic centers. The Paris region alone contains one sixth of the total population of France.

The present demographic position of France is a relatively recent development. For a long time she was by far the first country in Europe. At the beginning of the fourteenth century, France already had 23 to 24 million inhabitants. The Hundred Years' War, the Black Death, and the Wars of Religion caused a decrease, but in 1800, with 28 million, she was far ahead of Great Britain, with only 10 million, Germany with 22, and Italy with 17, and had been passed by Russia only a few years before. Sixteen per cent of all Europeans were French. But the population of France did not increase as fast as the others during the nineteenth century. Germany exceeded her in 1850, Great Britain in 1890, and Italy in 1930. Today, France has only eight per cent of the European population.

The last census was taken in 1946 and showed a population of 40,140,000. In 1950, it was estimated at 42 million. This is much more than in 1800, but Germany has 69 million, the United Kingdom 50, and Italy 46!

It is not necessary, of course, to be many to be happy. France does not have the recurrent fears of overpopulation entertained by other countries. But political, diplomatic, and military power, and maybe economic progress, are today more or less a function of numbers. The slowness of population development in France probably corresponds to the relative decline in her position among the major powers of the world.

But how did the French people grow more slowly than the other European peoples?

From 1801 to 1938 the population of France increased 50 per cent, from 28 to 42 million. This increase of 14 million, however, was not due to an excess of births over deaths, but to the gradual increase in the length of life and to immigration. The net reproduction rate, which was 1,110 per thousand in 1801, was only 860 in 1938, and for the whole period 1801-1938 stands at the average of 960. On the basis of reproduction alone, it is estimated that France would have had a 1938 population of only 22.5 million.

The population increase due to a greater life-expectancy, accounted for some 17 million inhabitants, and that due to immigration for 6 million. These accretions, added to 22.5 million, would give a total population of 45.5 million. But the actual population was after World War II only 42 million. The differential (3.5 million) is to be explained by the following facts: 1.5 million dead in the war of 1914-18, and 2 million fewer births as a result.

Thus the demographic situation of France is not bright. But it is not unique. The 1938 French reproduction rate of 960 was higher than that of Great Britain, Switzerland, and Sweden, while that of Germany was scarcely higher. What is important is not that the birth rate is low in France, for it is low in all the countries of western civilization. What is important is that birth control began in France long before it began in the other European countries, at least as early as the middle of the nineteenth century.

The general trend seems to have been reversed since World War II. For reasons which are partly unexplained, the birth rate and the net reproduction rate have both been higher since 1945 than they had been for a long time. The birth rate per thousand, which was 14.6 in 1938, and 13.3 in 1941, was 21 in 1948 and 20.7 in 1950. French natality is now the highest in Central and Western Europe, the Netherlands excepted. Between 1945 and 1950 there were 1,280,000 more births than deaths, and thus the deficit due to the war (some 1,130,000 persons) has been wiped out. It will take a long time, however, before the effects of the prewar deficit disappear.

French population could increase in numbers if the length of life were a little longer. The average life in France is six years shorter than in America, and is slightly shorter than in Great Britain, the Netherlands, and Switzerland. Among the abnormal causes of death should be mentioned tuberculosis, twice as deadly as in Great Britain and in Germany, infantile mortality, still too high in the poorer quarters of the main cities, and, no less unfortunately, alcoholism. There are more small "cafés" in France than primary school teachers. Wine drinking is not dangerous, if limited to a pint a day, but this limit is neglected by many farmers and industrial workers. Furthermore, they drink not only wine, but all sorts of liquors.

In discussing the demographic evolution of the country, it is necessary to make a distinction between southern and northern France, the Loire being the approximate dividing line. Northern France has always had a high reproduction rate, and some regions like Brittany have a fertility similar to that of French Canadians. Almost all the deficit in France, since the middle of the nineteenth century, comes from the south. It became a tradition in many regions, particularly in the southwest, to have only one child in order that he would inherit the entire possessions of the family. There was also a desire to enjoy life without the burden of many children, and secondarily, a rural economic crisis. In northern France the great source of deficit is Paris, which constantly drains the country to maintain her population.

National Characteristics. It is hard to give a good description of the French. Foreign impressions are often contradictory. As France has received so many different peoples and so many influences from outside, she is a compound of very different elements and exhibits very great diversity. Foreigners should know that Paris and the Riviera are just two aspects of France, greatly differing from the rest of the country.

The Capetian kings quickly built the unity of the nation around a common ideal. By the end of the Hundred Years' War the patriotic unity of the French was realized, and from that time on national sentiment has been the cement which binds all the inhabitants, even those of the provinces lately annexed to France. Even immigrant foreigners are quickly assimilated. The role of Paris as the capital has also been very important. It is by far the most populous city, and the center of the life of the country.

But even patriotic sentiment, reinforced after two German aggressions, and the diffusion of the Parisian ways of life do not suppress the many differences. There are parts of France where the French language is not the only one used. One million people speak Breton in the western half of Brittany, 125,000 speak the very old Basque tongue at the western end of the Pyrenees, 250,000 speak the Catalan dialect at the eastern end of the chain. Corsican is an Italian dialect used since the domination of Genoa. In the extreme north, Flemish is used around Dunkerque. Germanic dialects are spoken in Alsace and parts of Lorraine. The people speaking these dialects are practically all bilingual. Differences in speech are minor in the cities and towns, north and south, but the rural areas preserve many local dialects (*patois*), all stemming from common sources.

There is no minority problem in France. There has been an autonomist Breton movement and a separatist Alsatian party, but they were supported only by a very small number of individuals, most of whom passed into the service of the Germans in 1940. But within the framework of French unity there is a regionalist movement, asking from the central government only that regional languages and traditions should be encouraged to survive, or at least that they not be deliberately stamped out by stubborn over-centralists in Paris.

Besides the linguistic variety, there is also a temperamental diversity. The Parisian differs from the other Frenchmen. He divides France into two parts: Paris and the "Province," whatever this word used in the singular may mean. He has very quick emotions, a biting wit, a terrific pride, and a hidden desire to shock the foreign or provincial newcomer. The northern Frenchman is slow, sometimes shut within himself, and is not expansive. The southern Frenchman is vivacious, exuberant, gay, and demonstrative. It takes a long time to know all the sectional varieties, and generalizations are misleading, for there is now a great intermixture.

Physical types differ widely; there is, emphatically, no French race. Here and there may be found some homogenous groups, but there is as great a variety of Frenchmen as there is of Americans. When the Frenchman is represented abroad as a small, dark man, with a slightly protruding stomach, a moustache, and a Basque beret, widely gesticulating, talking fast and loud, more interested in politics, wine, and women than in anything else, it is just an oversimplified view and, as simplifications go, it is not very true.

The French love their liberty, which they have acquired only after bloody revolutions; national liberty as well as individual liberty. The Resistance against the occupying Germans was the expression of a very deep sentiment. This individualism makes them defiant of all mass movements, one-party systems, gregarious instincts, and the spirit of imitation.

France has always been a field of experiment for many philosophical and artistic new ideas which were later to conquer the world. Western civilization owes a great deal to the French, who are famous for their sure artistic sense. Good taste, lightness, vividness, refined luxury and elegance have made their reputation. They are also fairly broadminded and like to see all aspects of a problem. For instance, in politics they cannot have a two-party system, for they always find more than two solutions (generally they find more than a score of them) for every social, political, or economic question.

France is a country where tradition is very strong. The famous "plus ça change, plus c'est la même chose" is the right, if crude, expression of a true situation. To draw again an example from politics, the French attach little importance to the fall of ministries. They think first that in a democratic country no minister should stay who has not the confidence of the majority. They also know that even if several departmental heads change, all the bureaucracy stays, for there is no spoils system, and the traditional orientation of the national policy will not vary greatly. In fact, France seems to foreign diplomats to be one of the most consistently stubborn and hardheaded nations. The French, even if they do not care enough about comfort and sometimes cleanliness, love life in all its forms. They have tried to develop the art of living, the standards of which are very different from those adopted by Germanic or Anglo-Saxon peoples.

On the other hand they have inherited from their Gallic ancestors and from their Roman conquerors a number of defects: emotionality, fickleness, skepticism, lack of practical sense and of collective discipline. Too much individualism may not be an asset. An economic study will show that France is not wholly able to adopt the modern industrial processes of standardization and mass production. Frenchmen are also hampered by a great pride. They have every reason to point to their glorious past, their literary and artistic production, their good sense and wit, but have a tendency to despise all that is not French and to forget that they are less than 2 per cent of the population of the world, and have less than 6 per cent of the world's means of industrial production. But is not national pride also one of the defects of the British and, even now, of the Americans?

To have a clear picture of French life it would be necessary to add many national peculiarities and picturesque details: the café, either the small *bistro* or the large sidewalk establishment, the tiny shop, selling either expensive luxury goods or some grocery and produce, the *laisser-aller* in the way of dressing, the noise in the narrow streets, and the apparent total disorder of traffic. But these are outside the scope of geography.

Present Economic Life of France

Any study of the French economy must first begin with a fundamental consideration. During the last 50 years, the most decisive in the development of modern industrial economy, two terrible wars have broken down the economy of France. She has twice been the battlefield where has been fought the destiny of the world. Human and material losses have been tremendous and years have had to be spent in rebuilding the devastated country. From 1940 to 1944, when all the major nations were increasing their industrial potential, France was unable to increase her potential. Rather, she suffered a decrease because of the looting by the occupying enemy and because of the huge war-wrought destruction.

During the First World War, 1,500,000 Frenchmen were killed, most of them young; seven million acres were made unproductive (equal to the combined area of Massachusetts and Delaware); and the financial damage was estimated at 40 billion dollars. In World War II 200,000 soldiers were killed in battle, 160,000 civilians were killed, and 240,000 Frenchmen died in prison or in concentration camps. That is a loss of 600,000 lives. The material damage, which is almost impossible to evaluate, was certainly more than three times the French national income of 1938.

Between 1900 and 1950, more than ten years were years of war or occupation. The national energy spent in restoring the country, the loss in manpower, the birth deficit, and the exhaustion of financial resources also represent more than ten normal years of activity. France has thus been deprived of a total of 20 years of development during an extremely important half century in the development of the world. That the French economy should still be so buoyant today proves the remarkable resistance and the considerable effort of the French people. This should be constantly borne in mind while reading the following pages.

Distribution of the Working Population. In 1946, some 20,-780,000 French men and women were actively engaged in and derived their income from work, that is, one half of the total population. Of these 62.2 per cent were men and 37.8 per cent women. There were 535,000 more women working than in 1936, which could be explained by the slight increase in the proportion of females in the total population, the difficulties of living during and after the war, and the progressive accession of women to jobs which were once reserved for men. There were 140,000 less men working than in 1936.

The division of the working population according to kinds of work is the same as before the war. There are three equal groups: primary activities (agriculture, forestry, and fisheries) 36 per cent; secondary activities (mines and industry) 33 per cent; other (business professions, etc.) 31 per cent. It is interesting to note that the working population constitutes 70.5 per cent of the total adult population over 20 years of age. This is a greater percentage than in Great Britain and in the United States. More than one third of all French women have an active occupation (United States: 18 per cent). This is particularly marked in agriculture where almost one half of the agricultural workers are women (United States: 5 per cent). The back-breaking work done by the farmer's wife is always a subject of surprise to foreigners.

The number of French workers engaged in purely agricultural work is very high. There has been and there still is in most French minds a desire, voluntary or not, to keep agriculture on a par with industry. Rural tradition is strong in France, and the peasant mentality is still an essential part of the national character. By various means, the government has sought to stem the natural movement of labor from the country to the cities. During the nineteenth century, France kept her agricultural activity at a sufficiently high level to satisfy all her food needs, and this in spite of the example given by her northern neighbors, like Great Britain, Belgium, and Germany, and in spite of the growing competition of the recently settled continents, who could export and sell cheaply great quantities of agricultural products. Even today, among the countries of Western Europe, France is the one in which there is no real food problem.

Industry, however, is progressively gaining ground and the relative economic importance of agriculture is steadily decreasing. There are now as many industrial workers as farmers in France, a fact which is often overlooked. Weather and crop yields no longer determine the well-being of the country.

The National Temperament and Economy. The best aspects of the French spirit are a natural taste for order and equilibrium and a distrust of all forms of excess. The French do not like huge enterprises and risky adventures. France is still a country of handicraft workshops, small farms, small stores, made to the measure of the individual and not of the group. The insistence put on the necessity of human and personal relations—a fine intellectual and idealistic conception—and the desire to satisfy an art of living limited to simple pleasures and ambitions, are all precious virtues. But, of necessity, they restrict the horizon purely to individuals and families, and impose an obstacle to an American-like industrial development.

The average Frenchman is astonished but also shocked by the huge middle-western farms, the giant manufacturing plants and their production-line work, the powerful captains of industry, the chain stores and supermarkets, as well as by the skyscrapers and the straight, wide roads. They all seem to him to be aberrations of a large scale capitalism now out of touch with man. There is one word to sum it up and make him shudder: the "trusts" (a word he would be at a loss to define with precision). Workers in France dream of the day when they will have their own workshop on their own account; customers prefer their small grocery stores where they are personally known; farmers are satisfied with the ancestral inheritance. Their fierce individualism makes the French dislike being integrated into a community, and they really believe that they are singular beings. The great uniformity within the various classes of French society is deliberately denied, whereas America is somewhat despised for her uniform, material, and "modern" civilization. This, of course, is not the opinion of all Frenchmen, but does represent the opinion of a great majority.

Respectable as these ideas may be, they make France ill-adapted to a mechanized industry, and cause her to lag behind other, more progressive nations. Only 20 per cent of the working population finds employment in factories of more than ten workers and there are very few factories with more than 1,000. In her social structure France has barely entered the twentieth century. In many respects, she is in a precapitalist stage of evolution, halfway between the Mediterranean "handicraft" nations and the northern, overindustrialized nations.

Craftsmanship, small workshops and small farms greatly favor the development of artistic and original qualities, which are traditional in the French temperament. For centuries, French production has excelled in the making of high-quality luxury articles depending on the intelligence, the deftness, and the taste of her workers. Nowhere outside France has a fashion industry been created comparable to that of Paris. French perfumes, silk goods, and these various things called "Paris articles" are reputed throughout the world. The quality of the labor force is one of the greatest riches of France. But, truly, such qualities can be used only for a limited number and type of products, costly and luxurious and rather out of reach of the majority of consumers. The excellence of fashions, wines, and perfumes hides the fact that common products are not always very good and would greatly benefit from mass production and standardization. France could doubtless excel under such an economy, as she now excels in many other respects and she would, furthermore, have the advantage of lower prices, a higher level of living, and less social dissatisfaction. This is now understood by most French statesmen, but they have not yet decided whether it would be through a capitalistic, socialistic, or communistic system that such an aim would be reached.

Agriculture

We have already stressed the fact that agriculture plays a very important part in the French economy. It occupies about one third of the active population, whereas half of the total population lives in the country and is in many ways connected with agricultural work. Only 11.5 per cent of the national territory is not used by agriculture. Croplands cover 36 per cent of the total area, grasslands cover 22 per cent, and forests 20 per cent. France is normally able to satisfy all her food needs, except, of course, for tropical products, and even has some exportable surplus.

France is a country of small landowners: 4,500,000 farmers own less than 25 acres; 700,000 farmers own farms of a size between 25 and 125 acres; and only 100,000 farmers own farms of a size between 125 and 1,250 acres. Farms between 25 and 125 acres cover 54.5 per cent of the territory, those between 2.5 and 25 acres 15.4 per cent. Two thirds of the agricultural land is directly farmed by owners. The rest is farmed either by tenants, particularly in western France or by sharecroppers in the Basin of Aquitaine.

Often the farms are too small to derive sufficient income for the introduction of new techniques or machinery. The small scattered plots of land cause a great loss of time and are an obstacle to mechanization. There are a little over 100,000 tractors, which is certainly not enough for more than 7.5 million people working on the land. About one million oxen are still used to draw the carts and plows in the southern half of the country.

It seems obvious that France, gifted as she is with a mild climate and good soils, could liberate a good part of the rural manpower by increasing the productivity per agricultural worker, improving farm techniques, and making better use of the land. French economists point out that the United States not only feeds its population but still has an important food surplus while using in agricultural work only 18 per cent of the population. For France, agriculture is both a good asset and a waste of manpower, for it maintains on the land several million people who could better be used in industry, professions, and services—all activities which contribute to the advanced forms of civilized life.

The French farmer takes marvelous care of his fields and crops, loves his village and his ancestral plots of land, and, with the help of his wife, works very hard. But the results he obtains are not always among the best and yields do not correspond to the energy spent to obtain them. The chief causes for this are the extreme division of landownership and land holdings, the slow penetration

of modern ideas, machines and methods, the lack of capital, and
ingrained routine.

Agricultural Regions. In a broad generalization, seven types of
agricultural landscapes may be schematically described (Figure 59).

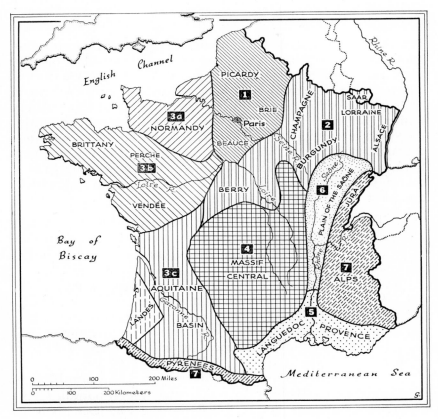

FIGURE 59. Agricultural regions of France.

1. THE NORTH AND THE WESTERN PARIS BASIN. A thick layer of
yellow loam covers most of this area, which stretches from Belgium
to the Loire River and includes such plains and plateaus as Inner
Flanders, Picardy, Beauce, Brie, and the Paris area. This is the most
modern and fertile agricultural area of France, with high yields,
good equipment, large farms, and permanent or temporary hired
workers. The basis of cultivation is wheat, associated with sugar
beets, which are cultivated on a large, mechanized scale. These
primary crops are associated with cattle and sheep raising in stables

and many secondary crops, included in the complex rotations. Numerous Belgian migrant workers come every year to help in the harvest of the beets, which are shipped to large sugar refineries. Beet pulp and molasses are given to the cattle. The landscape is one of perfectly open fields. The wide valley bottoms are used for truck and dairy farming. Along the eastern scarp of the Brie plateau stretch the carefully tended vineyards of Champagne.

2. THE NORTHEAST. Champagne, Berry, Lorraine, and Burgundy are predominantly chalk and limestone areas, but they are not covered with loam. Large sections of the plateaus are dry and fallow. Woods are extensive. Wheat is still the basis of the rotations and its cultivation is also associated with cattle and sheep raising. But there are no sugar beets and cattle are raised on pastures and not in stables. Yields are low, income poor, and rural depopulation is important. Two exceptions are the Vosges mountains, where woods are very extensive and there is some pastoral economy, and the very rich Alsace plain where wheat, sugar beets, hops, and vineyards grow on fertile lowlands.

3. THE "BOCAGE" AREAS OF WESTERN AND SOUTHWESTERN FRANCE. From the estuary of the Seine to the Pyrenees stretches a large, almost purely rural area. All fields are enclosed by hedgerows and trees.

(a) Normandy. Physically, Normandy includes a part of the Paris Basin and the northeastern corner of the Armorican Massif, but its agricultural landscape and economy are about everywhere the same. Normandy definitely specializes in cattle raising and dairy farming. In most areas meadows and good green pastures cover almost all the land.

(b) The Mixed Farming of Western France. The area between Normandy and the Basin of Aquitaine covers the Armorican Massif and the southeastern part of the Basin of Paris. Describing its rural economy is very difficult, for the very complex agricultural system was greatly transformed during the second half of the nineteenth century. Crop agriculture and animal husbandry are about equal. There is a great variety of crops, including wheat, many fodder crops, potatoes, and other cereals. Meadows and pastures also cover large acreages and the cattle density is high. Though this agriculture is on the whole very prosperous, it is still archaic in some parts of Brittany. Farms are small and limited to the working possibilities of the farmer's family. The peasants try to grow and raise a little of everything and generally aim to be self-sufficient, only the surplus being sold. High incomes, however, are derived in some districts either from vegetable growing as on the northern coast of Brittany and in the valley of the Loire, or from horse raising, as in Perche and northwestern Brittany.

(c) *The Basin of Aquitaine.* Here also the variety of crops is very great, but wheat and cattle are less important. Corn, tobacco, fruit trees, and vines are grown on small and intricate plots. The raising of poultry and pigs is important. Many farmers are only sharecroppers. Yields are rather low, agricultural techniques not very developed, and rural depopulation is considerable. Many human problems have changed this region from one of high prosperity in the beginning of the nineteenth century to one of constant decline in our day. There are three exceptional areas: the huge forested area of the Landes, the specialized vineyard region of Bordeaux, and the wide valley bottoms of the Garonne and its main tributaries, devoted to vegetable and fruits.

4. THE MASSIF CENTRAL. Poor soils derived from granite and schists, a climate which becomes harsh with increased elevation, and isolation due to the difficulty of establishing good communications, greatly restrict agricultural possibilities. The Massif Central has long been characterized by a self-sufficient economy, but poor crops, such as rye, are progressively replaced by better ones and cattle raising becomes predominant. There are good high pastures on the rounded mountain tops and slopes, particularly on the volcanic soils, and in the lower sections there are good meadows. The main cattle raising areas are Limousin in the west, Charolais and Morvan in the northeast, which export great quantities of beef, while Auvergne and Velay, in the center, specialize in dairying and the making of cheese. Sheep are raised in the drier southern region, especially on the Causses. Ewe milk is used to make the world-renowned Roquefort cheese.

5. THE MEDITERRANEAN AREA, OR MIDI. Climate is a decisive factor in the originality of this region. No meadows, no cattle, almost no pastures. There are two very contrasting types of agriculture. In Provence (east of the Rhone River) and Corsica, the old ways of life are still unchanged, almost the same as they were in Roman times, with an economy based on wheat on the narrow plains, vineyards and olive trees on the slopes, and sheep on the bare mountains. Traditional movements of transhumance bring the sheep in summer to the mountains of the Alps. On the plain of Languedoc, however, and along the lower Rhone there now is great specialization. Languedoc is now almost entirely covered with vineyards for the production of common wine. The plains

of the lower Rhone, as around Avignon, are devoted to truck farming and the intensified production of early vegetables, which are
sold everywhere in France. Roussillon, east of the Pyrenees, produces both wine and vegetables.

6. THE SAÔNE-RHONE CORRIDOR. Conditions in this agricultural region vary greatly. The soils of the upper plain of the Saône
are excellent and are covered either with cereal fields, particularly
corn, or with meadows. At the foot of the high Burgundy scarps
lie the famous vineyards of Burgundy. The morainic sand and
gravel area north and south of Lyon has been drained but remains
fairly poor. Poultry raising is very important. The small and interrupted plains of the Rhone Valley are well cultivated, and on
the wide terraces are planted fruit trees and vines.

7. THE HIGH MOUNTAINS. Agricultural possibilities are limited in the Pyrenees. The Jura and the Northern Alps contain
large forested tracts, and in the valleys many farms have developed
an important pastoral economy. Milk is used in the fabrication of
many kinds of cheese, particularly Gruyère and Swiss cheese. In
the inner and higher parts of the Alps, cows are driven in summer
to the upper slopes vacated by the melting snow.

Agricultural Production. Wheat is the leading crop of France.
It is grown in all parts of the country, even in those for which it
may seem poorly suited. This accounts for a great variety of yields,
the best being obtained on the loamy plateaus of the Basin of
Paris. The average yields for the country as a whole are below
those of England and the Netherlands. Total production varies
from year to year with climatic conditions, the average being
8 million tons. This gives France a rank of sixth among the wheat
producers of the world.[5]

With the steady increase of yields, however, the wheat area is
decreasing and now is about three fifths of what it was a century
ago. Wheat is the basis of most of the rotation systems, particularly sugar beets, corn, and fodder crops.

A present characteristic of French agricultural economy is the
decrease of the area in cropland, whereas that of grassland is increasing. On the cropland itself, fodder crops are taking a larger
share of the total, already covering an area greater than that devoted to wheat. Moreover, about one half of the area devoted to
cereals is used for cattle feeding. Thus animal husbandry is becoming the main interest in French agriculture.

[5] For statistical information see Appendix III.

France is the leading wine producer in the world, and vineyards are indeed typical of France. Climate limits them to the south of a line roughly drawn from Nantes to the Meuse River. They are really extensive only in the Basin of Aquitaine and the Mediterranean area, and are otherwise limited to specialized areas where production is of very high quality: Champagne—one per cent of the total wine production—Alsace, Bourgogne (Burgundy), the Rhone Valley. The Loire Valley produces wines of both high and common quality. Connoisseurs know how to distinguish the many local varieties of *crus*, which have made the world-wide reputation of France.

The production of vegetables, fruits, and flowers is greatly increasing and interests not only the Mediterranean region but also the valleys of the Garonne and the Loire, the coast of Brittany, and the Paris area. Vegetable marketing is more and more organized by cooperatives.

The livestock industry is slowly increasing. Although sheep are losing most of their importance and are now restricted to the drier and poorer regions, cattle are kept almost everywhere, for the production of milk, generally processed into butter and cheese (for the French drink very little milk), and meat.

Fisheries. There are about 65,000 fishermen in France. The main fishing ports are located on the Atlantic and Channel coasts, for the Mediterranean is very poor in fish. Southern Brittany is the leading area. Ships from Boulogne, Dieppe, and Fécamp go fishing in the Channel and the North Sea; many also go as far as Newfoundland and Greenland to fish for cod. Breton fishermen from Douarnenez, Concarneau, and Lorient have for their fishing grounds the western Channel and the Bay of Biscay, where they catch great quantities of sardine and tuna, which are canned in the ports. La Rochelle, Arcachon, and Bayonne also are important fishing ports.

Industry

French industry now occupies almost as many people as does agriculture. France has 6.4 million industrial workers. This number is considerable, for England, much more industrialized, has 8 million. In proportion to the total number of inhabitants, there are 10 per cent less industrial workers in the United States than in France. There is, consequently, no manpower problem as far as numbers are concerned. Yet there is a great problem of productivity, for with such a labor force French industrial production should be much greater. To the general causes listed in the general study of the economy above, there are several others which should be considered.

Power. Power is the main stumbling block in the French economy. France is obliged to import 38 per cent of her requirements of fuel and power. She is the only great nation which must import such a great amount, and there is, unfortunately, no immediate prospect of meeting this deficiency at home (Figure 60).

As is the case with the other Western European countries, France has but insignificant oil fields. The main one is that of Pechelbronn in lower Alsace, used mainly to produce motor lubricants. There is at present much research under way to discover new fields. Some wells are already productive along the foothills of the Pyrenees. Natural gas is exploited at St. Marcet, near St. Gaudens, on the upper Garonne. The total production of oil is only about 300,000 metric tons. Nineteen million tons are imported every year from Venezuela, Iraq, and the United States, the greater part of which is refined in France. The main refineries are located along the estuaries of the Seine, Loire, and Garonne rivers, in Languedoc, and near Marseille.

France produces only two thirds of the coal she needs. This is her greatest industrial handicap, particularly in comparison with Great Britain or Germany. There are three main groups of coal fields. The most important, producing about two thirds of the nation's total, is the *Bassin du Nord et du Pas-de-Calais*, located in a deep syncline along the northern slope of the Artois ridge. It directly continues, under chalk layers, the southern Belgian coal field. The seams are much broken and thin, and mechanical extraction is difficult.

The second important coal field is located in Lorraine and is the southern part of the great Saar coal field. Its production accounts for about one fifth of the French total. The field is much easier to work, for the coal seams are thick and modern equipment can be easily used. Production is steadily growing and the daily output per worker is twice the average output in France. The third group consists of scattered fields in the Massif Central, which account for about one fourth of the French production. Only three of these fields are important. They lie along the eastern edge of the Massif, and are located near Blanzy-Le Creusot, St. Etienne, and Alès. The other fields lie in the western part of the Massif, along the long dividing fault of the Hercynian "V," from Commentry in the north to Carmaux in the south. Except at Decazeveille, these fields are fairly deep, much broken and faulted, and their reserves are small. The importance of the coal fields of the Massif Central arises solely from the fact that they are located near the industrial centers of central France. For instance, the Creusot coal field is used by the great Schneider armament factory, while that of St. Etienne is the basis of its various metallurgical and mechanical industries.

All in all, the French coal fields cannot be compared to the huge British or West German fields. Since World War I, many technical improvements have been introduced and are still in progress. The two major fields in the north and Lorraine were nationalized in May, 1946, and there has been much concentration around the most productive shafts and a general development of mechanical excavators. In spite of this, the output is much lower than in other countries. In 1938, the output per miner per day was 1,900 pounds in France, compared to 3,600 in the Ruhr district of Germany and 9,100 in the United States. Many modern tools cannot be used in France and a great part of the coal crumbles into dust when excavated. Consequently, the cost of production is high.

Like the other European countries, France also suffers from a lack of mine workers. There are 210,000 workers on the Northern field and 42,000 in Lorraine, but it is difficult to recruit new miners. Between the two wars many Poles came to supplement the dwindling French manpower, but most of them have by now returned to their country. North Africans and Italians also work in the mines, but they suffer from the climate and their output is low. Manpower is a bottleneck in the French coal-mining industry.

Furthermore, the coal fields are not well located: 73 per cent of the coal is produced in the north, far from the rest of France. Before World War II, it was cheaper for all the western part of France to import Welsh coal than to use French coal because transportation by sea is so much cheaper than by rail.

Last, but not least, France produces only certain varieties of coal and those most important for industry are lacking. There is little anthracite and almost no coking coal. Since the war some metallurgical coke is obtained from the mixing of various coals through a process of "semidistillation," but France must still import most of the coking coal she needs.

The total production in 1952 was 57 million tons, but more than 15 million tons had to be imported. Before 1939, these importations came from Great Britain (38 per cent of the coal), from Germany (32.5 of the coal and 62 per cent of the coke), and the balance of the imports chiefly from Belgium, the Netherlands,

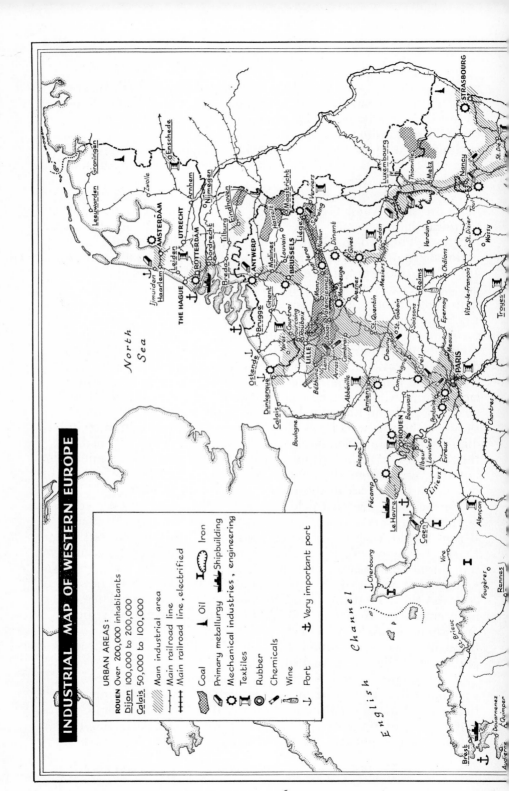

INDUSTRIAL MAP OF WESTERN EUROPE

URBAN AREAS:

ROUEN Over 200,000 inhabitants
<u>Dijon</u> 100,000 to 200,000
<u>Calais</u> 50,000 to 100,000

Main industrial area
┼┼┼┼ Main railroad line
┼┼┼┼ Main railroad line, electrified

Coal
Primary metallurgy
Mechanical industries, engineering
Textiles
Rubber
Chemicals
Wine
Port

Oil
Shipbuilding
Iron
Very important port

North Sea

English Channel

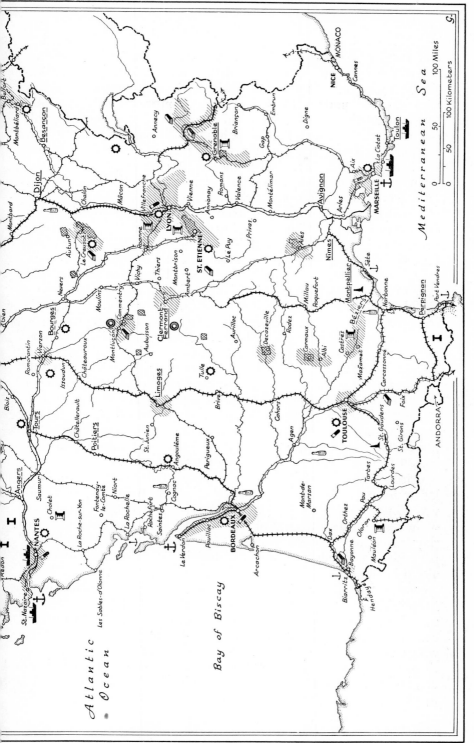

FIGURE 60

297

and Poland. France now has to do without British coal, on account of the British coal crisis. Furthermore, since the nationalization an ingenious system has made domestic or imported coal prices identical in all parts of France. Western France imports now only small quantities of American and Polish coal. Germany is still the principal supplier. The integration of the Saar into the French economy, bringing 16 million more tons, is extremely helpful and the Schuman plan for pooling the coal resources of France, the Ruhr, and the Benelux countries will be a most decisive remedy. (For a brief discussion of the Saar, see Chapter 6.)

Because of the acute coal problem, France has developed her hydroelectric resources. One half of her electric production comes from hydroelectric installations, but the production varies greatly from year to year depending on the amount of rains. The deep narrow valleys of the Massif Central have almost all been dammed, as well as many glacial valleys and lakes of the Alps and Pyrenees. Even the glaciers have been astutely tapped for their water. Hydroelectric production in 1950 was 16,170 million kw-hr. Impressive new dams, recently completed, will increase this production to about 24,000 million kw-hr. In 1949 the Génissiat dam on the upper Rhone, below Lake Geneva, was completed and has an annual output of 1,300 million kw-hr. The great Donzère-Montdragon dam on the lower Rhone, north of Avignon, is part of a general project to utilize this river, the most impetuous of all French rivers. There is also a great dam at Kembs on the Rhine. The Alps produce 45 per cent of French hydroelectricity; 15 per cent comes from the Massif Central, and 22 per cent from the Pyrenees.

Electricity generated from coal amounted to 15,600 million kw-hr in 1951. The total production of electricity in that year was 36,100 million kw-hr, twice that of 1938 and there are hopes of increasing this capacity in the near future. Progress has been slower than in many other countries, due to the damages and stoppage of work during the war. The electric power industry is nationalized in France.

However great her efforts, France will always be at a disadvantage in the total quantity of mechanical energy put at the service of her industry. If energy under its different forms is counted in tons of coal, in 1938 the United States had 6.5 tons per inhabitant per year, Great Britain 5.7, Germany 4.2, and France only 1.3. Unless there is a radical change in the present methods of producing energy, France will never be able to have a heavy industry comparable to that of Great Britain and Germany.

Raw Materials.   France is rich only in iron, bauxite, and potash. Even if the raw materials from her overseas territories were included, she has a very heavy deficit in raw materials. This places France very far behind the U.S.S.R., the United States, and the British Empire, which control three fourths of the raw materials of the world.

French industrial economy is fortunate only in one respect: she has the most important iron reserves of Europe. Except for the extraction of some excellent ores in western Normandy and the eastern Pyrenees, almost all (nine tenths) of the ore comes from Lorraine. The Lorraine iron ore, called *minette*, comes from Jurassic limestone strata, west of the Moselle scarplands, which stretch for 80 miles from north to south. There are four main fields: Longwy (which continues into Luxembourg), Thionville (the so-called Briey basin), Metz (west of the city), and more to the south, Nancy. The ore has a poor iron content (less than one third) and contains much phosphorus. It was only after 1878 that the Thomas and Gilchrist process permitted the use of such a low-grade ore. The production now is close to 30 million tons yearly. Important quantities are exported to Belgium and Germany. The greatest part of the ore is smelted into pig iron and steel in Lorraine, near the Lorraine coal field, though there are quite a number of blast furnaces in the North coal field.

France has important bauxite reserves, also the most important in Europe. In 1937 she was the world's leading producer, accounting for 42 per cent of the world output, but now she ranks only fourth. Bauxite is extracted in Provence (Les Baux, whence comes its name, is a picturesque half-ruined town south of Avignon), and near the Pyrenees.

France ranks third in the world (after Germany and the United States) in the extraction of potash. The mines are located in the southern part of Alsace, around the city of Mulhouse. The production of pure potash is almost equal to that of the United States. Salt reserves are important in Lorraine and forms the basis for an important chemical industry.

France has only very limited and scattered resources of other raw materials and their total production is quite negligible. The problem of the deficit or shortages of raw materials is grave, and combines with the paucity of energy and the lack of industrial spirit to place France at a great disadvantage in the world.

Production.   The iron and steel industry, employing some 1,400,000 workers, is not in proportion to the iron resources of

France, on account of the deficiency of coal and coke. Most of the steel works (70 per cent) are located in the Lorraine iron field (Figure 61) and in the North coal field (17 per cent). The others are located in the Massif Central and near the main ports. In 1951, 11.1 million metric tons of pigiron and 12.4 million metric tons of steel were produced, the production of the Saar being included.

FIGURE 61. Longwy, an important French industrial center located in the heart of the French Lorraine coal and iron-ore fields. (George W. Hoffman.)

Aluminum is smelted in the electric ovens of the Pyrenees and the Alps. There are scattered small copper, lead, and zinc refineries. One of the most active engineering industries is the automobile industry, with about 150,000 workers. France makes nearly 300,000 cars a year, of which more than one third are exported. The industry centers in the Paris area (70 per cent of French production), where are located the big Citroën, Renault, Ford, and Simca plants, and in the northern Jura near the Belfort Gap (Peugeot). Trucks are also made in Lyon. Shipbuilding yards are located in Dunkerque, Le Havre, Bordeaux, La Ciotat, but mainly in St. Nazaire and in Nantes.

There are many other engineering industries (Figure 60). Most of them are located in the coal fields, near the steel works, in the bigger cities such as Paris, Lille, Lyon, and Strasbourg, or in the ports of Nantes and Le Havre. In general, French engineering production is of good quality and is easily exported. But it is not diversified, is costly, and is not expanding fast enough to satisfy the country's needs. Whereas most French ships are built abroad, the automobile industry is now having a boom with large backlog orders.

Textile industries are an old tradition in France. Almost all the raw materials must be imported, the wool through Dunkerque and the cotton through Le Havre. Nevertheless textiles make up almost two thirds of French exports, in value. The cotton industry is the largest. Cotton yarn is spinned in three areas: eastern France in the Vosges and Alsace, northern France around Lille, and in Normandy around Rouen. It is woven partly in the spinning areas and partly in central France, around Roanne. The wool industries are more concentrated, chiefly in the north at Roubaix-Tourcoing. Other areas are Alsace, Champagne, and Normandy. Linen is also almost exclusively woven in the north. Silk weaving is a specialty of Lyon and has spread in a wide area around the city. Rayon first was made in this region but plants are also scattered in many industrial cities of southeastern and northern France. To these basic spinning and weaving industries are linked many others, some very specialized and widely renowned such as laces (le Puy, Alençon, Valenciennes), velvet (Amiens), ribbons (St. Etienne) and knitted goods (Troyes). Cloth-making is scattered everywhere.

Main Industrial Regions. 1. THE NORTH. This area, contiguous to Belgium, is similar in many respects to the great industrial regions of northwestern Europe. It benefits from a rich coal field, easy communications, British and Belgian capital, Flemish industrial tradition, and large reserves of manpower. All types of industry are represented and it groups one fifth of the metallurgical industries, one fourth of the food industries, one half of the textile industries, plus considerable chemical industries. Here 530,000 people live in the coal field, many in the monotonous row houses of the "Black Country," and in the conurbation of Lille, Roubaix, and Tourcoing live more than 700,000 people.

2. THE NORTHEAST. This region is not so homogeneous and contains at least four subregions: the iron area of Lorraine, the varied Nancy area and the textile area of the Vosges and Strasbourg. Here are located the most important iron and steel and cotton industries of France. Many foreigners work in the mines and steel plants.

3. THE LYON AREA. From the city of Lyon industries spread in all directions to the valleys of the Alps, to the St. Etienne coal

field, and to the upper Loire River. Metallurgical and textile industries are the main ones, but chemical and food industries also are very important. Approximately 725,000 people live in Lyon, 350,000 in or near St. Étienne, and 140,000 in the Grenoble area.

4. THE PARIS AREA. Paris has no raw materials and no power in its vicinity. Yet the Paris area is by far the nation's most important industrial region. Engineering industries come first, but most types of industrial work are also represented. Five and a half million people live in the Parisian metropolitan area.

There are many secondary industrial areas and centers around the ports, in the other major cities, and near the other sources of energy. However, 60 per cent of the industrial workers and 60 per cent of French factories with more than 100 workers are located northeast of the Seine River.

Communication and Trade

France has a very good network of railways, waterways, and roads. Its main drawback is the excessive concentration of all communications on Paris, which deprives some regions of easy access to other peripheral areas. The country has the densest road network in the world. Most of the roads are good, but they are not all adapted to heavy traffic. There are no superhighways. The railways are nationalized and are densest in the Paris Basin and in eastern France. The density of the lines is slightly inferior to that of Germany or Great Britain. The river-and-canal system is almost exclusively developed in the northeastern quarter of the country and is so arranged as to link the Seine and its tributaries with the rivers and canals of Flanders, the Rhine, the Saône, and the upper Loire. About 30 million tons of goods, chiefly bulk products, are carried every year on the canals and rivers. Unfortunately, most of the canals are small.

The airline system (Air-France) is one of the largest in the world. It has direct connections with the various overseas territories (West Africa, Madagascar, Indochina), North America, and South America. The French merchant marine now ranks fourth in the world, but is unable to carry much more than one half of the imports and exports of the country. The main ports are Marseille, Le Havre, Rouen, and Dunkerque, followed by Nantes-St. Nazaire and Bordeaux.

France trades with the whole world but, as a factor of her national economy, foreign trade is much less important to her than it is to many other European countries. She is able to satisfy most of her food needs and, though they are important, her industries do not export to a considerable degree. She must, however, import most of the raw materials she needs: great quantities of oil and coal, tropical foodstuffs, and many kinds of machinery. Her principal exports are textiles, machines and engineering products, pig iron and steel, automobiles, and wine.

Since 1880, the French foreign balance of trade has been unfavorable. Foreign assets and services could balance the payments, but France now suffers from a deficit with the dollar zone. Consequently, France has tried to develop her trade with her overseas territories. France imports mainly from the United States, West Germany, Belgium and Luxembourg, Australia (mainly wool), Great Britain, and Italy. She exports to Great Britain, West Germany, Belgium and Luxembourg, Switzerland, and the United States.

Overseas Territories

The importance of France in the world cannot be fully understood if no mention is made of her wide interests in her overseas possessions. Overseas France is 20 times larger than the mother country and includes 76 million people. Three fourths of the territories are located in Africa, and form a continuous block from the Mediterranean to the Congo River. The Sahara Desert isolates North Africa (Morocco, Algeria, and Tunisia) with almost 20 million people, from West and Equatorial Africa (24 million). In the Indian Ocean there is the island of Madagascar, larger than France, several islands (Réunion, etc.), and French Somaliland on the Red Sea. More than 4.5 million people live in Madagascar. The third group consists of the Indochinese states of Laos, Vietnam, and Cambodia, with a population of 27 millions. In the Pacific are New Caledonia and some very scattered islands. Finally, in America, France has the important islands of Guadeloupe and Martinique, part of Guiana and, off the coast of Newfoundland, the islets of St. Pierre and Miquelon.

Climatically speaking, only North Africa, some parts of Madagascar, St. Pierre and Miquelon, and the French islands in the Antilles may be permanently settled by Europeans. But North Africa and Madagascar already have a dense native population. There is therefore a limited settlement of French in their overseas territories, the only exception being Algeria, where French citizens (many of foreign descent) number about one million. France carries on almost one third of her trade with these overseas territories, and their economic importance is that of producers of raw materials (rubber, nickel, etc.) and tropical foodstuffs.

The Benelux Countries

Belgium, the Netherlands, and Luxembourg—or to use a recently coined and useful word, the Benelux countries—are three small countries which do not draw their geographic personality from shape, climate, or landforms. This fact was clearly set out in the first part of this chapter. But such a lack of physically distinguishing features does not by any means preclude the possession of a strong human unity and individuality.

Their common bond, their *raison d'être*, is commerce and it stems from their location. They are perfectly endowed for thriving trade relations. They are closely linked to France and thus to the Mediterranean lands. Located at the deltaic end of the Meuse and the Rhine, they offer easy access to Central Europe. They face Great Britain across the narrowest part of the North Sea. Furthermore, almost nothing in their landforms can stop the circulation of goods and men, but all invite it: streams, rivers, canals, estuaries and plains. Trade explains their population and their economic pattern.

Such a geographical position, however, began to exert its influence only at a fairly late period in European history. In Roman times, the location was eccentric: the lower Rhine flowed through a wilderness and the route from Rome to Britain passed across Gaul. The Germanic advance to the shores of the North Sea and then across the sea to Britain gave the Low Countries their first chance: they were then the hub of a completely different world, active and enterprising. When Charlemagne had his capital at Aachen and pushed the outer limits of Christian Europe as far as the Elbe, the Low Countries became one of the main foci of medieval civilization.

The first area to profit from these advantages was Flanders, south of the mouths of the Rhine and the Scheldt, because it was closer to France and England. First as the main relay of the land route between the Mediterranean and England, then at the beginning of the fourteenth century as the main relay on the sea route along Western Europe, Flanders became a land of high urban development, active textile industry, rich trade, and accumulated capital. Farther north, Holland was still but an isolated marshland between the Flemish and the German Hanseatic centers.

At the end of the fifteenth century, however, the astute and clever Dutch made Holland a stiff competitor of Flanders. Holland was better located to profit from navigation on the Rhine and the Meuse. The now open trade route through the Alpine passes, plus the development of the commercial centers of southern Germany, made the Rhine the most important route of Western Europe in the fifteenth century. In the sixteenth century, the Hanseatic fleet was outstripped by the Dutch and Amsterdam became the greatest port, mart, and banking center of Europe. During the seventeenth century, however, Great Britain began to assert her position as ruler of the seas and during the following century and the first part of the nineteenth century the Low Countries knew a long period of inactivity.

Thus along two parts of the western coast of Europe two stretches are of particular interest: around Brugge and Antwerp on the one hand, and around Amsterdam and Rotterdam on the other. These two cultural foci formed the core of two states whose development and whose greatness are not due to small and geographically poor territory but to the world extension of their trade relations. Inland limits were not sharply drawn. The Frisian area, north of the Rhine, was cut off from Germany by peat bogs and marshes and was early united to Holland. Flanders, as a region, continues across the present French boundary and it is due only to the hazards of war and diplomacy that the urban industrial area of northern France is now separated from Belgium. To the east of Flanders, Holland, and Friesland, the area lying between the Ardennes and the lowlands, had an autonomous regional development centering around the archbishoprics of Liége and Utrecht. The rich southern part was Gallicized and now forms the French-speaking Walloon area of Belgium. Finally, the central part of the Ardennes was divided between Belgium and Luxembourg and served as a buffer area between France and Germany.

It seemed reasonable to assume that these three pillars of trade, Flanders, Holland, and Wallonia, should have become united. But religion, as it happened, was the decisive factor in the creation of two national units. While the area north of the Rhine became Protestant, the south remained Roman Catholic. The Protestant area became independent in 1609 and annexed part of Catholic Brabant south of the Rhine, then, spreading across Zeeland, sealed the entrance to the Schelde. The Netherlands had won over Flanders, condemned to a long sleep under Spanish and Austrian rule. It is important here to stress that the dividing factor has not been language, but religion. Flemish is very similar to Dutch, and the Walloon area has always followed the destiny of the Flemish-speaking area. The artificial boundary between the Netherlands and Belgium, however, does not by any means follow the religious boundary.

The conquering of the mouth of the Schelde by Napoleon and the awakening of Antwerp to world-wide trade gave Flanders and Wallonia the awakening they needed. In 1830, under the cautious eye of their big neighbors, Great Britain, Germany, and France, they became independent and took the name of Belgium. Since then Flemings and Walloons have managed to live a kind of *mariage de raison*.

It is necessary for the student to have in mind these few historical notes in order to understand the national aspects of these particular countries today.

They are an offshoot of the Germanic world, but like the Scandinavian countries and like Great Britain, they have their own characteristics. Like the Germans, the Dutch and the Flemings are taciturn, their minds rather turned inward. They are obstinate workers, well knowing where their positive interests lie. But they differ from the Germans in that they don't like general ideas and mysticism. This draws them nearer to the British and Scandinavians. The same goes for their outward dignity, their self-control, their love for home and family life, their distaste for big political demonstrations and bitter public controversies, and their love of liberty.

The Dutch and the Flemings are not exactly similar; about three fifths of the Dutch are Protestant, whereas almost all the Flemings are ardent Roman Catholics. Furthermore, Flanders shows several traits which one may attribute to the long Spanish occupation: religious processions, carnivals, etc. As for the Walloons, they take after both the Flemings and the French. They are generally lighter spirited, more spontaneous, with a particular enjoyment of practical jokes and witty puns.

The Dutch and Flemish languages come from the Frankish dialect which has prevailed over Frisian, now spoken only in northeastern Netherlands and over Saxon, which has almost completely disappeared.

Physically, the people of the Netherlands have some Nordic homogeneity. Over 70 per cent of the Dutch have blond hair and blue or grey eyes, but the distribution of head shapes does not produce definite conclusions: 40 per cent long heads and 60 per cent round heads. Alpine-type people are most numerous in the southern part of the country. The Flemings in general have long heads, light complexions, and are tall. But the types are rather mixed, and probably have been since prehistoric times. The Walloons on the whole are shorter, more square-set, and have a browner skin.

The division of Belgium into Latin and Germanic population groups is the most geographically noteworthy fact about the country. The line between the Flemish- and French-speaking areas is almost stable. It begins in France, west of Dunkerque, passes slightly north of St. Omer, then through Courtrai, south of Brussels, Tirlemont, and north of Liége. For a long time the Walloons had primacy. In 1841 the Flemings constituted 42 per cent of the total Belgian population. However, the Flemish group has shown more vigor and persistence and has made a series of "conquests." In 1864 Flemish was admitted in schools; a Flemish university was founded in Ghent; and the Flemings finally succeeded in establishing the official bilingualism of French and Flemish. In numbers, the Flemish part of Belgium has also won out: the Walloon population has been decreasing since 1932. A deficit in births, plus Walloon emigration to Brussels and Antwerp in Flemish territory, an important factor since the war, have definitely reversed the demographic trend. The Walloon population, which was three million in 1932, is now slightly above 2.5 millions; the Flemish population is now more than four millions. To this demographic factor an economic one should be added. Belgian industry was previously located almost exclusively in the Meuse coal fields, but the development of modern industries, somewhat favored by new transportation facilities, and less dependent on coal, has taken place mainly in Flanders, and especially around Antwerp and Brussels.

The Walloon problem is one of the most delicate in present-day Belgium. Maintenance of the equilibrium between Flanders and Wallony has been one of the bases of Belgian economics and politics. Now the Walloons will have a "minority complex" and this will create uneasiness. Many have advocated, as a solution, some form of federalism modeled on that of Switzerland.

The development of trade in the Benelux countries, and the multiple opportunities for work thus created, have resulted in a considerable demographic increase. The population of the Netherlands has trebled in one century, from 3,000,000 in 1850 to 10,250,000 in 1950. Belgium did not increase so fast, from 3,785,000 in 1830 to a 1950 population of 8,600,000. Population densities here are the greatest in Europe and probably in the world: 823 per square mile in the Netherlands and 735 in Belgium. Furthermore, because some areas are not very densely settled, for instance the Ardennes and the marshy region of eastern Netherlands, real local densities are sometimes even larger, being 2,190 per square mile in the province of South Holland. Population is increasing rapidly. The Netherlands can boast of having, after Iceland, the lowest death rate in the world and the highest birth rate in Western Europe.

Yet this population, which for the three countries will soon be 20 million, lives on a naturally limited and poor territory. In fact, the majority of the population lives on lands which have been wrested from the sea, and are thus truly a creation of man. The mark of human labor is present everywhere, more so since there are no spectacular landforms to divert attention from the cultural landscape.

The growth of Belgian and Dutch cities corresponds to the increase of population and economic development. Two thirds of the population of Belgium and almost one half that of the Netherlands live in cities. Three cities in the Netherlands and five in Belgium have more than 200,000 inhabitants: 845,000 in Amsterdam, 685,000 in Rotterdam, 570,000 in The Hague, 900,000 in Brussels, 500,000 in Antwerp, 340,000 in Liége, 270,000 in Charleroi, and 250,000 in Ghent.

The Benelux countries have their minor but nevertheless interesting peculiarities. Cleanliness is striking. The Netherlands, like Switzerland, looks like a well-groomed park where nothing seems to be out of its place and uncared for. In such flat countries bicycles are very popular. Here people prefer the rather heavy bicycle where the rider sits upright, in contrast to the low and lightweight French bicycle. Special lanes are provided for them. Odors, also, are interesting. The Dutch house gives out a subtle mixture of spices, varnish, velvet, and cigars, with here and there a strong smell of herring. As in Germany and in some parts of the United States, cigars are extremely popular and the pervading odor is everywhere.

More important and striking to the casual observer is the high level of living—at least by European standards. There are no slums in the Netherlands and almost none in Belgium. Income per capita is very high.

The Present Economic Life of the Benelux Countries

Agriculture. In Belgium and in the Netherlands, agriculture gives employment to only a small part of the population: 20 per cent in the Netherlands, 17 per cent in Belgium. But this percentage is much higher than in Great Britain and these countries, which have trade and industry as their economic basis, did not sacrifice so much to the Industrial Revolution. Yet there are no naturally favorable soil conditions except in the loam-covered plains of central Belgium. Agriculture is here a result of transformations and even creations made by men. Furthermore, it is an agriculture of quality, with high yields and modern techniques, and a goodly part of it is devoted to the production of exportable products. These three characters: coexistence with industry, development in spite of unfavorable conditions, and a definite commercial interest, give the agriculture of the Benelux countries a strikingly original aspect.

Seven main types of agricultural landscapes may be briefly described, all corresponding to the main physiographic divisions of the country (see Figure 52).

1. LORRAINE. This landscape is found in but a very small area, on the limestone cuestas and subsequent clay vales (which are a prolongation of those in eastern France) in the southern part of Luxembourg (the Gutland) and in a tiny corner of Belgium. Open fields, a three-year crop rotation, and the importance of cereals survive but cattle raising and the cultivation of fodder crops is greatly increasing.

2. THE ARDENNES. A harsh and rainy climate and siliceous soils are mainly favorable to forests, moors, and marshes. There are, however, wide cultivated areas and the ancient and archaic economy is giving place to scientific stock raising (Figure 62).

FIGURE 62. A typical landscape of the Ardennes. (Belgian Government Information Center.)

3. THE HESBAYE. The central plains of Belgium, in contrast, are one of the most fertile areas of Europe. Like the Beauce in France, they are a country of open fields, large farms (200 to 400

acres), farmhouses looking like fortresses, intensive cultivation of wheat, sugar beets, and oats, and the raising of cattle and horses in stables and barns.

4. THE CAMPINE. These gently rolling sandy hills of northern Belgium and the southern Netherlands are but marshes and moors. Yet a great area of these desolate lands (somewhat like the pine barrens of Georgia) has been progressively conquered for forests and pastures by breaking the iron-like hardpan, burning the heather, and spreading vast quantities of manure and city garbage.

5. THE EASTERN NETHERLANDS. East of the IJsselmeer lie some of the largest peat bogs of Europe. Until recently there were but a few villages settled on the natural hillocks or *terpen*. By digging drainage ditches, taking off the peat, drying the bottom of the geometrical holes thus made, mixing the peat with sand and fertilizers and then replacing it to form a new soil, these *Veenkolonien* have been made into the best agricultural lands of the Netherlands. Potatoes, rye, and oats grow well. The potato crop forms the basis of an important starch industry (the Netherlands is the world's foremost producer and exporter of starch), while mats and cardboard are made from the oat and rye straw. Almost all this industry is carried on by cooperatives.

6. INNER FLANDERS. This is also a sandy region, but the sand is not thick and lies on clays and marls which, when mixed, give a fairly good soil. Ingenious small landowners have for centuries spent a tremendous amount of work on the land and have developed a great variety of cash crops. Stock raising and truck gardening are the two most important aspects of the economy. Flax is widely grown and Belgium ranks third in world production. Endives, chicory (which when roasted and ground is mixed with coffee), tobacco, and hops are but a few of the many crops. Furthermore, rich vegetables and fruits are grown in greenhouses. The famous grapes of Hoylaert, south of Brussels, are exported throughout the year.

7. POLDERLAND. Below the three-foot contour line above mean sea level, agricultural work is mainly an organized fight against the encroaching waters. The first defensive dams were built in the seventh century. In the fourteenth century offensive dams were built to conquer lands from the sea and some river flood plains as well. The word "polder," meaning an area completely drained and in which the water table is accurately regulated, appeared for the first time in 1219, but major progress was possible only when the Dutch

began to use windmills, adopting a technique brought from the Near East by the Crusaders, and adapted to pumping in the early 1400's. Beemster lake, north of Amsterdam, with an area of about 18,000 acres, was drained by Amsterdam merchants as a commercial venture in 1612. During the next forty years three other lakes, with a total of 23,000 acres, were drained and the land thus re-

FIGURE 63. Reclamation projects in the Netherlands.

claimed produced vegetables and fruits for the Amsterdam market. The masterwork has been the draining of the 46,000-acre Haarlemmermeer, between 1839 and 1856. The great work presently in progress is the draining of the Zuider Zee (Figure 63). The project was decided on in 1918 and work began the next year. In 1932 a 20-mile long sea wall closed the gulf and made it a lake, the IJsselmeer, and by 1937 all traces of salt had disappeared. The Northwest or Wieringermeer polder was the first to be reclaimed, in 1930. Deliberately flooded by the Germans in 1945, it was again reclaimed in 1946. The Northeast polder [6] was dry in 1942, and in 1949 work was begun on the remaining polders. When they are completed the area of the Netherlands will have been increased by 7 per cent. The draining is now done by electrically driven pumping stations and no longer by the picturesque windmills. Over the years the Dutch have constructed a complex system of dikes, dams, and walls wherever the coastal dunes were not capable of fending off the sea. Early in 1953, however, an exceptionally severe North Sea storm breached these defenses and inundated much hard-won land. The full reclamation of this land will take several years.

FIGURE 64. Schokland "island," now in the center of the newly reclaimed Northeast polder. (Netherlands Information Bureau.)

The new alluvial soil is very rich (Figure 64). In Zeeland fields of wheat, sugar beets, fodder crops, and vegetables are predominant. The island of Walcheren, flooded during the war, has since been reclaimed. In Holland, farmers are more interested in cattle raising. Meadows cover four fifths of the area and the production of

[6] For a detailed study see George W. Hoffman, "The Zuider Zee Reclamation Project," *Michigan Academy of Sciences, Arts and Letters*, XXXV (1949, issued 1951), 198–211.

milk, butter, and cheese is important. Southern Holland is principally an area of gardens. The tulip was brought from Turkey in
the sixteenth century and the hyacinth was added in the eighteenth
century. In the last 50 years vegetables have steadily gained ground
over bulbs and flowers. In 1913 the area devoted to bulbs was twice
that devoted to vegetables; today, the proportion is reversed (Figure 65).

FIGURE 65. Tulip field near Leiden. (Netherlands Information Bureau.)

The Benelux countries differ from France in that there are relatively few farmers who own their land. Except in Flanders, the
land in Belgium is largely owned by city people. The Netherlands
is about equally divided between land-owning farmers in the eastern part and tenants in the western part. Most of the farms are
very small, except in central Belgium. More than one half of the

Dutch farmers have less than 15 acres. There is also much part-time farming. Many industrial workers of southern Belgium own a plot of land and grow vegetables and raise cows, not only for their own use but also commercially.

Less than 6.5 per cent of Belgium and 12 per cent of the Netherlands is not farmland. This is an excellent proportion. Crop yields are very high: up to two or three times above the European average. This, however, is not sufficient to feed the population. In spite of considerable effort since 1930 to grow more wheat, Belgium must still import 80 per cent of the wheat she needs and great quantities of barley, oats, dairy products, fodder, and fertilizer. But at this latitude the growing of cereals is difficult and costly and it is more profitable to specialize in stock raising; hence, the area in wheat is now less than one half of what it was a century ago. Cattle raising is a large-scale enterprise and is very efficient. Dutch cows are among the best milk producers in the world. The Netherlands specializes in dairy and garden products and must sell them to other countries. To Germany, Great Britain, and Belgium the Dutch send cheese, fruits, vegetables, flowers, and cattle for breeding purposes.

Obviously, the Netherlands can live only under a free-trade system. During the war some markets were lost. The export of dairy products is now only one fifth of what it was in 1937-39, and that of vegetables only three fifths. Dutch butter, facing strong competition from Danish and New Zealand butter, has virtually ceased to be offered on the world market.

Industry in Belgium. There have been several stages in the development of Belgian industry. The first one began in the Middle Ages in the cities of Flanders. In the fifteenth century and down to the nineteenth century, industry was scattered throughout the country. Later it was concentrated in the coal fields. The present trend is toward decentralization in industry.

Belgium was fortunate at the time of the Industrial Revolution in that it possessed what were then considered impressive reserves of iron ore along the northern edge of the Ardennes, close to the coal mines. The Sambre and Meuse coal field is a Hercynian syncline. It is broken by many faults and the coal seams are thin, discontinuous, and of irregular depth. But reserves are abundant. Some mines, it is said, were known in Roman times, and coal was used for domestic purposes long before the industrial era. In 1845, Belgium was second to Great Britain in coal production in the world. Like Great Britain, Belgium must now pay the penalty for having pioneered in coal mining. There are too many mines, worked by outmoded methods and at high prices. These conditions generally are such that the production reached in 1913 has never been surpassed: 8 million tons in 1850, 23 million tons in 1913 and again in 1936, and now only 17 million. The number of miners is decreasing and foreign labor has not proved very satisfactory.

Fortunately, Belgium has another field in the Campine. The very deep but thick seams have been exploited only since 1920, and production is soaring: 3 million tons in 1929, 6 million in 1936 and 8 million in 1950.

The coal situation in Belgium, while not a great problem, is nevertheless not wholly satisfactory. More coal is needed than Belgium can produce, and not only coking coal but also several million tons of ordinary industrial coal are imported. More and more coal is being transformed into electric power, which is easier to use and transport. In Belgium the consumption of coal per capita is two and one half times that of France. This is evidence of the highly industrialized level of the country.

Yet Belgium has almost no other raw materials to support this industrialization. The Ardennes iron ore, exploited around Liége where John Cockerell in 1820 established the first puddling oven and in 1832 the first coke blast furnace, is now no longer exploited. The ore which Belgium uses comes from Lorraine and Luxembourg, and more and more from Sweden (a richer ore, which does not need so much coke). In spite of having to depend upon imported ore, Belgium is the fifth world producer of pig iron and sixth of steel. Charleroi and Liége are the main centers but the steel industry is spread all over the southern coal fields, except in the western part (or Hainaut) near Mons.

For a time, Belgium was also one of the main producers of zinc ore. The ore from Vieille Montagne near Liége was the basis of a sizable industry. Now the ore is imported from Sweden, Mexico, and Italy, but Belgium is still second to the United States in the production of refined zinc. Lead, copper, and aluminum industries have been added. Belgium is one of the main industrial centers of nonferrous metals in Europe. Two other important industries of Belgium are glass making, and cement making, also located on the coal field.

All these heavy industries, which are based on coal and which export considerable amounts of their production, are still the mainstay of the industrial life of the country. The new tendency, however, is for quality products, which are easier to export. The manufacturing industries of Belgium are more diversified than ever and are unable to cope with the tremendous demand of postwar Europe for locomotives, rolling stock, arms (an old specialty of Liége), ships, etc.

The textile industry, which is Belgium's oldest, is prosperous and operating far above its prewar level. Flanders is still one of the main world centers of the flax industry, but cotton is now much more important. Ghent as a canal port plays the role of another Manchester and has a cotton exchange which competes with those of Liverpool, Hamburg, and Le Havre. The Verviers area, east of Liége, is the center of the wool industry which was established there in the fifteenth century. The industry is also gaining in Flanders, where it had been progressively eliminated since the Middle Ages. With the exception of some flax from Flanders, all the raw materials of the textile industry are imported.

Besides these basic industries there are innumerable others, such as a prosperous chemical industry, rubber works, paper mills, electric plants, etc. For the time being, these new industries work mainly for the domestic market, but the country is striving to modernize, accumulate new capital for the making of high quality products, and is eager to compete with the United States exports to the European continent.

Industry in the Netherlands. Trade in the Netherlands is of great importance, but it is not directly from trade or from agriculture that the major part of the working population now makes a living. Thirty-seven per cent of all Dutch workers are now industrial workers. On a 1938 = 100 basis, the industrial production index was 145 in 1951, and this in spite of great damage caused by the war.

Dutch industry differs much from Belgian industry. At the end of the Middle Ages and down to the eighteenth century Holland, like Flanders, had famous industries, producing luxury goods like Utrecht velvet and Delft earthenware. But the Industrial Revolution had little effect, and in the nineteenth century the Netherlands was still a nation mainly devoted to commerce and agriculture. This was probably due to the lack of coal and to the absence of mineral resources. Population pressure, however, was so great that a different kind of industrialization process was set up. Industry began to evolve from Dutch trade and agriculture. Agricultural products were processed before being exported, and imported products, particularly colonial ones from Indonesia were processed in factories which were established around the ports.

This situation has changed in the last 50 years. The Netherlands now have enough coal for their needs. The Limburg coal field, east of the Belgian Campine field and very similar to it, provides 12 million tons a year, and the methods of extraction set up by the State during the First World War are among the most efficient in Europe. The Maurits mine is among the largest in Europe. The Netherlands is no longer dependent on the Ruhr for its coal supply and exports important quantities of coke.

The Netherlands is now second to Germany in petroleum production in Western Europe. The oil wells of Schoonebeek, near the German border, supply almost 25 per cent of the Netherlands consumption of petroleum products. Increasing production is expected, further improving the country's fuel situation.

The Dutch industries may be divided into four broad categories:

1. THE AGRICULTURAL INDUSTRIES. These industries (cheese, condensed milk, beet sugar, potato flour, and canned foods) are located chiefly in the eastern part of the country and in southern Holland. But they may also be found in the area south of the Meuse; for instance, the tanneries and shoe factories of Langstraat near 's Hertogenbosch. More than 800 cheese and butter factories are scattered over different parts of the country.

2. THE COLONIAL INDUSTRIES. Since the seventeenth century the Netherlands has imported from its overseas territories and from other tropical areas of the world, great quantities of agricultural and mineral raw materials. Before reshipping those, they are manufactured into many diverse products. The industries are located near the ports, Amsterdam and Rotterdam and their maritime canals, the North Sea Canal and New Waterway. Chief among the great variety of these industries are the manufacture of vegetable oil, margarine, cocoa and chocolate, the cutting of diamonds, and the preparation of quinine. A more recent development is the establishment of heavier industries such as tin smelting (the third largest tin smelter in the world is in Arnhem), superphosphates and synthetic fertilizers, petroleum refining (the largest oil refinery of Western Europe is found in Rotterdam). Another metallurgical industry, also based on imported ores, is steel making. Blast furnaces have been built at the entrance to the North Sea Canal which leads to Amsterdam.

3. SHIPBUILDING INDUSTRIES. For over four centuries, the Netherlands has been famous for her shipbuilding industry. At the beginning of the eighteenth century, four fifths of the ships built

in Europe were built in Dutch yards. Peter the Great, Tsar of Russia, studied in Amsterdam and learned how to build ships. More than 40,000 workers are engaged in shipbuilding in Rotterdam, Amsterdam, Dordrecht, and Flushing. As a corollary, Dutch naval engineering for boilers, ship, and port material is world famous.

4. SKILLED INDUSTRIES. During the nineteenth century the scattered textile industries of the Twente, in the northeastern section of the country, were progressively developed and very important cotton mills are now located around Enschede and Hengelo. These produce both for domestic consumption and for export. The wool industry is located in North Brabant around Tilburg and Breda. As to rayon, the Netherlands is one of the largest exporters in the world. The electrotechnical industry is centered at Eindhoven in the southern part of the country. The Philips factory at Eindhoven is the largest producer of radio equipment in the world and employs more than 20,000 workers. The Netherlands exports more than 300,000 radio sets every year throughout Europe. Other skilled industries are devoted to weighing apparatus, chemicals, drugs, etc. Diamond cutting has been discussed with the colonial industries because it began with stones brought from the Dutch colonies.

Industry in Luxembourg. In the preceding paragraphs this tiny country has been somewhat neglected for lack of more space. But industry in Luxembourg is also of an unexpected importance. The cuesta belt of French Lorraine continues into Luxembourg, and the Jurassic limestone formations are mined for *minette*, a phosphoric iron ore. Though about one half of the mined ore is exported to Belgium, Luxembourg is itself an important producer of pig iron and steel. There are, however, few engineering industries and the other industries of Luxembourg are mainly based on agriculture, such as tanneries, flour mills, and breweries.

Trade

The Benelux countries represent an eminently European type of civilization. Great numbers of people live on a land which cannot feed them all. Hence they must sell their work and skill to the whole world. They need a free international trade in order to live, and any hindrance to normal economic relations is deeply felt by them. They rank first in the world in volume and value of trade per capita. In 1938, in terms of U.S. gold dollars, the total of imports and exports per inhabitant was 106 for Belgium, 92 for the Netherlands. In comparison, in that same year, Great Britain had 81, Germany 37, France 31, and the United States 22. Since 1922, Luxembourg has formed a customs union with Belgium.

Normally, the foreign trade of the Benelux countries greatly exceeds their needs and transit trade is a very important element in the economic structure of the countries. Before World War II, 20 per cent of all German imports and exports passed through Rotterdam; three fourths of the trading activity of Rotterdam was for other countries. So were one third of the imports and one half of the exports of Antwerp.

This kind of trade has suffered much from the war. For one reason, Europe is poorer and Germany is divided. Rotterdam has lost some of its Central European trade; Antwerp is in a better position because the harbor had suffered almost no destruction when the Allies began to use it in September, 1944, and because it does not rely so much on German trade. Also, a part of the trade of northern France goes through Antwerp.

Before the war, the balance of trade in both Belgium and the Netherlands left some deficit, more important in the Netherlands than in Belgium. But the balance of payments, thanks to the many benefits derived from transit trade and from investments abroad, was always favorable. Belgium has regained her good prewar position. This is partly due to an astute policy of the government, which in 1946 used its large reserves of hard currency to make large-scale imports. The situation of the Netherlands is more serious, for Indonesia is no longer a colony but an independent country. Foreign and domestic trade depends not only on the location of the countries but also on having a highly developed transportation system.

Transportation

In the Netherlands, the waterways play a role unequalled elsewhere. The length of waterways per inhabitant is the highest in the world. It is impossible to travel 15 minutes without crossing some river or canal. Seventy-four per cent of the freight is water borne and only 26 per cent is carried by the railroads. The fluvial fleet in 1950 represented a tonnage of over 4 million tons. The trunk line, of course, is the Rhine, or rather its most important branch, the Waal. Wide canals link it with all parts of the country, for instance the Merwede Canal and the newly completed Amsterdam-Rhine Canal to Amsterdam, and the Wilhelmina Canal to the Meuse. Railways are a later development and, though they form a very dense network, have a total mileage only half that of the waterways.

In Belgium the railroad density is the highest in the world, three times that of France, and there is a dense traffic of goods and passengers. International routes cross Belgium in all directions, from France and the British Isles to Germany, from France to the Netherlands, from the Netherlands to Switzerland and Italy, etc. Waterways, while not as important as in the Netherlands, are still very dense. They carry about 38 per cent of the freight. The main lines of traffic are the canal from Charleroi to Mons on the southern coal field, the canal from Charleroi to Brussels and Antwerp, now being widened, and the important Albert Canal from Liége to Antwerp, which crosses the Campine coal field and its related industrial area.

Belgium has three main ports: Brugge, Ghent, and Antwerp. Traffic, which had been considerable during the Middle Ages, was greatly reduced until the nineteenth century because Brugge and Ghent were no longer accessible to large sea-going freighters and Antwerp was sealed up by the Dutch. Though maritime canals have been built from Brugge to Zeebrugge and from Ghent to Terneuzen, deep enough for vessels drawing 24 feet, 80 per cent of the traffic goes through Antwerp, thanks to a remarkable convergence of rivers, canals, and railways. The port lies in the Schelde estuary, 55 miles from the sea. For connections with the Rhine, river navigation has to pass through Dutch territory. By international treaty, the Netherlands now guarantees transit access to Antwerp (Figure 66).

The Netherlands has two great ports, Amsterdam and Rotterdam. For a long time Amsterdam was the main port. Once located on a gulf of the Zuider Zee, the city is built on marshy land and its successive development may be seen in the belts of canals which are its peculiar feature. But Amsterdam has two drawbacks: it is hard to reach from the sea and is not within easy access of the Rhine. Even though the North Sea Canal connects the port with the North Sea, and the Amsterdam-Rhine Canal with the Rhine, there is little transit traffic and most of the trade is for domestic purposes only. Rotterdam was for a long time only a fishing port. But the independence of Germany and the industrial development of the Ruhr region made it the exit of the Rhine area. Before the war, three fourths of the trade was in transit, mainly for Germany. Badly damaged in 1940, it is now better equipped than ever before. About 13,000 ships entered the port of Rotterdam in 1950.

Curiously enough, Belgium has a very small merchant fleet: only 6 per cent of the ships calling at Antwerp are Belgian. But the Netherlands has a fleet as important as the French merchant fleet. Most of the ships are very modern because the ships lost during the war have now been replaced. In 1950, the Dutch fleet totaled more than three million tons.

FIGURE 66. The port of Antwerp. (Belgian Government Information Center.)

The Most Urgent Problems Facing the Countries of Western Europe

Many of the present problems of the countries of Western Europe stem from their location. Unprotected by seas, like Great Britain, widely open to Central Europe, they have greatly suffered from the war with Germany, and are now directly affected by the unfortunate split between the Western democracies and the U.S.S.R. and its satellites in Eastern Europe.

Western Europe was an important battlefield of World War II. The war imposed very high costs of reconstruction, and left the countries considerably impoverished. Now they live under the constant threat of a new world war, well knowing that the risk of being invaded is great and that they would again be a battlefield.

From World War II these countries also have inherited inflation, which is their main problem of the hour. This causes a steady fall of the old values and marked social unrest. Meeting this financial difficulty would be the first step toward stabilization. Unfortunately, the rearmament imposed by the international situation will make a solution more difficult.

Their economy, badly shattered by the war, is at work again and production indexes are well above those of 1938. Yet the situation is not satisfactory, in spite of encouraging statistics. Production barely keeps up with an increased but limited demand for modern industrial products. Progress is not fast enough to bring a real betterment of the peoples' standard of living. Except in the Netherlands and in northern Belgium, most of the factories are too ancient, too small, and insufficiently equipped with modern machinery. The Netherlands and Belgium, on the whole, are better off, but the French industrial structure needs a complete overhauling. To attain this aim a plan for modernization, called the Monnet Plan, was set up in 1947 and established definite programs for an increase in production. Results have been satisfactory in many sectors, but have rarely reached the goals which had been fixed. The problem is extremely complex and only a total change in the economic structure of the country would bring a solution. Too many people work in agriculture, thus keeping many men and women who could be better used in services, commerce or industry. Productivity per worker, in both agriculture and in industry, is much below that of other countries. Most farms and factories are too small and do not have enough capital for improvement. The deficiency in coal has not been met. Consumer industries are overdeveloped in proportion to the basic industries. France simply does not produce enough machine tools, trucks, and other equipment.

The most noteworthy steps taken to improve the situation have been those for a more complete integration of the European economy. The Council of Europe in Strasbourg has not been invested with sufficient strength to impose profound changes, but much hope may be put into the Schuman plan for a pooling of all the coal and steel resources of France, the Benelux countries, and West Germany. It could be a prelude to other international agreements for a European economic union.

The Netherlands, Belgium, and Luxembourg have provided a most remarkable example of possible European union by their creation of the Benelux union. Yet it is taking years to iron out the difficulties, because taxation systems, social security organizations, and state controls are different. Furthermore, new industries in the three states fear competition. There are, however, great hopes that the union will soon be completely realized, for many problems are common.

The present outlook for Western Europe is not very bright. Yet it is better than anybody thought it would be when the war ended. Geography shows that these countries are sufficiently well endowed to keep hope for the future. Their problem is to become adapted in a completely different world. On a monument which stands on the enclosing dam of the IJsselmeer an inscription reads: "A people that is truly alive is busy building its future." In spite of their many difficulties, this is just what the Western European countries are doing.

BIBLIOGRAPHY

A. Books in English

Edelman, C. H. *Soils of the Netherlands.* Amsterdam: New Holland Publishing Co., 1950.

Evans, E. Estyn. *France.* London: Christophers, 1937.

Fleure, H. J. *French Life and Its Problems.* London: Continental Publishers & Distributors, Ltd., 1943.

Landheer, Bartholomeus (ed.). *The Netherlands.* Berkeley: University of California Press, 1943.

Martonne, Emmanuel de. *The Geographical Regions of France.* Translated by H. C. Brentnall. London: William Heinemann, Ltd., 1933.

Netherlands Ministry of Agriculture, Fisheries and Food, *Dutch Agriculture Facts,* The Hague, 1950.

Ormsby, Hilda. *France, A Regional and Economic Geography.* New York: E. P. Dutton & Co., 1950.

B. Books in Foreign Languages

Brunhes, J., and Defontaines, P. *Géographie humaine de la France* (Human Geography of France). Paris: F. Alcan, 1934.

Faucher, D. (ed.). *La France. Géographie, tourisme* (France: Geography and Tourism). 2 vols. Paris: Larousse, 1952.

Fourastie, J., and Montet, H. *L'économie française dans le monde* (French Economy in the World). Paris: Presses Universitaires de France, 1945.

Géographie Universelle

Vol. II: Demangeon, A. *Belgique, Pays-Bas, Luxembourg* (Belgium, the Netherlands, and Luxembourg). Paris: A. Colin, 1927.

Vol. VI, Part 1: Martonne, Em de. *France physique* (Physical Geography of France). Paris: A. Colin, 1942. Part 2: Demangeon, A. *France économique et humaine* (Economic and Human Geography of France). 2 vols. Paris: A. Colin, 1946, 1948.

George, Pierre. *Géographie économique et sociale de la France* (Economic and Social Geography of France), 2d ed. Paris: Editions Hier & Aujourd'hui, 1946.

Marcotte, V. *La Belgique dans le Monde* (Belgium in the World). Brussels: Anc. Établissements A. Pouvrez, 1946.

Schmitthüsen, Josef. *Das Luxemburger Land* (Luxembourg). Leipzig: S. Hirzel, 1940.

Vidal de la Blache, P. *Tableau de la géographie de la France* (A Geographical Survey of France). Paris: Librairie Hachette, 1903.

C. ARTICLES

AMERICAN GEOGRAPHICAL SOCIETY. *Readings in the Geography of France, Germany, and Netherlands.* Contributions by various authors. (Reprint Series No. 1.) New York: American Geographical Society, 1943.

BERKUM, E. VAN. "Reconstruction in the Netherlands," *Canadian Geographical Journal,* XXXIV (March, 1947), 140–45.

BUTT, L. "Belgian Agriculture," *Foreign Agriculture,* XI (July, 1947), 90–98.

CHABOT, G. "Flandre et Wallonie dans l'industrie Belge" (Flanders and Wallonia in Belgian Industry), *L'Information Géographique,* XIII (March-April, 1949), 43–47.

HOFFMAN, GEORGE W. "The Zuider Zee Reclamation Project," *Michigan Academy of Sciences, Arts, and Letters,* XXXV (1949), 197–213.

MORGAN, F. W. "Rotterdam and Waterways Approaches to the Rhine," *Economic Geography,* XXIV (January, 1948), 1–18.

RODRIGUES, D. H. "Agriculture in the Netherlands." New York: Netherlands Information Bureau, July, 1949.

———. "Communications in the Netherlands." New York: Netherlands Information Bureau, June, 1949.

———. "Of Ships and Men." New York: Netherlands Information Bureau, April, 1949.

chapter 6

CENTRAL EUROPE

THE TERM "Central Europe" (Mitteleuropa, Zwischeneuropa), so frequently misused by the Germans as well as by others, can hardly be mentioned without introducing political overtones. At best, it can be considered a flexible political-geographic term describing an area whose borders shift in accordance with changes in national boundaries. In this chapter the term is used as a common denominator for the following countries: Germany (Deutschland, Deutsches Reich) within its post-World War II boundaries, Switzerland (Schweiz, Suisse, Svizzera), Liechtenstein, and Austria (Österreich).

It should be pointed out that, while concepts of Central Europe have differed, many writers and especially German geographers have stressed its geographical and cultural entity, and the fact that Germany constitutes its core. Furthermore, Central Europe has always been held to include that part of Europe in which at least a portion of the population spoke a dialect of German. This region has at times included parts of France (Alsace and Lorraine) and the greater portion of Belgium and the Netherlands in the west, the territory of the former Austria-Hungary, Romania, Bulgaria, large sections of western Poland, the Baltic States, and some of the southern Alpine valleys extending into Italy, and coastal Yugoslavia. Some geographers have tried to base their delineation of Central Europe on its physical geography and have seen a common denominator in the east-west alignment of the Alps, Central Uplands, and Lowlands. Others have considered Central Europe as a central transitional zone located between oceanic or peninsular Europe in the west and essentially continental Europe in the east. All writers agree that Germany within its 1937 borders, Switzerland, Austria, Bohemia, and Moravia should be included in its area; Hilda Ormsby and

Henry Meyer have discussed the different interpretations attached to the elusive concept of Central Europe.[1]

The central position of the three countries—Germany, Switzerland, and Austria—in relation to other sections of peninsular Europe, is of great significance. The area is bordered by the Atlantic communities of France, Belgium, Luxembourg, and the Netherlands—all in Western Europe; by Denmark, Norway, and Sweden —all in Northern Europe; by Italy and the Free Territory of Trieste, which lie in Southern Europe; and by a great transitional region known by many names, but defined in this book as East Central Europe. The borders of Germany have constantly shifted while those of the Alpine countries (Alpenländer) of Switzerland and Austria have remained relatively stable for many centuries. The North German Lowlands, which form part of the great plain extending from northern France deep into the Soviet Union, have been used as a favorite invasion route from earliest historical times. The Vienna Basin has played an important role since the first century A.D., when the Romans used it as an outpost for offensive and as a base for defensive action. He who controls Vienna and its basin commands the narrows of the Danube, and gains access to the wide open spaces of the Great Hungarian Lowlands. Vienna also lies astride the lowland route between the Adriatic Sea and the headwaters of the Oder (Odra) and Vistula rivers, and guards the southeastern entrance to Bohemia and Bavaria. Farther south, the several low passes across the Alps have facilitated the free interchange of peoples between Central and Southern Europe.

Most of the peoples of Central Europe, including those of the greater part of Switzerland, are German-speaking. Their countries have a long and rich cultural tradition. Austria, with a glorious past and great power in the years of the Austro-Hungarian Monarchy, remained independent after 1919; Switzerland with its 25 cantons developed slowly from a nucleus (Urschweiz) formed in 1291 by a defensive alliance of the Forest Cantons (Waldstätten) Uri, Schwyz, and Unterwalden. Germany was politically unified in 1871.

However defined, Central Europe remains an area of transition. Structurally it ranges from sedimentary lowlands in north Germany covered by thick continental glacial deposits to crystalline highlands

[1] Hilda Ormsby, "The Definition of Mitteleuropa and Its Relations to the Conception of Deutschland in the Writings of Modern German Geographers," *The Scottish Geographical Magazine*, LI (November 15, 1935), 337-47; and Henry Cord Meyer, "Mitteleuropa in German Political Geography," *Annals of the Association of American Geographers*, XXXVI (September, 1946), 178-94.

(Alps) with cirques and valleys carved out by Alpine glaciers; climatically, from the marine west coast climates of Western Europe to the more continental climates in the east, or from the Mediterranean type prevailing in some of the valleys along the southern flank of the Alps to the more variable climates of the Alpine region proper.

Central Europe has considerable mineral wealth: coal in the Ruhr and the Saar, iron ore in central Austria (Erzberg). All three countries have ample hydroelectric power and valuable deposits of various metallic minerals and rare salts. The industries of the region are highly developed.

Physiographic Basis of Cultural Forms

Germany

Location and Size. No matter how one defines Central Europe, Germany forms part of it. In 1871, it covered an area of 208,189 square miles. At that time it was third in size among European powers. Since then it has undergone four territorial changes. By the Treaty of Versailles Germany lost 27,200 square miles with a population of 6.5 million. It expanded again under Hitler, who incorporated the Sudetenland, Austria, and many other parts of Europe into the Third Reich between 1938 and 1944. But after the military defeat of 1945, it was reduced to 136,000 square miles (approximately the combined areas of Minnesota and Michigan). Over five million people were killed or reported missing during World War II, and in 1946 Germany's population was down to 65,000,000. No one knows how long the Oder-Neisse river line will remain Germany's eastern border, or what the future holds for the Saar and other small boundary adjustments in the west.[2] In addition to losing territory, Germany is now divided into four occupation zones, and the city of Berlin is split up among the occupying powers. The western zones have been united economically and politically since 1949, and Bonn has become the seat of the German Federal Republic. The western zones are divided into länder or states. Since mid-1952, the eastern zone has been divided into Bezirke or districts. Among these many administrative changes resulting from the war and the subsequent occupation, the liquidation of Prussia is of special importance.

[2] Colbert C. Held, "The New Saarland," *Geographical Review*, XLI (October, 1951), 590-605; George W. Hoffman, "The Netherlands Demands on Germany, A Post-War Problem in Political Geography," *Annals of the Association of American Geographers*, XLII (June, 1952), 129-52.

Present-day Germany consists of eight länder and 14 districts (not including Berlin), with an area of approximately 136,000 square miles and 68 million people. It is divided into two major political units, the German Federal Republic (Deutsche Bundesrepublik) and the German Democratic Republic (Deutsche Demokratische Republik), the former consisting of the United States, British, and French zones of occupation, and the latter occupied by the Soviet Union. In the east, the former Prussian provinces of Pomerania, Brandenburg, and Upper and Lower Silesia have passed under Polish administration; East Prussia has been split up between the U.S.S.R. and Poland. Thus, present-day Germany is bounded by latitudes 47° and 55° N. and longitudes 6° and 15° E. Its greatest north-south extension is approximately 590 miles, and its maximum east-west extension 385 miles (Figure 67).

Climate. The climate of Germany is affected both by maritime and continental influences. In general, the full effect of the maritime characteristics is felt only in northwestern Germany. Toward the east, seasonal contrasts become sharper. The Central Uplands are not a climatic barrier. On the other hand, the Alps form a clear-cut divide between regions of Mediterranean climate and those with a marked Central European climate.

Temperatures vary according to a locality's latitude and its distance from the western seas. Southern Germany is six degrees south of the latitude of Kiel and therefore receives more sun heat than the northern part of the country. However, as southern Germany lies at a generally greater elevation, and because temperature decreases with altitude, the increase in sun heat is largely offset. Also, as the summer days in northern Germany are almost one hour longer than those in the south, the northern portion of the country benefits from additional daily warmth during that season. During the winter, conditions are reversed, and the north is much colder than the south. As a result, July temperatures are rather uniform over all of Germany: Kiel—62.9° F., Munich (München)—63.9° F., Leipzig—64.8° F.[3] The warmest areas are the protected valleys of southwestern Germany and those of the Rhine, Mosel, Main, and Neckar rivers; their climatic characteristics are often similar to those of Mediterranean regions, even though summer rainfall is heavier in these valleys.

The annual distribution of precipitation is characterized by a summer maximum. Spring and summer rains increase toward the east; fall and winter rains decrease in the same direction. Except

[3] See climatic graphs, Appendix II.

where influenced by relief, the total yearly precipitation in the North German Lowlands decreases toward the east. In the Central Uplands rainfall increases very rapidly with increasing altitude. This is well illustrated in the Alb areas bordering the Alpine Foreland. Rainfall differences between the windward and leeward sides of mountains are considerable, especially where the ranges are oriented in a north-south and northwest-southeast direction. Only during the winter, when cloudbanks are much lower than in summertime, do the summits show above the zone of maximum precipitation. The snow cover in the Central Uplands and in most of the Alpine Foreland is abundant and snowfalls continue as late as March.

German Rivers. The even distribution of precipitation and ample snow cover provide German rivers with sufficient water for navigation. Most of these rivers, for example the Ems, Weser, Elbe, and Oder, flow from the Central Uplands (and from their extension into Poland and Czechoslovakia) toward the North and Baltic seas. As a result of structural differences, the Rhine and the Danube have a different drainage pattern and direction of flow. As late as the Middle Tertiary, the Upper Rhine Plains and the Alpine Foreland were still covered by vast seas. When the waters receded, the Foreland was drained eastward by the Danube and northward by the Rhine. However, the lower altitude of the Upper Rhine plains and the very short distance to the North Sea enabled the Rhine to erode headward and to capture the drainage of the western Foreland and of the area around today's Lake Constance (Bodensee), which formerly fed into the Danube. This peculiar structural history also becomes apparent upon examination of the Rhine's course. The usual threefold division of rivers into upper, middle, and lower course is replaced in the case of the Rhine by a breakdown into five sections: Alpine Rhine (from its source to Lake Constance), High Rhine (to Basel), Upper Rhine (to Bingen), Middle Rhine (to Bonn), and Lower Rhine.

Brief mention should also be made of the regimes of streams, i.e., the changes in the amount of flow and in the water level. The rivers which rise in the Central Uplands—the Ems, Weser, Elbe, Oder, the right tributaries of the Rhine, and the left tributaries of the Danube—reach high-water stage shortly after the melting of the snow, usually during the early spring; their low-water stage comes in July and August, largely because of increased evaporation. Typical mountain streams as well as parts of the Rhine and of the Danube reach their crest in the summer because of the late melting of snows in the high mountains and the heavy summer rains; their low-water stage occurs during the winter. On the other hand, the Upper and

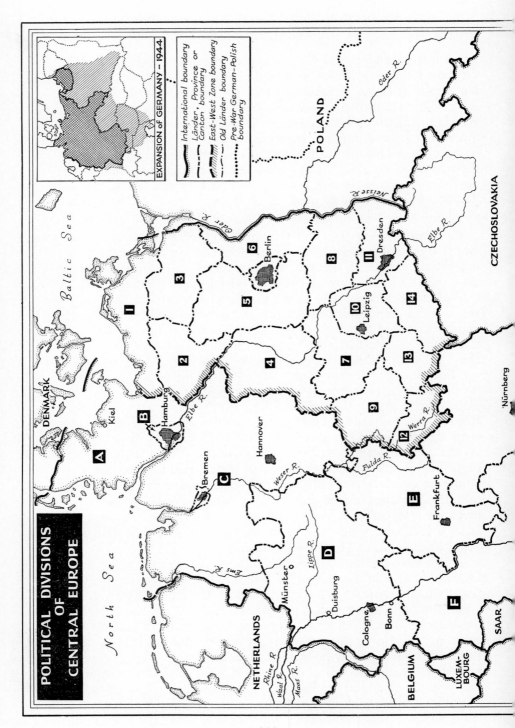

POLITICAL DIVISIONS
OF
CENTRAL EUROPE

POLAND

CZECHOSLOVAKIA

Oder R.

Neisse R.

Elbe R.

Baltic Sea

North Sea

DENMARK

Kiel

Hamburg

Elbe R.

Bremen

Hannover

Weser R.

Münster

Lippe R.

Ems R.

Duisburg

Cologne

Bonn

Rhine R.

Waal R.

Maas R.

NETHERLANDS

BELGIUM

LUXEM-
BOURG

SAAR

Frankfurt

Fulda R.

Werra R.

Nürnberg

Berlin

Dresden

Leipzig

3

6

8

11

5

10

14

2

4

7

13

9

12

1

A

B

C

D

E

F

330

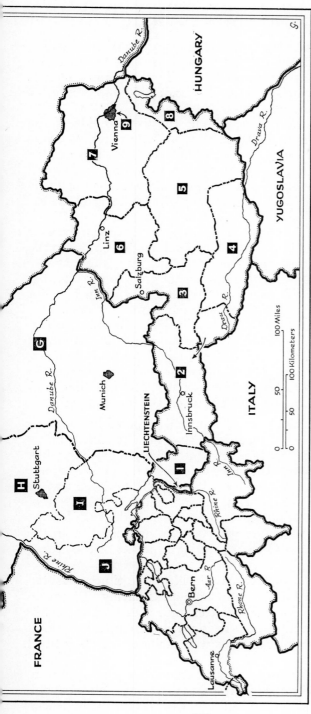

FIGURE 67. Political divisions of Central Europe. *East Germany* (districts): (1) Rostock, (2) Schwerin, (3) Neubrandenburg, (4) Magdeburg, (5) Potsdam, (6) Frankfurt, (7) Halle, (8) Cottbus, (9) Erfurt, (10) Leipzig, (11) Dresden, (12) Suhl, (13) Gera, (14) Chemnitz. *West Germany* (länder): (A) Schleswig-Holstein, (B) Hamburg, (C) Lower Saxony, (D) North Rhine-Westphalia, (E) Hesse, (F) Rhineland-Pfalz, (G) Bavaria, (H-I-J) Merged länder of Württemberg-Baden, Württemberg-Hohenzollern, and Baden. *Switzerland:* for canton names, see Figure 85. *Austria* (provinces): (1) Vorarlberg, (2) Tyrol, (3) Salzburg, (4) Carinthia, (5) Styria, (6) Upper Austria, (7) Lower Austria, (8) Burgenland, (9) Vienna.

331

Middle Rhine receives a considerable volume of water from numerous tributaries rising in the Central Uplands, so that the range between high and low water is reduced. The Lower Rhine is characterized by an even regime, a factor of considerable importance for the river's economic usefulness.

Compared with their windward side, the leeward side of the Central Uplands has an abundance of rain. The waters of many mountain rivers are dammed and stored in reservoirs (Talsperren), which provide protection against floods, storage for low-water periods, and water for industry and the generation of hydroelectric power. Most of these artificial lakes are within the Eifel, Sauerland, and the Bergischesland (south of the Ruhr).

The amount of ice cover on German rivers increases from west to east as expected, and impedes navigation. Great variations in the length of the winter freeze are characteristic. The Rhine at Cologne (Köln) is frozen over for an average of 20 days per year, the Ems for 27, the lower Weser for 37, the Elbe near Magdeburg for 45, and the Danube at Regensburg for an average of 37 days.

On the whole, Germany is fortunate in having a drainage pattern which connects remote parts of the land with all important economic regions, and whose great rivers, together with the numerous canals of the North German Lowlands, constitute a vital element of the country's transportation system. The fact that most of the rivers are navigable for long distances is of great importance.

Vegetation. The various vegetation changes noted in Germany are closely connected with climatic shifts which occurred during and since the Great Ice Age. Shortly after the postglacial period, birches (*Betula nana*) were the most widespread trees of the climax forests, but they were soon challenged by the Scotch pine and by certain types of oak, linden (lime), and maple (*Acer*), all of which extended across peninsular Europe and into the British Isles. Spruce (*Picea excelsa*) together with oak, fir, and beech from the south spread to northern Germany during a period of cooler and damper climate.

The vegetation cover of Germany in Neolithic times consisted largely of dense virgin forests, with some areas having little or no woodland. Even though some tree clearance goes back to prehistoric times, man found the border regions between forests and loess very attractive because the land was well drained and easily tilled with simple tools.

During Roman times, large parts of present-day Germany were impassable. The predominant forest types were distributed as follows: Scotch pine and spruce in the northeast and in the glacial valleys, oak and beech in the Baltic hinterland, and beech, birch, and oak in northwestern Germany and in the middle Rhineland. Beech was dominant in the lower parts of the Central Uplands, and spruce at higher altitudes. Fir was commonly found in southern Germany.

Three main periods of forest clearing (Rodung) may be distinguished: sixth to ninth centuries (early German period); ninth to fifteenth centuries (clearing due to population pressure); and eighteenth century (clearing due to industrialization and timber exports). Following the second period of clearings, oak was replaced by beech and spruce and forest conservation measures were initiated.

Thus, German forests in existence today differ widely from the virgin forests of Roman times. The great changes in the forest cover evident throughout Germany have been brought about largely by man. Once predominantly broadleaved, Germany's forests are now chiefly coniferous, the latter type having been found especially suitable for reforestation. One may generalize by saying that conifers are dominant in the east and southeast, while broadleaf species are more common in the west.

Plains originally covered by deciduous trees now have spruce or Scotch pine and some oak. Riverine forests are predominantly alder, poplar (*Populus*), ash (*Fraxinus excelsior*), and elm. A zone of larch (*Larix sibirica*), spruce, and Swiss stone pine (*Pinus cembra*) is commonly found in the Alps; one of silver fir (*Abies alba*), beech, and some spruce, in the Alpine Foreland. The Scotch pine has been found useful in the reforestation of sandy areas (dunes, heaths, and steppes). Certain tree types, such as the linden, poplar, willow (*Salix*), ash, and maple, which are commonly associated with German forests, occur only in small woods.

Thanks to effective conservation measures, more than 27 per cent of Germany is still forested, the ratio of coniferous to broadleaf species being 70 to 30. In general, the percentage of forest area increases from north to south. Bavaria, North Rhine Westphalia, and Lower Saxony are the most heavily wooded areas. Before the war, more than one half of the forested land was in private hands, one third consisted of state forests, and close to 15 per cent of village properties. Considerable changes have been made in the distribution of ownership since 1945. Furthermore, German forests suffered from overcutting, especially during the war and immediately thereafter.

A few words should be said about the grasslands — meadows and grazing land. The only true remaining grass formations are to be found along the dunes fringing the North Sea, on Alpine meadows above the tree line, and in marshes and sedges. A portion of the land that used to be in meadows is now cultivated, while many forested areas, marshes, and bays have been turned into meadows. In general, meadows are limited to those areas where the quality of the soil is such as to inhibit cultivation. Today such areas are found only in certain mountain valleys in scattered parts of the North German Lowlands.

Physiographic Divisions. Germany may be divided into three broad regions which resemble the main structural divisions: (1) The North German Lowlands, a glaciated plain; (2) the worn-down fragments of the Hercynian [4] system, collectively called the Central Uplands (Mittelgebirge); and (3) the Alpine Foreland, once covered by the Alpine ice cap, together with the Alps, a young folded mountain system of which only a small fraction lies within Germany's boundaries. Each of these three main regions is further subdivided according to structure, relief, climate, and soil characteristics. The central position of Germany is clearly indicated by these regions, inasmuch as all three extend deep into the neighboring countries (Figure 68).

Before discussing the regions and their subdivisions, it should be pointed out that in Germany the chief contrasts, both physiographic and cultural, appear between north and south. In the north, the glaciated lowlands include the transitional fertile borderlands. The south includes the diversified uplands of Central Germany, the Alpine Foreland, and the Alps. A dividing line, clearly marked on any physical map, may be drawn eastward from Aachen, along the southern margin of the Ruhr industrial area, along the edge of the Weser hills through Osnabrück and Hanover, along the northern edge of the Harz mountains, and around the Leipzig Bay to Görlitz on the Neisse River (Figure 68).

THE NORTH GERMAN LOWLANDS. The Lowlands escaped the uplift which has affected most of Southern and Western Europe since the Middle Tertiary. Unconsolidated deposits were laid down by the ice sheets which spread southward from Scandinavia in Quaternary times. Boulder clay, gravel, sand, and wind-blown loess deposits vary in thickness between 40 and 500 feet. In its successive advances the ice sheet encountered no obstacles short of the

---

[4] The name is derived from "Hercynia silva" (Hercynian forest) used by the Romans to describe the mountains north of Bohemia. In recent times the name has been applied to all massifs which are of similar age and origin. For details of all geological terms used in this chapter, see Appendix I.

Central Uplands, where it was halted by the Ore Mountains (Erzgebirge), Harz Mountains, Weser hills and other highlands. Subsequently, the ice movements across the Lowlands weakened. The various stages of glacial retreat are evidenced by moraines which give the region a hilly character. In its slow retreat northward, the ice sheet left two east-west oriented depressions east of the Elbe River. These abandoned glacial stream channels or spill-ways are called Urstromtäler by the Germans.

The North German Lowlands are generally divided into two subregions, one west and one east of the Elbe River:

West of the Elbe. Between the North Sea coast and the East Frisian Islands, which at one time formed a continuous dune wall, there are tidal flats or Watten which are flooded at high tide. Reclaimed areas, called Marschen, border the seashore and the estuaries of the Elbe, Weser, and Ems rivers. This land, like the polders in the Netherlands, has been reclaimed by diking and draining. The soil is rich and very suitable for grazing. Some sugar beets and vegetables are also grown profitably. Between the Marschen and the adjacent zone of Pleistocene sandy soils known as Geest there are usually extensive meadow moors (bogs), level, treeless, and covered with grasses. The Geest is located between the Elbe and Ems. Within it, a somewhat higher area extending from the Elbe to the Weser-Aller rivers is known as the Lüneburger Heath. Its highest point, the Wilseder Berg (1,663 feet), lies east of Bremen and has been made into a national park. The Geest is of limited agricultural value. Grazing is only of local importance. The climate is maritime, with cool summers and mild winters, considerable precipitation especially in winter, and strong winds (Figures 69, 70).

The Geest, particularly the part west of the Aller, is often interspersed with bogs. These bogs still cover a large area despite the application of modern, Dutch-inspired methods of cutting and draining. Thanks to these methods, which in Germany are known as Fehn or Behn cultivation, it is now possible to raise vegetables and cattle here. New agricultural settlements in former bog country are called fen colonies (Fehnkolonie). In the Netherlands they are called Veenkolonien (see Chapter 5). Papenburg, on the lower Ems, is such a settlement. More recent methods have shown that cutting is unnecessary and that, with proper drainage and the addition of sand and clay, bog soils can be made into valuable arable land. Peat is burned in nearby power plants or used for domestic purposes. Since 1941, petroleum has been found west of the Ems

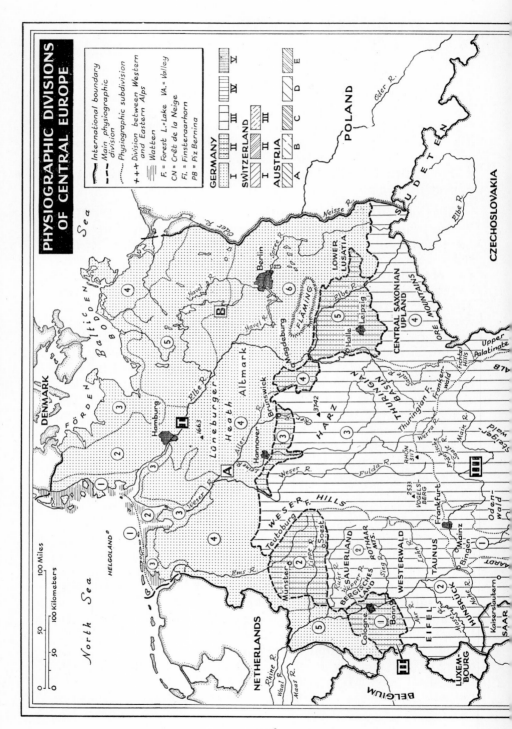

PHYSIOGRAPHIC DIVISIONS OF CENTRAL EUROPE

Legend:

— International boundary
– – Main physiographic division
· · · Physiographic subdivision
+++ Division between Western and Eastern Alps
▦ Watten

F. = Forest   L. = Lake   VA. = Valley
CN = Crêt de la Neige
Fi. = Finsteraarhorn
PB = Piz Bernina

GERMANY   I   II   III   IV   V
SWITZERLAND   I   II   III
AUSTRIA   A   B   C   D   E

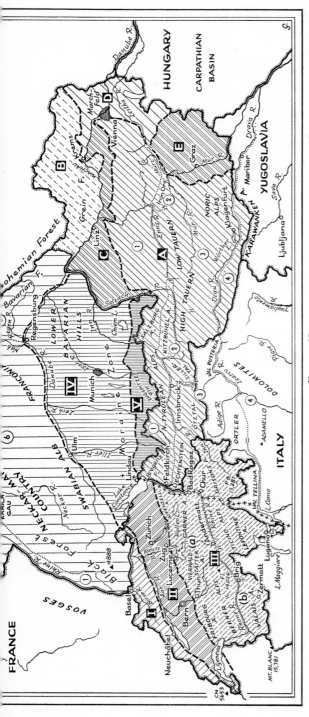

FIGURE 68

GERMANY

I. North German Lowlands
   A. West of the Elbe
      1. East Frisian Islands
      2. Watten
      3. Marschen
      4. Geest
      5. Lower Rhine Plains
   B. East of the Elbe
      1. Schleswig-Holstein Marschen
      2. Schleswig-Holstein Geest
      3. Schleswig-Holstein Förden and Moraine Zone
      4. Moraine Zone
      5. Baltic Heights or Lake Plateau
      6. Glacial Valley Zone

II. Southern Transitional Borderlands
    1. Cologne Bay
    2. Münster Bay
    3. Lower Saxony Borderland
    4. Magdeburg Borderland
    5. Halle-Leipzig Bay

III. Central Uplands
     1. Upper Rhine Valley
     2. Rhenish Slate Mountains
     3. Thuringian and Hessian Depressions
     4. Saxon Uplands
     5. Bohemian Forest
     6. Scarplands of Swabia and Franconia

IV. Alpine Foreland
V. German Alps

SWITZERLAND

I. Jura
II. Plateau
III. Alps: a, Northern; b, Southern

AUSTRIA

A. Alps
   1. Northern Limestone Alps
      Northern Longitudinal Valley
   2. Slate and Shale Ranges
      Central Alps
   3. Southern Longitudinal Valley
   4. Southern Limestone Alps
B. Granite Uplands
C. Alpine Foreland
D. Inner and Outer Vienna Basin
E. Styrian Basin

337

in the southern part of the Bourtanger Bog, and the wells of the so-called Emsland fields are bringing a further change to the cultural landscape of this once unproductive land.

FIGURE 69. Förden, Bodden, and Haff coasts.

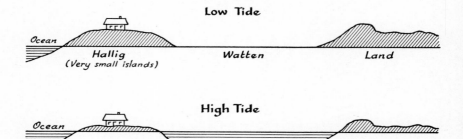

FIGURE 70. Low and high tide, Wattenland.

East of the Elbe. The country east of the Elbe River has a history of more recent glaciation; morainic ridges extend in several parallel bands along the southern shore of the Baltic Sea. Going from north to south the following subdivisions may be distinguished:

1. A ground moraine zone, consisting of glacial loams and forming a fertile rolling lowland belt. The many lakes in this zone are proof of its recent glaciation. The coast is clearly divided into a western and an eastern section, with the Oder River a distinctive boundary. The whole coastline is drowned, and the German section has many bays, gulfs, and islands. The western part of the Baltic coastline is usually further subdivided into a Bodden coast (irregularly shaped inlets behind irregular islands) between the Oder and Lübeck Bay in Mecklenburg, and a Förden coast (long, steep-sided drowned valleys formed by rivers underneath an ice sheet, similar to a fjord coast) so typical of the Baltic coast of Schleswig-Holstein. Climatic conditions along the Baltic are more continental than to the west; low salinity and a very small tidal

range allow the water to freeze over more readily. Stralsund was closed to traffic for over a month in 1947; most other ports are closed for at least two weeks (Figure 71).

2. South of this zone, extending 10 to 50 miles inland, is a strip of fertile lowlands covered with boulder clay. Crops such as sugar beets, rye, some wheat, and potatoes are grown here, and there are pastures for livestock.

3. Farther south, a zone of irregular hills marks a halt in the ice cap's last major retreat. This zone, commonly known as Baltic Heights or Baltic Lake Plateau, is characterized by many lakes and undrained hollows, gravel, sand, boulder clay, and coniferous trees.

4. Parallel to the main ridge of the Baltic Heights, a series of lower, more irregular, and less continuous terminal moraines marks the interruption of the slow retreat of the ice sheets.

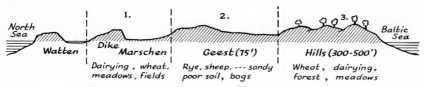

FIGURE 71. Profile across Schleswig-Holstein.

Glacial Valley Zone. Between the morainal heights and the Central Uplands there is an extended plain of broad valleys alternating with somewhat higher ground consisting mainly of sandy soils. Here are the previously mentioned glacial spillways extending in an east-west direction and interconnected by diagonal valleys. These glacial spillways form broad and flat depressions now occupied in whole or in part by various rivers, such as the Havel and Spree near Berlin (Figure 72). Originally, the main drainage paralleled the front of the continental ice mass, but during the retreat of the ice many streams adopted a north-south course. The glacial spillways, however, are of great value in the construction of canals; the need for locks is almost obviated by the slight gradient from east to west. The southern boundary of the area of the glacial spillways is formed roughly by the upland zones of the Fläming and Lower Lusatia. It is here that the last ice sheet was halted by higher ground.

Originally the whole Glacial Valley was forested. German settlers after the twelfth century drained the swampy valleys, consisting largely of peat swamps, wooded or heath covered sand dunes. Once drained, the alluvium itself offered more productive soil than that found in the sandy regions between the valleys.

FIGURE 72. Grosse Köris, in Brandenburg. Glacial spillways forming a broad and flat depression. The lakes serve recreation purposes. (Amt für Landeskunde.)

SOUTHERN TRANSITIONAL BORDERLANDS. North of the Central Uplands and south of the glaciated lowlands lies a belt of thinly layered morainic material and highly fertile soil.

The width of this zone varies, but it broadens to include several bays (lowland embayments): (1) the Cologne Bay which includes the Lower German Rhineland, (2) the Münster Bay, (3) Lower Saxon Borderland, (4) the Magdeburg Borderland, and (5) the Halle-Leipzig Bay.

This fertile belt consists of glacial soil covered by alluvial deposits which in turn are partially covered by loess. The whole belt has fertile brown forest and chernozem soils. Münster Bay has but a small area of loess near Soest. Situated between the dissected Central Uplands and the glaciated, moraine-covered lowlands, and cultivated since Neolithic times, this transitional belt is of outstanding importance to Germany and to the world.

Thanks to the natural quality of the land, to efficient crop rotation, and to the heavy application of fertilizer in less productive areas, this region has become a rich farm district in which wheat, sugar beets, barley, and vegetables predominate. The Transitional Borderlands also possess great mineral wealth, mainly bituminous coal and lignite deposits in the Ruhr and the Rhineland, lignite in the Leipzig Bay, low-grade iron ore and petroleum in the Peine-Salzgitter area between Hanover (Hannover) and Brunswick, and potassium and common salt deposits along the foothills of the Harz Mountains near Stassfurt and Halle.

This combination of great mineral wealth and valuable farmland supports a dense rural and urban population (500 to 600 per square mile). All the towns are old and have grown considerably in importance since the early Middle Ages. Situated for the most part at nodal points, where routes from the uplands fan out into the plain, these towns are also crossed by important east-west transportation arteries. The Midland Canal from the Ems to the Elbe is the most recent addition to the transport net; it provides a direct water connection between the Rhine, the Ruhr, Berlin, and the Oder.

CENTRAL UPLANDS. Between the North German Lowlands, the narrow belt of Transitional Borderlands, and the Alpine Foreland south of the Danube, there is a region of great diversity: rolling, dissected and forested hills, granite massifs reduced by glacial action, old volcanoes, basins, plateaus, scarped limestone ridges, etc., all belonging to the Hercynian zone—the Central Uplands. The hilly and diversified character of this zone is the result of block movements, uplifts and subsidence, upwarpings and recessions, resulting from fractures and horizontal dislocations. Numerous horsts are characteristic of this block landscape. Volcanic intrusions, which are especially noticeable in the western part of the Uplands, are closely connected with these movements. The heights near the center of the Uplands escaped the ice cover for the most part, but the peripheral valleys, particularly those in the north, were broadened by ice action. Only the highest portions of the Uplands were covered by mountain glaciers, as shown by the ridges and cirques of the Black Forest (Schwarzwald), Bohemian Forest (Böhmerwald), and Ore Mountains.

The Central Uplands may be divided into numerous topographic units, but for the purpose of presenting a generalized picture only the following distinctive parts will be recognized:

1. Upper Rhine Valley and its bordering mountains
2. Rhenish Slate Mountains
3. Thuringian and Hessian Depressions
4. Saxon Uplands
5. Bohemian Forest
6. The Scarplands of Swabia and Franconia

Upper Rhine Valley. The Upper Rhine Valley, extending from Basel to Frankfurt, has a length of more than 180 miles, but a width of only about 25 miles. Flanked by mountains, it was formed by the sinking of land between two roughly parallel faults in Late Tertiary times. This is called a graben. The Rhine enters the valley above Basel at an elevation of 800 feet above sea level, and leaves it near Bingen, 253 feet above sea level. The length of the regulated section of the river is 224 miles. The surface of the valley consists of drained alluvial land, dry gravels, and some loess deposits which have made it into a very rich agricultural region (Figure 73).

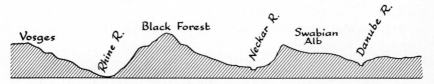

FIGURE 73. Profile—Vosges to Danube River.

The valley clearly forms a physical unit with its surrounding mountains. The Jura lies toward the south, the Rhenish Slate Mountains to the north, the Vosges and the Haardt to the west, and the Black Forest and Odenwald to the east. The mountains flanking the valley in the east and in the west are part of a massif whose center section was downfaulted. They are dissected by valleys and are heavily forested. The Odenwald is separated from the Black Forest by a depression, the Kraichgau or Neckar Bergland. North of the Odenwald is the Frankfurt Basin, drained by the lower Main River. The highest summit in this mountain complex is the Feldberg (4,888 feet) located in the Black Forest. West of the Rhine, and linked to its upper valley by the depression of Kaiserslautern, lies the coal-rich Saar Basin.

The Upper Rhine Valley's equable climate permits a highly diversified agriculture including the cultivation of wheat, sugar beets, tobacco, hops, fruits, and grapes; vineyards occupy the foothills of the bordering mountains, especially between Karlsruhe and Darmstadt. Winters are very mild and July temperatures average about 70° F. The mountains have long winters and abundant precipitation.

Rhenish Slate Mountains. The Rhenish Slate Mountains form part of the Central Uplands, but in terms of regional geography they belong to the Rhine Valley.

The mountains (sometimes called the Rhine Plateau) are cut in two by the Middle Rhine River which flows in a narrow, approximately 80-mile long gorge from Bingen to Bonn. The surrounding heights rise to an average of 1,500 feet above the gorge. From Mainz the Rhine flows westward for some 15 miles, skirts the Taunus as far as Bingen, and then continues northwestward through the gorge to Bonn and to the Lower Rhine Plains beyond. The course of the Rhine in this section is antecedent, the river having cut its channel at the same rate that the underlying peneplain was being uplifted (Figure 74). The Rhine gorge is often very narrow, and rapids had to be eliminated in order to make the river more navigable. Vineyards cover the terraced lower slopes of the steep-sided Rhine gorge; they are also found in terraces along the tributary valleys, notably along the Moselle, Lahn, and Ahr rivers. Today, the Rhine is not only a busy waterway for a great variety of craft, but its gorge is also an important tourist attraction.

FIGURE 74. Rhine Valley near St. Goarshausen. The view is upstream, toward the Lorelei. Two steps of the main terrace are clearly visible. (Bibliographisches Institute.)

The upland areas of the Rhenish Slate Mountains extend from the Main to the Ruhr and from the Ardennes to the Thuringian and Hessian depressions. The boundaries of the several subdivisions coincide with the courses of the Rhine's various tributaries. Severely weathered young volcanic deposits give the Westerwald better soils than are found in almost any other plateau region. In the

Siegerland, whose mines and forests supplied Germany's first industries with iron ore and charcoal, some iron is still mined. North of the Sieg River, the plateau drops off to the Sauerland beyond which the well-known industrial region of the Ruhr is located.

Thuringian and Hessian Depressions. This region is bounded by the Rhenish Slate Mountains in the west, the Saxon Uplands in the east, and the fertile Transitional Borderlands in the north. The Main River forms the southern boundary. The region is a mass of basins, broad forested uplands, and narrow but fertile plains, disturbed by volcanic activity, faulting, and to the north by much folding. Two subdivisions are commonly recognized: the Hessian Depression toward the west and the Thuringian Basin and Forest. Hesse is characterized by many individual forested mountain sections, the broad fertile river valleys (depressions) of the Weser and the Fulda, with the important crossroad town of Kassel, and the dissected volcanic Vogelsberg (2,533 feet) and Rhön (3,117 feet) mountains north of the Main River. In the north, two low wooded ranges, the Teutoburg Forest and the Weser Hills, protrude toward the plains between Münster and Hanover.

Thuringia is composed of three distinctive parts: The Harz Mountains, the Thuringian Forest, and the Thuringian Basin. These areas offer great contrasts. The Thuringian Forest is a densely populated, wooded mountain range, whose highly skilled inhabitants are engaged mainly in manufacturing demanding a high skill; there is only limited agriculture. In contrast, the Basin, which is drained by the Saale River and its tributaries, contains rich agricultural land, mainly degraded chernozem. The Harz Mountains are located between the Leine and the Saale and trend in a southeast-northwest direction. Their upper parts are still covered with forests, while elsewhere such crops as hay and potatoes are grown. The Brocken (3,742 feet) is the highest summit. Even today, the Harz Mountains remain a transportation bottleneck in an area of heavy traffic.

Saxon Uplands. South of the Halle-Leipzig Bay, the forested Ore Mountains reach an altitude of over 4,000 feet. These mountains drop off abruptly on the Bohemian side and slope gradually toward the bay. Their slopes, known as the Saxon Foothills support some agriculture, but the real value of this area lies in its mineral wealth, which includes uranium and lignite. The Ore Mountains, which run in a southwest-northeast direction, are separated from the Sudeten, which trend in a northwest-southeast direction, by the Elbsandsteingebirge, an area of great scenic beauty.

The Elbe River cuts through this sandstone range in a deep canyon formed by down faulting and later filled by clays and sandstones.

Bohemian Forest. Between the German-Czechoslovak frontier and the Danube and Nab rivers lies a sparsely populated forested region. This region, which is underlaid by granite and gneiss, is known as the Bohemian Forest. The forest reaches deep into Bohemia; within Germany it is subdivided into a southern and a northern part, the depression drained by the upper Regen River serving as a dividing line. Various names have been given to these subdivisions: We shall call the southern part the Bavarian Forest and the northern part the Upper Palatinate Forest. The Bavarian Forest consists of long, high ridges with wide basins, while the Upper Palatinate Forest has an irregular knob and valley topography and is generally lower than the former. Precipitation is abundant, ranging from 47 to 55 inches at an elevation of 2,400 feet and fogs are very frequent. Most of the region is occupied by forest, with beech, fir, and spruce dominant.

The Scarplands of Swabia and Franconia. East of the Black Forest and the Odenwald, there is a region variously identified as scarplands, plateaus, and basins. Most of it is drained by the Neckar and Main rivers. The scarps of the region face mostly toward the northwest, and the older formations are usually clearly visible.

As we proceed northeastward from the Black Forest and the Odenwald, we encounter various geologic formations, each of which leaves a distinct mark on the landscape. The scarplands of the Swabian and the Franconian Alb are cut out of limestone which forms a plateau up to 1,200 feet high. The scarps extend in a southwest-northeast direction from the Upper Rhine to the depression of the Ries, which divides the Swabian from the Franconian Alb; thence they trend from west to east until they veer northward toward the Main River.

Climatic conditions are influenced by elevation which varies from escarpment to escarpment. The Swabian and the Franconian Alb have considerably less precipitation (27 to 39 inches) than the escarpments farther west, while the leeward side facing the Danube receives less than 20 inches. Thanks to the latitude (48° N. to 50° N.) and to the protection afforded by the forested mountains on the west, the climate is well suited to the growing of cereals, tobacco, hops, and some hard fruits; even corn and vines do well on the plains. Except for deposits of lithographic stone found in the Franconian Alb, the region is almost lacking in economic minerals.

THE ALPINE FORELAND AND THE GERMAN ALPS. The German part of the Alpine Foreland lies between the Swabian and the Franconian Alb in the north, the Bohemian Forest in the northeast, and the Alps in the south. It forms a northward sloping plateau in continuation of the Swiss plateau. Relief differences are between 1,000 and 3,000 feet, but the Foreland has the appearance of a broad plain, with its lowest point (915 feet above sea level) at the confluence of the Danube and Inn rivers. The Foreland's geologic structure is closely related to that of the Alps. There also exist similarities in fauna and flora, and the Alpine climate influences that of the Foreland.

Morainic deposits—gravels, sands, and huge boulders—cover wide areas of the Foreland, in testimony of the extent of Alpine glaciers (Figure 75).

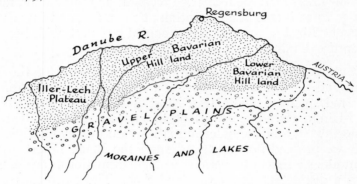

FIGURE 75. Sketch of the Alpine Foreland.

The northern part of the Foreland is covered by glacial outwash material and therefore it is hillier and better suited for agriculture (Figure 76). There are numerous bogs in the higher southern parts of the Foreland. Fingerlakes, at right angles to the trend of the moraines, are especially numerous east of the Lech River. All the rivers rise in the Alps and cross the Foreland in broad, marshy valleys. The main rivers, from east to west, are the Iller, Lech, Isar, and Inn. They are not navigable because of the irregularity of their flow. The Danube Valley occupies a depression 15 to 30 miles wide. Although it has a moderate gradient the Danube carries sufficient water for navigation to begin at Ulm.

The climate of the Foreland, noted for its cold winters, becomes more continental as one proceeds eastward. A comparison between Regensburg (1,125 feet) and Lindau on Lake Constance (1,329 feet) is of interest. The January temperature in Lindau averages 30° F., the July temperature 64.4° F., while the yearly mean is 48° F. In Regensburg, January temperature is 26.6° F., July 64° F., and the yearly mean 45.3° F. It should be added that the area has a milder climate, in part because of the influence of a large water body. Precipitation increases with elevation. The quantity of summer rainfall and of melting snow determines the rivers' summer volume.

FIGURE 76. Vilshofen, Lower Bavaria, in the northern part of the Alpine Foreland. Patches of forest are interspersed among small agricultural holdings. (Amt für Landeskunde.)

Mixed forests predominantly coniferous are at higher altitudes; forests occur mostly in small patches in the Foreland. Soils are generally poor so that barley, oats, and rye are the chief cereal crops, and dairy grazing is widespread. A few special crops are grown on better soils along several streams.

Only a small part of the Alps falls within Germany. The international boundary runs through the outer zones of the Northern Limestone Alps, from which rises Germany's highest mountain peak, the Zugspitze (9,711 feet). Many deep incised valleys facilitate travel to Austria and thence, through the Inn Valley and the Brenner Pass, to Italy.

The Alps

Location and Size. The Alps are Europe's greatest folded mountain system in terms of both elevation and extent. The length of the Alps along the inner edge of the arc is approximately 470 miles, and about 810 miles along the outer edge. The chord of the arc is approximately 340 miles long. Their width ranges from 80 miles near the highest peak (Mont Blanc, 15,781 feet) to 150 miles north of Verona. They cover about 85,000 square miles, or an area somewhat larger than Kansas.[5]

The Alps extend in an arc from the Altare Pass on the Gulf of Genoa to a line which approximates the railroad line Vienna-Graz-Maribor-Ljubljana. Southeast of Altare Pass they connect with the Apennines. In France, near Lake Bourget (Lac du Bourget), the Jura Mountains detach themselves for the main body of the Alps, forming a separate spur. Lying between them and the Alps proper, the plateau extends from Lake Geneva to southern Germany.

The interior of the arc is occupied by the Po-Adriatic depression, toward which the Alps slope rather abruptly. Along the outer edge of the arc there are a number of old massifs against which the Alps had been pushed during the folding process. This Alpine arc has scores of peaks reaching above 10,000 feet, and several peaks in the Valais (Wallis) chain of Switzerland attain an elevation of 15,000 feet. Despite their relatively low latitude (43° N. to 48° N.), the Alps carry the most extensive glaciers found on the mainland of Europe.

Politically, the Alps extend into seven countries: Italy, France, Switzerland, Liechtenstein, Germany, Austria, and Yugoslavia. Of these, Switzerland, Liechtenstein, and Austria are referred to as "Alpine countries" in a true sense. This section of the chapter concerns itself chiefly with the Alpine countries.

Major Divisions. A line running south from Lake Constance, up the Rhine Valley, and across Splügen Pass (6,923 feet) to Lake Como divides the Alps into two parts of very different topographic characteristics. West of this line, the Western Alps are narrower, more compact, and higher, with more and longer glaciers and more

---

[5] As far as possible the Alps are discussed as a whole in this chapter, since they form a physiographic unit. Their southern slopes are also discussed in the chapter on Southern Europe, and the French Alps in the chapter on Western Europe.

incised valleys. East of this line, the Eastern Alps are broader and lower; their longitudinal valleys are wider and interconnected across low watersheds. The highest peak in the Western Alps is Mont Blanc. Local relief, often exceeding 9,000 feet over a short horizontal distance, greatly contributes to the impressive picture confronting the visitor. The Eastern Alps, with their highest elevation at Piz Bernina (13,287 feet) in Grisons (Graubünden) canton of Switzerland, have several levels of summits (Gipfelfluren), and only near the previously mentioned line of division do they reach heights comparable to those in the Western Alps.[6]

Most of Switzerland falls within the Western Alps. Only the mountains of the eastern part of Grisons canton are included among the Eastern Alps. All of Austria lies in the Eastern Alps.

The Western Alps are further broken down into two divisions: the Franco-Italian Alps, which lie south and west of a line extending from the eastern end of Lake Geneva through the upper Rhone Valley, the Great St. Bernard Pass (8,110 feet), and the Dora Baltea Valley to the Piedmont lowlands and the upper Po River; and the Swiss Alps, which lie between the Great St. Bernard Pass and a line through Lake Constance-Rhine-Lake Como.

Germany's share of the Alps is limited to a narrow outer strip of the Northern Limestone Alps, between Lake Constance and Salzburg.

In addition to the transverse division described above, there are several parallel longitudinal zones separated by deep valleys and distinguished by differences in rock types. Thus the Alpine chains are broken up into several distinct groups.

Climate. The main trait of an Alpine climate is its great variability; it is influenced by the elevation, length, and width of the mountains. Situated between regions of Central European climate in the north, Mediterranean climate in the south, Marine climate in the west, and Short-Cold Winter type of climate in the east, the Alpine region has a complex and transitional climate pattern.

Typical of mountain regions in general are local differences in exposure to the sun and length of shade; in the Alps, these are especially noticeable in the east-west longitudinal valleys. This factor is of great importance for the distribution of settlements and crop lands on slopes: on sunny slopes (adret) settlements extend

[6] The division of the Alps into two parts is widely accepted. The Italians, however, prefer a threefold division: (1) *Alpi Occidentali*, with the Col du Ferret forming the boundary between it and (2) the *Alpi Centrali*, which in turn is separated by the furrow of the Brenner Pass from (3) the *Alpi Orientali*.

higher, while the colder, usually forested shady slopes (ubac) are avoided by settlers. This pattern is particularly evident in the Eastern Alps. The temperature lapse rate amounts to approximately 3° F. per 1,000 feet elevation; it is somewhat lower in midwinter and higher in early summer. It is also higher along the southern slopes and edges of mountain ranges. Wide valleys are warmer in summer, but suffer from temperature inversion in winter and are therefore colder than nearby slopes. This phenomenon is especially noticeable in the Engadine (Grisons, Switzerland) and the Klagenfurt Basin (Carinthia, Austria). Only at elevations above 3,500 feet are winter temperatures on slopes as low as those of adjacent basins. In fact, slopes and terraces enjoy many more sunny, bright, and dry days than the valleys or basins they overlook, which frequently are filled with cold, heavy air and thick mist.

For all these reasons, Alpine settlements are usually located on slopes, terraces, and alluvial cones for protection against low winter and night temperatures as well as flood danger. Temperature differences decrease and annual extremes are modified at increased altitudes largely because of exposure to sun, heating by insulation during the day, and earth radiation during the night, resulting in diurnal ranges of temperature. As a result, snow remains longer on the ground, August is often the warmest month, and late March the coldest month. The following table illustrates the foregoing statements:

I. Mountain Stations

	Alstätten	Gäbris	Rigi	Säntis	Sonnblick
Height in feet	1,509	4,100	5,873	8,202	10,171
January	−30°	−28.4°	−23.6°	−17.4°	−10° (Feb.)
July	64.6°	56.4°	49.5°	42.3°	34.3°

II. Valley Stations

	Locarno	Chur	Zermatt	Innsbruck	Graz	Bolzano (Bozen)
Height in feet	778	2,001	532	1,969	1,129	952
January	35.6°	29°	20.7°	26°	28°	32°
July	71.4°	63.7°	54.5°	64.1°	67.8°	72.5°

Source: Fritz Machatschek, *Länderkunde von Mitteleuropa* (Vienna: Franz Deuticke, 1925), p. 100.

Precipitation usually increases up to an altitude of 8,000 to 9,000 feet, and at times up to almost 10,000 feet, but it decreases at higher elevations. Interior valleys are much drier, often receiving less than 30 inches of annual rainfall. Cases in point are the Valais (Switzerland) or the Inn Valley (Austria), where irrigation is practiced. Furthermore, along most mountain chains precipitation varies from the windward to the leeward side. In winter, precipitation occurs in the form of snow which covers most of the Alps for from three to five months, and areas above 6,000 feet for as long as six months. Snow depths of 30 feet have been recorded in places.

A whole series of local winds is characteristic of the Alps. In addition to being swept by the westerlies, most valleys have a regular alternation of up-slope and down-slope winds. These winds are especially strong in transverse valleys open toward the margin of the mountains. Between Geneva and Salzburg, those transverse valleys which open up toward the north or the northwest are under the influence of the warm, dry föhn, a wind which occurs when a depression moving to the north of the Alps sucks air out of the Alpine valleys. This outgoing air is replaced by air from the southern side of the Alps. The föhn is responsible for the sudden melting of snow and for avalanches which endanger isolated mountain communities. It occurs both in midwinter and toward the end of the winter, when it usually heralds the coming of spring. It is accompanied by overcast skies, a sudden rise in temperature (40° F. within two hours is not unusual), and considerable dryness. High temperatures are due not only to the wind's southern origin, but also to the small loss of temperature incurred in rising to the summits and to the great increase in temperature resulting from the descent. Innsbruck has an average of 43 days of föhn. The föhn also accounts for the extension of agriculture into some high Alpine valleys. In the southern valleys of the Alps, one encounters a type of föhn which comes from the northern slopes. Its effect, however, is not as strongly felt as in the northern valleys.

Vegetation and Land Use. Alpine vegetation varies according to the climate of the different bordering regions. It is also characterized by vertical zoning. The central position of the Alps in relation to the different climatic types was noted in an earlier section. As a result, surrounding climatic types extend their influences into lower altitudes. On the eastern slopes of the Alps, the black pine (*Pinus nigra*) is common. In the hills of Styria one encounters alders and some true steppe plants. The greatest local differences are found in the Mediterranean Alps, along the upper Italian lakes and the northern shore of Lake Geneva, as well as in the southern French Alps, where drought-resistant shrubs replace forests and grasslands. Here the chestnut (*Castanea sativa* or *vesca*) occurs up to 8,850 feet, while on the north side of the Alps this tree is found only in the warmer valleys and on the sunnier slopes. Other trees characteristic of the Mediterranean Alps are the olive, mulberry, and cypress.

Three vertical vegetation and land use zones may be discerned (Figure 77): (1) an arable zone, (2) a zone of forests, and (3) a zone of pastures. Above these zones is an area of rock debris and eternal snow. The exact width and succession of these belts depend not only upon elevation but also upon latitude, exposure to the sun, degree of slope, temperature, precipitation, and the acts of man.

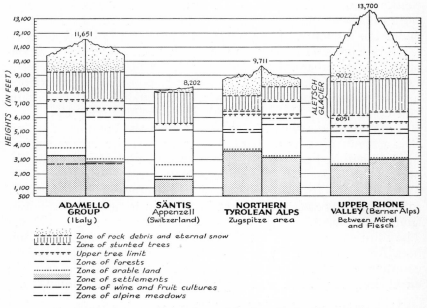

FIGURE 77. Vegetation and land use in the Alps.

1. The arable zone reaches an elevation of approximately 4,200 feet, but considerable variations are found from place to place. Its upper limit is at lower elevations in the northern part of the Alps, and at 4,600 to 5,600 feet in the south. In the North Tyrolean Limestone Alps rye, oats, barley, potatoes, beets, and flax are limited to areas below 3,280 feet. In the interior these crops are found as high as 7,200 feet. In the Eastern Alps the upper limit for cereals averages 5,100 feet, and it is somewhat higher in the Western Alps. On low sunny slopes grapes are common.

2. The forest zone is made up of coniferous trees at higher elevations and of deciduous trees at lower elevations. As one proceeds upward, the species change from the common beech, oak, and

birch to spruce and fir, then to larch, and near the tree line to the stone pine. In the Northern Alps, the forests thin out at 5,200 to 5,900 feet; in the Valais, Engadine, and Ötztal Alps, they reach as high as 7,200 feet. In the Eastern Alps, they seldom extend above 4,900 feet. The upper limit of trees is usually marked by a belt of stunted trees, such as the dwarf birch, dwarf pine (*Pinus montana*), juniper (*Juniperus nana*), etc. In the limestone zone, the Grünerle (*Alnus viridis*) and the rhododendron (*Rhododendron hirsutum* and *ferrugineum*) are especially numerous. The upper boundary of the forest zone is usually 2,600 to 2,900 feet below the snow line which it parallels, but this distance is often increased by man in order to gain additional grazing land. This practice is rather common along the southern slopes of the Alps. Timber cutting and sawmilling are of great importance, especially in the more accessible parts of the Alps. Ancient conservations laws have played a vital role in the preservation of this "gold of the mountains."

3. Alpine meadows are of great economic significance. On them dairy cattle are grazed, and in some localities special breeds (Allgäu, Simmental, Pinzgau, Lungau, etc.) are raised for export. Transhumance, a typically Alpine form of cattle raising, is called Senntenwirtschaft or Sennerei here. Either the village or the individual farmers own pastures (each one provided with a hut) at different elevations; these are used in successive stages during the warm season. With the beginning of the colder season, the herdsman returns to the village. When the cattle are returned to their winter stables in the valley, they feed on hay cut from meadows located at lower altitudes. Cattle pastures generally extend 900 to 1,600 feet above the forest zone, while sheep pastures extend close to the snow's edge.

Various colorful Alpine flowers with creeping and grasslike stems and woody roots are found in great numbers in the upper reaches of the Alpine meadows and among the rock debris during the very short growing season. They include primroses (*Primula*), buttercups (*Ranunculus*), gentian (*Gentiana*), monkshood (*Aconitum napellus*), and edelweiss (*Leontopodium alpinum*).

Glaciation and Hydrography. Precipitation, exposure to the sun, and latitude determine the extent of eternal snow in the Alps. The snow line ranges from 7,800 feet in the northern Swiss Alps to 10,500 feet in the central part of the Alps.

Precipitation in the mountains accumulates in the form of snow and ice, and is either quickly removed as dry or ground avalanches or more slowly as glaciers. Approximately 1,400 square miles, of which 600 are in the Eastern Alps, are covered by glaciers. Because of its altitude, the central zone has most of the large glaciers, while the northern and southern limestone zones have small cirque glaciers for the most part. Compared with the extent of glaciation during the Great Ice Age, the area covered by present-day glaciers

FIGURE 78. Wengen, overlooking the U-shaped Lauterbrunnen Valley (Switzerland). Some of the waterfalls have a vertical descent of close to 1,000 feet. The view is toward the Bernese Alps. (Swiss Tourist Office.)

is small indeed. The longest Alpine glacier is the Aletsch glacier (north of Brig, Switzerland) with a total length of 16 miles. The glacier which descends to the lowest elevation (3,500 feet above sea level) is the Lower Grindelwald glacier in the Bernese Alps. The effects of former glacial action are everywhere in evidence. The numerous steep-sided, U-shaped valleys found in the Alps have been eroded by glaciers; hanging tributary valleys owe their origin to the Ice Age. Indeed, the grand scenery of U-shaped valleys, abrupt slopes, and numerous waterfalls is entirely glacier-carved (Figure 78).

Alpine glaciers give rise to a great number of rivers. Many small torrents become mighty streams during the summer snow-melt season. Many Alpine rivers are regulated by lakes which they

FIGURE 79. View toward Rigi and Lake of Lucerne. Here Pleistocene glaciers carved a series of elongated valleys, now a series of beautiful lakes surrounded by high mountains. (Dr. Ernst Winkler.)

traverse and which keep their flow uniform. These lakes act as reservoirs, reduce the danger of floods, and contribute to the clearing of rivers by catching all the sediment carried in suspension. Among the largest lakes are Geneva, Neuchâtel, Thun-Brienz, Lucerne, and Zurich, all in Switzerland; Constance, divided between Switzerland, Germany, and Austria; Maggiore and Lugano in Switzerland and Italy; Como and Garda in northern Italy; Chiemsee in Germany; and Wörthersee in the Klagenfurt Basin of Austria.

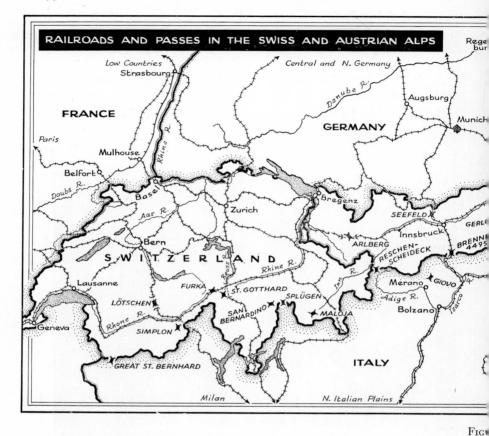

RAILROADS AND PASSES IN THE SWISS AND AUSTRIAN ALPS

Fig.

Numerous smaller lakes, mostly cirque lakes and lakes impounded by landslides (Figure 79), are scattered throughout the Western and the Eastern Alps.

Mention should also be made of the Alps' importance as a central watershed for several river systems which empty into four different seas. The Rhine rises in the Alps of Glarus (Garner) and Adula Alps and flows northward into the North Sea; en route it is joined by several northward-flowing tributaries of Alpine origin. All the right tributaries of the Upper and Middle Danube, notably the Inn, Salzach, Enns, Mur, and Drave (Drau), rise in the Alps and ultimately find their way to the Black Sea. The southern slopes of the Alps feed the Po and other rivers emptying into the Adriatic. And finally, the Rhone River, which rises in the Bernese Alps not far from the headwaters of the Rhine, flows west and south into the Gulf of Lion, an arm of the Mediterranean Sea.

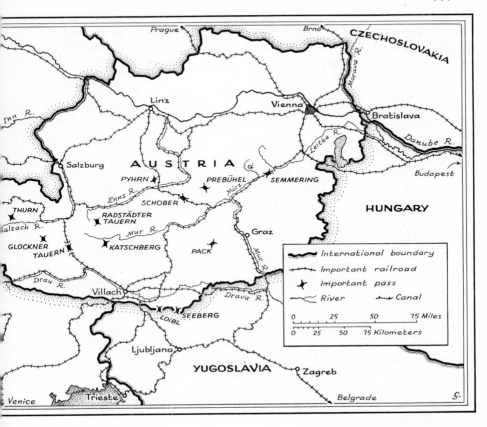

Alpine Communications. Despite the difficulties presented by the terrain, Alpine routes have been of great importance for transit traffic ever since prehistoric times. The few usable routes were first extensively traveled during the Roman period. Of the roads constructed at that time, some were not modernized until the late Middle Ages, and others not until the nineteenth century.

Three types of passageways, classified according to their orientation, may be distinguished in the Alps (Figure 80):

1. Longitudinal furrows which run parallel to the main trend of the ranges and contribute so much to the accessibility of the Alps. Their continuity is preserved by the low, easily traversable divides which separate one longitudinal river valley from another. Examples of such furrows are the valleys of the Inn, Salzach, and Enns rivers, which form almost a straight line from western Austria to the Danube; the Drave and Rienza valleys in southern

Austria, which connect Italian South Tyrol with Yugoslavia; and the Mur and Mürz valley chain in central and eastern Austria. In the Swiss Alps the most important such furrow follows the upper Rhone and the upper Rhine valleys from Lake Geneva to Lake Constance. Railroads follow most of these valleys and in many places use tunnels to penetrate the divides. The Arlberg Tunnel, which connects Tyrol and Vorarlberg in Austria, is a case in point.

2. Many transverse valleys, now of greatest importance in the transit traffic, were often obstructed by gorges which inhibited direct traffic until the Middle Ages. Along the Brenner Pass, the gorge of the Chiusa (Klausen) in the Isarco (Eisack) defile route, for example, necessitated a traffic detour across the Passo di Monte Giovo (Jaufen Pass) north of Bolzano until the fourteenth century. Similarly, the St. Gotthard route was not opened until the thirteenth century, when a bridge was built across the Schöllenen Gorge. Because the Alps are crossed by only a few direct north-south routes, these are of great significance. Several political units, notably Grisons and Tyrol, owe their existence to the establishment of pass routes. The Brenner Pass (4,495 feet) is the only Alpine crossing which a railroad can negotiate without the use of long tunnels. However, after it reaches the longitudinal valley of the Inn in Austria, one branch of the line uses several tunnels to pierce the ranges which bar access to southern Germany.

3. The diagonal routes are of lesser importance. One links the Upper Inn Valley with Lake Como, via Maloja Pass; another, a proposed route, would lead from Chur on the Rhine over a series of passes to the Upper Inn Valley and into the Val Venosta (Vintschgau) and Merano (Meran) in Italy. The diagonal line connecting the valleys of the Enns and Mur rivers via the Schober Pass in Styria is a link of some importance between the two Austrian cities of Innsbruck and Graz.

Today, railroads follow all the important old trans-Alpine routes, using tunnels to avoid difficult mountain stretches. It is now possible to cross any part of the Alps in less than four hours. Among the more important tunnels are the Mount Cenis (completed in 1871), which connects Genoa and Turin with Lyon and Paris; the Simplon and Lötschberg tunnels, which link Milan (Milano) with Bern; the 9.5-mile-long St. Gotthard tunnel (completed in 1882), which connects Milan and the Po Valley of Italy with northern France and western Germany via Zurich and the valleys of the Reuss and the Ticino; the Tauern tunnel for traffic between the Alpine Forelands and the Klagenfurt Basin, and the Karawanken tunnel for communication between the latter and Yugoslavia and the Free Territory of Trieste; and the Semmering tunnel, which constitutes the main connection between Vienna and the south.

Although the roads are snowbound for several months each winter, the Alps have never presented a serious obstacle to travel. Thanks to the modern roads and to the numerous railroads built since the beginning of this century, the Alps have become much more accessible to the peoples of the adjacent plains. Today, they attract an ever-increasing tourist traffic which provides new means of livelihood for their inhabitants.

Physiographic Divisions. As was pointed out in the introduction, the structure of the Alps is largely the result of the folding of sediments between the Eurasian forelands and the African land mass. Before this folding occurred, rivers had worn down the mountains of more ancient origin and carried the sediments into the adjacent seas. The mature surface thus created was very low and had little local relief, but during the later stages of the erosion cycle it was again uplifted and warped. Denudation and weathering have sculptured the mountains into the youthful forms we see today. These processes are much less evident in the Eastern Alps than in the Western Alps. During the Ice Age the whole mountain system was repeatedly covered by ice and only certain regions in the southeast and the southwest, such as Styria, Carinthia, and Provence, escaped the effects of glaciation. Ice sheets cut and dug away large portions of mountains, and, as warmer temperatures returned, moraines, U-shaped valleys, Alpine cirques, and pyramidal peaks were left as evidence of glacial action. Denudation by glaciers and streams is also responsible for such features as the broad, steep-walled hanging valleys, polished and striated boulders, and the many tongue basins blocked by morainic deposits at their outward ends. Glacial action has been especially important in widening and deepening what had once been a small longitudinal hollow into the present important central depression between Martigny on the Rhone and Chur on the Rhine. This same depression can be traced southwestward from Martigny into the high Alps and the Pre-Alps of France.

The transverse subdivision of the Alps into a western and an eastern part has already been described; more significant, however, is a division into several distinct longitudinal sectors along the deep valleys mentioned earlier. In many ways the lithological zones which we shall briefly describe here correspond to these longitudinal sectors. It should also be pointed out, however, that only in the

Eastern Alps can the following division into longitudinal zones be clearly recognized.

The Central Alps consists of resistant crystalline rocks (granite, gneiss, and schist), which form the principal chain of the Alps. These formations extend from the edge of the Carpathian Basin to the Pennine Alps just northwest of the Po Basin (Figure 68). In the Eastern Alps the zone of resistant rocks is interspersed with bands of shale and slate, which are more easily eroded and thus account for the gentler slopes.

North of the Central Alps lies a belt of generally lower ranges consisting of sedimentary rocks, especially limestone, and characterized by a very jagged skyline and deeply incised valleys. This belt is known as the Northern Limestone Alps. A Southern Limestone zone, which is not found in the Western Alps, begins east of Lake Maggiore, increases in width, and extends clear across the Karst into the Dinaric system of the Balkans. It contains volcanic extrusions such as the reddish-black rocks of the peripheral plateau of Bolzano.

North of the Northern Limestone Alps are the rolling Foreland hills, a narrow and discontinuous zone (called Flysch zone), consisting mostly of slate, clay, and sandstone. This zone widens in Austria, where it forms an outer zone of the Northern Limestone Alps. In front of the Flysch zone, in the Alpine Foreland, there are stream-deposited beds of Molasse, which consist mostly of sandstone and conglomerates. In places these deposits have been folded and have formed heights of considerable elevation (e.g., Rigi in Switzerland).

In order to further clarify these differences, we shall list the main physiographic divisions and point out some of their distinctive features. For the sake of better identification, this presentation will follow existing political divisions which, with the exception of a slight overlap in Grisons canton of Switzerland, follow the widely recognized dividing line between Eastern and Western Alps.

SWITZERLAND. Switzerland is normally divided into three distinct regions—the Jura, the Swiss Plateau,[7] and the Swiss Alps.

The Jura. The Jura trends southwest-northeast from the Rhone to the Rhine and consists of several parallel limestone folds. The folds are well developed along the southeastern rim but flatten out toward the northwest and gradually merge into the undisturbed strata of the Swiss Plateau. The eastern slopes facing

---

[7] This region is also known as the Plains, the Mittelland, or the Alpine Foreland (Alpenvorland).

Switzerland are steepest and highest. The ridges run in the same direction as the axis of the folds and are separated from each other by longitudinal valleys. They become lower and narrower toward Basel and the Rhine and are therefore easier to cross in this area. The highest point, Crêt de la Neige (5,653 feet), is located in the southwestern part of the Jura, just inside France. Its most important rivers are the Doubs, flowing almost entirely in France, and the Birse, which enters the Rhine near Basel. These rivers flow alternately in broad valleys and narrow gorges.

Thanks to abundant rainfall, the Jura's inhabitants practice dairying and lumbering and some winegrowing on the southeastern slopes facing the Plateau. Because of the karst-like topography and underground drainage characteristic of the Jura's limestone formations, relatively few streams and lakes appear at the surface.

The Jura occupies 10 per cent of the total area of Switzerland and has 13.2 per cent of its population. Its real importance lies in the fact that it is the home of the watchmaking industry.

FIGURE 81. Aerial view from Bern, on the Aar River. The view is across the Plateau to the Pre-Alps and the Bernese Alps. (Alpar-Berne.)

The Swiss Plateau. The Swiss Plateau, an "uplifted depression" between the Alps and the Jura, extends for 180 miles in a southeast-northeast direction from Lake Geneva to Lake Constance; it is up to 30 miles wide (Figure 81). The Plateau was dissected by rivers and covered by ice. Its many small lakes attest to the former presence and movements of the ice sheet; their shape indicates the advance of various ice tongues. Other typical features of glaciation are terminal and ground moraines, huge boulders or erratics, drumlins, and deepened valley floors. The Plateau varies in elevation from 1,200 to 2,200 feet, and has a mean altitude of 538 feet. It occupies 32 per cent of the total area of Switzerland but contains 67 per cent of the Swiss population.

The Plateau's climate is rather uniform; the mean January and July temperatures of Bern and Zurich are shown as examples:

	Mean January Temperature	Mean July Temperature
Bern, 1,870 feet	28.2° F.	63.7° F.
Zurich, 1,617 feet	29.5° F.	55.2° F.

Source: Marion I. Newbigin, *Southern Europe* (London: Methuen & Co., Ltd., 1949), p. 106.

Mist often covers the whole Plateau like a sea of clouds. Some localities have an average of 120 days of mist per year.

Precipitation ranges from 32 inches at Basel, 900 feet above sea level, to 46 inches at Lucerne (Luzern), 1,480 feet high, and to over 100 inches at Säntis, 8,202 feet high. However, only a small part of Switzerland has more than 47 inches of precipitation.

The Plateau is most suitable for dairying; it has excellent meadows and ample acreage on which forage crops are grown. In the southwest, there are sugar beet and tobacco fields, vineyards, and orchards.

The Swiss Plateau may be divided into three natural subregions of varying economic significance: (1) the northeast from Lake Constance to a line Baden-Zug, with wine growing on sunny slopes and considerable industry, (2) the center as far as a line through Solothurn-Bern-Thun-Brienz, largely agricultural, and (3) the southwest down to Lake Geneva, with specialized crops like tobacco and sugar beets.

The Swiss Alps. Much has been said about the Alps in general. That is why we shall list only the main physiographic divisions and discuss their location and main characteristics.

The Swiss Alps have no clear-cut boundary either in the direction of the Swiss Plateau or the North Italian Plains. Toward the Plateau, they become gradually lower, are often called the Pre-Alps, and acquire a different land-use pattern; unproductive land is rare. The Alps occupy 58 per cent of Switzerland, but only 18 per cent of its population resides there.

The Rhone-Rhine longitudinal trough divides the Swiss Alps into two parts: Northern Alps and Southern Alps. The Northern Alps may be further divided, as follows:

1. The Bernese Alps have the largest concentration of glaciers and reach their highest elevation (14,026 feet) in the Finsteraarhorn; the principal chain, 68 miles long, has numerous passes and falls off abruptly toward the Rhone Valley to the south, while in the north it gradually merges with the Pre-Alps which are dissected by deep valleys. The Fribourg Alps and the Waadtländer Mittelland are included within this division.

2. The Vierwaldstätter Alps are located between the Aar and the Reuss valleys. In the north they slope toward the Lake of Lucerne; in the south they are connected with the Gotthard massif. At Andermatt the transverse north-south route crosses the longitudinal route connecting the Rhone with the Rhine. A number of passes control this important transit area.

3. The Alps of Glarus (Garner Alps), between the Reuss and the portion of the Rhine Valley below Chur, consist predominantly of limestone mountains. The Linthal, a valley south of Wallensee, penetrates deep into the mountains.

4. The Appenzell Alps are situated between Wallensee and Lake Constance.

The Southern Alps, which lie south of the Rhone-Rhine trough, may also be divided into four main groups:

1. The Valais Alps are located between the Great St. Bernard and the Simplon. Their steep slopes are toward the north. The lower slopes are settled. Many lateral valleys give access to lofty peaks, notably the one to Zermatt which leads to the foot of the Matterhorn. The Simplon tunnel, which takes the Paris-Lausanne railroad line into Italy, is at the farthest end of the Valais Alps.

2. The Ticino Alps and the Lepontine Alps are pierced by the important Gotthard tunnel on the Zurich-Milan railroad line. These mountains slope toward the Po Plain.

3. The Adula Alps, west of Splügen Pass, form the connecting link with the Grisons Alps.

4. The Grisons Alps are divided into a northern and a southern chain which cover most of the area of the canton of Grisons. The peaks are not as high as other Alpine summits, but the valleys are less accessible. The hydrography of the area and the resulting pattern of dissection are quite complex. Many important passes connect the Rhine and the Inn valleys with Austria and Italy.

LIECHTENSTEIN. The small, independent principality of Liechtenstein lies between the Gap of Ragaz (Switzerland), the Schellenberg (west of the Austrian town of Feldkirch), the right bank of the Rhine, and the wooded and rocky heights of the western Rhätikon. Liechtenstein has been able to maintain its independence for a long time, largely because of its favorable location controlling the Gap of Ragaz, which in turn controls the valleys and passes of Grisons and the easy Rhine crossing west of Vaduz.

Until 1719, it was ruled by the lords of Vaduz and Schellenberg, and since then it has been independent. Its customs and railroads are now controlled by Switzerland. In spite of its size, 67 square miles, it has a healthy economic foundation. The valleys are fertile, pastures plentiful, and vineyards highly developed. Cotton spinning and embroidering are of exceptional quality, and tourist trade is ever-increasing. Liechtenstein derives most of its revenue from the sale of postage stamps, of interest to stamp collectors.

AUSTRIA. Earlier in this chapter we discussed the more general aspects of the Eastern Alps; both their geologic origin and lithologic divisions were described. Now we shall treat the various mountain groups and valley regions on the basis of their customary division into three longitudinal zones separated from each other by two longitudinal valley troughs. Following the standard works of Krebs, Sölch, and other geomorphologists, the country has been divided into regions, and the names which have been used describe their location and main characteristics (Figure 68):

The Alps
    Northern Limestone Alps
    Northern Longitudinal Valley
    Slate and Shale Ranges
    Central Alps
    Southern Longitudinal Valley
    Southern Limestone Alps
The Austrian Granite Uplands (Bohemian Plateau)
The Austrian Alpine Foreland
The Inner and Outer Vienna Basin
The Styrian Basin

The Alps. The Northern Limestone Alps form a belt of varying width across the northern parts of the provinces of Vorarlberg, Tyrol, the central and southern part of Salzburg province, and Upper Austria as far as the Vienna Woods. The outer zone, also called the Flysch zone, is characterized by rounded hills, gentle slopes, a very dense network of valleys, and many pastures. The limestone zone, which becomes wider toward the east, consists of many sharp peaks, barren high plateaus, fewer valleys, and much unproductive land.

The Central Alps, an interior crystalline zone, are separated from the limestone zone by the longitudinal valley depressions which run from Feldkirch and Vorarlberg over the Arlberg Pass, to the valleys of the Inn, Salzach, and Enns, then along the diagonal route of the Schober Saddle to the Mürz Valley, and finally over the Semmering Pass to the Vienna Basin. Important transverse valleys open into this important east-west highway, which is dotted with settlements and also contains the largest city of the interior Alps, Innsbruck. The longitudinal valley varies in width from a hundred feet to one mile (Figure 82).

At two places, slate and shale ranges are interposed between the Northern Limestone Alps and the Central Alps. These mountains are located between the longitudinal valley depression described above and a second, wider but discontinuous, depression which runs from the Ziller Valley in Tyrol to the valleys of the Salzach and the Enns rivers. Within these ranges are the Kitzbühel Alps and the rich ore mountains of the Eisenerz. The slate-shale mountains have rounded summits which rise just over 6,500 feet; they provide excellent pasture.

Between the Northern Longitudinal Valley, the southern edge of the slate-shale mountains, and the Southern Longitudinal Valley are the Central Alps. They consist of many mountain chains of varying length. They run from the transverse line which divides the Western and the Eastern Alps, to the Noric Alps of eastern Austria. Included in the Central Alps are the highest sections of the Austrian Alps, their numerous glaciated peaks rising over 10,000 feet. Routes across the Central Alps are not numerous.

The Southern Longitudinal Valley runs from Lake Como along the upper Adda River (Val Tellina), over Tonale Pass to the Bolzano-Adige-Isarco Valley, to the Puster Valley (Pustertal), and thence along the Drave River. The Klagenfurt Basin, a highly cultivated depression filled in Late Tertiary times, lies between the Central Alps and the Southern Limestone Alps. Frequent changes in rock composition make this zone a most picturesque one. Most of the mountains in this zone are located within Italy. The valleys of the Adige, Tagliamento, and Sava rivers offer the only through routes of any importance. With the exception of the South Tyrol, the entire zone is sparsely populated.

FIGURE 82. The Inn Valley, in the Austrian Tyrol. The view is west and northwest to the Karwendel and Wetterstein ranges of the Northern Limestone Alps. Note the Innsbruck-Garmisch-Partenkirchen railroad line incised on the flanks of the Wetterstein Range (right). (Stempfle, Innsbruck.)

The Austrian Granite Uplands. The Austrian Granite Uplands occupy the area between the Bavarian and the Bohemian border and the Danube, and also extend several spurs across the Danube. The Danube skirts the southern edge of the Bohemian Plateau and flows through a succession of narrows and basins. The river is swift and the country is unspoiled and very beautiful. Valleys are incised below rolling uplands covered by scattered dense forests and generally poor soils. The well-known Wachau is an example of such a valley (Figure 83). Water is abundant, and small farm patches are widely distributed. The eastern part of the Uplands has the better farmland. The Uplands are situated between 1,300 and 2,400 feet above sea level.

FIGURE 83. Spitz on the Danube. The view is toward the west. The Granite Uplands extend on both sides of the incised river valley. (Austrian Tourist Bureau.)

The Alpine Foreland. The Alpine Foreland is located between the Northern Limestone Alps and the Granite Uplands (Figure 68). Both the southern and the northern boundaries are very sharp and distinct. Covered by sediments of the Great Ice Age, the Foreland consists of numerous low hills, steep scarps, and terraces. Numerous glacial lakes reach the Foreland and remind the visitor of similar lakes in the Pre-Alps in Switzerland and in the German Alpine Foreland. The Foreland has forests and excellent farm land; south of Linz and below Krems there is a cover of loess.

The Inner and the Outer Vienna Basin. Included in this area is the territory north of the Danube—the Marchfeld and its extension eastward to the international border—as well as the land south and west of the Danube to the first Alpine slopes. This region has a dry, warm climate, a long growing season which permits some grape cultivation, and sufficient rainfall for high agricultural yields. It is also Austria's main sugar-beet region.

Because of the open character of the country, this area has been of great economic and strategic value since ancient times, and strong fortifications were built to control it. Carnuntum (Petronell), built in A.D. 73, and later Vindobona (Vienna) were Roman legionary fortresses which guarded the many routes which converge here. It was protected in the northeast by the slopes of the Vienna Woods, and on all other sides by the Danube and its many arms and tributaries, prior to the regulation of the river. Throughout history, the Vienna Basin has retained its importance in the political geography of Central Europe. Both from an agricultural and from an industrial standpoint, it is the most important region of Austria.

The Styrian Basin. The Styrian Basin consists of important valleys and of rolling hills which flatten out toward the Carpathian Basin. The region also includes southern Burgenland. There are broad valleys with fertile meadows, cultivated fields on terraces and gentle slopes, orchards and vineyards on steeper slopes, and deciduous trees on shady slopes. Settlements are scattered in the hill lands, while the larger villages and the cities are located in the main valleys. The climate is very favorable, less extreme than that of the Vienna Basin and conducive to intensive land utilization. The Mur Valley, with the important city of Graz (Slavic *Gradec* = fortress), is the center of this region.

The Cultural and Historical Background

The historical developments that are reflected in the changing political geography of Central Europe had in many areas certain broad trends in common. By following out these trends one may grasp the main characteristics of the historical geography of the region and gain as well a better understanding of its many present problems. The developments to be covered are: the migrations of the Germanic peoples following the decline of Rome; the conquests of Charlemagne and the establishment of the Holy Roman

Empire; the development of marches [8] to defend the main routes through the Danube Valley and the North German Lowlands from encroachments from the east; the growing independence of isolated regions, especially in the Alps, which resulted in the founding of the Swiss Confederation; the growth and decline of trade.

Decline of the Roman Empire and the Age of Migration. Central Europe at the beginning of the Christian era was inhabited by various German-speaking peoples such as the Saxons, Frisians, Goths, Vandals, Franks, and Alemanni. There were Celts in the mountainous regions of the south, and also Ligurians, Etruscans, and Illyrians. The Rhine became the frontier of the Roman Empire in the west after Caesar's conquest of Gaul (57-51 B.C.). Thus, a corresponding advance farther east to the Danube was strategically desirable for Rome, to secure the eastern frontier and command important passes of the Alps. A Roman force advanced through the Adige (Etsch) Valley into Tyrol and in 15 B.C. the province of Rhaetia was created. Shortly thereafter Noricum and Pannonia, both bounded by the Danube River and the crest of the Southern Alps, were added. At one period the Romans tried to establish their frontier as far as the Elbe River, but were defeated by Germanic tribes. With Roman fortifications acting as a check to their westward and southward movement, Germanic tribes added an extensive agriculture to their primarily pastoral economy. This brought about increased population pressures, which contributed to the unification of various tribes into more powerful units, and to the natural desire for additional settlement space.

Much has been written and many reasons have been given for the decline of the Roman Empire. Certainly the constant drain on its resources for defense against the barbarians from the north was a major contributing factor. The breakdown of the Rhine-Limes [9]-Danube frontier zone during the fourth and fifth centuries allowed colonization by the various Germanic peoples, a process which had begun peacefully under sanctions of the Emperors. The barbarian invasions brought new masters to Central Europe. The movement of the Germanic peoples toward the west and south also emptied wide stretches of land east of the

---

[8] A territorial border or frontier. The word is from the Old French word "marche" and is of Teutonic origin.

[9] Outer defense wall from Danube near Castra Regina (Regensburg) to the Rhine near Confluentes (Coblenz).

Elbe, which soon were occupied by Slavic peoples from the east—
an event of major historical importance in the relationship between
Central and Eastern Europe.

The Germanic peoples were quick to follow the Roman with-
drawal. Alemanni of Swabian stock proceeded from Brandenburg
into central Germany in order to attack the Roman fortifications.
They crossed into southern and southwestern Germany, occupied
the Rhine Valley, the Neckar lowlands, and the Swiss Plateau,
and also settled in parts of mountainous Switzerland and modern
Austrian Vorarlberg. Saxons moved from the plains between the
Ems and Weser rivers into Flanders and northern France; some
even crossed to the southeast coast of England. Others moved in
stages across the Thuringian Uplands and Plains to the Main and
Danube rivers. Bavarians [10] occupied the Alpine Forelands of
Germany and part of present Austria. Franks advanced from their
original homes on the Lower Rhine and in Westphalia across the
Rhine into France and the southern part of the Low countries.
Other German tribes migrated beyond Central Europe. The
Lombards traversed the Alps into the fertile Po Valley; the Van-
dals crossed into North Africa; the Goths settled in Iberia; and
Burgundians in the valley of the Saône in France. Often these
migrations were on a relatively small scale, with less than 25,000
people involved.

One effect of this resettling of peoples was the establishment
of many small political units. These were characteristic of medieval
Central Europe and are still evident today in the political organization of the German Federal Republic. Germanic influences
upon the political life of Europe and upon the visible landscape
were quite different from the Roman. But the influence of the
earlier civilization persisted and contributed to the more rapid
growth of nation-states in territory formerly occupied by the Romans. Roman influence in the practical sphere had also brought,
for example, a superior road network and a tradition of using stone
instead of wood for building.

Holy Roman Empire: Unity Versus Disunity. The Franks,
the westernmost of the Germanic peoples were greatly affected by
the centralized organization of the Roman Empire, their imperialistic ideas, and the spiritual powers of Christianity. After Charlemagne in A.D. 771 had united the Frankish Kingdom largely by
conquering and amalgamating other Germanic tribes and certain

---

[10] As the name Bavarians—Baioarii or Bajuvarii—indicates, they once inhabited
"Boriiland" (Bohemia).

Slavic peoples such as the Sorbs, Czechs, and Caranthanians, he felt it necessary to be crowned in Rome in A.D. 800 and to proclaim the Holy Roman Empire. The capital of this Empire was located at Aachen (Aix-la-Chapelle), an important crossroad city, but was later shifted to various places within the Empire. Many of its territories were only loosely bound to the Emperor and controlled by a weak bureaucracy. In 843 the Empire was partitioned, a division which laid the basis for modern France and Germany, but also for the many political units between the Netherlands and Switzerland. Owing to constant internal disunity—the struggle of local authorities against control—the Empire soon existed in name only, but did not completely disappear until 1806 when its last emperor, Francis II, laid down the imperial crown under pressure exerted by Napoleon.

Originally established as a strong centralized state on the model of the Roman Empire, the Holy Roman Empire never attained its goal. The many powerless member-states, most of them small in population and area but with leaders eager to play their role in the councils of the Empire, constantly fought against a strong unified state. There were numerous wars between the rulers themselves, between them and the Emperor during the Middle Ages and even during the early part of the modern era. Thus, with its exposed location, Central Europe became a battleground for foreign armies.

The Marches: Austria and Prussia. On the eastern frontier of the Empire, a system of Marches was established between the lands of sedentary peoples and those of nomads to the east (Figure 84). At first these Marches served only for defense, protecting the Empire against attack by peoples from the east, such as the Avars, Slavs, and Magyars. But once the eastern frontier became stabilized, the Marches served as bases for expansion. Constant fighting necessitated a large standing army and the rulers of the Marches used their special privileges to further their own interests. Out of these Marches grew independent kingdoms, two of which were later to play a decisive role in the fortunes of the Empire and of all Europe. In the south was the Eastern March (Ostmark), later to be known as Ostarichi (Österreich-Austria). Its boundaries were slowly extended to include the fertile Vienna Basin (1041), the approaches to it, and several Marches to the south. The margraves made their headquarters at Vienna which, due to its location, soon assumed a leading position as "a potential capital of the whole Middle Danube region." This city, by its "stalwart

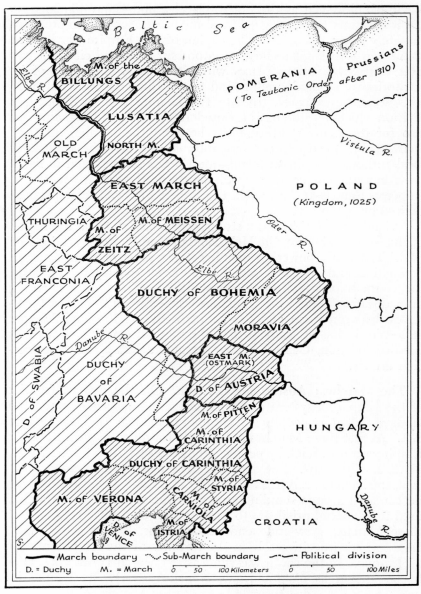

FIGURE 84. The Marches of medieval Europe.

resistance . . . has repeatedly earned the thanks of Western European civilization." [11]

After 200 years as the Eastern March of Bavaria, Austria became a duchy within the Holy Roman Empire. Its dukes were regularly elected as Emperors, and dominated the area roughly comprised by modern Germany, until Prussia, which included the Brandenburg March in the north, gained supremacy in 1871. Making use of the strategic location of the Vienna Basin and of the resources of its incorporated territories, the Habsburg rulers of Austria, through superior military strength and astute foreign policies, expanded toward Bohemia and Galicia (Poland) in the north and toward Italy in the south, defeated the Turks, and incorporated Hungary and parts of present-day Yugoslavia into a loose federation.

In the north, between the forested Ore Mountains and the Baltic coast, and the Elbe and Oder rivers, a series of Marches similar in origin and function to the East March was set up. The Old March (Altmark), in the vicinity of Magdeburg on the Elbe, was soon followed by the Middle March (Mittelmark) and the New March (Neumark), until territory given up by westward-moving Germanic peoples before A.D. 600 was reoccupied. In this way the Wendish territory of Brannibor (Brandenburg) was acquired. This expansion to the east, greatly aided by military religious orders (Teutonic Knights and Knights of the Sword), culminated after four hundred years of slow but steady advances and of intermittent warfare in the occupation of Prussia [12] and of Livonia further to the north, and in the re-establishment of the Vistula frontier. Only in 1410, at the battle of Tannenberg, were the advancing Germans stopped by the growing strength of Poland, a check to further expansion never since overcome. In spite of occasional territorial advances to the Vistula, the Germans were over the last five centuries slowly pushed back until at present the Oder River again serves as a border between the Germans and the Slavs. Germans also advanced along the Baltic coast but left the hinterland predominantly Slavic and under the control of the Polish Crown, a factor of importance in the establishment of the Polish Corridor in 1919.

In their advances into the North German Lowlands and the Transitional Borderlands, the Germans occupied the area of Meck-

[11] Derwent Whittlesey, *The Earth and the State* (New York: Henry Holt & Co., Inc., 1944), p. 218.

[12] Prussia at this time was a subdivision of Lithuania and its people spoke a language not unlike Lithuanian and Latvian. Their land was the former East Prussia, now divided between Poland and the U.S.S.R.

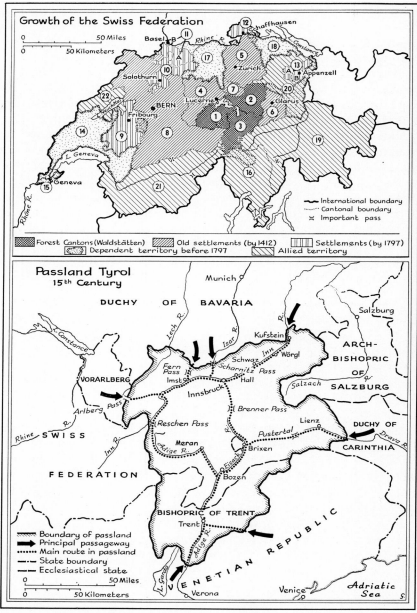

FIGURE 85 (*above*). Growth of the Swiss Federation. (1) Unterwalden, 1291; (2) Schwyz, 1291; (3) Uri, 1291; (4) Lucerne, 1332; (5) Zurich, 1351; (6) Glarus, 1352; (7) Zug, 1352; (8) Bern, 1352; (9) Fribourg, 1481; (10) Solothurn, 1481; (11A) Basel (rural), (B) Basel (urban), 1501; (12) Schaffhausen, 1501; (13A) Appenzell—Outer Rhodes, (B) Inner Rhodes, 1513; (14) Vaud, 1803; (15) Geneva, 1815; (16) Ticino, 1813; (17) Aargau, 1805; (18) Thurgau, 1803; (19) Grisons, 1803; (20) Saint Gallen, 1803; (21) Valais, 1815; (22) Neuchâtel, 1815.

FIGURE 86 (*below*). The Passlands of the Tyrol.

374

lenburg, Silesia, and present-day Saxony. The Slavs were absorbed, although some fled to the east, so that with the exception of two small areas no vestige of Slavic culture remained. Names ending in old forms, such as in -ried (marsh), -hagen (fence), -schlag (fill), indicate the advances of the Teutonic pioneers. The March of Brandenburg, with its core area between the Elbe and Oder rivers, expanded in a series of acquisitions until in the seventeenth century it extended its influence across the North German Lowlands, from the Rhine to the Vistula. It is not possible in this brief summary to account in detail for the rise of Brandenburg from a March to the Kingdom of Prussia, but toward the end of the eighteenth century Prussia became the most powerful all-German state and was rivaled only by the former East March of the south, which was ruled by the Habsburgs of Austria, heirs to the Imperial title. All other former Marches were now incorporated into these two, whose rise and decline show many similarities.

The "Passlands": Switzerland and Tyrol. Regional units, individual valleys, and such small administrative districts as the Gau, canton, or ecclesiastical division, make up the basis for the major political groupings in the Alpine regions of Central Europe. These units are often quite isolated and separated from each other by such barriers as high mountains, deeply incised valleys, or gorges. At various times several of these units were united, and if grouped around a pass controlling important routes were known as "Passlands." The Swiss Confederation around the St. Gotthard, and Tyrol around the Brenner (and originally also the Reschen Scheideck) are typical "Passlands" of the Alps. Their origin and importance are briefly analyzed.

THE SWISS FEDERATION. The area under modern federated Switzerland was once part of the Roman Empire and was afterwards integrated into the Holy Roman Empire. The passes of the Swiss Alps, for example Splügen, St. Gotthard, Great St. Bernard, and important valley routes such as those along the Rhine, Inn, and Reuss rivers, connect Germany and Italy and gave the emperors easy access to Rome (Figures 85, 86).

In 1291 the inhabitants of the mountain valleys controlling the most important of the north-south routes, the St. Gotthard, combined to fight the ambitions of the Habsburg Emperors. In that year the three valleys around Lake Lucerne which control the entrance to the St. Gotthard, comprising the cantons of Uri, Schwyz, and Unterwalden, solemnly formed the first federation (Bund der Eidgenossen). The Federation gained allies and dependents in expanding from this core area along the St. Gotthard route to the North Italian Plain, and to the east and west. Asserting its independence within the Empire with hard fighting, the Federation soon received additional help from Lucerne and Bern in the west, Glarus in the east, and Zurich and Zug in the north. Swiss independence was acknowledged by the major European powers in 1648; its neutrality was guaranteed in 1815. Modern Switzerland consists of nineteen cantons and six half cantons. This complex organization is due to the complex relief of the country. And the fact that these units differ greatly from each other in area and size of population facilitated the addition of new cantons and also contributed to religious toleration. The constantly increasing trade across the Alps added to the economic well-being and the importance of the Swiss "Passlands." Over the years cultural diffusion across passes, valleys, and gaps strengthened the unity of the Federation.

TYROL. The Tyrol, named for its first ruler, grew as a "Passland" around the network of the Inn, Isarco, and Adige rivers, with the Brenner and Reschenscheideck passes serving as connecting links (Figure 86). These routes were already extensively used by the Romans in their travel between the plains of Venetia and the Danube. The gorge of Finstermünz on the Inn and the Arlberg Pass are the exits to Switzerland and Vorarlberg. The two longitudinal valleys to Salzburg and along the Puster Valley to the Drau Valley are important routes toward the east, connecting with the rest of Austria. At the Inn ford, where the road from the Brenner meets the Inn River as well as the roads from Bavaria and Switzerland, a market-place, Innsbruck, was founded in 1180. Through its control of this important north-south route, Innsbruck became one of the leading cities of the Alps.

As the result of a series of successful wars and agreements, the borders of this triangular area were pushed out from its important roads; by the second half of the fourteenth century all borders of the Tyrol were located at the high mountain crests or at the constrictions of valleys. In this way the important "Passland" was kept under one rule until the end of World War I, when its southern part (South Tyrol) became Italian and the Alpine passes for the first time in history formed the border. This division also cut the direct connection from southern Austria (Carinthia) to the Inn Valley.

The Swiss "Passland" was able to obtain independence early in the modern era; but the Tyrol was too closely bound to the Habsburgs. However, its inhabitants received limited freedom early. For example, a Tyrolese assembly with full representation of the peasants was founded in 1342, and a deed (Freiheitsbrief, comparable to the Magna Carta) for its citizens' assembly (peasants and burghers) was also drawn up.

The Brenner and the St. Gotthard routes were the main north-south links between the German and the Italian parts of the Holy Roman Empire, and commerce along them brought considerable wealth. These routes, with their "Passlands," still play a vital role in the European transportation pattern (see Figure 80).

Settlement Forms. The beginnings of modern settlement forms may be traced back to the period shortly after the beginning of the Christian era, when various Germanic tribes occupied land with little or no woodland, such as in the fertile zone of Transitional Borderlands between the Cologne Bay and Silesia, the fertile river valleys, and the drier, sandy heathlands of the North German Lowlands.

The Central European cultural landscape is characterized by certain types of rural settlements: a nucleated village with the farm houses all centered on the village lands and the isolated farmstead surrounded by its own fields. Besides these two extreme examples many successions result from geographical, social, or economic influences which have shaped rural communities. The relief of the land, the fertility of the soil, and the original nature of the settlement (whether established by squatters or by well-knit groups) are among the factors which have determined the type of settlement evident today. Also significant are the type and layout of houses and the system of field ownership.

Houses of wooden construction, often with an artistic frame, are most common. Usually the houses have a stone foundation which extends to the first floor. The upper floors are usually of frame construction. In some parts of the country, and particularly in the east, clay houses are still common. Wooden houses or block houses, frequently protected by a slab of slate, are found at higher altitudes.

Some of the best-known types of habitations will now be described briefly (Figure 87). The typical Alpine single-unit house is a wooden or frame structure built on a stone foundation, with two stories, a balcony on the first floor, and small windows often protected by green shutters. The roof overhangs and is often protected against strong winds with heavy stones. The overhanging roof permits dry storage of wood. Under a single roof are the living quarters, kitchen (toward the front), stable, and barn. The space above the stable and the barn is usually used for storage.

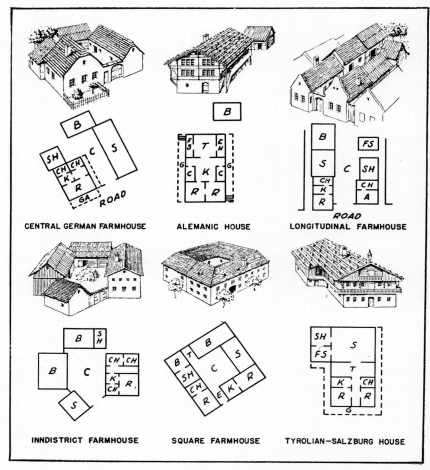

FIGURE 87. Selected farmhouse types in Central Europe. (Hans Slanar, Öster-reichischer Mittelschul-Atlas.) B—barn, S—stable, C—court, SH—shed, CH—chamber, K—kitchen, R—room, FS—forage storage, T—threshing floor, G—gallery, A—separate house for retired farmer, E—entrance, GA—garden plot.

In the Alpine Foreland, the Black Forest, and the Central Uplands, one encounters a second type of structure, the so-called Franconian house. Several units, the living quarters, stable, barn, storage facilities, etc., are grouped around a court, closed off by a heavy wooden gate. Wood and stone are the main construction materials, but the manner in which they are used differs from place to place.

The third group of structures, known as the Saxon or Lower German unit house, is found predominantly in the North German

Lowland. It is similar to the Alpine single-unit house in its interior make-up, but has only one story, while the Alpine house has two stories, with a space above the stable for storage. This building is normally built of timber with some brickwork; the latter is especially characteristic of the Frisian farms of the northern coastlands. There are many other types of modern farmhouses, but these are the three most widespread traditional types.

The isolated farmsteads and hamlets are probably the oldest known forms of settlement.[13] These farmsteads or hamlets consisted of one or several farmhouses, surrounded by woodland, meadows, common pastures, and arable land. Upon the breakup of a farm community, these farmstead lands were divided into small elongated strips and arranged in irregular furlongs or Gewanne.[14] Thus a hamlet was formed, a group of five to seven farmsteads, each with a number of such furlongs.

This type of hamlet was preserved until recently in northwestern Germany. In the Southern Transitional Borderlands and in central and southern Germany, the hamlet has grown into a "haufendorf."[15] Here newly cleared land with better soils was added by additional clearings during the Middle Ages. This newly cleared land was divided into furlongs and additional farms within the old hamlet were formed, so that a village soon had 15 to 25 farms. Near the end of the Middle Ages many such settlements disappeared again and their holdings were incorporated into existing settlements. In these ways larger, clustered villages were gradually developed.

During the Middle Ages other hamlets were also founded at higher altitudes. These often consisted of from two to five farmsteads with a number of small and widely scattered plots. At that time isolated farms also became more numerous. Two more regular forms of settlement, the shoestring village and the closely related roadside village, date from the twelfth and thirteenth century. Land for settlement had been originally donated by the large landowner and was then divided evenly among the new owners so that

[13] For a detailed discussion and illustrations of German settlements, see Robert E. Dickinson, "Rural Settlements in German Lands," *Annals of the Association of American Geographers*, XXXIX (December, 1949), 239-63.

[14] According to Eric Fischer and Francis E. Elliot, *A German and English Glossary of Geographical Terms*, Library Series No. 5 (New York: American Geographical Society, 1950), "Gewann" refers to the division of a village's communal lands into units of more or less uniform quality, thus enabling farmers to diversify their holdings by allowing each one to cultivate part of several "Gewanne."

[15] *Ibid.*, a haufendorf is a village in which the houses are irregularly clustered without any definite plan.

each peasant received a single compact holding rather than a number of scattered strips.

Other regular types of settlements include a roadside village in which the road widens to enclose a centrally located common, large enough for a church; the Runddorf, in which a group of houses connected by a wall enclose a central courtyard with but one entrance; the Marschhufendorf in which a row of houses faces a dike in a tidal marsh and the strips of land run at right angles to the dike; and the Waldhufendorf, which extends along a wooded river bank, sometimes for several miles.

Relatively few new areas were brought under cultivation after the sixteenth century. East of the Elbe marsh villages were founded in the glacial valleys and estates were organized by large landowners or *Junkers*, who concentrated on grain and dairy production. Earlier in this chapter, mention was made of the fen settlements which developed in the former peat bogs in the northwest. Some consolidation of holdings, particularly in mountainous areas, was accomplished, but has not progressed very far. Little alteration has taken place in the strip system of open fields. As Dickinson has pointed out, "The number of parcels was often reduced by the amalgamation of adjacent strips, but the strip system inside the arable land and the general grouping of the arable and, meadow, woodland and scrub invariably are the same today as they were hundreds of years ago." [16]

The Rise and Decline of Commerce in Central Europe. The importance of commerce in Europe and its main aspects are discussed in Chapter 10. The historical aspects of its development in the countries of Central Europe are briefly outlined here. As early as 1000 B.C. amber (a fossil resin), fur, leather, and other goods from the Baltic Sea area were carried to the Italian plains along the valleys of the Elbe, Oder, Morava, and the Danube, and through the Inn and other valleys of the Tyrol. During Roman times a variety of Mediterranean products, such as wine, parchment, and olive oil, was exchanged for hides, flax, timber, pelts, salt, etc. The barbarians beyond the Roman wall at times traded actively with the Romans. It is obvious that during the barbarian invasions and during times of war, trade was considerably limited. But by the end of the medieval period, as governments became more effective and towns more numerous, the exchange of goods increased in an unprecedented way. Many towns, for example, Munich, were founded at important junctions of inland trade routes; at outlets of passes,

[16] Dickinson, "Rural Settlements," *op. cit.*, p. 259.

as Innsbruck; and on the North German coastline, especially at the heads of navigation, such as Bremen, Hamburg, or Lübeck. Trade in Central Europe was also active in various local minerals. Commerce in gold and silver, and in copper and salt gave added importance to the "Passland" of the Tyrol. The Harz Mountains contributed lead, zinc, and copper, as did the Ore Mountains. While the total mineral trade was relatively small, it did affect several local communities. For example, it is estimated that nearly 30,000 men mined silver at Schwaz, and another 20,000 in other communities of the Tyrol. The widening and rebuilding of roads had much to do with increasing commerce and transportation.

Various parts of Central Europe participated in the ever-growing exchange of goods. Cities increased in population and importance. A canal system was started in the North German Lowlands; rivers and coastal waters were used increasingly. Trade, in the centuries before the Age of Discoveries, moved in three directions: (1) Trade with the north was in frontier products such as pelts, beeswax, hair, fish, honey. (2) Trade with the Levant was largely carried on through the principal Mediterranean ports of Venice and Genoa. (3) Some trade of minor importance moved up the Danube or through the highly dissected Balkan mountains. Vienna, with its protected Inner City, and big warehouses, was an important junction and distribution point. Europe's internal trade was of vital importance. Two major routes, both connecting the Alpine Forelands with the cities of the North German Lowlands and the Danubian lands, deserve special mention: (1) the Rhine, with its leading trading cities of Basel, Mainz, Cologne, etc., offered a direct route from the North Sea to the Alps; (2) the numerous navigable rivers of the North German Plain gave access to Vienna and the Danube by way of a portage between the Oder and the Morava rivers in the Moravian Gate.

Using the Baltic as its main route, the Hanseatic League was organized in 1256 as a loose association of about one hundred large trading towns of the North German Plain. The original aim of the League was to join forces in combating the pirates of the Baltic Sea, but it soon developed into a commercial and trade monopoly. Lübeck served as the League's headquarters, and during the three centuries of its hegemony trade flourished, roads and canals were built, and its trade spread westward and northward to British and Scandinavian ports and eastward as far as Novgorod in Russia. Its leading ports, many of which still retain the characteristic Hanseatic warehouses, are today among the ranking seaports and trade centers of Northern and Northwestern Europe. The League declined and eventually broke up as a result of discoveries in Africa and America which led to a reorientation of important trade routes, because of warfare with Denmark, the growth of British maritime power, and lastly because of internal dissension between strong-willed emperors and the League.

After the downfall of the Hanseatic League and a series of internal conflicts which culminated in the Wars of Religion, Germany played but a minor part in world trade for several centuries. Consequently, while Spain, Portugal, Holland, France, and England enriched themselves by trade with the newly won territories, the Holy Roman Empire was either torn by disunity or engaged in enlarging its southeastern holdings at the expense of the Turks. Not until the individual German states began to realize the importance of trade and undertook the formation of bilateral, then multilateral customs unions (Zollverein) after the Napoleonic Wars, did commerce once again play a more important role in Central Europe.

Disunity to Unity and Disunity. The Germanic migrations (A.D. 400-800) laid the basis for Central Europe's political fragmentation which lasted until the nineteenth century. The German tribes, and especially the Franks, had hoped to inherit the glory and power of the Roman Empire, but while they embraced a meaningful name, the area they controlled was divided among several hundred separate political units of which less than 30 were states of any size or consequence. The Holy Roman Empire was unable to control its constituent units, while they themselves were too small and powerless to make a decisive contribution to political or economic unity until late in the nineteenth century. Because of their location at Europe's invasion crossroads, and because of the dissected topography of the Central Uplands and the Alps, most political units remained small, often confining themselves to one small, narrow valley. The area occupied by these numerous powerless states stretches from the North German Lowlands to the Alps, and from the Rhineland to the Marches in the east.

The Swiss Federation was formed early in the mountains to the south. While the individual cantons and cities remained in control of their internal affairs, they stood united on questions of national policy. This was a living example of what a cohesive people could achieve.

While these small political units wrangled and fought each other, a number of strong leaders assigned to protect the Empire from newly organized borderlands (Marches) soon attained independence. Although the dukes of Austria had been the regularly elected emperors ever since 1273, the crown was meaningless and powerless in the face of opposition and the divergent aims of its many component states. Soon, therefore, disunity in Empire affairs was replaced by unity of purpose in the emperor's personal affairs, without regard to the welfare of the Empire as a whole. Religious disunity and foreign attachments by several political units added to the problems of the Empire. Meanwhile, the Marches of Austria and Prussia, both outgrowths of the Empire, began to fight for supremacy within it. They had expanded considerably from their original core, and each of them incorporated peoples of other language groups; in time they achieved some measure of national unity.

Only the threat of Napoleon brought the beginnings of unity to Central Europe. Almost two hundred minor political units disappeared, and for a time the Austrian Monarchy strove for greater centralization. Prussia incorporated many lesser German states, and the Federation of Switzerland received the promise of neutrality. By the end of the Napoleonic Wars, many rulers came to realize the need for greater unity, and various customs unions were established. This process was completed in 1844, when all German lands, with the exception of Austria, the free cities of Bremen, Hamburg, Lübeck, and Hanover, had joined the customs union.

Political unity, however, had to await the outcome of the contest for leadership between Austria and Prussia. The decision was reached in 1866, when Austria was defeated by Prussia on the battlefield. The cleavage between these two former Marches, ruled respectively by the Habsburg and Hohenzollern dynasties, was too deep. Austrians in general had nothing but contempt for Prussia, which in turn felt superior to Austria. When Prussia defeated France in 1871, all of the remaining German states joined it in proclaiming the modern German Empire (Deutsches Reich) with the king of Prussia as its emperor. Austria alone was not admitted.

Unity had finally been achieved in Germany, but not among Germans. During the centuries of disunity, political fragmentations, and conquests, many Germans had emigrated, especially to the frontier lands of East Central Europe. Hand in hand with a revival of German nationalism, these Germans pledged their eternal loyalty to the fatherland and began to work for a Greater German Reich. World War I, 1914-18, followed. It ended in the defeat of Germany, in the loss of its recently acquired colonies, and in important territorial losses in Europe. Alsace, the Saar, a large part of the area between the Oder and the Vistula, and parts of Silesia were gone. And a much-resented Polish Corridor split East Prussia from the rest of Germany. Austria, which had become a Dual Monarchy with Hungary in 1867, entered World War I on the side of Germany and lost all of the territorial acquisitions it had made almost from the time of its organization as a Marchland. Various members of the Austro-Hungarian Empire became independent. Austria proper, with a population of seven million of whom over two million lived in Vienna, began a new life of independence largely within the area of her former Alpine holdings.

A defeated but united Germany soon recovered from the havoc of World War I and, turning to a strictly centralized nationalistic regime, was determined once more to attain leadership in the world. After occupying Austria and Bohemia-Moravia, Hitler concluded an agreement with the Soviet Union to partition Poland, and thus brought about World War II (1939-45). This conflict ended in disaster for Nazi Germany and the world as a whole. Germany lost over five million people, its cities were destroyed, its families decimated, and its economy entirely disrupted. The aftereffects of this collapse are still visible. Aside from being occupied by foreign troops, Germany has lost most of the eastern territory it had acquired ever since the beginning of its eastward movement in the eighth century. All lands east of the Oder, including the Baltic port of Stettin, have gone to Poland, and East Prussia has been partitioned between Poland and the U.S.S.R. The German population of the lost territories from all parts of East Central Europe has been forced to flee into the reduced area of postwar Germany.

Austria, once more independent but still occupied by foreign troops, guards Central and Western Europe against incursions from the east. Thus her old function as a March is again being fulfilled.

We have now shown how Central Europe has gone through a full cycle from disunity to unity and again to disunity—from a conglomeration of numerous powerless states to a Germany split in two. Only Switzerland, which succeeded in keeping apart from the main stream of events, escaped the upheavals of the last century. Thanks to its location and to its spirit of defiance in the face of major threats, Switzerland progressed in peace, while the world around it was dislocated by wars.

Germany

Population

In discussing the population of Germany, the student should be aware of the many changes brought about since 1939 by political developments. For one thing, the factor of migration has been brought to the forefront of the demographic picture as a result of World War II. Millions of German refugees from the lost territories in the east, and Germans forced from East Central Europe, are crowding every one of the German states. This movement is by no means complete. Therefore, any conclusions regarding Germany's present demographic make-up can be no more than provisional.

On June 16, 1933 (date of the last regular prewar census), the population of Germany, exclusive of the Saar, was 65,140,242, or approximately 355 people per square mile. On September 13, 1950, the population of a much smaller Germany amounted to about 68 million.[17] In this connection we must remember that since 1945 all of the territory east of the Oder-Niesse line, including East Prussia, has been incorporated into Poland and the U.S.S.R., a loss of 24 per cent of Germany's 1937 territory and of 14 per cent of its population. While Germany's war losses amounted to more than five million people, this deficit has been more than made up by postwar immigration into a smaller Germany. Today, there are about 12.5 million German-speaking refugees in the country (9.4 million in the German Federal Republic alone). They consist of Reichsdeutsche, i.e., former citizens of German territories lost to the U.S.S.R. and Poland, and Volksdeutsche, i.e., ethnic Germans expelled from Czechoslovakia and from other countries of East Central Europe.[18] As a result of this immigration, both forced and voluntary, postwar Germany has to cope with a larger population, a complicating factor in the country's economic and political life. While the relative population distribution has changed but little during the last hundred years, the influx of the many refugees since 1945 has in some areas increased the population of what had been thinly settled rural areas (Figures 88, 89).

Migration has had an important effect on the population structure for almost a century. Overpopulation, wars, and religious and political persecution have been the chief causes of emigration. Close to six million people left Germany between 1830 and 1937; 5.4 million of these entered the United States during this period.

[17] Census data are available only for the German Federal Republic and for West Berlin; the 1950 population totaled 49,952,000. Official figures for Soviet-controlled East Germany are not available, but its 1950 population has been estimated at 18,000,000. For a detailed analysis of the population in the Soviet zone, see "Die Bevölkerungsbilanz der Sowjetischen Besatzungszone, 1939 bis 1949, und Nachtrag für die Volkszählung 1950," *Bonner Berichte aus Mittel—und Ostdeutschland* (Bonn, 1951).

[18] Gabriel Wülker, Friedrich Edding, Elisabeth Pfeil, Werner Essen, et al., *Europa und die Deutschen Flüchtlinge* (Frankfurt a. M.: Institut zur Förderung öffentlicher Angelegenheiten, 1952).

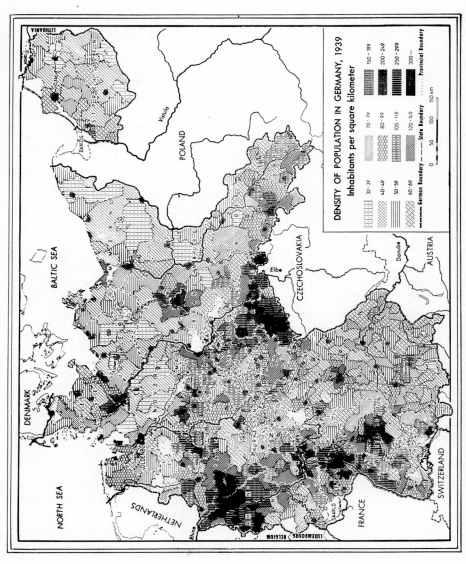

FIGURE 88. Germany, density of population, 1939. Census of May 17, 1939. (From Werner Essen, modified by Chauncy D. Harris. By permission of the Institut für Raumforschung, Bonn.)

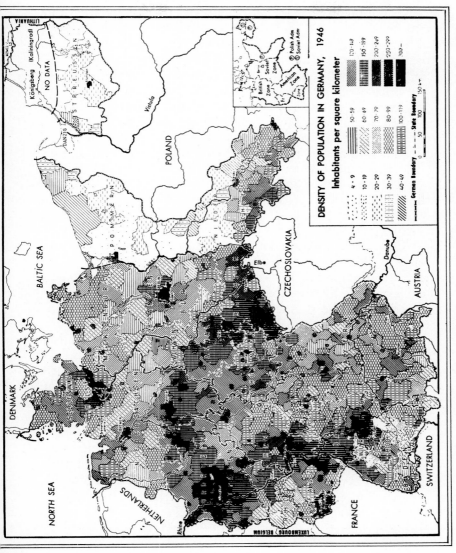

FIGURE 89. Germany, density of population, 1946. Census of October 29, 1946, in the four occupation zones of Germany and the Polish census of February 14, 1946, for the area under Polish administration. (From Werner Essen, modified by Chauncy D. Harris. By permission of the Institut für Raumforschung, Bonn.)

387

Some returned to Germany, especially in the years immediately preceding World War II. There has also been some immigration from other parts of Europe, notably between 1891 and 1911.

After Germany's catastrophic defeat of 1945, population movements took place on an almost unprecedented scale. Schleswig-Holstein alone absorbed almost one million refugees, a total which represented 38 per cent of its normal population.

It goes without saying that two world wars, a major depression, and a brief period of artificial prosperity during which a pro-natal policy was being advocated—all within one generation—have left a deep mark on Germany's population structure. The natural increase (excess of births over deaths), which in 1910 stood at 13 per thousand, diminished steadily until in 1933 it reached a low of 3.5 per thousand. Recovery followed, and by 1950 the German Federal Republic recorded a natural increase of 16.2 per thousand. Following a world-wide trend, rural areas have higher birth rates than urban areas. Like all other Western nations, Germany has an aging population; however, because of recent upheavals, an exact description of the country's population pyramid cannot be given.

In 1939, more than 31 per cent of Germany's population lived in cities of more than 100,000 inhabitants; the percentage figure for the territory of the present Federal Republic is 33.3. Because of wartime destruction and casualties, the 1946 ratio stood at 23.1 (23.3 for the Federal Republic). The 1950 census showed that this ratio had increased to 27 per cent—a noteworthy rebound. According to the same census, Germany's six largest cities (not including East German cities) were Berlin (3,334,000), Hamburg (1,-604,000), Munich (831,000), Essen (605,000), Cologne (590,000), and Frankfurt (524,000).

If we compare the 1939 and 1950 population totals of Germany's larger cities, we realize that the country's population increase occurred chiefly in rural areas. Between 1939 and 1950, the population of villages with fewer than 5,000 inhabitants had increased by more than 27 per cent, whereas the larger cities had barely reached their prewar totals by September, 1950. These trends are contrary to those registered in other countries, but they will probably be reversed as soon as the housing shortage in large cities is alleviated and surplus farm labor once more seeks employment in urban concentrations.

German is spoken by the entire population, although in 1933 a small number of people reported their native language as being Polish, Wendish, Danish, or Dutch. German may be divided into the following groups:

Low German (Niederdeutsch)		High German (Hochdeutsch)	
Lower Frankish	Lower Saxon	Middle German	Upper German
Lower Rhenish		East Middle German	Bavarian
		West Middle German	Franconian-Alemannic

The distribution of religions is extremely complex. North Germany is predominantly Protestant; south Germany is predominantly Roman Catholic. In the rest of Germany the two religious groups are intermingled. For Germany as a whole, the 1933 census listed 60.8 per cent of the population as Protestant and 33.2 per cent as Catholic. With the loss of large territories in the east (where 66.6 per cent of the population had been Protestant and 30 per cent Catholic) and the postwar immigration of Germans, the 1946 proportion had shifted slightly in favor of the Catholics: 59.7 per cent Protestant, 35.1 per cent Catholic.

While there are clear-cut differences of religion and of spoken dialects, there are no variations in the written language. Germans in Berlin, Cologne, and Munich, as well as those living in Zurich or Vienna, are united by the High German written language originated by Martin Luther. Illiteracy is negligible.

A few words should be added about the occupational distribution of the population. As Germany industrialized, more and more people, including women, entered the labor force. Between 1885 and 1939, the percentage of the population in the labor force rose from 42 to 51; the increase in women workers was even more spectacular, from 24 to 38 per cent of the female population. The 1950 figures for the Federal Republic show a further increase of 9.5 per cent in the working population since 1939. This latest increase reflects the high percentage of the working population recruited from the ranks of refugees. The most important conclusions to be drawn from employment figures is that there has been a relative decrease in stable agricultural employment over the last 50 years, while industry attracted most of the new recruits to the labor force. This development is characteristic of most industrialized countries.

In politics, the German population reflects great geographical disunity and diversity. While it would be an exaggeration to speak of a political cleavage between north and south Germany, there are unmistakable differences in character between the people of the North German Lowlands and those of the Alpine Foreland, between the inhabitants of the Rhineland and those of Saxony. Throughout history, these differences were reinforced by protracted feuds between ruling houses and by religious cleavages which originally followed lines of political division.

During the Hitler regime, every effort was made to obliterate these differences; the Nazis went so far as to change old-established political units, laws, and customs. Since the end of World War II, regional differentiation and decentralization have been advocated by the states (Länder) of the German Federal Republic; this trend has also been backed by various foreign powers, especially France, which in this way hopes to prevent a new dictator from assuming unlimited power over the German people. The government of the German Democratic Republic is highly centralized and in 1952 changed the administrative divisions of the area under its control. The German flair for militarism, their liking for discipline and organization have perhaps been subdued by the terrific destruction wrought by the last war, but no one can really be certain.

Germans are proud of their past, they are extremely hard workers, and they have highly scientific minds which qualify them as competent chemists, engineers, and physicists. Because they suffer from overpopulation and are heavily dependent upon vital raw-material imports, they are constantly looking for additional living space, using various means to accomplish their aim. It has often been said that the middle position in Europe has its dangers as well as its temptations.

Present Economic Life of Germany

Germany went through the industrial revolution after its political unification in 1871. Although other European countries had thus gained a head start, Germany with its vast reservoir of human and material resources, its fertile soils capable of feeding a growing industrial population, and its central position, soon overtook its rivals in production and trade. Despite the defeat and the territorial losses of 1919, which for a time greatly slowed economic activity, Germany maintained its determination to achieve economic as well as political leadership. At the end of World War II, Germany's economic life was once more almost completely paralyzed. The countryside was scarred by bombed-out cities (Figure 90) and destroyed industrial plants. The loss of territory resulted in the loss of important raw materials for industry. It is rather astonishing, therefore, to see the rise of new life amidst the burned-out ruins and dismantled plants [19] only a few years after the cessation of hostilities.

An analysis of the basis of Germany's economic strength will go far to explain her recuperative powers as well as her renewed importance in world affairs. The growth of agriculture and manufacturing after 1871 was made possible above all by the presence of domestic resources. Thanks to her pioneer efforts in applying scientific methods to agriculture, Germany greatly increased her wheat yields and attained world leadership in the production of sugar beets

FIGURE 90. The beautiful Cathedral of Cologne stands amidst bombed-out buildings.

and potatoes. She also became the world's largest rye producer. By 1937, Germany produced close to 85 per cent of its food needs. This was an extraordinary accomplishment for one of Western Europe's most advanced industrialized countries. Industry, Germany's greatest asset, owes its rapid growth to the extensive coal deposits of the Ruhr, the Saar, and Upper Silesia. Plentiful coal laid the basis for the iron and steel industry, which in turn supplied the basic

[19] According to the Potsdam Declaration of 1945, the four occupying powers—France, the United Kingdom, the United States, and the U.S.S.R.—were to dismantle many of Germany's industrial plants in order to reduce that country's war-making potential. By 1948, however, all four powers had discontinued this action. In fact, the United States, through the European Recovery Program, even restored some key plants in order to increase Germany's productive capacity.

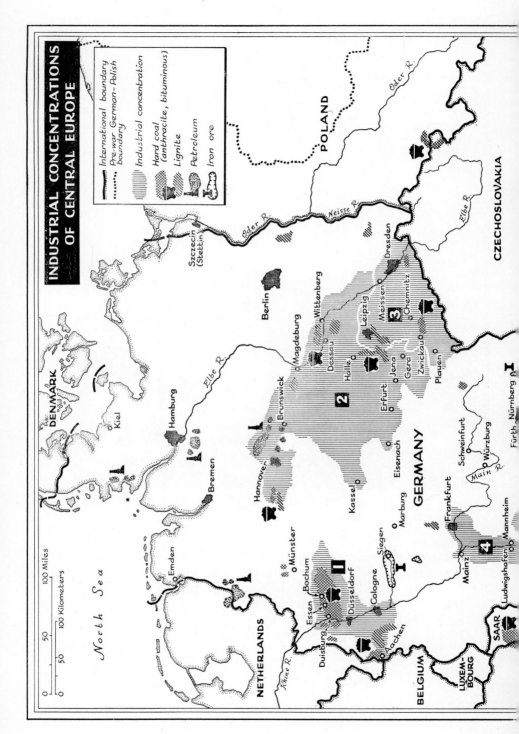

INDUSTRIAL CONCENTRATIONS OF CENTRAL EUROPE

Legend:
International boundary
Pre-war German–Polish boundary
Industrial concentration
Hard coal (anthracite, bituminous)
Lignite
Petroleum
Iron ore

DENMARK

North Sea

Kiel

Hamburg

Bremen

Emden

NETHERLANDS

Münster

Bochum
Essen
Duisburg
Düsseldorf
Cologne
Aachen
Siegen

BELGIUM

LUXEM-BOURG

SAAR

Ludwigshafen Mannheim
Mainz
Frankfurt
Marburg
Kassel

Hannover

Brunswick

Magdeburg

Berlin

Szczecin (Stettin)

Oder R.

Neisse R.

Elbe R.

POLAND

Dresden
Meissen
Chemnitz
Zwickau
Plauen
Gera
Jena
Erfurt
Eisenach
Halle
Dessau
Leipzig
Wittenberg

CZECHOSLOVAKIA

GERMANY

Schweinfurt
Würzburg
Main R.
Fürth Nürnberg

100 Miles
50
0

100 Kilometers
50
0

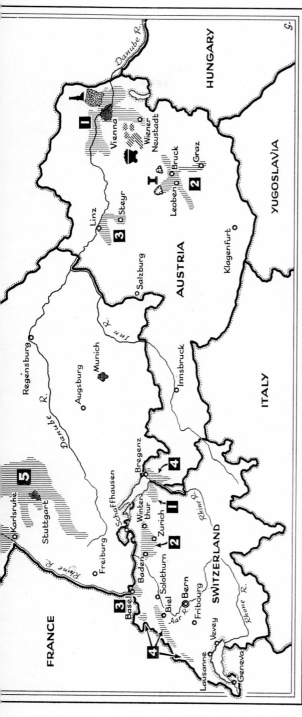

FIGURE 91. Industrial concentrations of Central Europe. *Germany:* (1) Rhine-Ruhr, (2) Central German Industrial Region, (3) Saxony, (4) Upper Rhine, (5) Neckar Basin. *Switzerland:* (1) St. Gallen, (2) Zurich-Winterthur-Baden, (3) Basel, (4) the Jura. *Austria:* (1) Vienna Basin, (2) Styria, (3) Upper Austria, (4) Vorarlberg.

materials for such vital industries as shipbuilding and the manufacture of rails, rolling stock, machines, tools, and armaments. Germany's other raw materials, including large potash and salt deposits
for the fertilizer and chemical industry, also contributed to its leading position among Europe's principal manufacturing countries
(Figure 91).

Germany's present economic situation has undergone extensive
changes from prewar days. Although the wartime loss of manpower
has been largely offset by a great influx of immigrants, and German cities and industrial establishments are being rebuilt, the territorial losses and the resultant loss of important raw materials constitute a serious impediment to the restoration of normal economic
life. Further obstacles to the country's rehabilitation lie in the fact
that Germany is divided into two economic and political units,
that it is still occupied by foreign powers, and that no peace treaty
has yet been signed.

On the other hand, mention should be made of the considerable
financial help which Western Germany has derived from participation in the European Recovery Program (Marshall Plan). The
Schuman Plan will also lead to the creation of a single coal and
steel market in much of free Europe and will undoubtedly benefit
the German economy.

In the following discussion we shall outline the facts of Germany's present economic life. Detailed statistics for all of Germany
are not available at present. Therefore, pre-World War II figures,
adjusted for postwar territorial changes, must sometimes be used
to point out the significant aspects of Germany's economic geography. Reference should also be made to Appendix III.

Agriculture. Two noteworthy features marked German agriculture before World War II: (1) the high percentage of land under
cultivation—61 to 63 per cent in 1939—and (2) the remarkably
high crop yields. Both of these characteristics contributed to the
country's high degree of agricultural self-sufficiency; in average years
Germany was 75 per cent self-sufficient, and in good years as much
as 85 per cent. Since 1945, however, considerable changes have
taken place. Territorial losses in the east, traditionally an agriculture surplus area, have had important repercussions on Germany's
postwar output. Of total prewar production, the lost territories had
supplied the following percentages: rye—30 plus, potatoes—30,
summer barley—29, oats—23, fodder—25, sugar beets—22, wheat—
15, horses—30, pigs—27, and cattle—20. Today these territories ship
almost no agricultural commodities westward. Furthermore, a Ger-

many considerably reduced in area has to feed a much greater number of people. Besides, the normal flow of complementary interregional trade has been hindered by various interzonal restrictions and by the fact that 32 per cent of the agricultural land of postwar Germany lies in the Soviet zone.

One conclusion is evident: More than ever before, Germany needs a large crop output, with high yields and intensive land use. It has been known for some time that higher yields could be achieved if the consolidation of the strips of land owned by one farmer and often distributed over a considerable area was carried out more rapidly. Hay fields and pasture lands could be improved with additional fertilizer. As stated in an official report, "The most important nutritional problem in the Federal Republic is the deficiency of protein in the diet; the expansion of fodder production, especially on grasslands, is needed to provide the additional feed for increased milk production. A higher rate of fodder production will also decrease the Federal Republic's dependence on imports of coarse grains and reduce the spending of foreign exchange correspondingly." [20]

A combination of factors is responsible for the high percentage of productive land and the high yields in Germany. Among them are the relief of the country, the climate, the nature of the soils, the distribution of population and the location of human activities, and governmental policies. There are considerable regional differences in rainfall and temperature. But the diversified type farming that is practiced yields a variety of products.

In Germany as a whole, the proportion of poor soil to total arable land is high (Figures 92, 93). However, by the consistent application of manure, commercial fertilizer, and various soil conservation measures over the last 150 years, an exceptionally high crop yield has been achieved on these soils. A good part of Germany has greybrown forest soils of various shades, mostly very light, leached, and acid, much like the soils found in New England. These soils can be used only for rye, oats, and potatoes, with oats cultivated only in the wetter areas. Loess soils (black and brown steppe soils) are found in patches, the largest of which is located between Brunswick and Leipzig (Soviet zone) in the zone of the Southern Transitional Borderlands. Although they have been in use since prehistoric

---

[20] Office of the U. S. High Commissioner for Germany, *Report on Germany*, 7th Quarterly, p. 82. During 1950-51 total food imports in the Federal Republic amounted to 41 per cent of all imports. See also Matthias Kramer, "Die Landwirtschaft in der Sowjetischen Besatzungszone," *Bonner Berichte aus Mittel- und Ostdeutschland* (Bonn, 1951), for an analysis of agriculture in the Soviet zone.

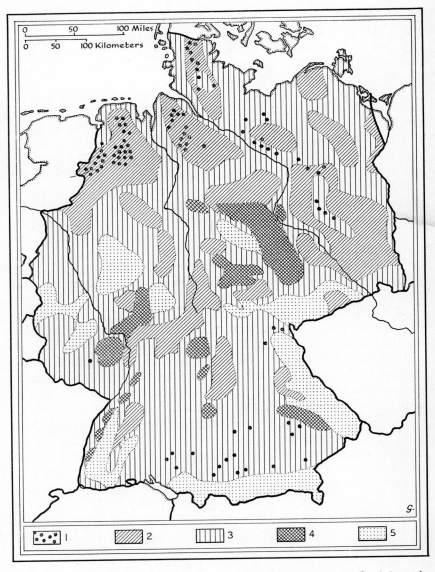

FIGURE 92. Soil regions of Germany and the Saar: (1) moor soils; (2) sandy soils; (3) mountain soils; (4) steppe soils (black and brown); (5) mixed types ranging from sandy loams to clay. (Figures 92 and 93 after H. Niehaus. By permission of the American Geographical Society.)

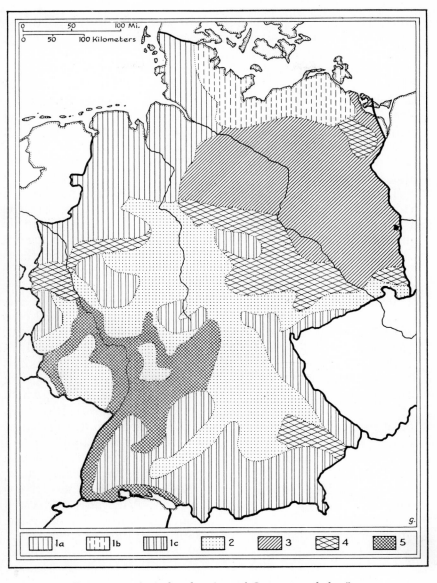

FIGURE 93. Agricultural regions of Germany and the Saar.

I. Humid and cool regions, receiving more than 60 per cent of the income from livestock
   1a. Lowlands: dairying and beef; pasture, hay, forage crops
   1b. Rolling land: dairying; forage crops, pasture
   1c. Foothills and low mountain ranges: dairying, hay, pasture

II. Drier and warmer regions, receiving 40 per cent or more of the income from crops
   2. Hilly: grain and livestock; forage crops
   3. Plain and rolling land: rye, potatoes, livestock
   4. Plain and rolling land: wheat, barley, sugar beets, livestock
   5. River bottoms and hilly land: wine, fruits, grain

times, these loess soils remain the most productive soils in Germany thanks to careful cultivation, good conservation measures, and the regular application of fertilizers.

The amount of land under cultivation has remained rather stable; it averages about 61 to 63 per cent of the total land area of Germany. In 1939, 44 per cent of the arable land was culti-vated, 27 in forests, 18 in meadows and pastures, 2 in gardens and orchards, and 7 per cent was unproductive. In the smaller area now comprising Germany (the four occupation zones plus Berlin), the land under cultivation equals roughly 58 per cent of the total land area.

The breadgrains (oats, barley, rye, and wheat) and potatoes, of which Germany used to be the world's chief producer, constitute the base of Germany's diet. Rye, the most important cereal, is made into dark bread. Wheat is grown on heavier soils and in regions with warmer summer temperatures, predominantly in the Southern Transitional Borderlands. In addition to playing an important role in the human diet, potatoes are used as feed for pigs and as a source of alcohol and starch. The distribution is similar to that of rye. Before the war, rye occupied close to 22 per cent of the total crop area (since reduced), oats 10 per cent, wheat and spelt 11 per cent. Barley, in special demand for beer brewing, grows predominantly in southern Germany. Oats is the typical crop of the moist regions along the Baltic coastlands and the North Sea. A great variety of other field products is grown in Germany. The sugar beet, which is the source of sugar and fodder, is grown for the most part on loess soil at the foot of the Central Uplands; its distribution is similar to that of wheat. Various grasses, such as clover and alfalfa, are of special value for stock raising and dairying. Vegetable production is widespread. Industrial crops, such as hemp, flax, tobacco, hops, and rapeseed have profitable uses. Soybeans are a relatively new crop, and corn is grown in only a few areas. Vineyards are located in the Rhine gorge and in the Neckar, Main, Moselle, and Nahe valleys. German wines (e.g., the Rhine wines) are of good quality and the production is not sufficient to meet domestic demand. Some of the warmer regions of southern Germany have extensive orchards, and in addition many roads throughout Germany are lined with fruit trees, especially apple trees. Before 1939, Württemberg had one sixth of Germany's apple and pear trees. Hogs, raised mainly in the North German Lowlands, fill a substantial part of German meat and fat requirements; in 1939, 65 per cent of all meat consumed was pork. Cattle are reared in the vicinity of large urban concentrations and in the Alpine Foreland.

Before the outbreak of World War II, Germany was able to limit its agricultural imports to milk products and some grain. To-day, the country has become a heavy food importer. In 1950-51 food products represented 40 per cent of the country's total imports. That is why a concerted effort was made—and is still being made— to restore food production to the high levels of the prewar period. Fish are being used increasingly to supplement the German diet. In recognition of this development, the occupying powers in 1946 encouraged Germany to rebuild its fishing fleet. This has been done and German fishing vessels are once again joining the fishing fleets of other nations on the high seas.

Germany has always had a large number of small farms. This is due partly to predominantly poor soil and partly to historical rea-sons. Larger holdings, e.g., farms with over 250 acres, were found chiefly in eastern Germany, in territories lost after World War II. The few large farms west of the Elbe, in the loess region of the Börde, have been broken up since 1945. If we compare the prewar (1937) percentage of all farms under five acres with the postwar (1950-51) figure we find almost no change in the general distribu-tion pattern in the Federal Republic. Figures for the Soviet zone, however, are not available. Medium-sized farms predominate in Bavaria and in the northwest. Small holdings of less than 12½ acres are common in the south, in central Germany, and in the west, especially in the Rhineland. The latter region, with its great urban concentrations, is dependent upon food imports. For example, most of the imported wheat is shipped upstream on the Rhine.

In conclusion, it may be stated that the food situation in West-ern Germany is highly critical. Prewar patterns of exchange within Germany have been broken up, and even under optimum conditions the Federal Republic is forced to import large quantities of food. The agricultural surpluses of former Eastern Germany are either nonexistent or else they are redirected to the Soviet-controlled coun-tries of East Central Europe.

Manufacturing. Germany is among the most important manu-facturing countries of Europe, next in rank to the U.S.S.R. and the United Kingdom. Despite two defeats in the span of a quarter cen-tury and the still recent destruction of a large part of its industrial facilities, Germany's rehabilitation has made great strides. Her iron and steel, textile, chemical, optical, and precision industries are once again in full or almost-full production. All four occupation powers have come to realize the value of and the need for increased German production. Postwar plans put forth for a "pastoral Ger-man economy" and a "transfer of her manufacturing facilities to other countries," were soon abandoned for increased German participation in industrial output. Generally speaking, German production has now reached prewar levels and in a number of items has exceeded them. In all four occupation zones dismantling of plants has given way to the building and modernization of new facilities. Such is the case in the Ruhr, at Fürstenberg on the Oder (Soviet zone) where a new steel mill has been constructed, and in many other industrial districts.

Germany's industrial achievements are due to a number of factors which will be discussed in the following pages.

THE RAW MATERIAL FACTOR. Coal is Germany's basic mineral resource and accounts for much of the early success in industrialization. Besides bituminous coal, sizable amounts of lignite or brown coal are mined. However, it should be realized that the heating value of lignite is considerably inferior to that of coal: about four and one half tons of lignite are needed to equal one ton of bituminous coal. Rich deposits of coking coal occur in three regions: in the Ruhr, in the Saar, now an independent political unit economically tied to France, and in Upper Silesia, now part of Poland. In 1937 the Ruhr accounted for 69 per cent of total production (127,-750,000 tons), the Saar for 12 per cent, Silesia for 16 per cent, and a smaller field in Saxony for the rest.

Lignite is widely distributed over Germany. It occurs in thick deposits close to the surface and is extracted mainly by open-pit workings. Its versatility gives it added value: for example, conversion into briquettes and electricity and various chemical products. Through a difficult process called hydrogenation, coal is converted into liquid hydrocarbons (gasoline, petroleum) and into the raw materials for synthetic rubber. As may be gathered from Figure 91, Germany's coal deposits are for the most part rather close to the country's frontiers. For strategic reasons and because of the tremendous fuel need in the prewar industrial expansion program, lignite production was greatly expanded in the 1930's, and high transportation costs called for its utilization as close to the deposits as possible. With the postwar loss of important bituminous coal mines, lignite has assumed an even more important position in the German industrial fuel picture.

Germany in 1951 produced approximately 122 million metric tons of coal (anthracite and bituminous) and 222 million metric tons of lignite.[21] This makes Germany the third largest Euro-

[21] It is estimated that three million metric tons of coal and 147 million metric tons of lignite came from the Soviet zone.

pean coal producer, despite the loss of Upper Silesia and the Saar. Part of this production is exported to the coal-poor countries of Europe. Germany's large supply of coal is thus an important reason for its key position in the European economy.

Despite the abundance of coal and the availability of potash, produced from large salt deposits around Stassfurt, northeast of the Harz Mountains, Germany suffers from considerable raw material shortages. One such shortage is in iron ore, which has been mined since 1850 southeast of Cologne in the Siegerland and in the Lahn region. In 1937, all the iron ore mined within the present-day territory of the Federal Republic provided but one fifth of total consumption. Even the tapping of poorer deposits could not supply the needs of the Ruhr industries. Imports came from Sweden, Lorraine, Spain, and French North Africa. The Democratic Republic imports its ores from the U.S.S.R. Other items which must be imported include lead, zinc, copper, tin, sulphur, and pyrites, as well as flax and silk for the textile industry. Germany became aware at an early date of the value of substitutes. Accordingly, many synthetic products and substitutes for essential natural resources were developed in Germany. Nevertheless, her dependence on raw material imports is an important economic handicap.

Water power is another important resource for German industries. It is concentrated in the Alps and in the valleys of the Central Uplands (dammed lakes). Even though much progress has been made in enlarging electric power-generating facilities over the last 20 years, a great deal of electricity must be imported, some of it in exchange for Ruhr coal.

Of great importance is Germany's new petroleum production. Output increased from 230,000 tons in 1933 to nearly 1,400,000 tons in 1951. The Emsland Field near the German-Dutch border is the newest of her productive fields, contributing almost 40 per cent of the country's total output. Oil has been also struck in the Aller River Valley, north of Hanover and Brunswick. There are minor fields in the western part of Schleswig-Holstein (Heide Field) and in Württemberg-Baden. Since the Potsdam Agreement specifically prohibited the production of synthetic oil in Germany, every additional barrel of domestic oil saves precious foreign exchange. At the end of 1951, Western Germany produced somewhat less than 30 per cent of the oil it consumed, but a considerable increase in production was hoped for.

THE LOCATIONAL FACTOR. Many scholars from different countries have analyzed the locational aspects and the interregional relationships of Germany's industrial production. Among the more important factors of industrial location are: raw materials, transportation, manpower, and the proximity of agricultural land. German industrial concentrations are characterized by a combination of several of these factors. Most of Germany's industries are concentrated in three regions (Figure 91): (1) A belt of unequal width extending from Aachen on the German-Belgian border to the Ore Mountains along the border of Czechoslovakia; this belt includes the Rhine-Ruhr region, the Central German Industrial region, and a large part of industrial Southern Saxony; (2) the upper part of the Rhine Valley, with chief centers at Karlsruhe, Mannheim-Ludwigshafen, Mainz and Frankfurt; and the Neckar Basin with Stuttgart as its industrial center; (3) the Saar, which now functions outside the German economy; Saarbrücken is its chief center. Several minor industrial regions have grown in importance as a result of the war and the postwar division of Germany. Most of these are centered on large cities including ports. Berlin is handicapped by its division into four occupation zones. Among the industrial territories lost since the war, Upper Silesia used to play an important role, though not comparable to that of the Ruhr. While this region contributed less than one sixth of Germany's over-all production before World War II, war damages have been comparatively light and its contribution to Poland's economy is, therefore, of major importance.

1. *The Rhine-Ruhr region* is most important for its coal and iron ore mines and for the production of coke, steel, chemicals, and heavy machinery. The core of the Ruhr area extends about 45 miles eastward from the Rhine to Dortmund and has a north-south extent of less than ten miles. A more recent expansion has taken place north of the core area, near the Münster coal mines. As may be seen from the following table, the Ruhr has been important for some time:

RUHR COAL AND COKE PRODUCTION

1,000 metric tons

Year	Coal	Coke	Year	Coal	Coke
1800	200	*	1929	123,600	34,200
1830	500	*	1932	73,275	15,323
1850	1,960	73	1937	127,750	31,600
1869	11,250	277	1939	130,500	36,000
1880	22,228	1,291	1942	131,183	35,000
1900	60,000	9,644	1945	33,380	5,338
1913	114,183	26,703	1948	81,106	18,920
1920	88,000	21,720			

* Not available.

Source: Wilhelm Helmrich, *Das Ruhrgebiet* (Stuttgart, 1949); United Nations, *Economic Survey of Europe in 1951* (Geneva, 1951).

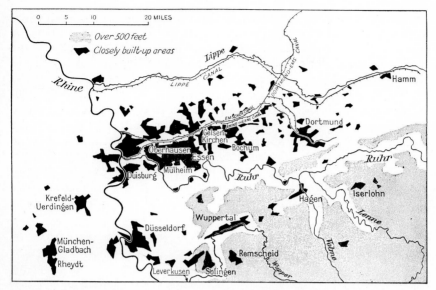

FIGURE 94. Industrial and mining areas, and waterways of the Ruhr. (From *Focus*, by permission of the American Geographical Society.)

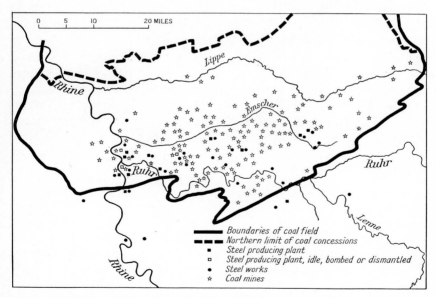

FIGURE 95. Coal mines and steelworks of the Ruhr. (From *Focus*, by permission of the American Geographical Society.)

In 1937, 70 per cent of the entire German output of steel originated in the Ruhr, a percentage which has barely changed despite altered postwar conditions. During the same year (1937), the Ruhr area produced over 25 per cent of Germany's electric power, 72 per cent of its coal tar, and 64 per cent of its crude benzene.

The importance of this region is due to its extensive and highgrade deposits of coking coal, its proximity to Germany's only source of iron ore, the unrivaled natural artery of trade provided by the Rhine, and its tributaries, the Lippe and the Ruhr, and the dense network of canals which connects the Ruhr with most parts of Germany. Its location in the very heart of Europe's commerce and industry has consistently encouraged the expansion of its industries (Figures 94, 95).

FIGURE 96. Aerial view of Duisburg. (Bibliographisches Institut.)

This area is remarkable for its large concentration of cities, fourteen of which have a population of over 100,000. Over six million people, nearly all of whom are dependent upon Ruhr industries, live in this region which is about the size of Delaware. Its chief city is Essen. Other large cities are Dortmund, Bochum, Duisburg (Duisburg-Hamborn), and Gelsenkirchen. Duisburg is the leading Rhine port; its 1950 population was 408,000. Before the war it had been the largest inland port (Figure 96) of Europe, handling more than 40 million tons of goods, with coal shipments alone amounting to 12.5 million tons. The Ruhr is dotted with iron and steel works, locomotive and chemical plants, and factories manufacturing equipment for mines and steel mills. Today, the Ruhr's huge output of coal and its industrial capacity are essential for the survival of the Western World. By the end of World War II, about 30 per cent of its productive capacity had been destroyed by Allied bombing. Transport had been disrupted and the normal pattern of interregional trade upset. The Ruhr was thus cut off from other parts of Germany upon which it had been dependent even in normal times for about one half of its food requirements. However, it soon became evident that without the rehabilitation of the Rhine-Ruhr region, the recovery of Western Europe [22] would be put in jeopardy. Therefore, early Allied policy aiming at reduced output had to be reversed. Today, all-out production is the chief goal.

Important postwar political developments include the unification of the entire Rhine-Ruhr region into the province of North Rhine-Westphalia (Land Nordrhein-Westfalen) within the British zone of occupation; the creation in December 1948, of the Ruhr International Authority to insure Germany's disarmament, hasten German as well as European recovery, and promote closer integration of its economic life; and the adoption of the previously described Schuman plan.

The Central German Industrial Region extends eastward from the middle Weser River along the zone of the Southern Transitional Borderlands to the Elbe River, and south into the Central Uplands. Its various industries are largely based upon lignite and mineral salts. The combination of raw materials has made this the most important chemical manufacturing region in all of Germany. Lignite is the basic fuel for the production of electric power and for other energy uses. In the 1930's, the low-grade iron ore deposits of the Peine-Salzgitter area near Brunswick attracted several heavy manufacturing establishments which also used the dense river and canal transportation system for imports of coal and additional iron ore. During the war the region gained added importance when important industries were relocated here from the Ruhr. In addition to a large number of chemical and heavy industrial establishments, there are many other industries dependent on the region's pool of skilled workers. The more important centers are Hanover (chemical and metallurgical industries), Salzgitter (steel mills, automobile and textile plants), Kassel (heavy machinery and locomotives), Magdeburg (chemicals), Dessau (aircraft center in the years before Germany was forbidden to build them), Halle (chemi-

[22] In this context the term refers to all the countries of Europe which are not Soviet-controlled.

cals), Erfurt and Jena (optical instruments, glass and chinaware, bicycles, typewriters, etc.).

The industries which developed in southern Saxony, on the northern slopes of the Ore Mountains, are largely based on lignite (formerly on minor bituminous coal deposits) and on a wide range of metallic ores, many of which are now exhausted. Lignite is still available and forms the basic source of power. A large number of skilled workers is employed in the numerous textile plants and in the woodworking and tanning industries which have grown up here. This region generally ranks second among German industrial districts, with textiles predominating. Before 1939, Saxony produced more than one half of all German textiles and Chemnitz is still called "the Manchester of Germany." Other cities of importance are Plauen (knitted goods, embroidery), Meissen and Dresden (porcelain), and Leipzig, a city of 700,000 people which is one of Europe's oldest trading centers. Before the war, Leipzig was a center of the fur trade; it was also known for its publishing and printing houses of high repute. Its famed international fair, while handicapped by the postwar division of Germany, is still being held annually. The Leipzig Bay is linked with other parts of Germany by a network of canals, rivers (including the Elbe), and railroad lines.

2. *The Upper Part of the Rhine Valley.* The second of Germany's industrial regions extends along the Rhine from Mainz and Frankfurt-am-Main (Frankfort on the Main) southward to Karlsruhe. It also includes several cities, notably Stuttgart, along the Neckar and its tributaries. The region's chief drawback is the lack of raw materials. However, this disadvantage is overcome by its excellent location, transportation-wise. The canalized Rhine, Main, and Neckar rivers give easy access to the east and to the Rhine-Ruhr region to the north. The region's industries manufacture precision instruments, tools, and typewriters. The twin cities of Ludwigshafen-Mannheim produce chemicals (dyes, fertilizer, nitrates, and pharmaceutical items). Mainz, Stuttgart, and Frankfurt are important centers for the manufacture of automobiles, railroad supplies, trucks, machines, and machine tools. Mannheim and Mainz are also active river ports, while Frankfurt was prewar Germany's leading commercial and financial center.

3. *The Saar Region.* Situated along the German-French border, this region (Figure 97) has changed hands several times in recent history. It owes its industrial development to the presence of coal deposits in proximity to the minette iron ores of Lorraine. Between 1871 and 1918, the region was part of Germany and the output of

its newly established industries was shipped eastward on canals connecting it with the main Rhine valley. By the Treaty of Versailles,
eastern Lorraine was returned to France; the Saar was made an autonomous territory administered by France under League of Nations supervision, but it reverted to Germany in 1935 as a result of a
plebiscite. After 1945, the Saar was made autonomous once more,

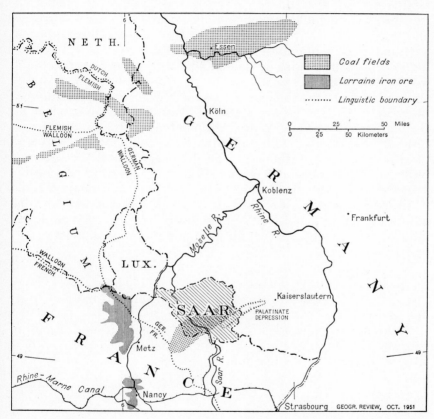

FIGURE 97. Location map of the Saar. (By permission, American Geographical
Society.)

but its economy is closely tied to that of France. The Saar now has
its own constitution and is governed by elected representatives.
While it is in full control of its internal affairs, all matters pertaining
to defense are in French hands. In 1950, the Saar entered the Council of Europe as a separate entity.

The constant political shifts have inevitably hampered production in this vital industrial region. The 1951 production of anthra-

cite and bituminous coal amounted to over 16 million metric tons —coal which is sorely needed by France's heavy industry. On the other hand, it should be remembered that the Saar had been Germany's second largest coal-producing region before World War II. Further impoverished by the loss of Upper Silesia, formerly its third-ranking coal region, Germany's agitation for the return of the Saarland is not unexpected. Her claim is also based on the fact that the overwhelming majority of Saarlanders are German by language and origin. Perhaps the integration of the Saar into the European coal and steel community under the Schuman plan will reduce political tensions and insure the fair allocation of its resources to all member nations.

In addition to the three major manufacturing regions, numerous other industrial centers are scattered all over Germany. Most of them are in or near large cities. As pointed out by Dickinson,[23] a certain distribution pattern is clearly visible: rolling stock and manufactures and repair shops are located near railroad yards; the principal agricultural market areas attract industries producing agricultural implements; Düsseldorf is such a center for the Lower Rhineland, Augsburg for the Alpine Foreland, Leipzig for the middle Elbe Basin, and Hanover for Lower Saxony. The electrical industry is represented in nearly all important cities and, above all, in Berlin, Cologne, and Munich.

West of Cologne, the rise of a number of industrial centers is closely linked to the coal basin extending from Belgium and Holland into Germany. Aachen is the center of a diversified industry, producing hardware, textiles, steel, etc.

In Franconia, a great variety of manufactures is found in Nürnberg and its suburb Fürth, in Würzburg, and in Schweinfurt. The latter two cities have important engineering works. Nürnberg is noted for its metallurgical products (machinery, motor cars, bicycles), foods, and toys. The city is also an important railway center.

Various industries are also concentrated in the many cities of the Alpine Foreland. Munich makes automobiles, optical equipment, machines, beer, and luxury items. Prewar Augsburg was the center of important aircraft industries. Regensburg, at the head of Danube River navigation, has several small shipbuilding works, machine and machine-tool industries.

Last but not least, there are important industrial concentrations in several German ports. Since June 1945, when Germany lost a

[23] R. E. Dickinson, "The Economic Regions of Germany," *Geographical Review*, XXVIII (October, 1938), 606-16.

major portion of its Baltic coastline and its main harbor, Stettin, the German ports on the Baltic have steadily declined. Hamburg, the easternmost North Sea port on the lower Elbe, has been hit hard by the loss of Czech transit trade which has been rerouted to Polish ports. Once a powerful member of the Hanseatic League, Hamburg has maintained to this day its position as a self-governing city. Before World War II it handled over 70 per cent of Germany's imports and 57 per cent of its exports (Figure 98). There are extensive shipbuilding yards, machinery and tool plants in all German port cities, with the greatest concentrations in Hamburg, Bremen, and Kiel. Each seaport has its own trade pattern, and old contacts

FIGURE 98. Hamburg is once more Germany's most important seaport. On the opposite side of the river are two large shipbuilding ways. (Amt für Landeskunde.)

are being actively renewed. Bremen was the major port for cotton imports destined for Central and East Central Europe. It was also Europe's leading importer of various tropical produce. Bremerhaven, its outer harbor, carried much of the traffic. Emden, the third of Germany's North Sea ports, was originally built to capture some of the trade going to Rotterdam. Direct access to the Rhine-Ruhr industrial region via the Dortmund-Ems canal has been an important factor in Emden's growth, but comparatively few industries are located within its port area. The port of Kiel is located on the Kiel Canal which connects the Baltic with the North Sea. It is the most important Baltic port of postwar Germany, the more so since Stettin, now called Szczecin, has become Polish.

THE TRANSPORTATION FACTOR. Germany's industrial growth would not have been possible without the development of an efficient, highly integrated transportation system; although considerably damaged by the war, the transportation system has made important contributions to postwar rehabilitation.

Germany's principal waterways are the country's oldest transport arteries. Four large, navigable rivers flow from south to north across the North German Plain; they are the Rhine with the Dortmund-Ems Canal extension to Emden, the Weser, the Elbe, and the Oder (now part of the German-Polish border). The three east-west arteries are the Danube and two canals: the Midland Canal and the Kiel Canal. The Midland Canal links the Ems with the Elbe and is extended eastward by various canals to the Oder. It is the most recent addition to Germany's system of waterways (Figure 99). Completed in 1938, the 224-mile long canal has a depth of nine feet. Germany's rivers and canals offer cheap transportation to all parts of the country and form an essential part of the country's communications network.

FIGURE 99. Entrance to the Kiel Canal. (Dr. C. Schott.)

The Rhine carries more passengers and freight than any other German waterway. Since the mouth of the river is in foreign territory, Germany constructed the Dortmund-Ems Canal as a bypass through German territory to the North Sea. However, because it is too shallow and too narrow for modern barges, most of the

Rhine shipping continues to travel down the river into Dutch territory. The Rhine flows through Europe's greatest industrial concentrations. The upstream traffic is heaviest, with coal, coke, and grain the bulkiest commodities. Timber, potash, and iron ore are the main downstream cargoes. The Elbe provides a natural link between the North Sea and landlocked Czechoslovakia. Hamburg, situated at its mouth, is still Germany's leading port. The Oder is of lesser importance today, largely because of the loss of the Silesian coal fields and of the port city of Stettin to Poland.

The Danube has always been of minor importance as an east-west artery, largely because of its isolation from other German waterways, the absence of a major industrial region along its banks, and the fact that it flows in the wrong direction, eastward. Many possibilities of connecting the Danube with Europe's other main rivers have been studied, but because of the high cost and technical difficulties little has been done so far. The only connection existing at present is the small Ludwig Canal which leads southward from the Main.

Germany's most important canal system is the Midland system, which crosses the North German Plain from the Ems to the Oder. Current political controversies between the occupying powers have reduced its usefulness as a transit route, especially in and around Berlin. In order to prevent interference with shipping, on the part of the western powers, an additional canal has been built to bypass the western zone of Berlin and thus afford a direct connection through the whole of the Soviet zone.

The physiography of Germany presented no major obstacles to the development of a dense rail network. This network connects all important cities and industrial areas. Rail densities are highest in the Rhine-Ruhr region, the Central Industrial region, and in the vicinity of Berlin, Leipzig, and Mainz-Frankfurt. In the Central Uplands and southern Bavaria, the rail net is not as dense. Only a small part of Germany's rail mileage is electrified, as compared with that of Switzerland and Austria.

Two general patterns of freight movement may be distinguished: (1) raw material imports and overseas exports move from and to the North Sea ports, and (2) raw materials and foodstuffs move from one region to another within the country and overland to other European countries.

Germany has excellent road communications. The density of the network is high, especially in those areas where rail lines are also very numerous. In addition to ordinary roads, Germany built a number of superhighways (Autobahnen) between 1933 and 1940. Although they were built primarily for strategic reasons—to facilitate troop movements—the superhighways are now used by an ever-increasing number of overland truck carriers. Finally, brief mention should be made of air transportation. Served by a dense air net before the war, Germany's airways are now controlled by foreign companies.

It should be stressed that the various means of transport are interdependent. While rivers and canals are highly suited for bulk traffic, their limitations as carriers must always be borne in mind. In effect, considering the present importance of railroads, waterways supplement rather than compete with overland transport.

Switzerland

Population

The great diversity in the relief of Switzerland has been described earlier. A study of the origins of the Swiss state shows that it grew from an aggregation of autonomous units which combined to defend the important mountain passes against external attack. Siegfried wrote:

> . . . the homogeneity resides in the principle of political resistance entrenched in a natural fortress, but the diversity is everywhere. . . . We find that each canton is different from its neighbor, whilst the various geographical areas are of such marked individuality that their inhabitants are fully conscious of the differences. In each neatly circumscribed valley, corresponding to the boundaries of a canton (I am thinking of Glarus, for example), each citizen knows instinctively why he belongs to his particular valley, to his particular canton. This is the solid basis of a democracy which has its roots both in the soil and in men's hearts.[24]

According to the census of December 1, 1950, Switzerland had a population of 4,714,992 concentrated in an area of less than 16,000 square miles—somewhat smaller than the combined areas of Massachusetts and New Hampshire. There are about 296 people to the square mile, but when it is realized that only 54 per cent of the total area is permanently inhabited (22 per cent unsettled and the rest inhabited only during the summer months), the density of 350 per square mile of productive land becomes the more significant figure.

[24] André Siegfried, *Switzerland* (London: Jonathan Cape, Ltd., 1950), p. 25.

The distribution of the population is very uneven, whether measured by its altitudinal distribution or by the size of populated centers. Some 54 per cent of Switzerland's inhabitants live below 1,500 feet, while only 5 per cent live above 3,000 feet. More than a third (36.5 per cent) of the population is found in towns of 10,000 and over. Bern, Zurich, Basel, and Geneva are the four largest cities. Bern, with 802,000 inhabitants, is the most populous canton; Appenzell-Inner Rhodes half-canton is the smallest unit of the Federation, with 13,383 inhabitants. Two thirds of the people of Switzerland live on the Plateau which comprises but one third of the total area.

The population is increasing slowly, at the rate of about one per cent per annum. During the decade of the 1940's the birth rate stood at 19.1 per thousand; the death rate dropped to 11 per thousand during the same period. In 1950, some 202,000 Swiss citizens lived abroad, the largest number of them in France and in the United States. Emigration has always played an important role in Swiss economic life, although the total has been far smaller on the average than that of most other European countries. On the other hand, many foreigners have immigrated into Switzerland. Many Swiss industries use foreign labor, largely of Italian origin.

Switzerland's unity, unlike that of many other nations, is not imperiled by the fact that people of different religions and languages live within the confines of one small country. The numerical ratio of the various religious groups has not changed significantly over the centuries: 58 per cent of the population is Protestant, 41 per cent Roman Catholic, and one per cent represents other faiths. Long-drawn-out religious controversies between several Swiss cities are recognized to have been extremely damaging to the country as a whole. Recognition of that fact, perhaps more than anything else, has convinced the Swiss people of the need of religious freedom.

The numerical language distribution is as follows: German dialects are spoken by 72 per cent of the population, French by 20.7, Italian by 5.2, and Romansh [25] by 1.1 per cent. The language boundary between the German- and the French-speaking parts of Switzerland runs in a north-south direction, diagonally from the Jura across the Plateau and the Alps. Italian is spoken in the canton of Ticino and to some extent in the adjacent areas of Grisons; Romansh is found exclusively in the valleys of Grisons. The linguistic line has changed hardly at all in the last century

[25] A Rhaeto-Romanic language (Celtic-Roman idiom) whose origin can be traced to the Romanization of Rhaetia.

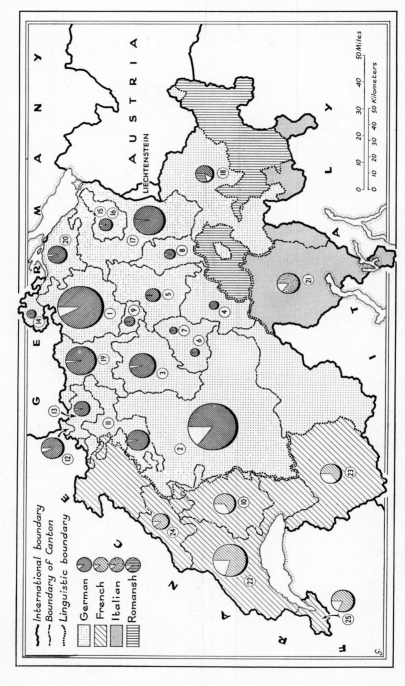

FIGURE 100. The linguistic pattern of Switzerland. The size of the circles indicates the cantonal population. For cantonal names, see table on opposite page.

and does not follow cantonal boundaries. However, the dividing line is sharp. One village may be German-speaking, a nearby one French (Figure 100). Romansh was recognized as one of Switzerland's official languages in 1941, when 46,400 Swiss citizens (of whom 40,000 lived in Grisons) were given permission to use it on a par with the other three languages. It is the consensus of many Swiss people that recognition of the Romansh language came just in time to save it from extinction. Official recognition includes the authorization to teach Romansh in public schools, a basic factor in the continuance of its life.

In the light of such great diversity of religion and language it is interesting to study the country's political unity over the last century. Since 1848, Switzerland has been a Confederation (Bundesstaat) of 19 cantons and six half-cantons. Of special significance, perhaps, is the active participation of the people in legislative matters. Frequent referenda give the Swiss citizen the feeling of

SWITZERLAND, LINGUISTIC DISTRIBUTION, BY CANTONS
(See Figure 100)

	Percentage Speaking				
	German	French	Italian	Romansh	Others
1. Zurich	91.2	5.11	3.4	.2	—
2. Bern	83.7	15.4	.6	.1	.3
3. Lucerne	97.6	.6	1.3	.1	.4
4. Uri	99.5	.2	.3	—	—
5. Schwyz	99.5	.2	.3	—	—
6. Obwalden	99.5	.1	.2	.2	—
7. Nidwalden	99.5	.1	.27	.13	—
8. Glarus	95.5	.65	3.6	.25	—
9. Zug	99.4	.2	.4	—	—
10. Fribourg	33.2	66.6	.1	—	.1
11. Solothurn	99.8	.1	.1	—	—
12. Basel—Urban	94.0	3.6	1.1	.1	.5
13. Basel—Rural	96.6	1.5	.8	.12	2.0
14. Schaffhausen	99.8	.1	.1	—	—
15. Appenzell—Inner Rhodes	99.8	.1	.1	—	—
16. Appenzell—Outer Rhodes	99.9	.1	—	—	—
17. St. Gallen	99.8	.1	.1	—	—
18. Grisons	55.0	—	12.7	37.3	—
19. Aargau	98.11	1.0	.89	—	—
20. Thurgau	98.61	—	1.0	—	.39
21. Ticino	8.15	1.5	85.1	3.0	2.25
22. Vaud	12.5	81.9	3.6	2.0	—
23. Valais	33.53	65.47	1.0	—	—
24. Neuchâtel	14.0	86.0	—	—	—
25. Geneva	13.56	80.58	2.45	3.41	—

direct responsibility for the actions of his government. The three highest authorities are the federal assembly, federal executive council, and federal court. In many ways there is similarity between Swiss democratic organizations and those of the United States. Each representative who sits in the Lower House represents 22,000 constituents, and each canton, regardless of size, has two representatives in the Upper House. The two Houses in joint session elect the federal council which consists of seven members, the federal court, and in case of war, the commanding general of the armed forces. At the head of the federal council is the president, elected from among its members for a term of one year. Bern is the seat of the federal assembly. The federal court, which acts on matters affecting the country as a whole, the cantons, or individuals sits in Lausanne. Equality before the law, religious freedom, the right of assembly, of free speech, and the right to open a business are guaranteed in the constitution.

Limitations of space keep us from describing the great strength of this democracy in greater detail. A foreigner is surprised to see what great responsibilities are shouldered by the people. Cantonal governments are elected by direct popular vote. The famous outdoor plenary assemblies (Landsgemeinden) of Glarus are as old as the first settlements in this region. Education is compulsory. Swiss citizenship puts cantonal loyalty first and federal allegiance second. Perhaps the Swiss system of government is best epitomized by the expression "the Swiss Confederation administers; the canton governs."

Present Economic Life of Switzerland

General Characteristics. Switzerland is poor in raw materials. Oil and coal are totally lacking, and hydroelectric power is the only important source of energy. Nevertheless, 47.2 per cent of the population is engaged in manufacturing, which is widely dispersed over the countryside and often found in remote valleys. The casual visitor will understand that this pattern is the result of an ample supply of water and of local manpower. Still, most of the larger industrial plants are concentrated in the Swiss Plateau, where communications are least difficult.

In general, Swiss industry is noted not so much for its methods as for its high-quality precision products which require skilled craftsmanship based on a long tradition, but yet are easily adaptable to modern techniques.

Only 22 per cent of the Swiss population is engaged in agriculture. As would be expected, agricultural methods vary from canton to canton in response to soil conditions and custom. Switzerland imports most of the cereals she needs and directs her efforts toward improving her livestock breeds and farming techniques. Whenever wars have cut off her imports, Switzerland has increased her cereal production, but only enough to feed her population. Farmers generally wield great power and are able to protect both their technical and political interests. Farmers' associations, unions and cooperatives, agricultural schools, etc. play an important role in the rural scene.

Agriculture and Forestry. The 22 per cent of the population still employed in agriculture continues to be a vital economic force. Agriculture is a flourishing part of Switzerland's economy despite the severe handicap of poor soils and the large percentage of unproductive land.

The arable land is divided into medium- and small-sized farms. Over 80 per cent of the farms occupy less than 25 acres. Fewer than 15 per cent of all the farmers are tenants. The great pride the Swiss take in their homes and barns is reflected in the fact that farm buildings represent close to one fourth of the entire capital investment of the farmer.

The relief, the climate, and the Swiss tradition combine to make the country outstanding in dairying. In a normal peacetime year dairying supplies about 50 per cent of the total value of the country's agricultural products. About two thirds of the milk produced enters market channels; nearly one half of the marketed milk is used in the manufacture of cheese, the rest in making butter, chocolate, etc. Such milk products as Emmental cheese and Linth chocolate have acquired world-wide renown.

Stock feeding is normally second in importance to dairying. Cattle feeding and fattening is followed in terms of value by hog, goat, and sheep raising. Orchard products include apples, pears, cherries, and prunes. Grapes are grown in several areas which have exceptionally mild climatic conditions: for example, along the shores of Lake Geneva, in the lower Valais, around the lakes of the Plateau, and in the sunny valleys of the Ticino.

Cereal production, though normally less than 5 per cent of the total agricultural output, has fluctuated greatly during the last few years. Since it is cheaper for Switzerland to purchase cereals abroad than to produce them, emphasis has been placed on such agricultural export items as dairy products. During the two world wars, however, cereals could no longer be imported, and great efforts were made to attain self-sufficiency in order to avoid a serious food shortage. During World War II much hay and pasture land was ploughed up for the production of staple crops, and grains assumed major importance; the dairying industry was greatly reduced; the acreage of land in cereals was doubled between 1937 and 1944, and the acreage in potatoes more than doubled. Slowly, the prewar pattern is again being re-established. Of the various grain crops, wheat takes up the largest area, followed by oats and rye. The potato crop is usually large enough to satisfy domestic needs but sugar, tobacco, fruits, and vegetables must be imported.

The forests of Switzerland are 70 per cent coniferous and 30 per cent broadleaved; the spruce has the widest distribution. As would be expected, 55 per cent of the area of the Swiss Alps is forested, but only 20 per cent of the Jura and 25 per cent of the Plateau. While lumber production is considerable, the output is insufficient to meet demands.

Raw Materials and Industries. Switzerland's hydroelectric power resources have played a very important part in the country's economic development. In 1950, Switzerland produced over 10 million kw-hr of electricity in more than 6,000 hydroelectric power plants. "White coal" supplies an ever-increasing share of the country's energy requirements. In 1938, coal and petroleum provided 83 per cent of the energy consumed; by 1950 this proportion had fallen to 76 per cent, the difference being accounted for by greater hydroelectric power capacity. A very hopeful sign for the future is the fact that, despite the increase in hydroelectric installations, less than 20 per cent of Switzerland's potential power has been harnessed to date.

Mineral resources are an almost negligible industrial factor (Figure 91). Only 14,000 people were engaged in mining in 1950. Coal deposits are insignificant. Peat is the most plentiful solid fuel. Annual imports of coal exceed two million metric tons, which represent more than 98 per cent of the country's needs. Iron ore was mined at one time, but today this activity is unprofitable. The ore is of very inferior quality—a considerable drawback in view of Switzerland's need for high-grade steel. Over 500,000 tons of ore—more than 80 per cent of industrial requirements—are imported annually. Some salt is found in the Rhine Valley and small amounts of asphalt are recovered in the Val de Travers of the Jura.

Industry is an element of major importance in the prosperity of the country, even though Switzerland must import its raw materials and export its products in payment for its imports. Swiss industry is highly diversified and employs 47.2 per cent of the total labor force. Until the turn of the century the textile industry was in the lead. During the last 50 years, however, the engineering industries have risen to the dominant position. Today, the manufacturing of machines, machine tools, and instruments outranks all other industries. Among the best-known Swiss-made products are electrical apparatus, textile machinery, engines of all types, locomotives, and agricultural machinery.

Watchmaking, which is centered in the Jura mountains between Geneva and Schaffhausen, is the oldest branch of engineering. The cantons of Solothurn and Neuchâtel lead in the production of watches. Today, there are more than 400 factories, 65 of which manufacture watch parts. The industry is highly mechanized. Switzerland has almost a world monopoly because of the fame of its big-name watches, e.g., Longines, Gruen. About 10 per cent of the country's industrial workers are employed in the watchmaking industry. The assembling of parts, which is the most important step in manufacturing, requires the great precision and technical skill characteristic of the Swiss workman.

Textiles, though a poor second in value to the output of the engineering industry, are nevertheless quite important. Many types of high grade silks, ribbons, laces, knitted goods, and cottons are produced. The quality of the thread, the intricacy of the design, and the skill of the worker combine to give these textiles a highly competitive position on world markets.

The substantial chemical industry had developed largely since 1929. The production of aniline dyes laid the basis for the industry. Today, production is varied and includes items such as plastics, dyes, insecticides, pharmaceuticals, cosmetics, and perfumes. The industry is centered at Basel, a key transportation hub.

The production of grease, oils, and soap, the shoe and leather industry, and the manufacture of chocolate and other food industries are also important but do not rank as high in terms of value added by manufacturing. The lumber and woodworking industry, which employs over ten per cent of the industrial labor force, in sawmills, paper mills, and woodworking establishments, deserves special mention. By rigid conservation measures and much scientific care this industry has operated on a sustained-yield basis for a long time.

In review, manufacturing in Switzerland is widely distributed. This is no handicap in view of the country's size and its excellent transportation system. Highly trained workmen are found in nearly every Alpine valley, and the watchmakers of Le Locle (Figure 101) and La Chaux-de-Fonds in the Jura, of Biel, Geneva, and Solothurn are world famous. In 1940, Switzerland began to build up her merchant marine; by 1950, the seagoing tonnage amounted to 71,000, with 60,000 more tons under construction. Thus Switzerland moves one step closer to the raw materials she must import. With these raw materials, with her financial resources, industrial know-how, and excellent system of technical education, Switzerland has all the ingredients for the high-value type of industrial output which has set a world-wide standard of perfection.

FIGURE 101. Le Locle, watchmaking town in the Jura Mountains, Switzerland. The watch factories are recognizable by the many windows which are necessary for precision work. (Dr. Ernst Winkler.)

The Tourist Trade. Switzerland is one country which can legitimately classify its natural charm and beauty as a financial asset, because the tourist trade furnishes a considerable part of the national income. Tourists have the choice of staying in one of the ultra modern or one of the many small- or medium-sized hotels, inns, or private homes. Generally speaking, the Alpine regions of the Bernese Oberland, the Ticino, Zurich, Lucerne, and Interlaken are the most important centers of tourist trade. But it is not necessary to cite individual places. All of Switzerland offers scenic beauty, winter sports, and recreation to satisfy the tastes of any visitor. Today, Switzerland's hotel industry alone employs 85,000 people, but the economic benefits of the tourist industry are derived indirectly by a considerable part of the population. The tourist industry is well organized; there are a central tourist bureau, numerous travel agencies, many hotel-trade schools, and a school for restaurant personnel. The tourist industry in Switzerland is big business.

Transportation. In the face of very obvious topographical difficulties, the Swiss have built an excellent transportation system. Tunnels and bridges of world renown have been constructed. About 75 per cent of the mileage is electrified and most standard-gauge lines are state-owned. Switzerland is famous for its many scenic mountain railways, some of which climb to heights exceeding 11,500 feet (see also p. 358). Water transportation is not lacking. Basel is a major Rhine River port; it handled over three million tons of freight in 1950. In the same year, more than 400 vessels of Swiss registry were plying the Rhine below Basel. Coal, coke, and iron ore are the chief commodities carried upstream to Basel; downstream traffic is much less important.

Austria

Population

Austria, with an area of 32,376 square miles, is somewhat smaller than the state of Maine. According to the census taken in June 1951, its population totaled 6,918,959, of which 1,737,893 lived in Vienna, the capital. The country is divided into nine provinces, with an international border 1,646 miles long. Its greatest east-west extension is 360 miles, and the average width (from north to south) is 37 miles in the western and 170 miles in the eastern part of the country. (See Figure 67.)

The 1951 population density equaled 209 per square mile, a relatively low figure. However, if we consider the mountainous character of Austria and the relative scarcity of fertile land, the density per square mile of agricultural land becomes substantially higher.

Three regional density groupings may be distinguished in Austria, Vienna excepted: (1) the agricultural and industrial areas of Lower and Upper Austria, Styria, and of the Burgenland are in the most-densely-populated category; (2) the valleys and scattered lowlands of Carinthia, Salzburg, Tyrol, and Vorarlberg belong in an in-between group; and (3) the mountainous parts of the latter provinces are either uninhabited or often populated only during the summertime. Villages and towns are concentrated in the plains, valleys, basins, and hill lands, while isolated settlements predominate in the higher regions. In recent years the population of the mountainous portion of Austria has increased considerably. Industries were relocated here during World War II in search of protection from Allied bombers, and since the war in flight from Soviet occupation forces in the eastern part of the country. Furthermore, most of the postwar immigrants from East Central Europe settled in the western, more mountainous, part of the country.

One third of Austria's population lives in cities of over 100,000; one third in villages of less than 2,000. It is interesting to record that 35 per cent of the population of the Tyrol and 20 per cent of that of Salzburg live at altitudes above 2,400 feet. The upper limit of wheat cultivation varies from 2,900 feet to 5,200 feet. Numerous small settlements may even be found at these upper elevations.

While the uneven geographical distribution of the population is a considerable handicap to the development of a balanced economy, the occupational distribution of the working population (according to the 1951 census) is a great asset to the country's economic strength: 40 per cent of the working population was engaged in industry and handicrafts, 14 per cent in commerce and transportation, and 32 per cent in agriculture and forestry.

One of the great difficulties of the Austro-Hungarian monarchy was its nationality problem. In contrast, the population of postwar Austria is predominantly German in character. Most of the non-Germans live in the frontier districts of Burgenland, Styria, Carinthia, and in Vienna (Figure 102). On the whole, the present ethnic composition gives strength to the country because the Republic is not beset by any language difficulties such as those which troubled the Monarchy. The Roman Catholic religion is dominant in Austria, claiming 94 per cent of the population.

Vienna is by far the largest city in Austria; it is about eight times as large as Graz, the second city in size. Linz, Salzburg, and Innsbruck are the other three large cities. Vienna has lost much of the glamour and importance it had under the Austro-Hungarian monarchy. Today, it is merely the oversized capital of a small, impoverished country—a city only two hours' drive from foreign territory. Graz, a provincial capital, has always been a rather quiet city. Many of its citizens are retired people. The population of Linz has increased by more than 60 per cent over the prewar total. It is the center of important industries, many of which were established after 1940. Salzburg, center of Austria's cultural life and site of the world-famous Salzburg Festival, has also greatly added to its population. Innsbruck is the capital of the Tyrol and the largest city of the Austrian Alps; its university and beautiful surroundings are well known to the many tourists who visit the city every year.

FIGURE 102. Folk costumes, still worn on national holidays and family festivals, are evidence of the great variety of local customs. (Austrian Student Goodwill Tour.)

The historical geography and past function of Vienna and Innsbruck deserve brief discussion. Vienna is mentioned in a record as old as A.D. 935 and in 1137 was cited as a city (stadt). In 1221 its citizens received the privilege of self-government. During the twelfth century, Vienna occupied no more than the site of a former Roman camp, protected on the northeast by the Danube and on the southeast and northwest by small rivers. There was no natural rampart to the southwest of the city. Situated at the crossing of important overland and river transportation routes, Vienna expanded rapidly.

Beginning in 1438, the emperors of the Holy Roman Empire usually resided in Vienna. Thus, the function of imperial capital and permanent seat of the Habsburg Monarchy gave added impetus to Vienna's growth and importance (Figure 103). Thousands of people moved to Vienna from all parts of the Empire to participate in the city's political, economic, and cultural leadership. As recently as 1934, the census reveals that at least 24 per cent of the city's inhabitants had their birthplace beyond the borders of post-World War I Austria; the majority of these had come from what is now Czechoslovakia.

Innsbruck is located in the Northern Longitudinal Valley in western Austria. The Inn Valley had been first inhabited during the Neolithic and Bronze ages. The city was founded near an Inn River bridge which controlled a road leading to the west and northwest. Since the thirteenth century the city has expanded southward in the direction of the Brenner Pass, on the alluvial fan formed by the Sill River. In 1239, it received city status and, as the route from Germany to Rome increased in importance, Inns-

FIGURE 103. The center of Vienna. The former fortified wall has been replaced by broad avenues. Rear, part of the Danube Canal; left foreground, the former Imperial Palace; center, St. Stephen's Cathedral. (Austrian State Tourist Office.)

bruck expanded rapidly. Situated at the natural focus of the whole North Tyrol, the city has always been a trading rather than an industrial center. Its population grew from 4,000 in 1600 to a present population of more than 95,000.

Many of Austria's better-known towns of today owe their origin to a monastery. Examples are Melk, Klosterneuberg, and Krems, all on the Danube. Other towns date back to strategically placed medieval castles, e.g., Graz, Kufstein, Steyr. Several others, such as Linz, Wels, and Salzburg, began as Roman settlements. In

Lower Austria a number of fortified towns such as Tulln or Ybbs grew up along the Danube; their location may have been determined by the routes of the salt trade or by the existence of fords. The border fortifications (Burgen) established along the rolling wooded hills of Lower Austria and Styria (later Burgenland) became villages, but none of them assumed any real importance. Thus, as early as the fourteenth century, the pattern of the population distribution and the location of Austrian cities had been fixed.

Present Economic Life of Austria [26]

When, in 1918, Austria emerged as one of the "Succession States" of the former Austria-Hungary, serious problems of an administrative and economic nature had to be solved in order to provide a livelihood for her six and a half million people, nearly one third of whom lived in Vienna. The task of adjusting to a much smaller area was the major problem facing the government and the people of Austria between 1919 and 1938, when the country was incorporated into Germany. Thus, the newborn Republic of Austria had to struggle with problems of how to increase food production, reorganize the industrial structure, modernize and expand raw material production, and establish a new basis for Austria's foreign trade. It is generally agreed that Austria did succeed fairly well in re-establishing her economy, despite the serious economic and political crises of the interwar years.

In 1945, when Austria re-emerged as an independent country after seven years of occupation and complete absorption into the German war economy, it found itself in an entirely different situation, as compared with 1919. Although industrial capacity had increased, Austria's economy had been further unbalanced because most of the new facilities had been constructed to fit Germany's war needs. One favorable result was the fact that many new industries had been established in the western part of Austria and were thus beyond the reach of Soviet occupation forces after the war.

Starting once more from scratch, Austria's economy had to be completely rebuilt. The job has been many times more difficult than after 1919. Not only is Austria occupied by four powers (the Soviet Union, the United States, the United Kingdom, and France),

[26] Parts of this section are taken from George W. Hoffman, "The Survival of an Independent Austria," *Geographical Review*, XLI (October, 1951), 606-21. By permission of the American Geographical Society.

but the so-called Cold War between the West and the East has affected every step taken to rebuild the shattered economy.

Unfortunately for Austria, it occupies one of Europe's most strategic areas. No great power can afford to have it dominated by another power. That is why postwar Austria was occupied, divided into four zones, and given a minimum of freedom to shape her own future. The U.S.S.R. occupies the key area of the Vienna Basin, while Vienna proper is jointly administered by all four occupation powers. The Western powers occupy the mountainous and hilly regions of southern and western Austria, including the new industrial region of Linz and the Upper Styrian industrial area centered on the Erzberg.

Food Supply. When peace was restored in 1919, and an independent Austrian Republic was organized, the new country found itself cut off from all of its former sources of supply. Old trade channels within the Austro-Hungarian customs union and with the rest of Europe were severed, agricultural areas were cut in two by new international boundaries, and the new countries carved out of the former Empire were unwilling to export agricultural products except on a strict barter basis. Bowman summarized Austria's losses by stating that "The Czechs were the chief producers of sugar beets. . . . Maize (corn) and wine were produced in the Slovene region of Alpine forelands; barley was produced chiefly in Bohemia and Galicia. Istria was famous for its maize and wine; Gorizia yielded wheat and maize. . . ." [27] Special attention was given to increased food production, but in view of the climatic conditions and the generally poor soils in this mountainous country, there were sharp limitations to any plan of agricultural expansion. In the valleys, winter lasts three to four months; the higher parts of the Alps are covered by snow for six to nine months. The basins of the eastern and southern part of the country are hot and dry during the summer. Forests cover about 37 per cent of the total area of Austria and about 47 per cent of its productive land. Nevertheless, agricultural production increased despite the lack of capital and the never-ending internal party strife. Before World War II, Austria had become about 75 per cent self-sufficient, an achievement which represented a new high in the country's agricultural economy.

World War II wiped out all the previous gains in Austria's food producing capacity. Further shortages, loss of farm machin-

[27] Isaiah Bowman, *The New World* (Yonkers, N. Y.: World Book Co., 1926), pp. 212-14.

ery, destruction wrought by moving armies, mass slaughter of live-stock, and a shortage of man power combined to bring about a situation similar to that experienced twenty-five years previously. Only the immediate postwar intervention of such international relief agencies as the United Nations Relief and Rehabilitation Administration and the aid given by private relief organizations and the occupation armies saved the Austrian population from malnutrition. Later, the Austrian government, in close cooperation with the Economic Cooperation Administration (ECA) undertook to provide seeds and artificial fertilizer, initiated measures to control cattle tuberculosis, began a program of mechanization and electrification of farm equipment, and improved rural roads. Furthermore, laboratories and farm educational institutions were established. By the end of 1951, total agricultural production had risen to about 98 per cent of the 1937 level. Austria's chief crops are rye, wheat, oats, and barley, in that order of importance.

The problem of Austria's self-sufficiency in food supply has already been touched upon. While food production increased steadily after reaching a low in 1946, consumption kept on exceeding these higher production levels. It is estimated that Austria had become 78 per cent self-sufficient by the end of 1951. Nevertheless, with a population approximately 3.5 per cent larger than in 1934, and reduced American economic aid, Austria must face and somehow solve the problem of how to increase acreage and agricultural output.

Various studies have been undertaken to determine how Austria's food producing acreage might be increased. They have all come to the same conclusion: By improving existing acreage through reclamation and irrigation, enough new farmland can be brought under cultivation to make Austria self-supporting; only the corn acreage cannot be expanded substantially, for climatic reasons. Since 1945, more than 52,000 acres have been reclaimed or brought under irrigation, and an additional 12,500 acres were marked for improvement.

A substantial increase in agricultural acreage and output per acre would not only save the country valuable foreign currency otherwise needed for food imports but would also bring additional income to the state treasury, increased employment, and possibly arrest the constant numerical decline of the farm population (the number of people employed in agriculture and forestry fell from 285,600 in 1937 to 237,000 in 1951). Seasonal agricultural labor, which before 1938 was recruited from adjacent countries, may now be drawn from among the more than 300,000 displaced persons still living in Austria.[28] While modern farm machinery could possibly be used in greater numbers, it is questionable whether its utilization would be economical if at all feasible, in view of the smallness of most farms and the country's rugged relief.

Minerals. With the exception of coal, Austria is fortunate in having considerable mineral deposits: iron ore, salt, talc, gypsum, magnesite, and oil (Figure 91). The iron ore deposits of Styria are of excellent quality and suffice to meet domestic requirements (Figure 104). Also mined in increasing quantities are antimony,

FIGURE 104. The Erzberg (Ore Mountain) in Styria. Open-pit mining has been carried on here since Neolithic times. (Austrian State Tourist Office.)

bauxite, china clay, graphite, lead, and pyrite. Many of these minerals are exported, thereby contributing to Austria's growing foreign trade. The lack of adequate coal is a primary cause for many of the country's economic difficulties; four to five million tons must be imported annually.

Water Power. Austria is one of the most important sources of hydroelectric power in Europe. Its potential is estimated at

[28] According to the *Report of the United States High Commissioner*, Statistical Annex XVIII, First Quarter 1951, No. 53, p. 5, this figure includes all displaced persons and aliens in Austria, regardless of date of entry, with the exception of those granted residence permits by the Austrian government.

more than 30 billion kw-hr annually, as compared with Switzerland's 20 billion kw-hr. In 1951, Austria produced a total of 7.4 billion kw-hr, an output 150 per cent above that of 1938. More than 15 per cent of this power is exported, principally to Germany. Upper Austria ranked first in production and was followed by Styria and the Tyrol. The country's power capacity is being expanded at a rapid rate (Figure 105).[29]

FIGURE 105. Mooserboden Reservoir at the head of the Kaprun Valley, under construction in 1949. This dam, now finished, is part of the Glockner-Kaprun hydroelectric power project. (Austrian State Tourist Office.)

The expansion of Austria's hydroelectric capacity assumes special importance in view of the country's coal shortage. Experts have come to the conclusion that by increasing the capacity, expanding the high tension grid, and creating ample storage capacity, it may become possible to reduce bituminous coal imports by more than 50 per cent.

Petroleum. Austria's most recent fuel discovery is petroleum, which takes its place, as a major source of energy, with hydroelectric

[29] See Alice F. A. Mutton, "Glockner-Kaprun Hydroelectric Project, Hohe Tauern, Austria," *Geographical Review*, XLI (April, 1951), 332-34.

power and imported coal. Most of Austria's petroleum and refining facilities are in the Zistersdorf area, thirty miles northeast of Vienna (in the Soviet zone of occupation). Between 1937 and 1950, production increased from 32,000 metric tons to 1.5 million metric tons. Since minimum domestic needs are estimated at 1,000,000 metric tons, a sizable export surplus should be available under normal conditions, in exchange for coal imports. Were such a barter arrangement feasible, it would greatly benefit the Austrian economy. Unfortunately, the Soviet occupation forces release an insufficient quantity of Austria's own oil to cover the country's minimum needs. The huge quantities of oil sent to the Soviet Union bring no benefit to the Austrian economy.[30] Hence, a great deal of foreign exchange and foreign-aid funds (ERP, etc.) must be expended to make up the deficit.

Forest Products. Austrian forests cover 37 per cent of the country. Spruce is the most important tree, with the Scotch pine and the beech of secondary importance. Her forests make it possible for Austria to be one of the few European countries which export timber and paper. Before the German occupation, these forests yielded 32.5 million board feet annually. During the war, annual felling exceeded the annual increment, but by 1950 lumbering was back to its prewar level; overcutting remains a serious problem. New forest areas are now being tapped in the less accessible parts of the country, and great improvements are being made in timber hauling and evacuation methods. Exports of timber and timber products, prefabricated houses, cardboard, and paper are slowly rising above the 1937 total of two million metric tons. By 1950, the export of lumber had increased so greatly that domestic consumers found it difficult to procure adequate supplies.

Industries. Austria's present and future industrial outlook is unquestionably more favorable than that of many other European countries. During World War II, the iron, steel, aluminum, and chemical industries were expanded, and, despite considerable bomb damage and destruction caused by early occupation excesses, the country's total industrial capacity is now much larger than it was in 1938. However, a large part of this expansion was for military needs, and many of the country's industrial plants which were unfortunate enough to be located in the Soviet zone of occupation

---

[30] Late in 1952, the Soviet administration in Austria announced that the U.S.S.R. would sell to Austria in 1953 more than 1,000,000 tons of oil products. Austrian experts said this was about half of what the Russians had confiscated from Austrian fields as former German assets.

have been dismantled and shipped to the U.S.S.R. or forced to produce for the sole benefit of the Soviet Union. It is estimated that the equivalent of 12 per cent of Austria's present industrial capacity has been removed by the Soviet Union. The Western powers, on the other hand, restored all the plants in their zones to Austria in 1946.

Among the plants built during the war, several had been intended to serve a Europe under unified German control. Most of these plants are now in Austrian hands, since they are located in the American and British zones of occupation. Two are at Linz, where port facilities have also been greatly expanded. The United Iron and Steel Works has some of the most modern blast furnaces and steel-processing mills; their combined capacity exceeds both Austria's needs or its ability to supply iron ore. These facilities, together with the modernized furnaces and rolling plants in Styria, make Austria one of the more important steel-producing countries of Europe. The large nitrogenous fertilizer plant near Linz is now producing upwards of 400,000 metric tons of fertilizer, a considerable portion of which is available for export. An aluminum plant at Ranshofen, Upper Austria, has a capacity of 60,000 tons, but because of a shortage of bauxite and electric power has been only in partial production since its completion.

Austria's successful efforts to increase its industrial output have been strengthened by shipments of modern industrial equipment from the United States. A large rolling mill in Styria was perhaps the most important addition. This new machinery, while greatly contributing to the industrial output, at the same time created a greater dependence upon imports of industrial raw materials, most of which must be obtained from the countries of East Central Europe.

Austria has also become the recipient of industries established by Germans who, before the war, had lived in the Czech Sudetenland, in Hungary, and in Yugoslavia. For example, the famous Gablonz glassware, formerly a noted export item of Czechoslovakia, is now produced in Salzburg and in Upper Austria and is a fillip to Austria's foreign trade. Most of the industries established since 1940 are located at some distance from the old industrial core—the Vienna Basin—a fact which is partially responsible for the population growth of Austria's western provinces.

The Tourist Trade. The tourist trade constitutes an important source of income for Austria. In this respect, Austria is in sharp competition with Switzerland although it does not have the latter's long experience in accommodating visitors. While the province of Styria has experienced the greatest influx of visitors, most of these have been Austrians; the Tyrol, Salzburg, Vorarlberg, and Carinthia have attracted more foreign visitors. Although the number of tourists visiting Austria since the war lags behind prewar figures, there has been a marked revival of the trade in the past two or three years. Hotels, inns, and tourist homes are high on the priority list for postwar construction, and many of the country's beautiful and scenic spots are being opened to tourists.

Transportation. Austria's strategic location involves a special responsibility for the upkeep and modernization of its transportation system. Both domestic traffic serving the important tourist trade and transit traffic serving the rest of Europe must be considered. Several important international rail lines cross the country, and their modernization goes hand in hand with the further electrification of Austrian lines. Here again competition with Switzerland is keen. Electrification of the main east-west line from Vorarlberg to Vienna is largely completed, and many other lines have also been electrified. Of even greater importance, perhaps, is the double-tracking of important rail lines including numerous tunnels. The improvement of the highway net is of equal importance to a country so dependent upon transit traffic and tourist trade. Most parts of Austria are accessible by modern roads, and up-to-date highways crisscross the country. Because of its mountainous character, the construction and maintenance of roads is not only difficult but costly.

The question of linking the Danube by canals with other European rivers has been discussed earlier in this chapter. Only when oil and surplus grains may be exchanged for the coal and machinery of the Ruhr and Silesia will the Danube become a traffic artery of major importance. However, such an exchange is based on relatively free trade, and it is doubtful whether such a project can be carried out in a Europe divided into so many national units, each with its special interests. It is clear, however, that a link between the Danube and other trafficable waterways is as badly needed for Austria and for the rest of Europe today as it was in the seventeenth century when Austrian and Bohemian merchants first proposed the Morava-Oder (Danube-Baltic) Canal.

Summary. The gradual substitution of waterpower and petroleum for imported coal is a key to Austria's postwar development. If it can be carried out successfully, the foreign trade balance will be restored and Austrian industries will be guaranteed a steady supply of domestic fuel. However, Soviet control of the country's petroleum production is the key to the whole problem.

With Austria included in the European Recovery Program, the United States has assumed a major responsibility for the restoration of its economy. Thus far, results have been satisfactory, both for the United States and for Austria. Her production index has climbed steadily. Unemployment has been held down, the tourist trade has improved, and a stable government has been in charge.

The Most Urgent Problems Facing the Countries of Central Europe

We have completed the analysis of the countries of Central Europe. While it is natural for a region so artificially delimited to contain a great deal of physical and human diversity, certain common characteristics are nevertheless discernible. A final survey of these characteristics will also be helpful in pointing up the major problems facing Germany, Switzerland, and Austria. The most important common features will now be listed:

1. Location and control of transportation systems. Because of their location in the heart of Europe, Germany, Switzerland, and Austria embrace important roads, passes, and rivers within their territories. Austria and Switzerland control the key Alpine passes, Germany the east-west passage across the Northern Lowlands, and Austria the Vienna Basin with its many radiating routes. In addition, some of Europe's most important rivers flow through these countries. Although traffic on some of these rivers may be curtailed (e.g., the Danube cut in two by the Iron Curtain), or may have decreased as a result of changed economic conditions, greater use of river traffic is of paramount importance for postwar Europe.

2. Dependence upon important foreign raw materials. With the exception of coal available in Germany, water power, timber, petroleum (controlled at the present time by Soviet Russia), and some iron ore found in Austria, and water power and timber in Switzerland, all raw materials must be imported.

3. Economies based on industrial surpluses. German steel, chemicals, and other heavy manufactured products, Swiss high-quality products such as engineering equipment and chemicals, and Austrian machinery, textiles, and forest products must all be exported in order to pay for raw material imports.

4. Food deficit. Austria reached 75 per cent of self-sufficiency before the war. Switzerland's main emphasis is on dairying and cheese manufacturing; it is cheaper for Switzerland to import cere-

als than to produce them at home. Germany, with an increased population and less arable land per head than in 1937, faces a tremendous food-deficit problem; at the present time it is a substantial food importer.

5. Highly skilled labor for the production of high-quality items. Without such a labor force the three countries could not compete with cheaper mass-produced goods coming largely from the United States.

6. Homogeneity of population in Germany and Austria. Switzerland, whose different ethnic groups live in peace and mutual respect, also has no nationality problems.

7. World War II and postwar problems. Switzerland, though neutral, was at times completely cut off from the outside world and had to adjust her economy to self-sufficiency; she suffered no direct war damages. Germany, whose economy was totally disrupted at the end of the war, is occupied by four powers, has lost territory, has acquired millions of refugees, and has to repair extensive war damages. Austria re-emerged as an independent country after seven years of occupation and complete absorption into the German war economy; Austria, too, is still occupied by four powers.

8. Postwar economic rehabilitation. Rehabilitation is relatively simple in Switzerland, since no industries have been damaged and no manpower has been lost through warfare. The Swiss economy is reverting slowly to the prewar pattern—concentration on high-quality exports. Western Germany, which was just recently granted a great deal of freedom in guiding its economic destiny, suffers considerably from the east-west split; moreover, it has lost economically important territory. On the other hand, Germany's extensive industrial plants are urgently needed to increase production all over the world, thus giving the country an excellent bargaining position. Eastern Germany is controlled by the Soviet Union. Its industrial plants are also urgently needed by the rest of the world, but its economy is closely integrated with that of Soviet Russia and of other East Central European countries. Austria, which the Allies had not declared an enemy country during World War II, is greatly hampered by Soviet control of its important industries and petroleum resources. Not unlike Germany, however, Austria's strategic location gives added importance to her raw materials and her industrial capacity. Not only has the United States encouraged Austria's quick rehabilitation, but it has contributed large sums and technical aid to the modernization of existing facilities, the construction of new plants, and the rehabilitation of agriculture.

9. East-West controversies. The split, which has widened since the Korean War, affects the life of all three countries to varying degrees. Germany and Austria, both occupied in part by Soviet Russia, have been politically and economically divided since 1945, though Austria to a lesser degree. Switzerland has been under United States pressure to reduce its trade with the countries behind the Iron Curtain, especially in strategic materials. As East and West move further apart in Europe, each of the two halves appears to be gaining a certain unity.

Other urgent problems could be cited, but those listed seem to be the most important ones. It is not the purpose of this brief summary to discuss all the problems in detail, but rather to indicate those important trends and possible solutions which may enable the student to anticipate future developments in Europe.

How each of these countries will solve its problems depends to a considerable degree on the future course of international relations and on the outlook for orderly trade relations. If a political rapprochement in Europe and in the world at large were in the offing, political stability and closer ties between European nations could be achieved, and the problems of economic rehabilitation could be easily solved. Switzerland would again concentrate on its specialized exports; Germany and Austria would exchange manufactured products for raw materials and direct their trade toward East Central Europe, Soviet Russia, and many overseas countries. Unfortunately such a solution is not in sight.

As long as the country is divided, Germany's future is clouded. Two entirely separate governmental and economic structures are in the process of being erected. One, controlled by the Western powers, is largely based on pre-Hitler economic organizations; the other, controlled by Soviet Russia, is modeled after and closely tied to the economy of Soviet Russia. The main problem in divided Germany is how to increase production—both agricultural and industrial. Apart from that, both sections of Germany have to pay considerable occupation costs. In addition, the German Democratic Republic is forced to ship sizable amounts of both light and heavy industrial products as reparations to the Soviet Union; and many other industrial facilities are now either partially or totally owned by the Soviets. With considerable United States help the German Federal Republic has succeeded in rehabilitating a large share of its damaged production facilities. As a participant in the European Recovery Program, Western Germany has benefited from various economic and political schemes, most of which are aimed at strengthening the West economically and unifying it politically.

In addition to recapturing its prewar markets, Switzerland hopes to attract an ever-increasing number of foreign visitors. The tourist trade is rapidly becoming a ranking industry. The problem is how to increase exports in the face of world-wide trade restrictions. Switzerland will need a great deal of ingenuity in order to keep its competitive position at a time when nearly every Western country is bent on furthering its own exports.

Austria has special problems, largely because it is an occupied country. As long as Soviet troops live off the land and the U.S.S.R. draws off almost 12 per cent of Austria's industrial capacity, it is extremely difficult to see how the country can become solvent. Either the United States will have to pay the bill, or else Austria's economy will collapse, entailing serious domestic and international repercussions. Because of inflated raw material prices, Austria has been forced to increase her exports, reduce domestic consumption, and curtail her imports. However, with a limited amount of American financial help, and by straining all sinews to increase its productive facilities and its exports, and at the same time increase the standard of living of its inhabitants, Austria will be able to carry on until such time as its position in a unified Europe is more secure.

BIBLIOGRAPHY

A. Books in English

DICKINSON, ROBERT E. *The Regions of Germany.* New York: Oxford University Press, 1945.

HARPHAM, W. *Switzerland, Economic and Commercial Conditions in Switzerland.* London: H. M. Stationery Office, 1948.

MAYER, KURT B. *The Population of Switzerland.* New York: Columbia University Press, 1952.

MORGENTHAU, HANS. *Germany and the Future of Europe.* Chicago: Chicago University Press, 1951.

OESCHLI, WILHELM. *History of Switzerland, 1499-1914.* London: Cambridge University Press, 1922.

PARTSCH, JOSEF. *Central Europe.* New York: D. Appleton & Co., 1903.

POUNDS, NORMAN. *The Ruhr.* London: Faber & Faber, 1952.

ROTHSCHILD, K. W. *The Austrian Economy Since 1945.* London: Royal Institute of International Affairs, 1950.

———. *Austria's Economic Development Between Two Wars.* London: Frederick Muller, Ltd., 1947.

RUSSELL, FRANK M. *The Saar: Battleground and Pawn.* Stanford: Stanford University Press, 1951.

B. Books in Foreign Languages

BLANCHARD, RAOUL. *Les Alpes Occidentales* (The Western Alps). Tours: Arrault et Cie, 1938-45.

BRAUN, G. *Deutschland* (Germany), 5 parts. Berlin: Gebrüder Bornträger, 1926-34.

DOPSCH, ALFONS. *Die Ältere Wirtschafts-und Sozialgeschichte der Bauern in den Alpenländern Österreichs* (The Early Economic and Social History of the Farmers in the Alpine Provinces of Austria). Oslo: Aschehoug (Nygaard), 1930.

FRÜH, J. *Geographie der Schweiz* (Geography of Switzerland). St. Gallen: Fehr, 1929-45.

GSTEU, HERMANN. *Länderkunde Österreichs* (Regional Geography of Austria). Innsbruck: Tyrolia Verlag, 1948.

GUTERSOHN, HEINRICH. *Landschaften der Schweiz* (Regions of Switzerland). Zürich: Büchergilde Gutenberg, 1950.

HAUSHOFER, ALBRECHT. *Pass-Staaten in den Alpen* (Pass Countries in the Alps). Berlin: K. Vowinckel, 1928.

KOBER, L. *Bau und Entstehung der Alpen* (Structure and Origin of the Alps). Berlin: Gebruder Bornträger, 1923.

KREBS, NORBERT (ed.). *Landeskunde von Deutschland* (Regional Geography of Germany), 3 parts. Leipzig and Berlin: B. G. Teubner, 1923-35.

———. *Die Ostalpen und das heutige Österreich* (The Eastern Alps and Today's Austria). Stuttgart: J. Engelhorn's Nachfolger, 1928.

LEITMEIER, HANS (ed). *Die Österreichischen Alpen* (The Austrian Alps). Vienna: F. Deuticke, 1928.

MACHATSCHEK, FRITZ. *Länderkunde von Mitteleuropa* (Regional Geography of Central Europe). Enzyklopädie der Erdkunde, ed. O. Kende. Vienna: F. Deuticke, 1925.

MAULL, OTTO. *Deutschland* (Germany). Leipzig: Bibliographisches Institut, 1933.

NUSSBAUM, F. *Geographie der Schweiz* (Geography of Switzerland). Bern: Kümmerly und Frey, 1940.

PENCK, A., and BRÜCKNER, E. *Die Alpen im Eiszeitalter* (The Alps During the Great Ice Age), 3 vols. Leipzig: Tauchnitz, 1909.

C. ARTICLES

CAROL, HANS VON, and SENN, ULRICH. "Jura, Mittelland und Alpen, Ihr Anteil an Fläche und Bevölkerung der Schweiz" (Jura, Mitteland and Alps, Their Share in the Area and Population of Switzerland), *Geographica Helvetica*, V (1950), 129-36.

CLARK, RONALD W. "Liechtenstein Thrives on Stamps," *National Geographic Magazine*, XCIV (July, 1948), 105-12.

"Das Deutsche Flüchtlingsproblem" (German Refugee Problem), *Sonderheft der Zeitschrift für Raumforschung*, Bielefeld: F. Eilers Verlag, 1950.

DICKINSON, ROBERT E. "Economic Regions of Germany," *Geographical Review*, XXVIII (1938), 609-26.

———. "Rural Settlements in the German Lands," *Annals of the Association of American Geographers*, XXXIX (1949), pp. 239-63.

GARNETT, ALICE. "The Loess Region in Central Europe in Prehistoric Times," *Geographical Journal*, CVI (1945), 132-43.

GRADMANN, NORBERT. "Das mitteleuropäische Landschaftsbild nach seiner geschichtlichen Entwicklung" (The Central European Landscape in Its Historical Development), *Geographische Zeitschrift*, VII (1901), 361-77, 435-47.

HARRIS, CHAUNCY D. "The Ruhr Coal Mining District," *Geographical Review*, XXXVI (1946), 194-221.

HASSINGER, HUGO. "Boden und Lage Wiens" (Site and Situation of Vienna), *Mitteilungen der Geographischen Gesellschaft in Wien*, LXXXIV (1941), 359-84.

HELD, COLBERT C. "The New Saarland," *Geographical Review*, XLI (1951), 590-605.

HOFFMAN, GEORGE W. "The Survival of Independent Austria," *Geographical Review*, XLI (1951), 605-21.

KUEHNELT-LEDDIHN, ERIK M. R. VON. "The Southern Boundaries of Austria," *Journal of Central European Affairs*, V (1945), 243-59.

MUTTON, ALICE F. A. "Hydro-Electric Power in Western Europe," *The Geographical Journal*, CXVII (1951), 328-42.

NIEHAUS, HEINRICH. "Agricultural Conditions and Regions in Germany," *Geographical Review*, XXIII (1933), 23-47.

OFFICE OF THE U. S. HIGH COMMISSIONER FOR GERMANY. "Improving Germany's Agriculture," *Report on Germany*, 7th Quarterly Report (April-June 1951), 77-85.

POUNDS, NORMAN. "The Ruhr Area: A Problem in Definition," *Geography*, XXXVI (1951), 165-78.

RESEARCH AND PLANNING DIVISION, ECONOMIC COMMISSION FOR EUROPE. "Pre-War Regional Interdependence and Post-War Interzonal Trade in Germany," *Economic Bulletin for Europe*, I (1949), 25-62.

SÖLCH, JOHANN. "The Brenner Region," *Sociological Review*, XIX (1927), 318-34.

STOLZ, OTTO. "Der deutsche Raum in den Alpen und seine Geschichte" (The German Area in the Alps and Its History), *Zeitschrift des deutsch-österreichischen Alpenvereins*, LXIII (1932), 1-36, and LXIV (1933), 240-76.

VALKENBURG, S. VAN. "The Rise and Decline of the German 'Lebensraum'," in *New Compass of the World*, Hans Weigert and others (eds.), New York: The Macmillan Co., 1949, pp. 205-18.

WOPFNER, HANS. "Die Besiedlung unserer Hochalpentäler" (The Settlement of Our Alpine Valleys), *Zeitschrift das deutsch-österreichischen Alpenvereins*, LI (1920), 25-86.

chapter 7

SOUTHERN EUROPE

THIS CHAPTER deals with the area within the present political boundaries of European Turkey, Greece, Italy, Spain, and Portugal, as well as with several minor political units closely connected with them such as the Free Territory of Trieste, the republic of San Marino, the Vatican State, the island of Malta, Gibraltar, and the republic of Andorra. This is, obviously, an arbitrary definition. However, a short review of all possible and actually proposed delimitations of Southern Europe will show that all are arbitrary, whether they are based on topographic or hydrographic features, on climate or vegetation, on language or cultural traits. Using any one of these criteria, several different boundaries can be justified. A grouping based on a combination of several features would result in showing a boundary belt instead of a line, a concept which has many merits but is impractical for our purpose. Political boundaries have the advantages of being definite, of coinciding for long stretches with linguistic and cultural boundary lines. They often coincide with climatic and vegetation boundaries and sometimes even follow orographic and religious boundaries.

Physiographic Basis of Cultural Forms

Southern Europe consists of three separate peninsulas without territorial connection. Regarded as the European half of a circum-Mediterranean region, it has many uniting and characteristic features which stand out clearly. Only once in history, during the Roman period, did the whole area form a political unit, although its essential unifying traits of climate, vegetation, and way of life have persisted. At other periods, African states extended over parts of the opposite European shores, or European countries reached

439

into Africa. When the enmity between Christianity and Islam disrupted this unity most completely, the disruption was felt as something unnatural and both parties tried to correct the situation, though, of course, each acted in its own interest.

Location. Peninsular location means that some of the Southern European countries have a land boundary in common with no more than one neighbor (Portugal, Gibraltar, the Vatican State, and San Marino) or with two (Free State of Trieste and Andorra). On the other hand, very short distances across the sea separate most of these nations from several other territorial units. It is less than one hundred miles from Italy to Albania, Greece, Malta, Tunisia, and French Corsica, or from Spain to Morocco and Algeria. And it is less than 250 miles from Portugal to Spanish or French Morocco; between the Spanish Balearic Islands and Italian Sardinia; between Sardinia and Algeria; and between Greece and Cyrenaica, Egypt, or Cyprus. Add to this the fact that the Greek and Turkish coasts, as well as those of Italy and Yugoslavia face each other across narrow seas for much greater distances than the length of their land boundary. All these factors illustrate the intimate interpenetration of land and sea in Southern Europe.

The longitudinal extent of this region is rather wide, namely 2,200 miles from the Atlantic coast of Portugal to the Dodecanese Islands. That is almost as far as from New York to Hoover Dam or from San Francisco to Detroit. When it is noon at Rhodes (Rhodos) it is 9:30 in the morning in Lisbon. The north-south distances are much shorter. From Malta to the Brenner Pass on the northern border of the Italian Tyrol is roughly 800 miles, the distance from Atlanta to Detroit. Crete's southern coast is still farther to the south, but the distance thence to the northern frontier of Greece is only about 450 miles.

The maritime character of Southern Europe is pronounced. It explains why, despite the distances involved, the land area is only somewhat larger than that of Texas and New Mexico combined. Of this area, more than 75 per cent is peninsular, eight per cent is islands and another 15 per cent belongs to the mainland of Europe.

Land and Sea. The inland point located farthest from a coast (230 miles) lies in the Iberian Peninsula, roughly fifty miles southwest of Madrid. This fact is a good indication of the general character of the region. Though land and sea interpenetrate over the whole area, this is least true of the Iberian Peninsula and most true of Greece. Only on the plateaus of Spain do people live largely unconscious of the sea and its life. Everywhere else the proximity of the sea is felt in some subtle way. The Mediterranean Sea with its deep, clear, blue waters, its unending variety of bays, forelands, and islands; its fishing boats with their triangular white sails; its small white towns surrounded by cordons of single trees or small groves in a bare mountain landscape—all this belongs to the typical picture of Southern Europe. The peculiar coloring of the countryside is largely a result of the prevailing dryness of the air throughout a great number of sunny days. The azure color of the sea is caused by the high salt content.

Like the sea, the mountains belong to the landscape and typify the region. There are hardly any coastal points where mountains are not visible at some distance inland, nor is the view of mountains absent in the largest lowlands, the North Italian Plain. For the most part, hills and mountains come quite close to the coast, with small towns overlooking the sea from some summit. In northern Italy the famous lakes repeat the general character of the Mediterranean, their ultramarine expanses surrounded by oases of Mediterranean vegetation. The vivid clear colors, together with the exquisite shapes of the mountains rising out of the sea, account for the early development of the artistic sense in many of the Mediterranean peoples. The distinctive way in which they developed established a tradition to which we are heirs.

Structural Elements

Old Structural Elements of the Iberian Peninsula. Most of Southern Europe was shaped by the great mountain-building processes of the Tertiary period.[1] A different landscape exists only in the high plateaus of Spain. As a matter of fact, the central and western parts of Iberia also belong structurally to another world. The western section took its form essentially during the Hercynian revolution at the end of the Paleozoic period (Figure 106). It was probably connected at that time with the Hercynian massifs of Brittany, the French Massif Central and old mountain structures in western Morocco. It was lifted to its present altitude in the Tertiary period and at that time some warping took place in the rigid block. The deep gorges of the Duero, Tagus, and Minho rivers near the Spanish-Portuguese border are a result of rapid erosion induced by this uplift. Only on the northern margin, in the Cantabrian Cordillera, were the Hercynian masses involved in the Tertiary folding of the Pyrenees. The evidence of this folding

[1] For geologic terms see Appendix I.

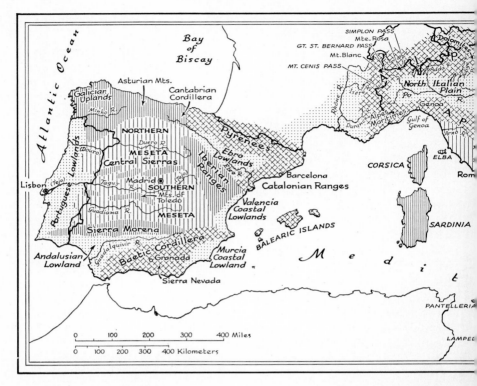

FIGURE 106. Physiographi

process becomes less and less pronounced toward the west in the mountains of Asturia. The old Iberian massif was, however, broken by later tectonic movements into many smaller blocks. The two largest pieces constitute the Mesetas. They form wide uniform plateaus, largely dry and treeless, a landscape with African affinities (Figure 107). The southern Meseta is somewhat lower and slightly tilted toward the southwest, where the transition to the Portuguese coastal plain is rather gradual. The northern Meseta is higher (on the average, 2,500 feet above sea level) and almost completely surrounded by rugged land. In the northwestern corner of the peninsula, erosion by numerous small rivers, draining into the Atlantic Ocean, has completely destroyed the original level surface. Galicia is a country of bold hills and meandering valleys. Stream erosion also played a great role in the dissection of the Cantabrian Cordillera.

Numerous smaller blocks were lifted high above the surface of the Meseta. For the most part these segments are narrow and ar-

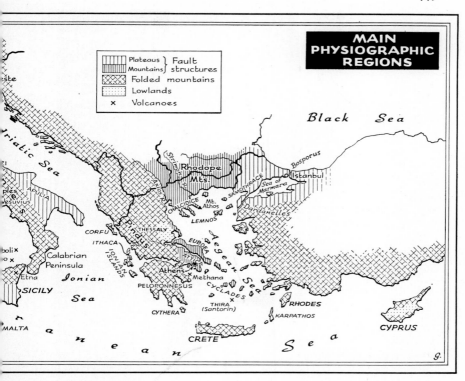

MAIN PHYSIOGRAPHIC REGIONS

Plateaus ⎱ Fault
Mountains ⎰ structures
Folded mountains
Lowlands
x Volcanoes

divisions of Southern Europe.

ranged in elongated rows. Thus they form the long ranges of the
Central Sierras between the northern and the southern parts of
the Meseta, the Iberian Ranges at the northwestern edge of the
Meseta, the Sierra Morena at its southern rim, and the shorter
ranges of the Montes de Toledo and their western continuation.
As they are not a single chain of mountains, there are many low
passes between the individual ranges. Fluvial and, in the higher
parts, glacial erosion has almost completely destroyed the original
plateau surface. As their name, *sierras* (saws), indicates, they appear as saw-toothed ridges. The least passable are the Iberian
Ranges. They can be bypassed through the gap of Burgos, between
the Cantabrian Cordillera and the Iberian Ranges. The eastern
part of the Mesetas is buried beneath horizontal layers of Tertiary
material, and there is no visible break between the Tertiary deposits
and the old structural surface.

The triangular Ebro Lowlands are presumably a depressed block
buried beneath deeply dissected Tertiary deposits (Figure 108).

FIGURE 107. The treeless, flat Meseta. The village of Vico di Segovia is sheltered in a small valley. (Spanish Tourist Office.)

Its western, innermost corner is a dissected hill country; only in the eastern part does the Ebro Valley merge with a somewhat extended plain.

Least conspicuous of the sierras is the Sierra Morena, at least when viewed from the Meseta. In the south, the Sierra Morena fronts the Andalusian Lowland along a straight faultline several hundred miles long. Thus it appears from the Andalusian side as a formidable mountain chain. At its foot is another triangular area of subsidence, which in its innermost corner is a country of low hills, but otherwise is an alluvial plain wide open toward the Atlantic Ocean.

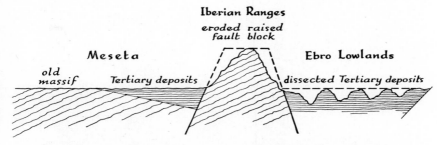

FIGURE 108. A west-east geologic profile of the Iberian peninsula.

Other Areas of Faulted Structure. There are other areas of old rocks scattered over the Mediterranean region, although they do not belong to such a uniform mountain system as the Hercynian system. Under the tremendous stresses and pressures of the Tertiary folding, they have been broken into many small pieces. Many of the fragments were submerged, others, mostly small ones, are still standing, and possibly have even been elevated. We can distinguish here three groups:

The first group, though its geological unity is disputed, consists of the islands of Sardinia, Corsica, and Elba, and some of the hill country in western Tuscany. The islands are high and rugged. In Tuscany the country is lower, though hilly and interspersed with small rolling plains. On the border of this fault block and the Apennines, a row of extinct volcanoes trends from northern Tuscany southwards. In Tuscany and Latium circular crater lakes bear witness to former volcanic action. This structural line of volcanoes continues southward to Vesuvius, which was thought to be extinct when it erupted in A.D. 79. The ashes of this famous first explosion buried and preserved the city of Pompeii for posterity. At present, the volcanic activity of Vesuvius is centered

in a cone which was built within the central caldera.[2] Still farther
south, Stromboli is one of the few known volcanoes constantly
active. Etna in Sicily erupts mostly through parasitic cones on its
slopes. The lava flows have frequently destroyed orchards and
towns but have also produced some good soils. Some cities, like
Messina in 1908, have been victims of severe earthquakes connected
with volcanic activity.

FIGURE 109. Mount Athos rises precipitously to a height of more than 6,000
feet above the sea, which is here more than 3,000 feet deep. (Press Department,
Greek Government.)

A second area of old structures is the Thracian block, culminating in the Rhodope Massif. It occupies central and eastern Macedonia and Thrace. This block is broken by numerous fault lines,
and though some parts are raised, others are depressed and have
either been buried under recent alluvial deposits or have subsided
below sea level in the deep northern part of the Aegean Sea. The
northernmost islands and the finger-like forelands of the Chalcidice
(Khalkidhiki) Peninsula, especially the steep, dark heights of Sam-
othrace (Samothraki) and Mt. Athos (6,349 feet) rise sheer out of
the azure sea (Figure 109) in striking contrast to the dazzling white

---

[2] A *caldera* is a large basin (caldron) resulting from volcanic activity.

limestone plateau of the nearby island of Lemnos, in the folded zone.

A third group are the Cycladic islands (Kikladhes) and small parts of Boeotia, Attica, and the island of Euboea (Evvoia). Between these components the land has subsided relatively little to form the shallow central part of the Aegean Sea. Fault lines have extended from this area and have also broken the Tertiary ranges into numerous small uplands and basins. Many basins, such as that of Thessaly, have been filled in and are now small lowlands. They are especially frequent in the inner corners of bays, where short streams enter the sea. A famous example is the Gulf of Lamia. Here the Sperkhios River has advanced its mouth approximately ten miles since historical time (Figure 110). The walls of the mountains which once made the few hundred feet of narrow Thermopylae an easily guarded pass, today face the deltaic plain.

The group of the Cyclades ends in the south at a fault line marked by active volcanoes and heavy earthquakes. In historical times only the volcanoes of Methana and Santorin (Thira) have erupted. The latter island is the remainder of the outer rim of a tremendous explosion crater, with steep walls facing the interior. The sea has broken through this wall and now occupies the interior crater. In recent times, submarine eruptions have occurred within the crater, thereby creating two small islands (Figure 111).

Deep Sea Basins. Subsidence, the contemporaneous counterpart of the uplift of some blocks, created in the Mediterranean area several caldron-like basins, some more than 10,000 feet deep. Some parts of the rising Alpine folds, but mostly the older structures, were carried along into the depths. The Mediterranean has several well-defined basins, frequently surrounded by semicircular gulfs and secondary subsidence features, closely connected with the main depressions. Bold headlands between them help create the type of coastline so characteristic of South Europe from Gibraltar to the heel of the Italian boot.

The Folded Mountain Zone. The Mediterranean Sea is not wholly a recent area of subsidence. In part, it is the successor of an old ocean which extended between Hercynian Europe on the north and Africa on the south. It is assumed the African landmass moved northward, narrowing the space of the sea, breaking up some island massifs, and squeezing out the sedimentary layers. Where the sediments were plastic enough they were folded; where they were too rigid they broke into blocks such as are to be found in the southern limestone Alps. In all South European peninsulas

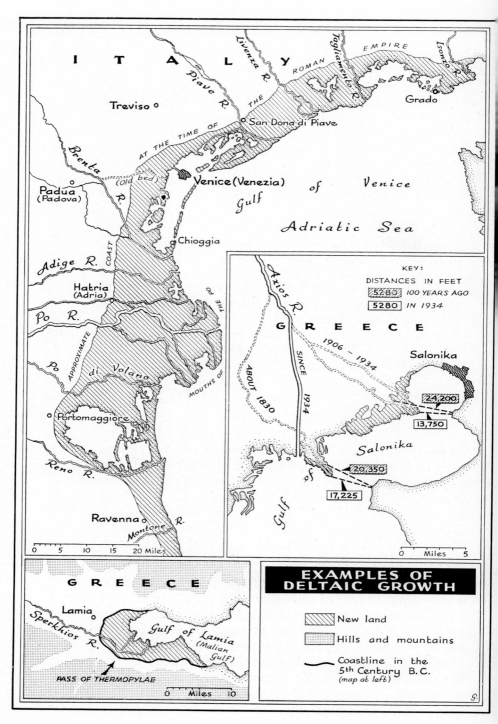

FIGURE 110

448

FIGURE 111. Santorin, an active island volcano. The island forms an interrupted circle around the gigantic old crater, now invaded by the sea. The island in the center of the crater is one of two islets created by recent eruptions. Note the style of the Greek church, with its cupola, free-standing bell tower, and crosses with arms of equal length. (Press Department, Greek Government.)

chains of folded mountains are outstanding. With the Alps, they form a continuous zone, extending eastward throughout the entire length of Asia. The manner of their connection with the Catalonian Ranges and the Baetic Cordillera (Cordillera Penirética) is debated. Several submarine connections stand out, such as those from the Apennines via Sicily to the Atlas Mountains, from southern Greece via Crete, Karpathos, and Rhodes to Asia Minor, and from the Baetic Cordillera to the Balearic Islands.

Landforms of the Folded Mountains. As soon as the mountain folds emerged from the sea, erosion set in, modeling and wearing down the mountains. Stream erosion was succeeded in the Alps and, to a lesser degree, in the higher parts of the other mountains by glacial erosion. Stream erosion has, of course, resumed its importance, but has not as yet been able to destroy the features of glacial erosion. The great lakes of northern Italy are fjord-like terminal basins of ancient glacier-tongues, with morainic amphitheaters at their lower ends. The valleys have steep walls and terraces, which protect villages and fields from floods. Tributary valleys end high above the floor of the main valleys and offer naturally favorable conditions for hydroelectric power works. Because of the proximity of the sea the base level for erosion is everywhere near, and steep slopes and narrow valleys abound, offering but poor means of livelihood amidst splendid beauty.

The Alps. Highest among the folded mountains of Europe are the Alps. Only parts of them, primarily their southern and their western ends, belong to Southern Europe and thus most of their aspects are discussed in detail in Chapter 6. The boundary of Italy encloses most of the drainage basin of the Po and its tributaries, following the divide more or less closely. The tributary valleys allow Mediterranean vegetation, climate, crops, Italian language and cultural habits to penetrate deep into the Alps. The same sort of penetration occurs in the French Alps to the west. These features are especially visible in the broad longitudinal valleys such as those of the Dora Baltea, Adda, Adige, Rienza, Durance, and Isère rivers. Valleys which bear names different from those of their streams, such as Val d'Aosta, Val Tellina, Val Venosta, and Val Pusteria (Pustertal), preserve names of very ancient tribes. These valleys lead to easy passes, some used since prehistoric times. They have helped to minimize the barrier function of the Alps and have been the routes of numerous invasions from the north.

Valleys and passes break up the Alps into numerous well defined groups. In the west they are mostly bare, steep, jagged mountains, with relatively small glaciers, forming two closely connected arcs, their convex side facing France. They gain in height from the Alpes Maritimes inland to Mont Blanc (15,781 feet). A group of passes, of which Mont Cenis Pass is the best known, provide the main connection from France into Italy. Curving east, the Alps trend from Great St. Bernard Pass to Simplon Pass. Here, on the Swiss-Italian border, is the highest peak of Southern Europe, Monte Rosa (15,271 feet). But the largest glaciers face northward, and the tremendous Italian slopes are largely bare rock in their higher parts.

East of the Simplon, the Pleistocene glaciers have carved deep furrows, which cup the blue waters of the famous Lake Maggiore, Lake Lugano, Lake Como, and Lake Garda. Eastward from Lake Como a separate zone of limestone mountains constitutes the inner arc of the Alps. Among these, the Dolomites are the most famous group because of their bizarre towers and crags, their white-and-pink walls standing above the green Alpine meadows, and the afterglow of the summits at sunset. Other limestone groups form bare, karstic plateaus with steep walls over fertile valleys. In between are old volcanic extrusions such as the reddish-black rocks of the porphyry plateau of Bolzano. Farther in the interior, crystalline schists, similar to those of the Western Alps form dark, high, glaciated massifs. Their highest peaks, however, do not attain the altitudes of the Western Alps.

Pindus System. In the Eastern Alps a southern chain of limestone mountains is well discernible and is generally regarded as the beginning of the Dinaric ranges which trend southeastward along the eastern shore of the Adriatic Sea through Yugoslavia and Albania into Greece, culminating in the Pindus Mountains. In Greece, smaller ranges fork from the parent chain, most of them swerving eastward in arcs open toward the north. These arcs have been cut into many isolated parts by large-scale faulting and subsidence. Thus, parts of the chains are often below the level of the Aegean Sea, whose islands are the lofty peaks of submarine ranges. The main chain can be traced through Cythera, Crete, Karpathos, and Rhodes (Rhodos). This interpenetration of sea and land has helped to make the Aegean coasts and islands of Greece one of the earliest centers of mutual cultural contacts. In sharp contrast are her western coasts, parallel to the axis of the mountains, and difficult of access. Along the coast trend the Ionian Islands, of which Corfu (Kerkira) is the largest, and Ithaca (Ithaki) the most famous. Like their Aegean counterpart, they prospered in ancient times and prosper again at present, in strong contrast to the physical and cultural bareness of the adjacent mainland. Many of the mountains of Greece rise almost isolated from the sea, thus appearing very high and impressive. Yet they would be little known were it not for the ancient writers and poets who peopled them with gods and heroes.

Many ranges of the eastern Italian Alps and virtually all the young mountains of Greece are made of limestone. Limestone mountains are poor. They have no mineralization and water tends to sink rapidly underground so that little is left on the surface. If

FIGURE 112. The rocky coast of an Aegean island. Lapiés visible at the right. (Press Department, Greek Government.)

deforestation occurs, and it did occur at one time or another in highly civilized, densely populated countries, the shallow soil is easily washed away and the typical limestone or karst phenomenon of "lapiés" (Figure 112) becomes apparent. In the central Peloponnesus many rivers disappear in sinkholes to reappear at some distant point, occasionally at the other side of a range as a strong spring. All over Greece are karst lakes without visible outlet. Many of them dry up in summer, leaving fertile but malarious plains. At other periods, the sinkholes become blocked and their lakes flood the surrounding country. Some, like Copais Lake in Boeotia have been drained to reclaim land for agriculture.

The Apennines. The Apennines are the southeastern continuation of the Western Alps. The two form a semicircle around the western end of the North Italian Plain. They run through the entire Italian peninsula in a bow-shaped chain. They first hug the shore of the Gulf of Genoa in Liguria, the famous Italian Riviera and then cross the peninsula and sweep close to the shore of the Adriatic Sea. Continuing further, they form the toe of the Italian boot, the peninsula of Calabria, and reappear in northern Sicily.

Throughout their length, the Apennines are a rather narrow and rugged mountain chain, though of moderate height. Limestone

FIGURE 113. The Vallata del Sinni. Note the braided stream in its floodplain, the bushes and scattered trees on the slopes, and the cultivated terraces. No human settlements are visible. (Attraverso L'Italia, Italian Touring Club.)

and sandstone formations are prevalent and this explains the lack of water in the higher parts. Where the Apennines recede from the Adriatic coast, extremely dry limestone plateaus of nearly horizontal strata form the spur of Mount Gargano and the plain of Apulia (Figure 113). They resemble the karst plateau of Yugoslavia across the Adriatic Sea, of which they are virtually a part in their geological structure. Along the eastern Italian coast a straight almost harborless coastline has developed.

The Apennines are the longest—though by far not the highest— of the South European folded mountain chains, extending approximately 600 miles from the group of low passes north and northwest of Genoa, which mark the boundary between them and the Alps. Another 175 miles of mountain ranges stretch across Sicily and continue as the Atlas Mountains in northern Africa.

Folded Mountains of the Iberian Peninsula. There are three Tertiary mountain chains on the Iberian Peninsula, two of them of almost equal and considerable height. The Mulhacén Peak in the Baetic Cordillera rises to 11,240 feet, the Pico de Aneto in the Pyrenees to 11,169 feet. The third chain, the Catalonian Ranges, are much lower. Because of their trend parallel to the coast they nevertheless constitute an important orographic feature, isolating the coastal area from the enclosed, subhumid Ebro basin.

The Pyrenees are for most of their length a fairly uniform mountain range, crossed by high, difficult passes. The central part is the highest and only near the ends are passes which have been used frequently. Railroads had to use the narrow space between the mountains and the sea on both ends until some twenty years ago, when engineers pierced these ramparts with two tunnels. The western end of the Pyrenees is accompanied by a lower parallel chain. Here a few longitudinal valleys exist. Elsewhere, short transverse valleys descend in grandiose steps from the glacial cirques near the main crests. The valleys of the southern and northern flank rarely originate on opposite sides of the same mountain and this explains the lack of good passes. Most valleys end against a steep towering wall. Because of their steepness and lower altitude, the Pyrenees were not as heavily glaciated in the Pleistocene period as were the Alps, and lack the many beautiful lakes of the latter.

The third range, the Baetic Cordillera, has a similarly complicated structure, broken into numerous individual groups, separated by transverse and longitudinal valleys. In a central depression, irrigated gardening and cities such as Granada have developed. The settlement pattern, therefore, resembles the Alps rather than any of the other folded mountain ranges. The highest group of the Baetic Cordillera is the Sierra Nevada (the snowy crest). In the northeast, the higher parts of a submarine continuation emerge from the sea to form the Balearic Islands (Islas Baleares). In the west, the Baetic Cordillera comes close to the Rif Mountains of northern Morocco at the Straits of Gibraltar. The Straits have been regarded by some as a low, flooded pass in a recurving chain. However, they seem rather to be a structural depression parallel to the trend of the mountains.

North Italian Plain. Different from the structures so far discussed is the northern third of the Adriatic Sea, which is a zone of downwarping between the uplifted folded zones of the Apennines and the Dinaric system of Yugoslavia. The Adriatic Sea once extended farther inland. Sediments brought by rivers from the Alps and the Apennines filled in this upper part and created the North Italian Plain. This process is still going on at the combined delta of the Po, Brenta, and Adige at the pace of almost 30 feet a year (see Figure 110, page 448). The northern part of the North Italian Plain was buried later under the moraines and outwash plains of the great Alpine glaciers of the Ice Age. Rivers cut into this unconsolidated material, lowering thereby the groundwater table. It emerges in a line of springs (*fontanili*) at the border of the morainic, dry and unfertile zone, and the alluvial materials (Figure 114). The Po meanders in the flood plain, confined by natural and man-made levees.

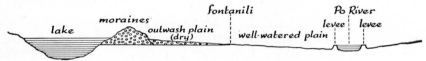

FIGURE 114. Diagram showing the location of fontanili on the North Italian Plain.

Climate

Owing to the existence of the Mediterranean Sea, the typical subtropical West Coast climate penetrates farther east in the Old World than anywhere else. During the summer Southern Europe lies in the region of the horse latitudes, the zone where the air of the dry antitrades sinks down and dries out even more in the process of descending. Thus the summer is characterized by sunny, hot weather with extended calms or light winds from varying directions. Trade winds blow over Sicily from the northeast and over the Greek peninsula from the northwest. A stable summer depression over Cyprus causes this deflection. The ancient Greeks called these light steady winds summer winds ("Etesians").

During winter the horse latitudes move southward. Thus the rainless period is usually restricted to July on the Riviera, lengthens to three to four months in Sicily and southeast Spain, and to four to five months in Malta and the Peloponnesus, causing the parched, semiarid appearance of these regions.[3] In some, especially in the limestone areas of southern Italy, rivers stop flowing in summer. Small mountain streams are in spate after heavy rains. During winter a few cyclonic depressions enter the Mediterranean Basin,

[3] See climatic graphs, Appendix II.

usually through the gap between the Pyrenees and the Alps, less frequently through the Straits of Gibraltar. Most of the cyclonic disturbances seem to develop over the Mediterranean area—for instance, the North Italian Plain and the Gulf of Genoa—moving along both Italian coasts and across Greece.

All these cyclonic depressions cause moderate rains but do not change the mild and frequently sunny character of the Mediterranean winter. As they sweep eastward they bring to the western coasts a generally more moist climate and higher winter temperatures. Locally and for short periods, temperatures are lowered by cold strong fall winds breaking down from the limestone plateaus of Yugoslavia, the *bora* of the northern Adriatic. The analogous *mistral* of southern France rarely extends to the Italian Riviera and the northeastern Spanish coast. A lasting cooling effect is precluded by the high temperature of the sea (about 57° F. in winter), which persists because little cold ocean water can enter through the narrow Straits of Gibraltar. Less spectacular but more persistent are the cold northeast winds which reach the Bosporus area across the Black Sea from the Russian plains. Their influence does not extend beyond the Sea of Marmara. Another characteristic wind is the south wind called *sirocco* in southern Italy and *leveche* on the Spanish east coast. Coming from the Sahara, it is a very warm, oppressive wind of the spring or fall but arrives as damp wind after crossing the sea. It is not to be confused with the African desert storms which on rare occasions bring their dust masses across the Mediterranean Sea.

Exceptions to the Mediterranean climate are found in the higher regions of the Alps and other mountain areas. More important is the continental climate of the North Italian Plain and that of the Spanish Mesetas. The North Italian Plain forms a basin enclosed almost on every side, in which cold air sinks to the bottom and stagnates for prolonged periods. Temperature inversion develops, the plain is covered by cold air and dense fog, the surrounding hills reaching into sunny, slightly warmer air layers. The Spanish Mesetas, on the other hand, create an independent air circulation system. During winter, a stable anticyclone develops there, causing low temperatures and light winds blowing outward from the center of the peninsula. In some winters this Iberian high is connected with the so-called Azores high. In summer the Mesetas are much more heated than any other part of the Mediterranean lands. Temperatures and dryness develop which place the interior of Spain in summer on a par with parts of North Africa. On the other hand, the northern and northwestern coastal landscapes of the Iberian peninsula definitely belong to the maritime climatic province of Western Europe.

Vegetation and Animals

As is the case with its climate, the vegetation found all around the Mediterranean Sea constitutes a distinctive and uniform type. During the Ice Age the general level of the oceans was lowered, and that of the Mediterranean Sea even more, since the influx of water through the Straits of Gibraltar was stopped. Plants and animals crossed over land bridges connecting Spain and Morocco, Sicily and Tunisia, as well as Greece and Asia Minor.

Mediterranean vegetation is characterized by evergreen trees and bushes with leathery, drought-resistant leaves, such as some types of oak (*Quercus ilex* and *Quercus inber*), laurel (*Laurus nobilis*), oleander (*Nerium oleander*), myrrh (*Commiphora*) and junipers (*Juniperus oxycedrus* and *macrocarpa*). Among conifers is the Aleppo pine, looking like a big, somewhat ruffled umbrella, standing alone on limestone rocks, and the cypress (*Cupressus sempervirens*) rising as a high, narrow, dark cone. Grass and meadows are almost completely absent.

The landscape, as we know it, is almost entirely man made. The original forests have been destroyed, and in many areas the unprotected shallow mountain soil has been washed away and bare limestone rocks remain, especially in Greece. In other places a secondary growth of low bush with few trees has developed. The bushes, which are thorny and grow in a dense tangle, difficult to penetrate, are called *maquis* (French), *macchie* (Italian) or *monte* (Spanish). If growing conditions are still less favorable the garrigue appears, a thorny bush with only very few, low trees interspersed. The bushes stand far apart and herds moving and feeding between them contribute to the further deterioration of the vegetation.

Most important, however, are the large areas occupied by trees bearing edible fruits. A few, such as apple trees (*Malus domestica*), fig trees (*Ficus larica*), and the glittering silver-gray olive trees (*Oba europaea*) (Figure 115) are indigenous. Most were brought in at different times, such as pears (*Pirus communis*), prunes (*Prunus domestica*), cherries (*Prunus avium*), apricots (*Prunus armeniaca*), peaches (*Prunus persica*), mulberries (*Morus alba*), and all citrus fruits. Most of the field crops, like the fruit trees, are Asiatic immigrants, either early ones such as presumably wheat and barley or later arrivals such as sugar cane (*Saccharum officinarum*) and cot-

458 A GEOGRAPHY OF EUROPE

ton (*Gossypium*). Corn (*Zea mais*) and tobacco (*Nicotiana tabacum*) were imported from America only a few centuries ago. From America also came the cacti, which can hardly be dissociated from the characteristic picture of the present Mediterranean landscape.

FIGURE 115. The olive tree reaches maturity in about six years. It is easily recognized by its gnarled and twisted trunk and small, silver-gray leaves. (Spanish Tourist Office.)

In the higher mountains, Mediterranean vegetation gradually gives way to Central European and Alpine forms. The interior of the Iberian peninsula is steppe. Whether it is a natural feature or man-induced by the destruction of original open forest and bushland is a debated question. The prevalence of esparto grass (*Lygeum spartum*) shows affinities with the North African steppe. There are also cultural landscapes of North African character such as the *huerta* of Murcia, with irrigated groves of date palms.

In these ancient cultivated countries the wild life has been reduced to the smaller animals, which are not conspicuous in the landscape. Poisonous snakes unknown to the rest of Europe, and scorpions belong to them. The domestic animals are the same as in all of Europe, but those better adapted to rocky, semiarid hill country such as sheep, goats, asses, and mules are more prominent than cattle, pigs, or horses. The uniformly high temperature of the sea, its great depth and little vertical circulation, plus the lack of plankton as fish fodder, exclude many fish which live in shoals, such as herring, cod, or salmon. An almost tropical variety of fish lives in the upper layers, but only tuna fish and sardines appear in large shoals.

Historical Geography

Despite obvious differences, the countries of Southern Europe have been influenced time and again by a common set of geographical factors, namely their location on the same land-locked sea, their connection with the European continent, and their relationship to Africa and Asia. There were periods when none of these factors exerted a decisive influence and each peninsula could develop autonomously. We shall discuss these autonomous developments by individual countries.

The Mediterranean Sea as Unifying Factor

The Mediterranean Sea exerted its unifying influence very early, when seafaring nations, the Minoan Cretans, Phoenicians, and Greeks founded trading posts and colonies all around its shores. Owing to the difficulties of land travel, the foundation of trading posts meant the economic domination of the hinterland by the sea power. Where such trading posts were closely spaced a whole empire developed, centered around one or the other of the various basins of the Mediterranean. Thus the Minoan Cretans apparently ruled effectively the area around the Aegean Sea, and the Phoenician settlers of Carthage the western Mediterranean basin. The Athenians established their rule around the Aegean Sea, Corinth and its colony Syracuse around the Ionian Sea. The oldest urban settlements in Southern Europe have grown from protected centers of some small landscape, such as Athens or Rome, or from the outposts of these trading empires such as Cadiz, Malaga, or Palermo. Many Greek tribal centers developed into merchant cities, and colonies such as Salonika (Thessaloniki), Corfu, Syracuse, and Naples were founded.

These older mercantile empires were replaced by the Roman Empire. The contemporary attempt of the Carthaginians to build an empire around the western Mediterranean basin did not succeed. The Romans based their rule on the sea, but at the same time they penetrated inland, building roads and cities as military

FIGURE 116. This Roman bridge, near Salamanca, is still in use. (Spanish Tourist Office.)

strongholds and bases of colonization. Some of these Roman roads have survived and served as main lines of communication up to the age of the railroads. Several bridges still stand and are used (Figure 116), and many railroads follow rather closely the alignment of

Roman roads. It is almost unique that no modern road follows the trace of the Roman road from Durazzo (Durrës) to Salonika.

Most Roman cities have survived. While many of the Greek cities such as Paestum, Emporium, Cnossus, and Phaestus were destroyed or at best left their names to small villages, this fate befell hardly any of the larger Roman cities. Some Roman cities replaced older fortified towns and tribal centers in Italy and the Iberian peninsula, such as Toledo, Lisbon, Bologna, Florence (Firenze). Most cities, dating from Roman times, are inland. On the coasts the Romans took over Greek and Phoenician cities, Genoa and Trieste being exceptions.

No later empire succeeded the Roman feat, although the Arabs in the ninth and the Turks in the sixteenth centuries almost did. In the nineteenth century, Great Britain virtually dominated the Mediterranean Sea from her bases at Gibraltar (1704), Malta (1815), the Ionian Islands (1815-64), Cyprus (1878), and Egypt (1882-1924), but it can hardly be said that she ruled over the adjacent countries. Other attempts were on a less ambitious scale. The Turks did succeed in making the eastern Mediterranean a Turkish sea; Venice ruled the Adriatic and Aegean seas; Spain dominated for a short time the western Mediterranean. The Greek attempt to convert the Aegean Sea into a Greek sea was defeated by the Turks in 1922. The Italians succeeded in making the Adriatic sea their *mare nostro* in 1919, but later met defeat when they strove to rule the whole Mediterranean.

The South European Peninsulas and the Continent

Time and again, attempts have been made to rule peninsular Southern Europe from a broad continental basis. Time and again, German kings crossed the Alps to gain the coveted imperial crown in Rome. They established a firm hold over the North Italian Plain and parts of central Italy for long periods, but only at the peak of their might over the south. Later the kings of France, Napoleon, and finally the Austrian Habsburgs repeated these attempts. The French succeeded in dominating Spain for much shorter periods by installing a relative of their rulers on the Spanish throne. Culturally more significant are the positions French monastic orders held in northern Spain in the wars against the Mohammedans. But in general the Pyrenees proved to be a better protection than the Alps with their deeply indented passes.

Greece, too, was annexed to northern empires for some short periods. Philip of Macedonia and Dushan of Serbia are the two famous conquerors from the north. On the other hand, there is no clear instance of any of the peninsulas serving as the basis for a dominion over the adjacent parts of the continent. The Romans did so only after they had founded their circum-Mediterranean empire. The Spanish attempt could succeed for a short while only because of the dynastic connection with the Austrian Habsburgs.

The domination of the South European peninsulas from the continent should not be confused with their use as land bridges between Europe and Asia or between Europe and Africa. They have served as such from prehistoric times, when people from North Africa took advantage of the disappearance of the ice from Europe to push northwards. In the last war, the Germans first used Italy as a bridge to Tunisia and Libya. The Americans and British, starting from Tunisia, fought their way through Sicily and then crossed to Italy. In the many centuries of recorded history there were many such movements in both directions. Some peoples merely moved through these countries. The Vandals, when they migrated across Spain into North Africa, left ruins but little else, as did Celtic tribes in Greece on their way to Asia Minor. Other peoples, such as the Turks in their advance to Central Europe, stayed on to rule over Greece for centuries. Still others, blocked in their advance, settled down as did some Celtic tribes in the North Italian Plain and other Celtic tribes in the Iberian Peninsula. Langobards and Visigoths are later examples. The Arabs passed through Spain into France, were finally thrown back, but remained in the peninsula from the eighth to the end of the fifteenth century.

Turkey (in Europe)

In a geographical sense, European and Asiatic sides of the straits formed by the Bosporus, the Sea of Marmara, and the Dardanelles cannot be treated separately. The Bosporus is only 800 yards wide at its narrowest place and the Dardanelles not much over one mile. Both are flanked by steep hills, and a strong surface current flows through them from the Black Sea to the Aegean Sea. They were river valleys in the geological past and, like a river valley they unite their banks rather than separate them (Figure 117). The character of the landscape is the same on both sides. No wonder that since very early times peoples and empires have tended to extend over both banks: the Persian Empire, some of the Hellenistic states, Rome, Byzantium, the Latin Empire, and the Ottoman Turkish Empire. The Straits hardly ever were more than provincial boundaries. Since Turkey's loss of most of her

European provinces in the two Balkan Wars of 1912-13, Eastern Thrace, the European part of Turkey, is only an enlarged bridge-head to safeguard the Straits.

The importance of the Straits lies in their function as the most important gateway through the great Eurasian mountain belt east of Marseille. Even the relatively easy mountain passes cannot rival their importance. Routes from inner Asia have used this gateway. The northern borderlands of the Black Sea, the Ukraine of today, exported their grain to the deficit areas around the Mediterranean

FIGURE 117. The Bosporus, looking from the Anatolian side to European Turkey. This narrow strait has all the characteristics of a river. The villas bespeak the period of Ottoman grandeur and power; the modern gun emplacement is grim evidence of modern Turkey's determination to defend the strait. (Turkish Information Office.)

Sea from antiquity to the Bolshevik Revolution in Russia. On the other hand, these great plains have been dependent upon many wares, luxuries and necessities for a higher standard of life, and before the age of the railroads there were few other channels of import. Thus, since prehistoric times, cities have been founded to guard this pass. The oldest was Troy. When the Arabs besieged Constantinople twice, they were prompted as much by the desire to expand Islam as by a desire to open the trade route to the Black Sea.

There have been interruptions in this Black Sea-Mediterranean Sea trade, either at times when the South Russian plains were invaded by barbarian hordes from the east, or when order and civilization broke down in the Mediterranean basin in the Dark Ages. More insidious were such interruptions when war and trouble on the Straits closed them and jeopardized the interests of both the Black Sea and Mediterranean partners. Fortunately such periods never lasted long because of the interest of the rulers of the Straits to profit from the passing traffic. Sometimes it meant only the replacement of one trading power by another. Venetians and Genoese alternated with the change of the rulers, Byzantines, Latin Emperors and Turks.

The situation changed when the Russians reached the north shore of the Black Sea. The Russians were well aware that their quest for the open sea was thwarted as long as they depended on the good will of the Turks for an exit from the Black Sea. There have been various legal arrangements in the last hundred years to safeguard the free transit through the Straits. None of them has proved satisfactory either for Russia or Turkey. As a consequence, the problem of the Straits continues to disturb the relations in this part of the world, though it may be shelved for shorter or longer periods.

The Crossroad City. Several cities rose to prominence and disappeared, from the fall of Troy to the selection of Byzantium by the Roman Emperor Constantine as the new capital of the Roman Empire in A.D. 330. The advantages of Istanbul—this nationalistic Turkish name is a corruption of the Greek *eis tan polin* (into the city)—over its competitors are local: a deep protected harbor, the drowned valley of the Golden Horn, which together with the Bosporus and Sea of Marmara surrounds a peninsula which could easily be defended. Since the establishment of Constantinople as capital and guardian of the crossroad, all other cities in this area have dwindled to insignificance. Today Ankara, Turkey's new capital in Asia Minor, outshines Istanbul politically and traffic between the Black Sea areas and the outer world is at a low ebb. The Near East–Central European trade route, which has suffered many ups and downs during history, is virtually dead at the moment. The Berlin-Baghdad railroad, which had been launched with high expectations, was completed during the last war, but never functioned as an effective link between northwestern Europe and the Near East. The nearby Turkish-Bulgarian boundary has indeed become the frontier between two worlds.

Population. There is probably no other country whose population has changed so completely within a generation as has that of European Turkey. Today there are living in all of European Turkey probably less people than lived in Istanbul alone some thirty years ago. Istanbul, whose population was estimated variously between 1,200,000 and 1,800,000 has today a little over one million people.[4] Although the Greek population of the city was exempted from the population exchange between Greece and Turkey, many left. When Istanbul ceased to be the center of a multinational state, many Serbs, Bulgars, Albanians, and Arabs also left. Government agencies and foreign embassies moved to Ankara and banks, shipping concerns, and great business firms closed their Istanbul offices. The decline of its population was speeded by an appallingly high death rate in the unsanitary older sections of the city. Although conditions have improved, there is not sufficient immigration to replace the deficit of deaths over births because Istanbul's European hinterland is lost to the Balkan countries and the Asiatic hinterland to the new capital of Ankara. Some smaller waves of emigration have also affected the city, such as the return of Armenians to Soviet Armenia and the Jewish migration to Israel. The majority of its White Russian refugees have also moved on.

These changes have made Istanbul more than ever a Turkish city. Forty years ago Istanbul had a majority of non-Islamic inhabitants; today, the majority belongs to the modernized and nationalized Mohammedan creed. A small but significant industrial population has recently developed, and indicates another turn in the city's fortunes. In all this Istanbul reflects developments in Turkey as a whole, which has become overwhelmingly a uniform Turkish state in which industrialization has made significant progress with American help.

If the population of Istanbul has shrunk considerably and is recovering slowly, that of Thrace has been changed completely. Before 1912 it was a thinly settled area, whose peasants spoke Bulgarian. In the small towns along the coasts Greeks prevailed. Only Edirne (Adrianople) and a few small places had Turkish garrisons. Greeks and Bulgarians have disappeared and an entirely Turkish population from Macedonia has taken its place. The land is more densely populated and better utilized.

The Economic Position of European Turkey Within the Turkish Republic. It should be obvious from the preceding paragraphs that European Turkey has little to contribute to the eco-

[4] Population statistics are to be found in Appendix III.

nomic life of Turkey. In every respect the center of gravity of modern Turkey is in Asia Minor (Anatolia). New roads, new railroad lines, irrigation works, prospecting for mining, the growth of new urban centers, experiments with new crops and new industries all are going on in this area. A few modern factories have been founded in Istanbul, mainly because of the presence of skilled labor.

Istanbul has retained part of its position as gateway to foreign commerce. Although its location has become too marginal to be the most convenient port for large parts of Turkey, it is still the home port of most of the Turkish merchant marine. Formerly Turkey relied almost exclusively on foreign ships for its overseas trade. Its own marine consisted of fishing vessels and a few small coastal vessels operated by Greek subjects of the Sultan. This has changed. Despite the loss of the seafaring Greek population the Turkish merchant marine has shown a slow, but continuous growth and the Turkish flag can be seen in all ports of the eastern Mediterranean.

Despite promising starts in mining and industry Turkey is still a predominantly (82 per cent) agricultural country. Here again, Asia Minor has more varied and valuable products to contribute to the nation's economy. European Turkey produces mainly wheat and corn and has truck gardens near Istanbul. Olive and fig orchards indicate the Mediterranean character of the country. However, the typical Mediterranean landscape is rather to be found in the coastal areas of Asia Minor, where large orchards produce fruits for export, fields are intensively cultivated, and most of the population is concentrated.

Greece

Greece in Ancient Times. The most important geographical factor in Greek history is the interpenetration of sea and land. Inland areas more than a few miles away from the coast remained backward and without recorded history into late antiquity. The oldest civilization rose on Crete and the Cycladic islands. It is almost certain that the earliest inhabitants spoke a non-Indo-European language, related to languages spoken in Southeastern Asia Minor. When the Greek tribes moved into the peninsula and on to the islands they soon developed a high civilization but they never succeeded in creating a unified state. The separation of the various cultural nuclei by arms of the sea or by difficult mountain terrain contributed to this development. The small city states on the peninsula were virtually more isolated than the island states. The areas least favored by access to the sea, primarily in the west, remained the most backward, a development which is duplicated in modern Greece.

Greece Under Foreign Rule. When unification came, it was the result of foreign domination. From the fourth century B.C. onward Greece was a part of the Macedonian, Roman, Byzantine, and Turkish Empires. Some of its islands were ruled by Arabs, Crusaders, Genoese, Venetians, British, and Italians. These foreign rulers have left surprisingly few vestiges, except negatively by the destruction of old monuments. A few Byzantine churches, Crusaders' and Venetian castles, mostly in northern Greece and on the islands, recall their rule. It has been surmised that the neglect of drainage and the consequent spread of malaria had something to do with the decline and depopulation which took place in Roman times. In the long war of liberation from Turkey (1821-28) Greece won liberty for only a small part of its area, but this time was unified as a nation. Ancient Greece had been a land of cities. In 1821 virtually all of them were faint memories, at best small villages. Only a few have regained the status of cities. The ancient Greeks had built their cities on protected sites, isolated steep hills, or slopes, looking inland, but at the same time not far from the sea. No bay, only a sandy beach, was needed as a harbor. Now such sites are no longer sufficient and the cities of modern Greece are often successors of latecomers among the ancient cities, such as Patras (Patrai) or Salonika. In the case of Athens historical tradition was strong enough to insure its victory over rival Nauplia in the bay of Argolis, and Hermoupolis on the island of Syros (Siros).

Modern Greece. Greece owed its independence to the valor of its people, and to external aid given by the liberal movements of the period. So the Greek constitution was fashioned after liberal patterns. Despite these liberal ideas, the heritage of subjection by the Turks and the long years of guerrilla war, resulted in personal feuds, in assassinations, revolutions, and civil wars. A number of external wars had to be fought before the whole Greek-speaking area (except Cyprus) was liberated (Figure 118). Western Asia Minor lost its Greek character by expulsion of its Greek population, as a result of the Turkish defeat of the Greek forces in Anatolia, in 1922.

The development of the new state has started from the well-protected islands and deeply indented parts of the peninsula and

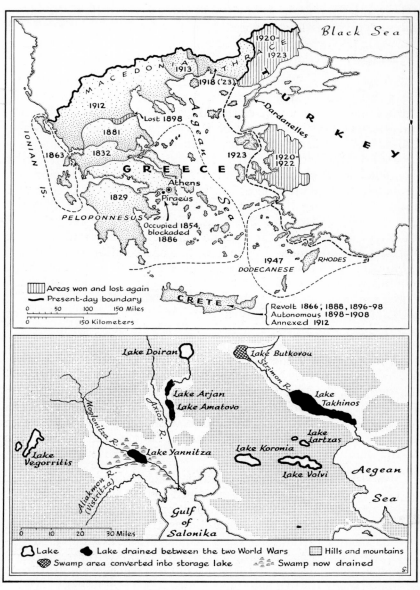

FIGURE 118 (*above*). The changing political boundaries of Greece.
FIGURE 119 (*below*). Lakes of southern Macedonia.

has absorbed parts of the continental Balkan Peninsula and some islands on the fringes. Athens is more than ever the geographical center. The ecclesiastical center, however, has remained in Constantinople, as the Greeks still call Turkish Istanbul.

Population

The demographic development of Greece has been radically upset by the political events of the last decades. In the early 1920's, when Greece had only five million people, it had to accept 1,220,000 Greek refugees, expelled from Turkey and Bulgaria, while only 430,000 Mohammedans and Bulgars left the country. With the help of the Nansen committee of the League of Nations, health and starvation conditions improved rapidly and by 1940 the population had increased to 7,344,000. The losses of World War II amounted to the tremendous figure of approximately 870,000, i.e., at least 12 per cent of the prewar population.[5] However, Greece has one of the highest birth rates in Europe, and a falling death rate, though the figure is still tremendously high. This high net increase, and to a minor degree the incorporation of the Dodecanese, explains why, in 1950, the population was estimated to have reached close to eight million. This means a density of 155 persons per square mile, a very high figure for a mountainous, by no means fertile, little industrialized country. External and civil wars have contributed to keep people very poor and the living standard very low, especially in the rural districts. Low living standards are the result, but also the cause of, the use of primitive tools and implements, small and often unsanitary houses, and primitive means of transportation. Food is simple, containing much fish, vegetables, and cheese. The cooking is done with olive oil. Lamb is the meat most frequently eaten. Wine is the common drink, partly because of the lack of good water. The per-capita income of $128 per year is the lowest among all European countries and less than a tenth of the average American.

Sixty-four per cent of the population lived in rural communities of less than 5,000 in 1940, and 52 per cent were employed in agriculture and stock raising. Only 27 per cent of the area was under cultivation—an area that had been doubled between 1923 and 1937, but may now almost have reached the possible limit. It has been estimated that another 600 square miles was available for drainage and 1,000 square miles which could be protected from

[5] Greek Office of Information, *Greece-Basic Statistics* (London: 1949), pp. 22-23.

floods. The density of population for the cultivated area amounted
to 796 per square mile. Under these circumstances emigration has
always played a great role, both by actually diminishing population
pressure and through remittances. At present, outlets for emigration exist for small numbers only. Another remarkable by-product
of this rapid population increase is the fact that 57 per cent of the
population was in the productive age group of 15 to 60 years in
1940, and is expected to increase to 64.5 per cent in 1970.

Illiteracy is still widespread. However, this is rapidly changing
due to the higher literacy of the children, though obligatory school
attendance is still on paper. Despite these handicaps the average
Greek is quick and open minded. Politics is the burning interest
even in the most remote village. Political strife is bitter between
the numerous parties. Newspapers and discussions in public places
and inns play a great role in daily life. Coffee houses and inns
have their tables and chairs outside the houses and are frequented
mostly by men. Women have equal legal status, but custom makes
the man predominant in all public places and affairs. In the villages women often do the hard work while men look on or direct.
Work pauses during the noon hours, even the work in the fields.
Shops, banks, and offices reopen at 3 or 4 o'clock and business and
life goes on far into the night. Streets and squares in cities and
villages are noisy and vivid, accentuating the natural vivacity of
the landscape, its bright colors, and entrancing shapes. Everywhere the deep blue of sky and sea, the white of the bare limestone, the silvery green of the olives, the darker green of other
trees, and the red hollow bricks of the roofs blend with the manifold forms of mountains and hills, the curving bays and beaches,
and the skyward-pointing cypresses and pines. Man almost disappears in this landscape, except where he puts his monuments
on dominating heights such as the Acropolis of Athens, the St.
George's monastery of Lycabettos, the temple to Poseidon on
Cape Sounion, the Crusader castles of Mytilene, or the Venetian
fortresses at the entrance of Corfu harbor. Towns are frequently
built on slopes, but disappear into the landscape because the
houses of native stone blend with the rocks. Villages are usually
large, hamlets or dispersed settlements existing only in a few sections of northern Greece. The scarcity of water has forced people
to live around the wells; centuries of insecurity have contributed
to the habit of gathering on protected sites. Many of the war-
ravaged villages are now being rebuilt, often more sanitary though
less beautiful, and on less spectacular sites in the valleys near the
fields and roads.

It is impossible to speak of a Greek racial type, as we know how many elements have been absorbed throughout historical times. Nevertheless, a swarthy type of moderate height, often rather heavy-set with a round face is frequently found. Anthropologists have classified the majority as belonging to the Mediterranean subrace of the white race.

There have been periods when immigration was more important to Greece than emigration. From the sixth century on almost all of continental Greece had a Slavic speaking population. At one period, many islands and harbor towns were largely Italian speaking and Albanians settled in the regions devastated in the struggles against the Turks. Spanish-speaking Jews, Turks, Romanian nomadic herdsmen, Russian Tsarist refugees, and Armenian refugees came in smaller groups. Greek higher civilization succeeded in assimilating most of these groups, especially those belonging to the Greek Orthodox church. The population exchange with Turkey and Bulgaria removed other minorities. The Romanians are linguistically Hellenized and recognizable only by their way of life. Similarly, their Roman Catholic religion alone reveals descendants of Italians. In the 1940 census 93 per cent recorded Greek as their mother tongue and 96.5 per cent were members of the Greek-Orthodox church. Nevertheless, the small Macedo-Slavic group proved to be a source of trouble, associating itself first with the Bulgarians, and later with the Communists. Today most of them are gone and with them a group of Mohammedan Albanians. The Spanish-speaking Jewish community of Salonika was destroyed by the Germans. Many Armenians followed the call of the Soviet Union to return. Greek is an Indo-European language, but without any close relationship to other languages of this group. The Greek written language has changed surprisingly little in historical times, though Homer's speech would be unintelligible today. There are a number of dialects, and there is a struggle going on between those who adhere to a language patterned after Classical Greek and those whose speech is more popular.

The Present Economic Life of Greece

There is no part of the Greek economy which has not suffered from the last war and its aftermath. Whole villages and towns have been destroyed, men were drafted into the army, fled abroad or were deported, cities were bombed, ships sunk, and fishing equipment deteriorated from nonuse. Recovery was much delayed by the Communist rebellion and Civil War. British and later American aid was necessary. At present, the economy is on its way back and in many segments emerges healthier and modernized.

Agriculture. Unfortunately for Greece, bare rocks and thorny brush constitute 55 per cent of the surface of the land. The cultivated land is badly exhausted and the poor owners for the most part are unable to procure needed fertilizer. There are no large estates, and the prevalence of small owners, though socially preferable, is an obstacle to efficient management. Agriculture is confined to the river valleys, delta plains, and few intermontane basins. Level areas are not very extensive and are often swampy and malarial. Drainage work has been going on, more rigorously since the middle 1920's, primarily in the plains of the Axios (Vardar) and Strimon (Struma) in Macedonia. Flood control played a great role in this work. Malaria has been fought successfully and new land for the expellees from Asia Minor was won. The Axios delta has been converted into a densely settled, well drained, and well cared for landscape. The mouth of the Axios was shifted so that it no longer threatens to bar the entrance to the Gulf of Salonika. The bed of the Strimon has been shortened and its flood waters are stored in Lake Butkovou, formerly a swamp area. The Takhinos lake in its course, and several other lakes such as Lake Yannitza west of Salonika, and Lake Copais in Boeotia have been drained and their area utilized for tobacco, corn, barley and some cotton (Figure 119). There are numerous other swamp and shallow or periodical lake areas which can and will be drained.

The main products of Greek agriculture are cereals, olives, grapes, and tobacco in that order. However, the restricted size of the plains is not sufficient to provide Greece with both exportable cash crops and the needed food. Thus the greater part of the arable land is devoted to cash crops. The harvests of tobacco, wheat, and corn are back to prewar levels and are steadily improving. However, the partial loss of the United States market and that in Germany is threatening the basic tobacco industry. Very serious is the loss of two million olive trees and three million other fruit trees which were cut down during the hostilities and will take many years to grow again.

Tobacco is the main export of Greece, furnishing as much as 54 per cent of the value of export in prewar times. Many of the tree crops serve to produce exports. The silver-gray leaves and knotted trunks of the olive trees are a characteristic sight, as are the terraces of the vineyards. Exported are seedless currants

(Corinthian raisins) from the western Peloponnesus, as well as raisins and wine, mainly products of the islands. The wine of the mainland is used for home consumption only. Currants and raisins amounted to 12 per cent of the value of the prewar exports. Seldom are large areas all under the same crop. Thus citrus fruits, mulberry groves, orchards of fig trees, peaches, almonds, etc., alternate frequently. There is less variety in the more continental area of northern Greece, where tobacco, grains, and some cotton replace the typical Mediterranean products and fields quite generally take the place of gardens and orchards. In these northern areas agricultural machinery is slowly replacing animal and man power.

Forestry. Less than a fifth of the country is in forests, of which the state owns two thirds. This is only a small remnant of the woods which covered the land and were destroyed back in antiquity. During the last war, 30 per cent of the remaining forests were cut down, a loss hard to replace. Many of the preserved forest areas are in the dissected Pindus Mountains. Reforestation is still in the beginnings and hampered much by the goat, which is almost indispensable for the poor peasant.

Animal Husbandry and Fishing. There is no large-scale animal husbandry. However, because of the little mechanized agriculture and the condition of the roads, asses, horses, and mules are still numerous. Oxen and the water buffalo are primarily work animals. In numbers, work animals have recovered from wartime depletion far less than have pigs, sheep, and goats. In the remote mountain districts, a few shepherds still migrate between winter and summer villages. They used to roam far into the Balkan peninsula in Turkish time and a few groups managed to do so until the last war. The closing of the frontiers and the increasing utilization of much winter pasture land for agriculture have sharply curtailed their way of life.

The resources of fish should not be overestimated. As everywhere in the Mediterranean, there is a great variety of fish, but few fish in great numbers. Fishing is done on a small scale by many small crafts. Tunny fishing is the most important. The fishing is done at night, the fish being attracted by open fires on board the boats, and caught with nets or speared. The only marine product for export are sponges obtained by divers from clear shallow waters.

Merchant Marine. The poor natural endowment of most of Greece, the existence of many sheltered bays, and the short distance between the islands and across the bays have always made seafaring important. However, Greece is no longer on one of the highways of world traffic, and none of the Greek harbors is visited by the great ship lines. In spite of this primary handicap and the fact that much shipping was destroyed during the war, the Greek merchant marine is being rebuilt and expanded. As was the case before the war, a large proportion of the Greek merchant marine consists of cargo vessels and tankers which, in tramp shipping, have an important share of the world's maritime commerce. The Greek fishing fleet is larger and better equipped than it was before the war years. Furthermore, in the present air age, Athens has become a convenient stopping point on the way from Western Europe to the Near East and from East Central Europe to Egypt.

Among the Greek harbors that of the Piraeus (Piraievs), the harbor of Athens, is foremost. Its modern development and importance date from the growth of Athens. The main harbor of northern Greece is Salonika. Located at the southern end of an easy corridor through the Balkan peninsula, it once served an extended hinterland. Political conflicts, however, have restricted its trade area to Greek Macedonia. The latter's increased settlement and production make up partially for loss of the tributary area. Patras at the western exit of the Gulf of Corinth is the main export harbor for currants and the port of call for ships going into the Adriatic Sea. Traffic between the east and west, in small- and medium-sized vessels, is greatly helped by the existence of the Canal of Corinth. There is no harbor at either end of the Canal. The ancient city of Corinth has remained an insignificant town. The Canal was blocked by the sinking of ships and an artificial landslide during the war. It was reopened in March, 1949. Some harbors are specialized, such as Kavalla for tobacco, or serve particular areas or islands, such as Corfu on the island of Corfu, Canea (Khania) on Crete, Rhodes on the island of the same name, and Volos on the plains of Thessaly.

Land Transportation. The Greek network of railroads and roads is not well developed. Railroads over the mountains coming close to the coast cannot compete with shipping around the deeply indented gulfs and inlets. Obviously, the islands have to rely on shipping. But even Epirus is without a railroad and the Peloponnesian and other railroads are narrow gauge. There is a single main line from Piraeus-Athens to Salonika connecting through the Vardar Valley with Central and East Central Europe and east to Istanbul. The total road net comprises roads on the islands and its mileage is given as five times that of the railroads. But as only one seventh was hard-surfaced before the war, it was obviously inadequate. It is now being considerably improved, with an increased mileage of hard-surfaced roads.

The wartime destruction of the railroads was similar in severity to that of the merchant marine. Of 1,664 miles of track only 522 miles was left serviceable at the end of the war. Almost all railroad bridges were destroyed. Only 35 of 353 locomotives were left and 494 out of 7,337 railroad carriages. In December, 1950, however, it was announced that traffic had been resumed on all lines. Cars and engines have been salvaged and much new rolling stock has been added, among them a number of diesel engines delivered by the Italians as reparations.

Industry and Mining. In 1944, it was estimated that 12.5 per cent of the population were industrial workers and their dependents, and as many handicraftsmen and their dependents. This gives some measure of the small development of mining and industry in Greece. Most manufactured products come from small artisan shops. Much is connected with processing of agricultural products such as the pressing of olive oil, the curing of tobacco, and the manufacture of wine. However, there are also some larger industries, many started by the refugees from Asia Minor, such as weaving of the famous Smyrna rugs. However, the leading products are chemicals, textiles, cement, and potteries. Except for Piraeus-Athens, hardly a city can be considered industrialized.

Mining too is done on small scale. There is a great variety of minerals (Figure 120), but almost all deposits are small, either by nature or because they have been exploited for many centuries. Greece has little indigenous fuels, lignite of moderate quality being the only one available in small mines in Thessaly and the Peloponnesus. Its production has considerably surpassed prewar figures. Of some slight importance are the lead and zinc mines near Athens and the magnesite, molybdenite, and chromium deposits on Euboea.

Commerce. Throughout all its history as an independent nation, Greece has been in a difficult economic situation. Wars and revolutions occurred frequently and interrupted recovery every time it showed some prospects. Thus Greece had to rely on invisible imports, first of all remittances from abroad by its emigrants, merchants, and seamen, many of them serving under foreign flags. Many rich communities contributed generously, either as communities or as individuals.

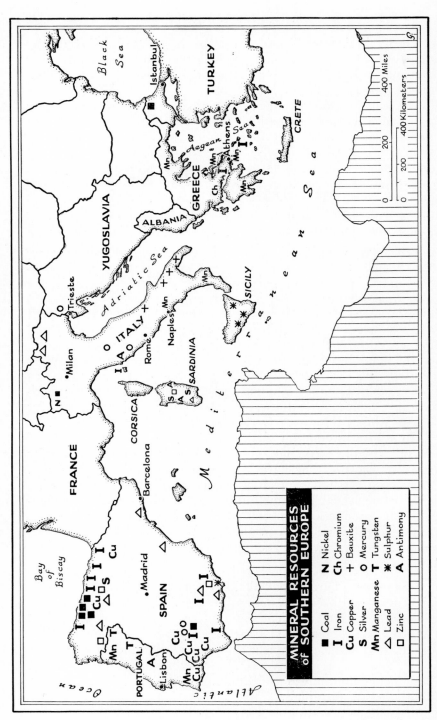

FIGURE 120

Another source of income came from tourist traffic. Tourists from Europe come primarily to see the relics of classical antiquity. Others come to enjoy the pleasant climate. Visitors come from Central and Western Europe, especially in winter, to places such as Corfu; people come from the Near East in summer to places such as Rhodes.

Italy

Unity and Diversity. Unlike Greece, the middle peninsula of the Mediterranean has many places where human settlement could develop without recourse to the sea. Indeed, both coasts stretch hundreds of miles without harbors, made still less favorable for human habitation by malarial swamps, while a few miles inland fertile basins provide the basis for self-contained development. Only in southern Italy and Sicily do small secluded plains look toward the sea, offering a habitat comparable to that of Greece. They provided points of access for Phoenicians and Greeks, and later for Arabs, Normans, and Spaniards. All these nations have left their impress upon the landscape, some only in names, more in ruins and buildings, and all in the character of the people.

Throughout much of its history Italy was split into many states. The mountainous nature of the peninsula and its long narrow shape account for it. However, the obstacles to unification are less rigid than in Greece. Tuscany (Toscana), ancient Etruria, was split into city states, which have been united in the twelve-city federation of the Etruscans, and since the Renaissance under Florence (Firenze). Other regions emerge as political units, such as Latium and Umbria, to break up again under certain historical conditions into minute units. The largest natural unit of the peninsula, the North Italian Plain, achieved unity only when it was imposed from the outside.

Cultural Unification. In spite of the geographical obstacles to unification, and in contrast to the persistence of numerous political units in the nineteenth century, cultural and linguistic unification came early. This was accomplished as an accompaniment of the first political unification of Italy under the Romans, and later foreign invasions did not change this fact. This fact is the more remarkable because the Romans conquered people of different origin, civilization, and language. The Etruscans, Sards, Ligurians, and Sikels spoke non-Indo-European languages of unknown origin. But only the Etruscans had advanced culturally. Other languages the Romans encountered were Indo-European, Greek in the south, Celtic in the north, Illyric, the predecessor of Albanian in the northeast and southeast, and languages related to their own Latin language in the rest of the peninsula. Most of these languages disappeared from Italy in ancient times. Greek was spoken in a few places until recently, and there are still a few Albanian-speaking villages. The map of Italy shows the variegated story of naming the geographical features, from Ligurian Genoa (Genova), Illyrian Venice (Venezia), and Celtic Bologna in the north to Greek Syracuse, Phoenician Palermo, and prehistoric Sicily and Sardinia in the south.

Italy entered the period of the Renaissance with a common literary language, which had been coined in its final literary form by Dante. At the same period city states gave place to somewhat larger political units. Two of the tiny medieval states, however, have survived to the present day—San Marino and Monaco. In many places, the boundaries established at that time survive as internal boundaries. The greatest obstacles to further unification were the States of the Church, ruled by the Pope and separating northern from southern Italy. Rome became the seat of the Pope when it was the center of the Roman Empire. The Papacy survived the empire, inheriting the central location and prestige of ancient Rome.

The French Revolution gave a decisive impulse to unification, which was accomplished in 1871 despite temporary reverses. From 1871 to the rise of Fascism Italy was a constitutional monarchy. The king compromised with the Fascist dictatorship and fell with it; today, Italy is a republic. After 1871 the remaining national problem was the northern boundary. The linguistic, historical, and physiographic boundaries nowhere coincided. The result was the irredentist movement, born of the desire to unite all Italian-speaking areas. In the northwest the physiographic boundary of high Alpine ridges against France was maintained, sacrificing Savoy, historically a part of Italy, and Nice, linguistically Italian (1859). Some tiny districts were ceded to France in 1947 and the French-speaking Val d'Aosta was given restricted autonomy. The Swiss border, though neither a physiographic nor linguistic boundary, remained unchanged.

The main struggle developed in the northeast. World War I brought Italy a boundary which, for strategic and economic reasons, was largely drawn through German-, Slovene- or Croat-speaking areas. Italianization was pushed into the German-speaking Alto Adige (Southern Tyrol) region. The emigration of Germans, agreed upon with Hitler, was only partially carried out. The economic connections of this area with Italy had been strengthened so much that a reannexation by Austria would have meant an economic catastrophe.

Thus the peace treaty of 1946 left the area with Italy and provided for a restricted autonomy. The artificial boundary of 1919 has become a reality in many respects.[6] On the other hand, Italy had to yield to Yugoslavia her Dalmatian acquisitions of 1919, among them unquestionably Italian cities such as Pola. Trieste and vicinity was made a Free Territory.

Italian irredentism has also claimed Corsica and Malta. The first is Italian speaking and belonged to Pisa and Genoa for several centuries until it was annexed by France in 1768. Today it is closely integrated with France. Malta belonged to Sicily only from the end of the eleventh to the beginning of the sixteenth century, otherwise it was independent or belonged to African states. It became British in 1800 and remained a main anchor of the "lifeline" to India through World War II. Its population is Roman Catholic. The language, however, is basically Arabic although the vocabulary has many Italian words.

Urban Development. Dispersed settlement is rare in Italy and restricted to a few regions. Even villages look like cities, with their houses of stone several stories high and built closely together without barn or farmyard. Where possible, small towns are built on top of hills or spurs. Such locations, despite the lack of drinking water, were chosen for protection and because of the danger of malaria in the plains. The history of most cities goes back to antiquity. A few of the ancient sites have been deserted, such as Greek Sybaris and the famous victim of a volcanic eruption, Pompeii. Ancient ruins are still the great attraction, foremost in Rome and Ravenna. Few new sites have been added since Roman times. Towns as adjuncts to ecclesiastical institutions were added, such as Monte Cassino or Loretto, but they are exceptional. Livorno (Leghorn) and Venice have been founded on the growing deltas. There has been a shift in importance. Naples (Napoli), a minor Greek colony, became the seat of a kingdom and is the third city of Italy today. Merchant emporia such as Amalfi and Pisa won prominence and lost it again, Amalfi for lack of hinterland and Pisa because it is now cut off from the sea by the growth of the Arno delta. Venice is struggling hard to maintain its position in the lagoon, which is threatened by the deposits of the Brenta, Adige, and Po rivers.

  [6] Guido G. Weigend, "Effects of Boundary Changes in the South Tyrol," *Geographical Review*, XL, No. 3 (July, 1950), 364-75.

Of the great medieval maritime cities Genoa alone has maintained its importance, due to its deep harbor and easy access over low passes to the main Italian industrial area. The Renaissance palaces and churches of Siena, Perugia, Urbino and many other cities are witnesses of a greater past as independent cities or capitals of petty states. Others such as Florence, Milan (Milano), Verona, Bologna would be interesting cities even without such relics because they became industrial and administrative centers or crossroad towns. There are, however, a few cities which make a thoroughly modern impression such as Turin (Torino), Novara, or Livorno, though they, too, are old urban sites. Rome has again become the largest city of Italy, largely due to its political and religious position.

Population

From this great variety of peoples and languages a rather uniform nation has grown. Many racial strains have contributed to the making of the Italian people. Small, dark, stout types prevail in the south; taller lighter ones in the north. But numerous local and individual variations also occur.

The Roman Catholic creed is confessed by the great majority of the people (99.6 per cent), though many pay only lip service. The Roman Catholic Church is the state religion and is taught in the public schools.

Hardly less impressive is the linguistic uniformity. The Val d'Aosta with its French-speaking population, and Alto Adige with its German majority, are the only areas where minority problems exist, and the Republic has granted to these areas autonomous status and bilingual administration. The small group of Romansh-speaking Ladins in Alto Adige has allied itself closely to the Germans. The small groups of Albanians in scattered villages of Apulia (Puglie) and Catalans in a corner of Sardinia are insignificant.

Although there is one Italian written language, there are many spoken dialects, widely different. An illiterate peasant from Sicily is unable to communicate with a man from Piedmont, and the latter may not be able to understand the dialect of Friuli, the area northeast of Venice. With the spread of literacy, these dialectical differences, tied to historical traditions, are decreasing as a menace to unity. Illiteracy is still widespread in southern Italy, where the obligatory school attendance is difficult to enforce. While northern Italy has virtually no illiteracy, the general average was still 21.6 per cent in 1921, with a slightly better showing of the male population. Later figures are unavailable.

This difference in educational standards and the great poverty of the predominantly rural south have kept alive the lingering antagonism between north and south. Dispersed settlement is to be found in northern Italy and even predominates in Tuscany, Umbria, and parts of the Emilia. In most parts of Italy, however, large agglomerations are characteristic and the peasant often has to walk several miles to his fields. The scarcity of springs and (formerly) better protection are probably as much responsible as the gregarious nature of the people for these large agglomerations. Italians, even the illiterate among them, are much more aware of their glorious history than most other people, as it is hardly otherwise possible in a country where the monuments of the past are everywhere present. There is hardly a village where the church or the palace of the lord does not remind one of the past, few churches which do not possess a picture, a statue, or some votive piece by some great master. Thus, an understanding of artistic values is widespread, though often unconscious. Many Italians have great appreciation for dramatic performances, for example, a good speech. Therefore, they are apt to applaud a political speaker for his oratorial performance rather than the content of his speech.

It is difficult to give examples of national characteristics which apply to all Italians. Foreigners are apt to take the mentality of guides and other people catering to tourists as typical. Most Italians resent such a generalization. A definite trait is the general frugality, which is partly a result of poverty. Meals from wheat, such as macaroni and spaghetti, or corn, such as polenta in northern Italy, and dried rice in some regions, constitute the main food. Vegetables, fish, and cheese are often added. Until recently, light and cheap wine has been the only unpolluted drink available in many areas. The food is usually cooked with olive oil. The one-sided nutrition, especially in the corn- and rice-eating areas gave rise to many deficiency diseases such as pellagra and tuberculosis.

Italy has a very high birth rate, which declined rapidly in pre-war years. While it stood at an average of 36.9 per thousand during the years 1866 to 1872, it sank to 23.8 per thousand as an average during 1935 to 1939. However, the death rate declined still faster, from 29.7 to 14.1 during the same period. Infant mortality is still very high, 103 per thousand just before the war, and about 80 per thousand in 1947. These rates mean a net increase of approximately 400,000 persons each year, an almost unbearable burden in years of crisis.

Emigration has played a great role in Italian population movements, although the countries of destination have changed frequently. The mass emigration to the United States was stopped in the early 1920's. Since the war, France and Argentina stand at the head of the list. Other South American republics take considerable numbers, too. Many emigrants, especially those to France, Britain, Belgium, and Luxembourg, expect to return. Such expectations are not always fulfilled, but in some provinces such as Sicily or Piedmont the re-emigrants play a very important role economically and socially.

The Present Economic Life of Italy

When the unified Italian kingdom came into being it was primarily an agricultural country. Numerous cities had degenerated into local market centers. Only a few administrative centers (Turin, Venice, Milan, Parma, Florence, Rome, Naples, Palermo), and university towns (Padua, Bologna) had survived as cities. Tourist trade took the place of manufacture and export of products of high artisanship, both because of the unfavorable political conditions and the competition from western European industry. Modern industry had hardly started.

Agriculture. By far the most numerous group of Italy's population is employed in agriculture, as in other less industrialized Southern European countries. There are many people on farms who are not needed and stay on with the family because they have no other choice. This "hidden unemployment" is especially characteristic of the backward areas of southern Italy. The result is a heavy concentration in the countryside of about 400 per square mile.

Another characteristic of Italian agriculture is the extended use of manpower. Much agriculture is only gardening, partly because of the traditional attitudes, which originated in the natural conditions of agriculture in a mountainous country of Mediterranean climate. Plains have been, and some still are, malarial. They are also exposed to cold winds in winter and do not allow the planting of the typical Mediterranean plants, while the summer drought makes it difficult to grow other products. Therefore unirrigated cereal production is restricted to certain regions. Where the land needs irrigation a network of narrowly spaced ditches requires much manual work. The same is true of work on the terraces and on the small plots wrung from stony slopes. On the other hand, the mild winters allow and require work the year round, though it never results in peak work loads such as harvesting within a short period.

The prevalence and natural advantages of intensive cultivation on small plots contrast with the low yield of the great estates (*latifundi*) of southern Italy and Sicily. This is caused partly by the well known evils of absentee ownership. The situation is worsened by the use of at least part of the land for crops needing intensive care, which cannot be expected from scarcely supervised landless laborers and sharecropping tenants.

Among the fruit trees, olives and figs are best adapted to the climatic conditions as, likewise, are the grapevines which grow to considerable height and are often trained on stone pillars, over which beams are laid. Trees and vines are planted at considerable distances, leaving space for other crops, which thus receive enough light and sufficient protection from direct sun radiation. Occasionally three different crops are planted simultaneously on the same plot, and during an entire year a succession of as many as five crops may be grown. Vegetables and grains are equally important for such intercropping. Among industrial crops sugar beets, flax, and hemp are important. Italy is the only rice-producing country of Europe of any importance, having produced more than 60 per cent of the 1936-40 average, though this was hardly one half of one per cent of the world crop. The average yield per acre, however, was by far the highest in the world, more than one third higher than that of Japan, its next competitor for rank in yield. The postwar yield per acre, while showing some decline, is still the world's highest. The yield per acre of corn, in prewar years, was also the highest accomplished anywhere. In most of the North Italian Plain corn and rice need irrigation, but can be grown without it along the lower Po and in the Roman Campagna. These growing conditions influence the distribution of the grain areas. Rice and corn are most abundant in the North Italian Plain, while wheat is grown in the drier parts of the Plain and in the dry limestone areas of southern Italy and Sicily.

Except for olive and fig trees, most fruit trees and the citrus fruits especially, need irrigation or special protection against the winter cold. They are outside their natural habitat in many cases and, like the oranges of the Riviera, are cultivated more for the tourist trade than because of their crop value. Their market has been endangered recently because refrigerator service permits shipment from more distant countries.

Other Nonindustrial Resources. Like all countries of Mediterranean climate, the Italy of the Apennine peninsula has few forests. Many so-called forests are of the *maquis* (Italian *macchia*) type, which at best furnish wood only for charcoal. Fortunately, Italy possesses some good forests in the Alps, though timber still must be imported.

Animal husbandry plays a minor role in Italian economy. However, on the irrigated meadows of the Lombardy plain, cattle are abundant. This is the only area where milk and butter replace olive oil in general consumption. Most Italian cheese, such as gorgonzola or parmesan (*parmigiano* from Parma), is exported.

In Alto Adige, transhumance is the usual mode of cattle raising. Transhumance with large sheep and goat herds also occurs between the summer dry plains of southern Italy and the Apennines. Advancing irrigation and reclamation, however, continuously narrow the area available for transhumance. As in all Mediterranean countries, donkeys and mules are widely used, and horses are used in the North Italian Plain. The small plots and the location of fields on terraced slopes gives these domestic animals a good chance to compete with mechanized equipment.

Fishing is carried on all along the Italian coast. For the most part, small boats are used and the haul is of moderate size, for reasons discussed on page 473. Only the small Italian sardines are caught in large numbers. Fish is an important ingredient of Italian food supply because of the scarcity of meat and the strict observance of the Catholic fast days. Meat and fish combined, however, constitute a minor portion of the food.

Traffic and Communications. At unification, Italy lowered its tariff. Though this proved a handicap for the agricultural southern provinces, Italian industry and commerce developed rapidly. At the same time the Suez Canal was opened. Naples and Genoa rose to become important harbors on one of the world routes; Trieste, still Austrian at the time, Venice, and—as a passenger embarkation point—Brindisi profited too. Genoa had the advantage of easy access to the rapidly developing industrial centers of northern Italy and even of Switzerland and southern Germany. Naples and Palermo became embarkation points for the increasing emigration. Venice and Trieste were rivals for the commerce of their overlapping hinterlands. Until 1914, Trieste profited from its political attachment to the Austro-Hungarian monarchy. Venice was threatened by the silting of the shallow lagoon, but favored by shorter routes to the Italian hinterland. Trieste and Genoa became the seats of the large shipping companies of Austria and Italy.

The railroad net, and somewhat later the road net, was expanded and improved. Because of the shape of the peninsula, no one center arose. The railway lines crossing the Alps focused on Turin, Milan, and Bologna. The route from southern France follows the coast of the Riviera (Figure 121), although many tunnels are needed. From Genoa it ran parallel to the coast to Rome and Naples. The important lines from the north join it either at Genoa, or from Bologna via Florence at Rome. From Turin an

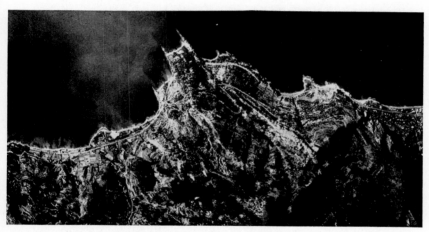

FIGURE 121. Air photo of Cape Mortola, on the Italian Riviera. Note the characteristic promontories and semicircular bays. The slopes have only a sparse vegetational cover. (Attraverso L'Italia, Touring Club of Italy.)

important route follows the outer edge of the Apennines through Bologna along the Roman (Emilian) Way and along the Adriatic coast to Bari and Brindisi. Before the air age this was part of the shortest route from western Europe to India. Another important international route crosses the North Italian Plain via Milan, Verona, Padua, and Venice to Trieste and the Balkans. Many Italian railroads are electrified, especially in the north, close to the water power from the Alpine rivers. The largest hydroelectric installations are in the Piedmont, Trentino, and Alto Adige regions. Italian roads are among the best in Europe, partly due to the skill of the Italian road worker, who has found employment for this kind of work all over Europe.

Mining and Heavy Industry. Hydroelectric power was developed in Italy mainly because of the scarcity of oil and coal. There are a few coal mines in Sardinia and in Val d'Aosta. Lignite deposits in the basins and broad valleys of Tuscany have been exploited also. But all this together furnished less than 15 per cent of the prewar needs. Coal came to Italy both from the Ruhr and England by sea, and from the Ruhr and Polish Silesia by rail. Economically Italy is no longer in a position to buy coal freely. The other mainstay of modern industry is iron and steel. Iron ore is in short supply, the few iron ore mines being found on the island of Elba and in Tuscany in the Catena Metallifera (the name means ore-bearing range). The need to import iron ore has caused much of the heavy industry to locate near Genoa and its neighboring harbor Savona. Shipbuilding is important here, and also in Trieste and vicinity. The great wharves of Monfalcone, a few miles northwest of Trieste, are still on the Italian side of the border. Another branch of the metal industry is the production of automobiles. The FIAT factory in Turin is one of the leading European firms in this field. Though the production figures are low when compared with American ones, they are not so with respect to the small European market. Italian heavy industry has specialized in a few lines requiring little raw material. Ball bearings are an excellent example.

There are a few minerals which are abundant and can be exported. Foremost among them is sulphur from Tuscany and especially Sicily (Figure 120), where the small port Agrigento specializes in it. American competition, however, threatens to ruin the sulphur trade. Another export product is mercury, coming from mines in Tuscany. Bauxite is found on Monte Gargano and in the southern projection of Apulia, both in the limestone areas closely related to that of the Dinaric system. All other mineral output, such as that of manganese, lead, and zinc is insignificant.

Other Industries. Because the lack of coal and iron has hampered the development of Italian heavy industry, other industries took the lead. Foremost has been the textile industry in most of its branches, especially silk and rayon products. This industry is centered in the Lombardy center of the North Italian Plain, in the cities of Milan, Como, Brescia, and Bergamo, and many others of less importance. Here hydroelectric power and skilled workers are available. The division of the land into tiny parcels, and the large number of children in the family forces many members, frequently the father, to earn money outside the farm. The basis of the silk fabrication, the silkworm, is tended in all parts of Italy. Mulberry trees are especially frequent in northern Italy.

Cotton and woolen industries are only a little less important than silk weaving. More recently, the chemical industry has also come into prominence, especially the manufacture of sulphuric acid and copper sulphate, which could draw on the native resources just at the moment when the external market for these mining products was shrinking due to American competition. Among the food processing industries, sugar refineries and fish canning should be mentioned.

Though Italian industry gives work to a substantial number of workers—more than six million, one third of them in large concerns —the possibilities for further expansion of most industries seem definitely limited because of the lack of raw materials. Imported raw materials can be used for the internal market but can be used in competition in the export market only when wages are kept at a starvation level. Italy's attempt to create a protected market overseas through acquisition of colonies ended in failure. The Italian colonists still remaining in Eritrea and Libya can, however, be relied upon to buy as much as possible in the Italian market.

Trade Balance. Italy is comprised of some very productive but small and several poor regions. Therefore, in all periods of progress, population quickly outran domestic supply, in Roman as well as in modern times. The present population density of nearly 900 per square miles of cultivable land is one of the highest known in Europe. The handicaps which the nation faces in its development of large-scale industries are also responsible for the inability to pay for food imports by exports. In prewar times, the Italian economy was kept going by remittances from Italians abroad, the savings of the returning emigrants, the earnings of the merchant marine, and by the earnings of some Italian insurance companies which had branches all over Europe and the Near East. The restrictions on emigration have caused the first two sources to dwindle in importance.

Destruction and Reconstruction. World War II put a heavy stress on the Italian economy. Actual destruction by bombing was less severe than in many other European countries, and some of the famous historical sites, especially Rome, were spared. The total destruction of Monte Cassino remained a solitary case. However, the neglect of plants and installations, the drafting of manpower, and a general slump in morale caused a substantial lowering of production. Recovery was slower than in many other countries. Demobilization of the armed forces threw millions of men out of work in an already overpopulated land. Many demobilized men did not return to their rural homes, but looked for work in the cities. Industry recently has increased its output by mechanization and, despite a present greater output than in 1939, fewer workers are employed. Italy is unique in postwar Europe for its continuously large number of unemployed. The government has concluded emigration agreements with Argentina, Brazil, Venezuela, and Canada, and on a temporary basis with Belgium, France, and Switzerland. The numbers involved in such emigration plans, however, are utterly insufficient.

Railroads and roads have now been repaired. Some new mileage has been added to the road net but none to the railroads. Their rolling stock is still much lower than before the war, but nevertheless provided 13,800 million passenger miles in 1948-49 compared to 7,270 in 1938-39. A few lines are being electrified, an improvement which is now used on more than a third of the Italian railway mileage. On the other hand, the number of registered automobiles has almost doubled. Industrial output, which in 1945 declined to only 40 per cent of the prewar level, advanced to 117 per cent by 1950. This should be regarded as rather unsatisfactory in view of the increased population and the low living standard of many regions.

There are, however, some brighter spots in the picture. The reclamation of swampy, malarial areas, which had a good, though overadvertised start under Mussolini, is progressing, and with the help of the Rockefeller Foundation produced good results in Sardinia. A settlement program is under way which will double the population of this island within the next few years. The land reform in southern Italy had a very slow start and is still in its beginnings. The brightest picture is offered by the steadily increasing tonnage of the merchant marine. Many of the larger vessels are new or completely reconditioned. War damage in harbors has been repaired.

Colonies in the Italian Economy. Somaliland has been restored to Italian trusteeship for another ten years. It is a small semidesert coastal strip and therefore does not amount to much. However, a significant number of colonists has remained in the former colonies, Eritrea, Libya, and even in Ethiopia. Though the position of the Italians in Libya seems rather precarious, those in Eritrea and, strangely enough, in Ethiopia seem to get along with the natives well enough to be sought out for work requiring technical skill.

Trieste. The most surprising economic survival is that of Trieste, despite the continuing hostility of Yugoslavia. Thanks to the routing of all ERP cargoes for Austria through the harbor of Trieste, the port traffic figures approach those of the peak year 1913 before World War I, which had never been reached since. This is, however, a transitory condition. The Free Territory of Trieste was created after World War II, because no agreement concerning its annexation either by Yugoslavia or Italy could be reached. For all practical purposes, only the city and a narrow corridor connecting it with Italy have a separate political existence. The majority of the population is Italian, but the Yugoslav minority is by no means negligible. The rural area, mostly inhabited by Yugoslavs, is practically incorporated into Yugoslavia. Northern Yugoslavia, Hungary, parts of Czechoslovakia which have been served in the past as hinterland are cut off and only Austria is left. It remains to be seen whether the Territory's favorable geographical location as the maritime outlet of Eastern Central Europe can overcome its political handicaps.

The Iberian Peninsula

The fact that the interior uplands tower high above the narrow coastal lowlands has played a great role in Spanish history. The last civil war showed again how difficult it is to defend these lowlands. On the other hand, a strong sea power such as Great Britain could hold on to a part of the fringe, the isolated rock of Gibraltar. British seapower was also a major factor in helping Portugal preserve its independence from Spain. Portugal's face is turned seaward even more than that of other marginal regions of Europe. It has, with one exception, the only rivers of the peninsula which can be entered from the sea, and its territory extends as far inland as the headwaters of river navigation, beyond which deep gorges hinder further river communication. The boundary between Portugal and Spain passes through some of the most thinly settled parts of the peninsula. Portugal conquered the area south of the Tagus (Tejo River) long before Castile penetrated as far south, acquiring in war a distinct national consciousness which became indestructible in the great age of discoveries. Portugal's interest overseas took quite a different turn from that of Spain. Its colonial empire was genuinely based on sea power, and never became another overseas continental empire. The Portuguese language became an established literary language through the influence of the poems of Camoëns, the Dante of Portugal.

When the Spanish Christians gradually recovered from the Arab conquest of the eighth century they formed a number of small states in the northern mountains. These states became united under the crown of Castile from the time they expanded onto the plateau, which made unity feasible and also imperative in order to resist Arab pressure. From this center Castile imposed unity upon the coastal lowlands as ancient Rome had forced it upon Italy, not from a national feeling of community. The coastal regions, however, have retained their peculiarities, either in dialect and character as the Gallegos of Galicia, the Asturians, and the Andalusians, or in the political separatism of the Catalans and Basques.

Roman and Arabic Influences.   Many peoples and cultures have influenced Spain and Portugal. Many names, sites of cities, racial peculiarities, and the Basque language of the western Pyrenees, survive from the prehistoric and the early Celtic and Iberian population. Along the coast Phoenician and Carthaginian colonies left their imprint. Some institutions and a few buildings can be traced to the Vandal, Visigothic, and Suevian invaders of the fifth century.

The strongest and most lasting influences, however, came from Romans and Arabs. The most impressive monuments of Rome's rule are the Spanish and Portuguese languages. The Romans built roads around their main centers, Caesarea Augusta (Saragossa), Asturica (Astorga, north of Valladolid), Emerita (Mérida), Hispalis (Seville), and Olisipo (Lisbon). The Roman provincial capital Tarraco (Tarragona southwest of Barcelona), the pre-Roman center Saguntum, and the Carthaginian capital Carthago Nova (Cartagena) were connected by a coastal road. Some of the paved roads and arched stone bridges are still usable. Scarcely a city of any importance in Roman times has disappeared from the map. Of much later foundation are the fortress cities of the Christian-Islamic wars—Castile is the land of castles—religious centers such as Santiago di Compostela, and administrative centers such as Madrid.

The Romans also brought some of the cultivated plants to Spain, for example, several fruit trees. Far more important, however, was the contribution of the Arabic-Moorish period. In the coastal areas citrus fruits, sugar cane, and cotton are outstanding contributions, closely connected with an elaborate system of irrigation. Water rights are still administered according to Moorish customs, while in every other respect Roman law prevails. Many of the Moorish castles and mosques still stand, the latter converted into churches. Christian artisans, trained under Moorish rule, influenced Spanish architectural styles decisively.

More difficult to trace is the racial mixture, undoubtedly strong, but hard to separate from earlier Phoenician and Jewish admixture. Arabic names are most frequent in southern Spain, and southern and central Portugal, but appear occasionally in both countries as far as north of the Douro (Duero). Examples among rivers are Guadalquivir (Wadi al kabir = the great river), among mountains Mulhacén (Mulay Hassan), among regions Algarve (al gharb = the west), among settlements Gibraltar (gebel al Tariq = rock of Tariq). A less fortunate inheritance is the survival of large estates bestowed upon knights, religious orders, and bishoprics by the conquerors.

The eight centuries of war against the Mohammedan Moors have also molded the character of the Spanish and to a lesser degree the Portuguese people. Religious fanaticism, intolerance, and the idealization of the fighting life characterized certain periods of the history of all European nations, but nowhere with such lasting effect. The Roman Catholic Church became so intimately connected with national liberation that it could survive the attacks of the Reformation with comparative ease.

The Colonies. The two Iberian countries led in geographical discoveries and became the first truly colonial powers. The waxing and waning of their colonial empire has historical as well as geographical causes. The discoveries were, in their first phase, virtually the continuation of the struggles of the reconquista.[7] After having reached the southern coast, the Portuguese crossed into Morocco and continued along the West African coast. The Iberian Peninsula was the most advanced vantage point of Europe toward the southwest, either on the route to India or to the Antilles. It had a seafaring tradition because of its Mediterranean coast, and Catalonia participated in the great period of Italian shipping and expansion to the East, in the late Middle Ages. The peninsula also had an Atlantic front, and both Seville and Lisbon became leading European ports for a while. However, conquest, emigration, and the expulsion of the Moors and the Jews sapped the manpower of both Spain and Portugal. The decline in Spain's national vigor was accelerated by her close connection with the Catholic Church, a connection which involved the nation in unproductive European

---

[7] The period in Iberian history when the Christians reconquered the country from the Moors.

wars. The easy influx of American gold accustomed people to look down on arduous, less rewarding work. Finally, it turned out that the mountain barrier of the Pyrenees made the peninsula difficult to reach from most of Europe, and hence unfit to serve as a permanent basis for overseas shipping. The national liberation movement in the Americas overthrew the weakened colonial empires.

The Atlantic island possessions of both Spain and Portugal, and the Portuguese colonies of Goa, Diu, and Daman in India, Macao on the Chinese coast, and half of the island of Timor in Indonesia, are the only relics of this great period together with a few coastal way stations and fortified points. Based on the latter, Portugal was able to win and hold new colonies in Guinea, Mozambique, and Angola in the nineteenth century. Spain did the same in northern Morocco, Rio de Oro, and Guinea.

Constitutional Development. The rule of one province over others seems best assured by a central absolute power. On the peninsula, Castile occupied such a central geographical position. Thus many Castilians came to uphold absolutism in both its traditional form and as modern dictatorship. Liberal ideas are mainly French importations, brought to literary circles in the eighteenth century, and to the masses by the armies of Napoleon. But in this respect Spain, behind the barrier of the Pyrenees, seems rather remote from Europe, more so than countries not contiguous to France.

Portugal, with her face to the Atlantic Ocean, maintained closer contacts with France and England, and was somewhat more influenced by Western European thought. After a protracted struggle, it became a republic in 1910. At present it is governed by an attenuated form of dictatorship, based on a social program developed by the Catholic Church.

Urban Developments. The distribution of Iberian cities is also strongly determined by the position of the central highlands. Most large cities are located on the periphery. Of these peripheral cities the most important is Barcelona, the nation's thriving industrial capital. The dominating center has concentrated all functions in the only large city, Madrid, which has replaced the older, similarly central city of Toledo as the capital. Toledo, located on a detached part of the plateau, surrounded on three sides by the deep and steep-sided Tagus Valley, was an excellent site as long as defense was imperative. When the Moorish wars ceased the disadvantages of cramped space and obstructed communications became obvious. Some cities of the northern Meseta, such as León, Burgos, Valladolid, and Salamanca played their part at a time when a frontier crossed it, and since have stagnated.

All Iberian cities show the influence of past history in their architecture. French Romanesque and Gothic style came with feudal knights and fighting orders to the northern half of the peninsula. All along the pilgrims' road to Santiago di Compostela are the splendid churches of this period. Other cities, too, have grown around ecclesiastical foundations. Arabic architecture contributed splendid monuments in the south from the Alhambra (the Red one) of Granada to the mosque churches of Córdoba and Seville and the Alcazár (the castle) of Toledo. The wealth of the Indies made possible the erection of famous works of Renaissance and Baroque all over the peninsula.

Each coastal region has its own well-developed center. The importance of some of these centers dates back to Phoenician times with Cádiz and Cartagena, to Roman days with Saragossa, Pamplona and Seville, and to the early Middle Ages with Barcelona and Valencia. Some cities, though much older, have acquired real importance only with modern industry and mining, such as Bilbao, Santandér, and Oviedo, and their harbors Gijón and Portugalete. In Portugal only Lisbon (Lisboa) and Oporto (Porto) became large cities. The old university town of Coimbra has remained small, and Setúbal a specialized fishing port.

Spain

Population

It has been stressed in the historical section that the apparent uniformity of the Spanish people covers many differences. Dialects differ widely and regional consciousness is very strong. The Gallego dialect of Galicia is closer to Portuguese than to Castilian, Catalan is claimed to be a separate language, and Castilian is used as the official language only. There is only one undisputed linguistic minority, the Basques, living in three small provinces off the Bay of Biscay. Spain's religious uniformity is even more pronounced, Roman Catholicism being not only the state religion, but in fact the creed of an overwhelming majority. Tensions result, however, from anticlerical attitudes of both workers and intellectuals.

Like that of all Southern European nations, the Spanish population is increasing rapidly. However, because the birth rate and the death rate are falling at the same pace, the proportion of increase has not changed much between the average of the years 1876 to 1882 and those of 1935 to 1939. As the same percentage refers to a larger population, absolute numbers are increasing rapidly. The Civil War checked this movement only temporarily. The infant mortality, for example, rose from 117.5 per thousand in 1932 to 140.3 per thousand in 1939. In 1947, however, it was reported as having decreased to 76.1 per thousand. This was the lowest rate in Southern Europe, though still double that of the United States. Spanish vital statistics are generally somewhat more favorable than the Italian figures, but still reflect the social problem of a backward, largely illiterate peasantry. School attendance is obligatory and illiteracy among the younger generation is definitely decreasing.

Density of population varies. The whole interior, with the exception of the urban agglomeration around Madrid, is very thinly populated, most sparsely on the steppe of the upper Ebro Basin and of La Mancha southeast of Madrid. In contrast, several coastal regions have very high densities. This is the case in the mining and industrial areas of Catalonia and the Basque provinces, and somewhat less in Asturias. Areas of intensive irrigation around Valencia and Murcia and the coastal strip from Málaga to Almería show a high concentration of population. None of these favorable conditions, however, can explain the equally high densities of preponderantly rural Galicia and Andalusia. The unhealthy overpopulation in these areas has led to continual emigration. Most of the emigration to the Americas originates here, although many emigrants also come from the Basque provinces. Argentina and Cuba are the main countries of destination. However, emigration does not play as important a role in Spain as it does in other Southern European countries.

It is difficult to describe the Spanish character. The popular concept of the proud, dignified, rather lazy, serious, even melancholic, quixotic or fanatical Spaniard is primarily that of the Castilian, and fits only in certain respects the shrewd, hard-working, parsimonious, but imaginative and superstitious Gallego, or the simple, down-to-earth, intransigent Basque, the exuberant, enterprising, progressive, and even adventurous Catalan, the open, stubborn Aragonese, or the easy-going, aesthetic, gay Andalusian.

Most Spaniards are very conscious of the past glory of their country. The memory of the fight against Islam, as well as the golden age (*siglo de oro*), is very vivid. The century-old state of affairs has fostered a widespread feeling of resentment and suspicion of foreign nations. Together with the actual remoteness from

Europe, this has contributed to the peculiar Spanish brand of isolationism.

In most areas the climate permits many activities to go on outdoors, and most Spaniards seem to enjoy the crowd. However, less loud and vivacious talk is heard than in Italy or Greece. Traditions still have a firm hold on many groups of the population. It is often difficult to find people who are willing to do certain necessary but lowly work. They do not regard it beneath their dignity to live from charity. The lag in mining development, and of industry in some areas, is partly due to this reluctance to do manual work outside of agriculture because it is regarded as socially degrading.

FIGURE 122. Pedraza, a small village near Segovia. Note the characteristic architecture, with its columns, stone-paved porches and balconies, the barren slopes in the background, and the lack of women in the dusty courtyard. (Spanish Tourist Office.)

Spanish houses show oriental influence, especially in the south. Designed to keep women secluded, the enclosed yards and walls with few windows are reminiscent of Mohammedan cities. The patios of the more pretentious houses have gardens and fountains. The custom of having iron lattice work in the windows is found far into northern Spain and many of the lattices are often true works of art. Flat roofs, on which to spend the cooler hours, are confined to the south. Elsewhere in Spain, the round tiles of Roman derivation are used to cover gently sloping roofs (Figure 122). Stone and brick houses prevail in most parts of the country, except in the northern mountainous region where native wood is available. The bricks are often unbaked, of the type called *adobe*. Walls are frequently whitewashed and the lime kiln is a characteristic adjunct of the town.

In the drier parts of the Mesetas, windmills are another characteristic feature of the landscape. Towns and cities of northern Spain frequently have enclosed squares, which are entered through passages and which give the feeling of an enlarged *patio*. Balconies and arcades are much used in town houses. Outside the closely built towns there are few buildings except for the amphitheater used for bullfighting. The older parts of cities and towns are irregular and narrow, although sections built up since the Renaissance show rectangular patterns. There is scarcely a Spanish city which does not harbor architectural treasures from the Moorish, Romanesque, Gothic, or Baroque periods, more rarely from Roman or Renaissance periods, hardly any from the Carthaginian or Visigothic era.

The Present Economic Life of Spain

Mediterranean landforms and climate are ideally suited to a garden economy based on manual work and irrigation. Such an economy, however, is very susceptible to disturbances from the outside. In addition, only part of Spain is truly Mediterranean. Spain was not involved in World War II, but had its own Civil War in 1936-39, and the devastation was so terrific that its industry could not profit from the war, as other neutrals did. The general stagnation of Spanish economy dates back to the exhausting accomplishments of the sixteenth century. Since the seventeenth century, Spain has been economically behind other European countries.

Agriculture. Despite the potentialities of industrial development, agriculture is and will probably remain Spain's main economic activity. It has unexploited possibilities. The effects of the Civil War are still more visible here than in any other activity. Though the number of animals and the volume of some minor crops have increased, the harvest of the key crops, barley and wheat, is still only half of the pre-Civil War level, and that of rice and corn substantially lower. The areas of these crops are partly exclusive. Wheat is the main crop of the better soils of the dry northern Meseta, while the shallow soils of the southern Meseta and its still

greater aridity permit only the cultivation of barley. Moist northwestern Spain is a land of corn and of pastures. Most of the cattle
of Spain are found in Galicia, Asturia, and the Pyrenees. The
southern half of the country is characterized by olive groves, vineyards, and orange groves. Spain is the world's greatest producer
of olive oil and the largest exporter of oranges (Figure 123). The
orange groves are closely confined to the southern and eastern
coasts, although the olive tree is also found inland. Other Mediterranean fruit trees such as almonds, pomegranates, and figs are found

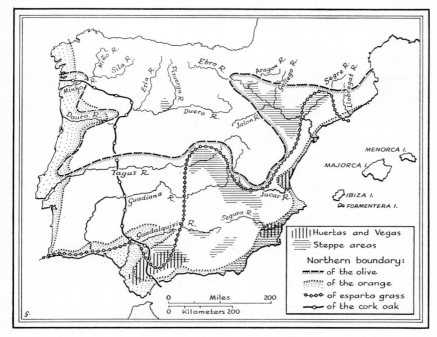

FIGURE 123. Mediterranean products of the Iberian peninsula.

in the same general area, and also tropical ones such as carobs and
date palms. The date palm, though it grows in a wider area, bears
fruit only in the famous groves of Elche near Murcia. All these
tropical and subtropical products need irrigation and are most
plentiful in areas where the old Moorish irrigation installations are
well preserved, around Valencia, Murcia, Almería, Málaga, and inland in the mountain valley of Granada, and the plains of the Ebro
and Guadalquivir. The intensively cultivated oases in semiarid surroundings are called *huertas*, where two crops are harvested, or the
Arabic equivalent, *vegas*, where only one crop is possible. From

these areas Western Europe receives its early spring vegetables. The products of the vineyards are exported either as grapes and raisins or as wine. Sherry received its name from Jerez de la Frontera. Intercropping is less frequent than in Italy, though it occurs especially in the open olive groves.

A few other products of secondary importance are interesting for one reason or another, some because of their importance in Moorish times. Examples are cotton, sugar cane, mulberry trees, and the cork oak, which grows along the border of Spain and Portugal. Until recently, these two countries had a monopoly of its products, but French North Africa has become a serious competitor in the last two decades.

It is still questioned whether the steppe of the interior upland is natural or a product of the destruction by man and his animals at an early period. One argument for the existence of a genuine steppe is that the Mesetas share the esparto grass, a coarse bunch grass, with the North African steppe. It is used for mats, baskets, braided shoes, etc. Great herds of sheep and goats are kept in these areas. The merino sheep is a native of Spain, though the best merino wool no longer comes from this country. In summer the flocks have to be brought to the sierras. The wide tracks of these migrations are characteristic of many parts of Spain, and the strife between the *mesta*, the organization of the big sheepowners, and the peasants fills many pages of Spanish history. In this instance modern technology has brought beneficial changes to Spain. Today, the animals are shipped by railroad, and much land can be reclaimed for agriculture. On the other hand, the goat is still unrestrained from damaging tree growth, more so than in any other Mediterranean country.

Another reason for the backwardness of Spanish agriculture is the large estates owned by absentee landlords. They are interested only in a carefree existence and do not care to improve their land. The great estates were created in the later phases of the reconquista; northern Spain remains a land of small landowners. Several attempts of land reform have been undertaken, yet nothing decisive has been accomplished so far.

Traffic and Fishing. A great obstacle to the development of industry in Spain is the peripheral distribution of the main population centers. Shipping around the coasts is inexpensive, but slow. Railroad and truck traffic are both undeveloped. Spanish railroads are slow, irregular, and the trains are infrequent. There is a well-developed road and railroad net on the map, but its efficiency is very low, and the meshes of the grid are rather large. This is partly due to the mountains which must be crossed and partly to the broad gauge. Prompted by her fear of invasion, Spain chose a very broad gauge in the early years of railroad building. This necessitates very great curves and makes construction of tunnels and bridges very expensive. Therefore, seldom more than one track can be laid. Because of the high costs, about a quarter of the tracks were laid in narrow gauge. Some of these lines, once regarded as feeder lines, could do better today if through service could be given. All these factors make railway traffic slow and expensive. The rolling stock of the railroads, as well as the mechanized road vehicles, deteriorated during the Civil War, and economic conditions since that time have not permitted a thorough overhauling or replacement.

Although it has numerous good natural harbors, Spain has a merchant marine which totals only a little more than one million tons, most of them fishing vessels and small coastal steamers. The bulk of the traffic to other countries is carried on in foreign bottoms.

In the Basque provinces and Galicia, Spain has a coastal population with a long maritime tradition. They have been engaged mainly in fishing, the only economic activity not significantly interrupted by the Civil War. The volume of catch has more than doubled since 1928, despite domestic and world economic crises. The destruction of livestock which occurred during the Civil War may have had something to do with the replacement of meat by fish in the general diet.

Mining. In many respects, Spain possesses a better basis for a modern economy than any other South European country. Its power basis is assured by rich coal deposits, and the large rivers, even in the dry south, are a permanent source of water power. The iron ores of the Cantabrian mountains are among the best in Europe—41 to 57 per cent iron—and are exported from Bilbao to several countries (Figure 120). Those of Asturias are located close to coal mines. Nevertheless, little smelting is done in Spain itself. This is due partly to the fact that the mines are owned by foreign, mostly English, capital, and partly to the precapitalistic psychology of many Spaniards. The rich aristocrats are not ready to invest money in anything other than land, and the poor man, especially the Castilian, is not ready to work in mines. Oviedo, Bilbao, and Santander are the main centers of the northern Spanish mining districts. Other mining districts are the Sierra Morena, where mercury, copper, and lead are the main products, and the Baetic Cordillera, which has a great variety of products. Almadén is one of the world's richest mercury mines and has a close Mediterranean competitor only in Idria, now in Yugoslavia. Despite century-old exploitation, Spain still produces more than a fourth of the world production. In other metals such as gold, silver, lead, and copper, Spain lost its leading position either in late antiquity or as late as the nineteenth century, and its resources of zinc, tin, and tungsten have never played a very important role. It is surprising how little this mineral wealth contributes to Spain's economy. However, there has been a steady though slow increase in coal production. Also, the number of miners, approximately 150,000 in 1948, is by no means insignificant.

Industry. The main center of Spanish industry, including heavy industry, is Catalonia and its capital Barcelona, rather remote from the mining districts. This industrial vigor is commonly attributed to the different psychological attitude of the Catalans. Coal from northern Spain must be shipped around the peninsula so a number of the hydroelectric plants and imported coal furnish most of the power basis for this industry. Textile industries lead, with many small-scale light industries following. Cork processing and fish canning are especially important. Minor industrial areas include a metal industry in the northern part of Spain, and textiles in Andalusia and the larger cities along the Mediterranean coast.

Overseas Spain. The small Spanish overseas empire has little economic value, the Spanish Sahara none at all. The most important possession is the Canary Islands, which are officially a part of metropolitan Spain. Their products are similar to those of Mediterranean Spain. They are a frequented tourist resort and have a certain importance as a halfway station on the route to South America. The islands in the Gulf of Guinea produce cocoa and coffee. Northern Morocco is of strategic and prestige value rather than an economic asset.

Portugal

Population

The people of Portugal have attained a uniformity in religion and language unequalled elsewhere. The religion of Portugal is overwhelmingly Roman Catholic. Portuguese is a separate Romance language, with an ancient and valuable literature. It may be true that Portuguese is more closely related to Castilian than is

Catalan, but it certainly cannot be regarded as a Spanish dialect. Within Portugal, dialect differences are insignificant. The linguistic boundary between Portugal and Spain coincides very closely with the political boundary, a natural consequence of the fact that the political boundary antedates the written fixation of both Spanish and Portuguese. The political boundary is one of the most stable in the world. Except for one small correction, it has not been changed since the thirteenth century.

The Portuguese birth rate and death rate are both high. Though the latter has shown a considerable decline lately, it is still the highest in Southern Europe. The high mortality does not begin to offset the far higher number of births, and hence Portugal has one of the highest known net reproduction rates.

This overpopulation has led to a large emigration. Though Portuguese statistics are rather unsatisfactory, it appears that proportionally more Portuguese have emigrated during the last decades than have emigrants from any other country except Ireland. The bulk of the emigration went to Portuguese-speaking Brazil. As there is considerable unauthorized emigration, available figures tell only part of the story. Some of the successful emigrants return later with their savings. It is not without significance that literacy among these emigrants was higher than the average of the country. Thus, emigration takes away from the country a higher proportion of its better educated and presumably more ambitious and more intelligent elements. It is obvious that the center of cultural activity in the Portuguese language is no longer Portugal but Brazil. Illiteracy in Portugal is high, and is higher among women than among men. Even among boys of from 10 to 14 years of age about 33 per cent are illiterate. Among women of 60 years and over the percentage is 71.5.

The population is unequally distributed. Northern Portugal is a land of dense population on small holdings. In the south, in the area of large estates, low density prevails. Only the extreme south, Algarve, is a land of small proprietors. About 17.5 per cent of the whole territory is in the hands of large landowners. The density of population decreases in most regions from the coastal plain toward the interior upland. The international boundary runs through a very thinly inhabited area.

The Portuguese resemble the Spaniards in physical respect, and on an average are only slightly taller. There are also more individuals of Near Eastern type. How much this is due to Phoenician colonization and how much to later Arabic and Jewish admixture is unknown. Likewise, it is debated whether the Negroid features of many individuals should be traced to a prehistoric Negro population or to the influx of slaves in the age of discovery.

The Portuguese have many traits in common with their Castilian-Spanish cousins. They are a proud, sensitive people, given to vainglorious daydreaming, and are easily discouraged by obstacles. The weight of tradition is felt here even stronger than in Spain, especially among the illiterate peasants, who are reluctant to accept improvements. The Portuguese, however, are gayer and more accommodating than the Castilians. The conservative nature of the country is seen among other things in the retention of many costumes, or at least parts of them, such as the strawbraided raincoats, the leather apron worn to protect the legs in the thorny *maquis*, and the colorful woolen caps or felt hats. Agricultural tools are often primitive, unchanged for centuries. No other European country has among its fishing boats such a large proportion of sailing vessels and rowboats. They often have high bows and sterns and are gaudily painted. Farmhouses are often several storied, the first story serving as a barn. There is a great variety of house types in this small country. They are adapted to the various local building materials, ranging from granite and limestone to sun-baked clay. In some areas walled-in small plots (quintas) are characteristic. They enclose the house, orchard, fields, and a small pasture. Only Lisbon and Oporto should be called modern cities. Although monasteries and churches are not conspicuous in the landscape buildings of ancient architecture are numerous, though less so than in Spain. Ruins of castles are frequent north of the Tagus, where the war with the Moors lasted longer than in quickly overrun southern Portugal.

The Present Economic Life of Portugal

Portugal is a poor country. The great age of discovery exhausted its material and population resources and was followed by a period of dependence on Spain (1580-1640). Portugal has never recovered from the losses suffered during this period. It profited in a moderate way from its neutrality during both the Spanish Civil War and World War II. The dictatorial regime has maintained rigid economic controls and secured a surplus of revenues over expenditures since the war. The economic situation has improved, but has not changed basically.

Agriculture. Of all the countries of Southern Europe, Portugal is the most uniform, not so much because of its small size but because it belongs entirely to the western fringe of the Iberian Peninsula. There is a gradual transition from the typical Mediterranean climate in the south to the Atlantic humid climate of Galicia. Most of the important Mediterranean products, such as olives, grapes, oranges, cork oaks, and fig trees grow in low-lying parts of the country (Figure 123). Cork oaks and olive trees are planted in open stands and between the olive trees vegetables and occasionally grain is grown. The vines are trained on trellises in the northern part of the country, elsewhere kept continuously trimmed as low bushes. Wine and cork are among the three main exports, fish being the most important. Port wine is so-called because its export is legally restricted to the port of Oporto. Madeira wines also find a good market abroad. Other significant products are turpentine and resin from the large pine forests in the sand dunes. Other forests are mostly *maquis*, which furnish only some wood for domestic fuel. Portugal is, however, one of the few countries where reforestation has a rather lengthy record.

Grains are widely planted, corn in the wetter north on small terrace plots, and wheat on the large estates of southern Portugal. Irrigation is slowly spreading and with it the cultivation of rice. Only in northern Portugal can the spring flood of the rivers be used for rice cultivation. The grain crops, however, are not sufficient for the needs of the growing population and more has to be imported. Neither the cultivation by small landowners working without capital and with antiquated methods nor that of tenants on large estates of absentee landowners produces good results. The per acre yields are the lowest in all of Europe except Greece, and nearly the lowest known anywhere. About half of the cultivated area is left fallow every year. Other areas could be drained or improved. Taken all together, Portugal could increase its agricultural production considerably.

The small area of Algarve, between the south coast and the Sierra de Monchique, the last spur of the Sierra Morena, is the orchard of Portugal. Mediterranean and some tropical fruit trees, such as bananas and date palms, are grown here in well-tended small plots. The agriculture of Madeira and the Azores is of similar character; the latter specialize in pineapples, the cultivation of which occupies 60 to 70 per cent of the population.

Fishing. Portugal is dependent for part of its food and for much of its export revenue on the products of its fishing industry. Among the fish, sardines occupy the first place. When the shoals of sardines did not appear along the Portuguese coast in the 1948 and 1949 seasons, it caused a serious crisis in the entire economy. There was some apprehension that this shift of the sardine migration might be permanent, connected with the reported warming up of the Arctic and a shift of life zones northward. However, such cyclical occurrences have been reported in earlier periods and 1950 was a satisfactory season. The importance of the fishing season for the Portuguese economy may be judged by the fact that, according to value, an average of 83 per cent of the entire production of the country is agricultural, and 4 per cent products of the sea, but for exports the figures are 60 and 20 per cent respectively. The ancient participation of Portuguese trawlers on the Newfoundland Banks is declining and codfish is now imported.

Mining and Industry. There are many small mines in Portugal (Figure 120). Only wolframite, the mother ore of tungsten, is important and probably the dependence of both the Axis and the Allies on this metal helped to keep Portugal out of the war. Coal is mined in some quantity, but this is not sufficient. Though little coal is needed for heating or industry, and charcoal is used for cooking in the villages, coal has to be imported, mostly for the railroads. Most of the industry is on a small scale, and concentrated in Lisbon and Oporto. But even in these two cities workers constitute only a small proportion of the population. Portuguese industry is beginning to supply part of the needs of the colonies, which repay primarily in badly needed foodstuffs.

Traffic and Communications. Although much work has been done on improving roads, the dirt road is still predominant in Portugal. Many of the new roads are not connected with each other or have been constructed from two terminals, the median piece being still missing. On the dirt roads two-wheeled wooden carts are used. In many mountainous sections donkeys and mules on bridle paths are the only means of communications. The railroad net is sparse. Portugal uses the Spanish broad gauge and the two nets are connected by five lines. On these lines only a few trains cross the boundary in each direction each day. The only railway line used to any extent is the internal line connecting Lisbon and Oporto.

Colonies. Portugal was able to save some parts of its colonial empire, and in the nineteenth century extended its rule inland from the coasts of Angola and Mozambique. Portugal has not been able to invest much capital in the development of these colonies. As we have seen, their foodstuffs and other products contribute in a modest way to the economy of the metropolitan country. On the other hand, Portugal has little part in the commerce of its smaller colonies in Asia, and in that of Guinea and the Cape Verde Islands. The most prosperous possessions are the two islands of São Tomé (St. Thomas) and Principe in the Gulf of Guinea, and Madeira and the Azores in the Atlantic. The latter two groups are regarded officially as parts of European Portugal. Both their population and their products are similar to those of the mainland.

The Most Important Problems Facing the Countries of Southern Europe

There are certain problems which trouble all the countries of Southern Europe, with the partial exception of Turkey. Underlying most of these troubles is the rapid increase in population which threatens to outrun any possible increase in productivity. All these countries have reached the stage where modern medicine and hygiene are lowering mortality rapidly. In Italy, and even more so in Greece, the drainage of swamps wipes out the scourge of malaria. At the same time the birth rate has begun to fall only a little, and in Portugal hardly at all. Birth control, industrialization, increase of agricultural production, and emigration, all have very definite limitations as means of improving the geographical conditions of these countries.

Birth control, apparently the most obvious remedy, is a rather long-range solution, and its application is blocked in countries where the Roman Catholic Church is influential and a considerable percentage of the population illiterate. It cannot be dismissed, but it may take decades before it can become effective.

Industrialization in these countries has very definite limits, especially in Italy and Greece, where very few mineral resources are available. How far industrialization can still be driven under such circumstances is shown by the Italian example. It seems doubtful whether further industrialization can keep pace with population increase. The situation is somewhat more hopeful in Turkey, Spain, and even in Portugal. In these countries lack of capital, poverty, which restricts the internal market, and psychological attitudes are the main obstacles.

In all these countries, new land can be won, and cultivated land better utilized. All except Greece have large, little utilized latifundia. Though mechanization would be possible and would increase yields, the problem of giving work to the greatest possible number of people seems overriding and indicates the probable further direction of developments.

Other areas may be reclaimed. Drainage and improvement are rather slow working methods and have definite limits. In the first years, results may be spectacular, as was Mussolini's drainage of the Roman Campagna, and the reclamation of the Axios delta in Greece. Very soon, regions will have to be attacked which give only diminishing returns. There is also a definite limit to the amount of land which can be reclaimed. Everywhere in the world there is a tendency to extend methods of large-scale work to agriculture, mechanization foremost among them. Mediterranean agriculture is primarily tree culture and largely done on small plots and terraced steep slopes where mechanization is not possible. This puts Mediterranean countries at a disadvantage in competition. Many of the typical Mediterranean tree crops, such as oranges, have to be irrigated, while in Florida or Southeast Asia this is not necessary. With improvement of transportation facilities there is even danger that the basis of some staple products may be undermined and that Mediterranean agriculture will have to give up areas which cannot be used for other products. This applies not only to citrus fruits but also to Greek tobacco, Spanish and Portuguese cork, and even to wine.

Finally, emigration has played a considerable role in the alleviation of population pressure. With immigration restrictions in many countries, however, especially in the United States, this is no longer a solution to be relied upon. Turkey is different since it still can absorb the recent immigration from the Balkan countries, though this is no longer true in European Turkey.

Compared with these basic problems, other problems such as nutritional deficiencies seem of less importance. Animal husbandry seems condemned to shrink because the climatic conditions do not favor pasture land. Sheep raising requiring transhumance is threatened by the land reclamation program. Goats have been recognized as enemies of the forests and their number, except in Spain, is being restricted. Thus animal husbandry will not furnish enough animal products for a growing population. To replace proteins from this source, fishing had to be expanded. For reasons discussed above, the Mediterranean Sea does not provide good fishing. In this respect Spain and Portugal are in a better position, but only insofar as they are not Mediterranean countries. Connected with these problems is the general backwardness of the rural population and, in the Iberian peninsula and in Turkey, of a large segment of the urban population. Here rapid improvement is most likely, although the decrease of illiteracy does not tell the whole story.

Italy is the only Southern European country which has good connections with the rest of the continent. The Iberian countries are hampered by the natural barrier of the Pyrenees and by the broad gauge of their railroads. Turkey and Greece are rather remote and, for political reasons, have at present to rely on shipping for contacts with Western Europe.

Threats to a peaceful development are a recurrent feature of the history of the South European peninsulas and are at present urgent for Turkey, Greece, and Italy. The last faces danger no longer from the Germans beyond the Alps, but rather from the northeastern Slav block. For Turkey, external pressure has been the overriding problem for 250 years with varying intensity. Spain's lingering distrust of a France looming from across the Pyrenees as well as from Morocco, has become pointless in the foreseeable future.

There are also a number of national aspirations of the South European nations. Though most of them simmer below the surface of the political cauldron, the facts of human geography and, in some instances, of topography make it unlikely that they will be forgotten. From time to time there is talk of Spain's desire to win back Gibraltar, Italy's agitation to reacquire Trieste, and Greek demands for the complete union of all Greeks by being accorded political control of Cyprus. Other objects of Greek and Italian irredentism, such as Eastern Thrace, Istanbul, Asia Minor, Fiume, and Dalmatia, seem to be buried. But it is hard to believe that this is true of Italian aspirations for Corsica and Malta or Greek demands for northern Epirus, even though they are not the subject of agitation at the moment. Neither Portugal nor Turkey entertains territorial claims.

BIBLIOGRAPHY

A. Books in English

American Geographical Society. *Readings in the Geography of the Mediterranean Region.* Reprint Series No. 2. Contributions by various authors. New York: American Geographical Society, 1943.

King, Georgiana G. *Heart of Spain.* Cambridge: Harvard University Press, 1941.

Moodie, A. E. *The Italo-Yugoslav Boundary.* London: George Philip & Son, Ltd., The London Geographical Inst., 1945.

Newbigin, Marion I. *The Mediterranean Lands,* 3d ed. New York: Alfred A. Knopf, Inc., 1948.

Semple, Ellen Churchill. *Geography of the Mediterranean.* New York: Henry Holt & Co., Inc., 1931.

Thornburg, Max Weston, Spry, Graham, and Soule, George. *Turkey: An Economic Appraisal.* New York: The Twentieth Century Fund, 1949.

B. Books in Foreign Languages

Dantin-Cereceda, J. *Regiones naturales de España* (Natural Regions of Spain). Madrid: J. Cosano, 1922.

Echeverria, Martin, L. *España: el pais y los habitantes* (Spain: The Country and Its Inhabitants). Mexico: Ed. Atlante, 1940.

Krueger, Karl. *Die Türkei* (Turkey). Berlin: Safari-Verlag, 1951.

Marcotte, A. *Le Portugal dans le monde* (Portugal in the World). Brussels: Anc. Etablissements A. Puvrez, 1944.

Philippson, Alfred. *Das Mittelmeergebiet, seine geographische und kulturelle Eigenart* (The Mediterranean, Its Geographic and Cultural Character), 4th ed. Leipzig: B. G. Teubner, 1931.

————. *Die Griechischen Landschaften* (The Regions of Greece), Vol. I. Frankfurt am Main: Vittorio Klostermann, 1952.

Touring Club Italiano. *Attraverso l'Italia* (Going Across Italy). Milan: Touring Club of Italy, 1927.

C. Articles

Almagia, Roberto. "The Repopulation of the Roman Campagna," *Geographical Review*, XIX (1929), 529-55.

Dobby, E. H. G. "Agrarian Problems in Spain," *Geographical Review*, XXVI (1936), 177-89.

Fels, Edwin. "Landgewinnung in Griechenland" (Land Reclamation in Greece), *Petermanns Mitteilungen*, Ergänzungsheft No. 242, 1944.

Frost, R. S. "The Reclamation of the Pontine Marshes," *Geographical Review*, XXIV (1934), 584-95.

Giusti, Ugo. "Lo spopolamento montano in Italia" (The Mountain Depopulation in Italy), Studi e monografie n. 16. Rome, Istituto Nazionale di Economia Agraria, 1938.

Hoffman, George W. "South Tyrol: Borderland Rights vs. World Politics," *Journal of Central European Affairs*, VII (1947), 285-306.

Houston, J. M. "Irrigation as a Solution to Agrarian Problems in Modern Spain," *Geographical Journal*, CXVI (1950), 55-63.

Lautensach, Hermann. "Portugal auf Grund eigener Reisen und der Literatur (Portugal, a Description Based on Travel and Literature), *Petermanns Mitteilungen*, Ergänzungsheft No. 46, 1932; No. 50, 1937.

Lovett, F. Edwards. "Trieste: International City," *Geographical Magazine*, XXIV (1952), 464-72.

Ogilvie, A. G. "Physiography and Settlement in Southern Macedonia," *Geographical Review*, IX (1921), 172-97.

Patterson, Rosina M. "The Balearic Islands," *Journal of Geography*, XLV (1946), 153-56.

Weigend, Guido G. "Effects of Boundary Changes in the South Tyrol," *Geographical Review*, XL (1950), 364-75.

chapter 8

EAST CENTRAL EUROPE

THIS CHAPTER concerns itself with Albania, Yugoslavia, Bulgaria, Romania, Hungary, Czechoslovakia, and Poland. All are well-known geographical entities, even though their political boundaries have often changed. Other terms are also used to designate the region: "Shatter Belt," for instance, which is a political expression depicting the fragmentation of the region into many small countries. "Devil's Belt" is a term used by the peoples of East Central Europe to reflect their expectation of being overrun, destroyed, or exterminated at any time by the great powers which border them. The term "South Central Europe," which is sometimes applied, does not include Poland and Czechoslovakia, while the "Balkans," a term attached geographically and historically to the area once controlled by the Ottoman Empire in the Balkan Peninsula, excludes Czechoslovakia, Poland, and Hungary. None of these terms fully reflects the present political distribution pattern of the countries concerned, their physiographic unity, or their common historical background.

Thus the name "East Central Europe," while in a way arbitrary, is perhaps the most satisfactory from the general geographical point of view. An additional circumstance which arose after World War II gives the area a completely unified aspect: East Central Europe is at present the major zone of interest of the Soviet Union. It is communist ruled, and has a new political, social, and economic face. Despite Yugoslavia's defection, East Central Europe can still be considered as the western security belt of the Soviet Union.

East Central Europe also coincides closely with an historical corridor or transit land. Eastern expansion had to narrow down here before reaching the oceanic regions; western movements, in contrast, had to fan out toward the continental areas, a necessity imposed by the Black Sea, which has divided the possible routes of eastward movement into a northern one (toward the Urals and central Asia) and a southern one (across the Bosporus into the Middle East).

Nothing is stable in the area: everything is mixed and changing, unconsolidated in space as well as in time. Shifts are felt in races, peoples, clans, and individuals, ideals and languages, the way of thinking, the habits, the religions, and customs. Not the least variable, as a result, are East Central Europe's political life and the political boundaries.

Three main physiographic regions compose East Central Europe: the Northern Lowlands, the Danube Valley basins with their mountain girdles, and the Southern Highlands. Relief, rock formations, soils, climate, and vegetation are different in each of these three regions. These differences are also reflected in the ethnic groups. Northern Slavs inhabit the Northern Lowlands and the Bohemian-Polish Uplands. Southern Slavs live in the Southern Highlands, while non-Slavic peoples fill the Danube Valley basins and their connecting regions.

The mineral raw materials are fairly well distributed among these three divisions. Coal and uranium constitute the principal riches of the northern region; petroleum, rock salt, and bauxite are the wealth of the central area; various ores, like chromium and copper, are plentiful in the southern section.

Yet agricultural activities are dominant, which again gives a common character to the entire area. Under the new rulers the agriculture has been dedicated to an industrial type of farming. Industrialization and urbanization are also developing considerably in their own right. This gives East Central Europe a strong transitional character: from agriculture to industrialization, from capitalism to socialism, from political independence to subjugation. Under the pressure of the Soviet Union, forces are now at work within each of the countries to bring about a uniformity in way of life and thinking. This transitional uniformity gives the final touch of unity to the region.

Physiographic Basis of Cultural Forms

Situation and Location. In terms of the surface distribution of continents and oceans, East Central Europe has a continental situation. The Baltic, Adriatic, and Black seas bordering some sections of the region are all inland waters and do not change significantly its continental character, reflected both in physiography and in human actions. Compared with the surrounding major regions the region has a central location on the European peninsula.

Size and Form. The total area of East Central Europe is 450,000 square miles, containing approximately 90 million people. But from the physiographic point of view, 5,000 square miles should be added for Ruthenia, now the Transcarpathian Oblast of the Ukrainian S.S.R. The whole region is therefore equal in size to the combined areas of Great Britain, France, the Benelux states, and Germany, an area which is only a little less than that of the North Central states of the United States of America. The longest north-south distance, i.e., between the Baltic and Ionian seas, is 1,000 miles, the greatest east-west distance, between the Adriatic and the Black seas, is 640 miles.

The present form is irregular, with a longer north-south axis and a narrow neck between Austria and the Soviet Union. Within a 500-mile radius of the geographical center of the area (Karcag in Hungary), are the shores of the Baltic, the Adriatic, and the Black Sea coast of Bulgaria and Romania. A circle with a radius of 350 miles would include all capitals with the exception of Tirana (Tiranë) in Albania. The smaller circle would also contain the most important mineral wealth of the area: the petroleum of Romania, Hungary, and Poland; the bauxite of Hungary and Yugoslavia; and the Silesian coal basin.

Structure, Relief, and Natural Regions. East Central Europe is a mosaic of the main European structural elements (Figure 124). The western edge of the Fenno-Russian block, undisturbed since the Cretaceous,[1] forms the projecting arm of northeast Poland. Caledonian structures enter from the western Baltic and extend as far as the Polish uplands; Hercynian remnants are represented by the Bohemian Massif, the Sudeten, the Holy Cross Mountains (Gory Swietokrzyskie), the Dobruja, parts of the Rhodope Massif, and small structural islands in the Carpathian Basin.

All these structural elements are split by the Alpine mountain system, which crosses the region. The great arc of the Alps, the Carpathians, and the Balkan ranges forms the northern branch. The southern branch is formed by the Dinaric ranges, which extend southeastward into the Pindus Mountains. These two branches begin to diverge in Austria and meet again in the Armenian knot in Asia, as the Pontic and Taurus chains. Along the way they enclose several Tertiary or Quaternary depressions.

[1] For geological terms see Appendix I.

These structural elements and surface configurations make it possible to divide the region into four natural regions: (a) the Northern Lowlands (North Polish Lowlands), (b) the Bohemian-Polish Uplands, (c) the Danube Valley with its basins and the Carpathian Mountains, and (d) the Southern Highlands of the Balkan Peninsula.

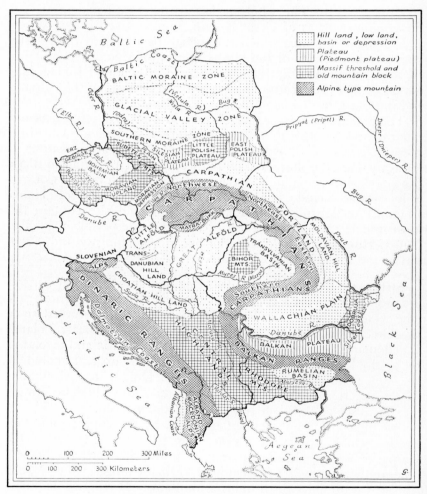

FIGURE 124. Structural map of East Central Europe.

Northern Lowlands. The Baltic section of the German-Polish lowland can be subdivided into three main belts: the northern or Baltic Moraine Zone (Baltic Plain), the Glacial Valley Zone, and the narrow Southern Moraine Zone, which includes the Silesian Plain along the upper Oder River.

THE BALTIC COAST AND BALTIC MORAINE ZONE. Between the estuaries of the Oder (Odra) and Pasleka (former Passarge), extends the fairly straight shore line of the low Baltic coast. Characteristic long narrow sandbars, caused by the strong sea currents, tend to enclose as lagoons the depressions of the low coastal platform. The most remarkable features of this coastal belt are scattered lakes in the western half, and large lagoons with single sea inlets in the eastern section. High dune ridges, shifted inland by the onshore winds, bar the way to the interior (Figure 125). Southward, the land ascends gradually into the gently undulating ground-moraine zone, with an average altitude of 150 feet. Drumlins and morainic hills 250 to 500 feet high, left by the retreating ice sheet, reach their highest elevation near Gdansk.

FIGURE 125. Shifting dunes of the Polish Baltic Coast.

East of the Vistula (Wisla), in Masuria, extensive lakes are rare, in contrast to thousands of lakes sprinkled over the western coastlands (*Pomorze*). The irregular land surface lacks large flat sections, and the characteristic glacial till is cut everywhere by gullies and creeks. This coastal zone is limited inland by the terminal moraines, an almost continuous west-east band of hills pushing tongues into the southward lying sandy outwash plain, which has resulted from the erosion of the moraine by many ice-fed rivers of the glacial epoch.

THE GLACIAL VALLEY ZONE. South of the Baltic Moraine Zone or Baltic Plain, lies the central belt of the glacial valleys (*Pradoliny* in Polish and *Urstromtäler* in German). There are three glacial valleys, each drained by one or two large rivers: Posnania-Kuyavia, Masovia, and Podlachia. Despite their broken courses, the general alignment of the rivers is a west-east one. Because of the general low relief, the broad and flat valleys and extensive marshes have no clearly marked watershed. The Bug Valley, running first south to north along the western edge of the Pripet marshes, turns westward at Brest (Brzesc). The valleys, the loamy soil interspersed with moraines and erratic rocks, sandflats, and dunes give a monotonous appearance to this extensive plain of Central Poland.

THE SOUTHERN MORAINE ZONE AND THE SILESIAN PLAIN. The broken character of the surface, caused by postglacial erosion, gives a transitional aspect to this narrow southernmost extension of the great north European glaciation, which graduates almost imperceptibly into the southward extending Silesian Plain. The latter is limited on the southwest by the foothills of the Sudeten and on the east by the hilly section of the Upper Silesian Plateau. Glacial and fluvioglacial deposits typify this part of the region, which is crossed at its longer axis by the Oder River.

Bohemian-Polish Uplands. Lying between the Northern Lowlands and the Carpathians are the Bohemian-Polish Uplands. A zone of great structural variation, these Uplands can be divided into two larger sections, the Bohemian Massif and the Polish Uplands, each with a number of smaller subregions.

BOHEMIAN MASSIF. The Bohemian Massif, sometimes called the Bohemian Plateau, is one of the most ancient structural features of Europe. Its center is an intermontane basin (Bohemian Basin) whose undulating surface has an elevation of from 1,500 to 1,800 feet, and is surrounded by mountain ranges of varying height and age. The northern portion of the depression is a dissected tableland drained by the Elbe (Labe) Valley. The basin is bordered on the southwest by the Czecho-Moravian Upland and the Bohemian Forest, a rolling hill country with a few peaks over 4,000 feet, and with several shallow longitudinal depressions. To the northwest, the basin is bounded by some basaltic uplands (Středohori) and the Teplice heights.

West of these heights extends a terrace, incised by many rivers, and beyond that are the crystalline Erz Gebirge (Ore Mountains), with their fairly steep slopes containing valuable pitchblende (uranium ore) at Jáchymov. On their northeastern end the Elbe cuts its way into Germany. To the east of the Elbe the Sudeten begins.

One hundred miles long, strongly eroded, these horst-type mountains (composed of crystalline nuclei, surrounded by gneiss, slates, and limestones) form the northeastern wall of the Bohemian Basin. The western portion of the Sudeten, including the headwaters of the Elbe, is composed of several longitudinal blocks with altitudes of from 3,000 to 5,000 feet. The lower, more compact eastern portion, from which flow the Oder and Morava rivers, ends suddenly at the Moravian Gate (930 feet high), which connects the Oder and Vistula valleys with the Moravian Depression.

The Bohemian Basin is limited toward the Moravian Depression by the relatively broad Czecho-Moravian Upland, whose low and indefinite watershed joins the Bohemian Forest in the Granite Uplands of Lower Austria. The complete encirclement of the Bohemian Basin is remarkably compact and well defined, whereas the Moravian Depression is a longitudinal pass between Silesia and the Basin of Vienna, and forms part of the Carpathian foreland.

POLISH UPLANDS. Between the Northern Lowlands and the Carpathians are the Polish Uplands, which begin in the west with the upper Silesian Plateau. Cut by the Oder River between Racibórz (Ratibor) and Opole (Oppeln), the western portion of this plateau has an average altitude of 1,000 feet and a thick loess cover, while its eastern portion bears the famous Silesian coal formation, overlain by Tertiary marls in the south. The eastward ascent from the Upper Silesian Plateau into the Little Polish Plateau is gradual. This high plateau, composed largely of Cretaceous limestones covered with loess, reaches its top elevation in the Lyso Góry, a hill group over 1,800 feet high, composed of Paleozoic strata. A similar though lower region is the East Polish Plateau, extending north as far as the Pripet marshes. The two plateaus are bisected by the broad north-south upper valley of the Vistula, which, with the San Valley to the east, forms the boundary between the plateau region and the Carpathian foreland.

The Danube Valley. This region includes the Carpathian Basin and the Wallachian Plain, both girdled by the Carpathian ranges. The Carpathian Basin comprises the Little Alföld (Small Hungarian Plains), the Hill Lands of Transdanubia and of Croatia-Slavonia, the Great Alföld (Great Hungarian Plains), and the Transylvanian Basin.

Characterized by a strong diversity in relief and structure, the Carpathian Basin is cut in unequal portions by the Danube Valley: the larger, northern section is encircled by the Carpathian arc, whereas the southern section is limited by the Alps in the west, the

Dinaric Alps in the southwest, and the Central Highlands in the south. Its complete and compact encirclement makes this basin one of the most uniform physiographic regions of the globe.

THE CARPATHIANS. With their foreland, the Carpathians extend in a thousand-mile arc, with a continuous Tertiary outer sandstone belt, and a central zone, composed mainly of crystalline rocks and limestone. On the basin side of the central zone there is an almost continuous volcanic inner belt. The variations in relief and general landscape offer a basis for division into the following sectors: Northwestern, Northeastern, Eastern, and Southern Carpathians.

1. The Northwestern Carpathians begin near the Morava River. Their sandstone belt comprises the White Carpathians and the Western Beskids, a bundle of monotonous parallel ranges of medium elevation, cut into smaller ridge sections by many transverse valleys. Their minor ranges constitute the Danube and Baltic watershed, with the Dukla Pass, 1,641 feet high, as an eastern limit. The northern part of the Carpathian foreland, a sandstone hill zone with an altitude of 1,600 feet, flattens into the valley plain of the Upper Vistula.

The central zone has three almost parallel ranges: the northern range comprises the crystalline nuclei of the Little Fatra, the Liptov Alps, and the High Tatra. The true alpine High Tatra ranges show crests from 6,000 to 8,000 feet, notably Stalin Peak (8,737 feet), highest of the Carpathians. The central range is composed of the Tribec, the Great Fatra, and the Low Tatra. The southern range consists of the Slovakian Ore Mountains. But these are thoroughly knitted to the volcanic belt with its Mátra-Bükk and Presov-Tokaj mountain groups.

East of the Low Tatra, belonging to the central range group, runs the Danube-Tisza watershed. Its rivers have, first, an alignment facilitating the west-east traffic and then turn south into the plains of the Carpathian Basin. Little intermontane basins, deep valleys, alpine pasture, and coniferous or mixed forests make the landscape picturesque.

2. East of the Dukla Pass, as far as the Borsa Pass and the crystalline massif of the Alps of Rodna, extend the less high and more rounded Northeastern Carpathians. These are composed of an inner, volcanic belt and a very broad zone of parallel sandstone ranges which contain rock salt, as well as some petroleum. On the inner or basin slope of the Northeastern Carpathians, the Tisza

starts its way toward the Great Alföld; on their outer, gradually flattening slopes the Prut rises, while not far to the southeast are the headwaters of the Siret. The San and Dniester originate close to each other in the Eastern Beskids, taking their course across the rolling but remarkably incised Galician foreland of the Northeastern Carpathians.

3. From the Alps of Rodna, the Eastern Carpathians strike south-southeastward as a continuation of the Northeastern Carpathian ranges, and end near Stalin (Brasov). Covered by Quaternary strata in the undulating foreland, the oil-rich sandstone belt

FIGURE 126. The wooded Southern Carpathians, near Roznau in Transylvania.

narrows and then gives place to the central limestone and crystalline zones and to the consistently broad Tertiary eruptive belt. Deep valleys and gorge-like passes, and peaks 4,000 to 7,000 feet high, characterize this mountain area of pastures, mineral springs, and virgin forests (Figure 126). From the strongly incised outer slopes of the Eastern Carpathians the Siret collects its tributaries, and runs parallel to the Carpathian chain in a long and well-marked valley across Moldavia.

4. West of Stalin, the sandstone and limestone zones disappear. The mountains strike first east to west, then southwest. Here called the Southern Carpathians (or Transylvanian Alps), they are

composed of two crystalline ranges, with elevations of over 5,000 feet and peaks exceeding 8,000. Crossed only by the Olt River, they form a natural barrier between the Transylvanian Basin and the Wallachian Plain. They end abruptly at the Danube water gap famous for its two gorges, the Kasan Pass (Klisura) and the Iron Gate. The southern slopes of these ranges merge into the foothills of Wallachia, which are cut by parallel rivers flowing southward across forest and pasture land, well known in its eastern section as the oil region of Ploesti.

THE CARPATHIAN BASIN. This basin, so well enclosed by the Carpathian ranges we have discussed, has an area of 100,000 square miles, with centripetal drainage. It is not, however, uniform in its relief. Three minor basins, divided by hill lands or mountains, can be distinguished: the Little Alföld, the Great Alföld, and Transylvania.

The Danube, on leaving the Basin of Vienna, builds a huge alluvial fan of gravel and silt southeast of Bratislava. This is the central portion of the Little Alföld, a flat to gently undulating lowland bounded on the west by the foothills of the Alps and on the southeast by the Bakony Mountains. In its western corner the large marshy Fertö (Neusiedler) Lake, surrounded by mud flats and swamps, bars cross-country movement.

South of the Little Alföld lies Transdanubia, a rolling hill land covered mainly by loess, and drained by hundreds of creeks with a general north-south alignment. Bordered on the east by the Danube and on the south by the Drava River, Transdanubia includes low forested mountains. Along a longitudinal faultline stretches Lake Balaton, the largest body of water in East Central Europe.

Southward, between the Drava, the Danube, the Sava, and the Slovenian Alps stretches the Croatian-Slavonian Hill Land, which is really more an undulating lowland with interspersed limestone and crystalline hills. Mention need be made only of its rolling basin of Zagreb in the west and the level Sava Basin (Posavina) reaching as far as Belgrade (Beograd) to the east.

East of these hill lands, between the Danube, the foothills and volcanic belt of the Northwestern and the Northeastern Carpathians, and bounded on the east by the Bihor and Banat mountains, lies the Great Alföld, 40,000 square miles in area, and irregularly shaped. This plain is a constantly sinking block covered by thick Tertiary and Quaternary strata. Cut by the meandering Tisza, the western portion, called *Duna-Tisza-Köze* (Mid-Danube-

Tisza),[2] is a long, partly sand-covered Mesopotamian region. The eastern larger part, the plain in the true sense, is called Transtisia. Near Debrecen is situated the *Hortobágy*, a steppe with blown sand of high soda content. To the south are completely flat areas crossed by the meandering and flood-dangerous Körös and Mures (Maros) rivers. The black soil region of the Banat extends still farther southward, while between the Tamis and Danube rivers lies the blown-sand area of the Deliblato.

East of the Great Alföld and the Bihor Mountains is the Transylvanian Basin with its Tertiary clay strata. In contrast to the Great Alföld and the Wallachian Plain, Transylvania is an elevated intermontane basin open only toward the Great Alföld along the broader Somes (Szamos) and the Mures (Maros) river valleys. This is a region of rolling deforested hills yielding salt, gypsum, and natural gas.

WALLACHIAN PLAIN. The Wallachian Plain, also called the Lower Danube Plain, is a trenchlike basin limited by the Southern Carpathians and their southern foothills, by the piedmont plateau of the Balkan Mountains, and by the Dobruja. This latter steppe plateau blocks the straight outlet of the Danube to the Black Sea. The basin is an undissected low diluvial plain with broad terraces along the Danube. It is limited in the north by the Moldavian Hill Land.

The Southern Highlands. The comparatively simple structure and compartmental relief of the Danube Valley regions are lost in the Balkan Peninsula. Nothing but steep mountains and a few narrow and small intermontane basins compose the Southern Highlands, broad on their northwestern and southwestern ends but narrowing to a neck of 200 miles between the Gulf of Drin on the Adriatic and the Wallachian Plain. Three great components, mainly structural, can be distinguished: the Dinaric Ranges in the west, the Central Highlands, and the Balkan Ranges in the east.

DINARIC RANGES AND ADRIATIC COAST. The Slovenian Alps begin at the border of the Venetian Plain and the Basin of Klagen-

[2] As a result of Sumerian-Magyar affiliations in early historical time the Magyars, when occupying the Carpathian Basin in the ninth century, named it the Mesopotamian region between the Danube and the Tisza rivers (*Duna-Tisza-Köze* = Mid-Danube-Tisza, or Danube-Tisza-Mesopotamia) and, based on the old tradition, regarded this area as the center of their country. East of the Tisza the region was named *Tiszántúl* (Trans-Tisza, or Transtisia), the area west of the Danube got the name of *Dunántúl* (Transdanubia). This explanation will clear some of the errors and misunderstandings of these terms in various literature. Hungarian (Magyar) verbiage, customs, and place names reflect, even at present, a strong Sumerian affinity.

furt. Two branches can be recognized, the Karawanken and the Julian Alps, which enclose the Basin of Ljubljana. These mountains form the northernmost section of the Dinaric ranges, which trend southeast parallel to the Adriatic coast. The crystalline Pohor (Bacher) Mountains, an eastward extension of the Karawanken, slope gradually into the rolling plain between the Transdanubian and Croatian hill lands.

The Dinaric Ranges, folded in the late Tertiary era, are composed of three segments: (a) a coastal limestone zone, broken for two thirds of its length into thousands of islands, showing a strongly indented shoreline with many peninsulas, submerged valleys, and deep channels; (b) a central karst zone consisting mainly of Triassic limestones; and (c) an inner limestone-serpentine belt, the so-called Bosno-Macedo-Albanian mountain region. This third zone is the highest. The over-all landscape of the Dinaric Ranges is rocky, desolate karst with poor surface drainage and sparse vegetation. A few but not extensive longitudinal troughs, called *polja* (= plains, fields), are filled with alluvial deposits or *terra rossa* (red earth). The Dinaric Ranges have an average altitude of from 4,000 to 6,000 feet. Their sharp and rocky heights, crossed by only a few difficult passes, form a tremendous barrier between the inland valleys and the Adriatic Sea.

The Dalmatian coast of Yugoslavia is indented, and deep water is close to the shore line. Albania has a lowland coast with extensive marshy deltas, dunes, beaches, sand bars and barriers with long spits, which enclose many shallow lagoons. The Adriatic main coast is roughly a thousand miles long, while the island coasts have a total length of over three thousand miles.

CENTRAL HIGHLANDS. The Balkan Peninsula's Central Highlands are perhaps the roughest mountain area in Europe. The boundary between them and the Dinaric Ranges is marked by a band of metamorphic rocks called the Kopaonik-Vardar Zone. East of and parallel to the Kopaonik-Vardar Zone runs the narrow mountain strip of the old and massive Rhodope block, which broadens southeastward, then, farther south, changes to an east-west direction. Its irregular drainage runs through deeply incised valleys, which broaden only rarely to valley plains.

The Morava-Vardar trench divides the Balkan highland and is the only feasible though rough passage for north-south traffic. East of the trench, just south of Sofia, ranges from 3,000 to 5,000 feet high form the Rila Mountains, which show marks of glaciation. Stalin Peak (Musalla), 9,597 feet, is the highest point of East

Central Europe. Farther to the east, the Rhodope fans out into several broken, dissected ranges, which enclose the Thracian Basin and, together with the Balkan Ranges, the basin of Rumelia. Both areas are drained by the Maritsa River, which leads their waters to the Aegean.

BALKAN RANGES, DOBRUJA, AND BLACK SEA COAST. Bounded by the Rhodope block and the Wallachian plain, the arc of the Balkan Ranges, which are a prolongation of the Carpathians, trends south-southeast and then eastward. The northernmost section, the Northeast Serbian Mountains, is a rough, poorly drained, high plateau. The Bulgarian section comprises two parallel chains, a northern Balkan Range and a southern Anti-Balkan Range. Though only of moderate altitude, their aspect is rough, with deeply cut valleys, gorges, and abrupt slopes.

All along the northern slopes of the Balkan Ranges, and as far as the flood plain of the Danube, stretches the undulating piedmont plateau of Danubian Bulgaria, crossed by rivers with broad valleys. Flattening in the east, the plateau joins with the Balkan Ranges to enclose the little Basin of Stalin (Varna), open toward the Black Sea. The Dobruja, which displays Hercynian structure, is a steppe plateau limited to the east and north by the marshy Danube section of the Balta and the Danube delta region. Southeast of the Dobruja appears a *liman* (= lagoon) coast with extensive sand barriers. Farther south the sandy, flat, and straight shore is called the Silver Coast. From Cape Kaliakra south, the Balkan Ranges and the Rhodope form an abrupt mountain coast, with many bays opening into intermontane basins.

Drainage

A main water divide crosses Europe from the Iberian peninsula to the northern Urals. North of this line the waters empty into the North Sea and the Baltic Sea; south of it they flow into the Mediterranean Sea and the Black Sea. The waters of the northern drainage area of East Central Europe are carried mainly by three large rivers: the Elbe, originating in the Western Sudeten, drains the Bohemian Basin, and flows through Germany into the North Sea. It has a drainage area of some 19,800 square miles along the 246 miles of its course through Czechoslovakia.

The other two main north-draining streams, the Oder and the Vistula, start at the Moravian Gate. The Oder crosses the Silesian plain, then cuts through the Southern Moraine Zone, and, in the

Glacial Valley Zone, is joined by its main right bank affluent, the Warta. It flows into the lagoon of Szczecin (Stettin) connected to the Baltic Sea through the inlet at Swinoujscie (Swinemünde). The Vistula takes up first the torrential Dunajec and the San, then breaks through the Polish Uplands and is joined in the Glacial Valley Zone by the Pilica and by the Bug, coming from the Podolian plateau. It empties into the Bay of Gdansk. The Vistula drains 76,500 square miles in its course of 861 miles, while the Oder (561 miles in length) collects waters for 48,100 square miles.

The Mediterranean drainage area of East Central Europe is much smaller, although the mainland coast exceeds in length those of the region's Baltic or Black Sea coasts. Adriatic drainage is mainly represented by the Neretva, the Shkumbi, and the Drin, which, through its Black Drin branch, broaches Lake Ochrida (Ohrid). The Moraca is the main inflow river of Lake Scutari (Shkadar), from which the Bojana leads into the Adriatic. The poor drainage is partly due to the fact that the water divide between the Adriatic Sea and the Danube Basin runs close to the Adriatic shore line. As in every typical karstland, the subsurface drainage is very extensive, thus leading precipitation rapidly into subterranean channels and emptying a huge amount by the way of submarine springs close to the shore.

Aegean drainage rivers include the Vardar, the Struma, the Mesta, and the Maritsa. All except the Vardar have their headwaters in the Rila Mountains. They cover a drainage area of about 30,000 square miles, two thirds of which lies in the nations of East Central Europe.

The Carpathian Basin, Moldavia, Wallachia, Danubian Bulgaria, and a great part of Yugoslavia, is all drained by the Danube. Of its 1,776-mile total length, 1,160 miles belong to East Central Europe, with a drainage area of 729,000 square miles. The more important tributaries of the Danube, north of the Iron Gate, are the Morava, the Drava, the Tisza (596 miles long and itself draining an area of 61,000 square miles), the Sava, and the (Serbian) Morava. After cutting its way through the Carpatho-Balkan arc, the Danube enters the Wallachian Plain. The main right bank tributaries here are the Isker and Yantra. On the left they are the Olt, the Siret, and the Prut. Accompanied here by huge lakes and swamps, the great Danube now discharges its average 227,000 cubic feet per second through three delta branches into the Black Sea.

The rivers of East Central Europe vary greatly in character. The northern ones are frozen over for long periods each winter, while in the Mediterranean coastal area the mild winters serve as a defense against the ice. The Danube and its tributaries mark the transition line. The abundance of water and the course also vary. Thus, rivers which flow toward the North Sea and the Baltic collect their waters from areas of oceanic climate, with precipitation evenly distributed throughout the year, so that the resulting water level is stable. But their current is changeable, especially in the areas of alluvial deposits. On the other hand, considerable fluctuation of the water level is shown by the Adriatic and Aegean rivers, which will rise suddenly in winter and early spring and show low periods during the summer. Because the Danube and its affluents drain regions of various climatic zones, the currents and the velocity of the different sections change tremendously.

Lakes, marshes, swamps, and bogs are widely distributed in the Northern Lowlands. But they also accompany the Danube in the plains, and may be very extensive in flat regions like the Upper Tisza or the Balta Danube section. The largest, although a shallow body of water, is Lake Balaton in Transdanubia. Others are the Fertö in the Little Alföld; Lake Scutari on the Albano-Yugoslav frontier close to the Adriatic; Ochrida and Prespa lakes in eastern Macedonia; Greaca, southeast of Bucharest, and Lake Serban in the Balta region.

Weather and Climate

East Central Europe has four main climatic types: the short cold winter, the Mediterranean, and the long cold winter types, in addition to the varied mountain and boreal climates. Mild and foggy winters with abundant precipitation and temperate summers of the short cold winter type (oceanic) mix with the long cold winter type (continental), represented by hot dry summers, a precipitation peak in early summer, and with frosty winters in the northern lands. In the Balkan Peninsula, the mountain climates and short cold winter type are balanced by the Mediterranean, with hot and dry summers, mild winters with a lack of snow, and a double peak of precipitation, one in spring, the other in the fall.

On the Adriatic coast, the mean annual temperature is 61° F.[3] From there the northwest-southeast trending isotherms show a concave, arc-formed series, with decreasing temperature toward Belorussia (White Russia). The temperature decreases rapidly in the Dinaric Ranges and the Rhodope to 55-57° F., and even lower in the Carpathian Basin, Wallachia, and southern Moldavia

---

[3] See climatic graphs, Appendix II.

to 50-53° F. The Bohemian Basin and Carpathians show 48-50° F., while the Sudeten, the Tatra, the Transylvanian Basin, and the greater southwestern part of Poland have 45-48° F. Only in Masuria does the mean annual temperature drop below 44° F. The difference between the coldest and warmest month is greatest at the Vistula-San confluence, in the Carpathian Basin, Wallachia, Moldavia, and around Skoplje in Macedonia (76-79° F.). The least difference appears on the Dalmatian and Albanian coast (57-63° F.).

AVERAGE OF APPROXIMATE JANUARY AND JULY TEMPERATURES OF LARGER REGIONS IN EAST CENTRAL EUROPE

Area	January (F.)	July (F.)
Adriatic Coast	39	76
Basins of the Carpathians, Danubian Bulgaria, and South Moldavia	28-30	68-76
Bohemia	25-28	below 61
Sudeten	19-20	61-64 and below
Carpathians, Eastern Poland, and North Moldavia . . .	17-20	61-68

The outstanding characteristics of the precipitation are its great abundance in the mountain areas and the relative absence in the basins, and, even more important, its seasonal distribution. There is no completely dry month in the course of the year in any of the regions of East Central Europe. The late spring (April-June) rainfall reaches 6 inches even in the driest basins. Over almost the entire area there is a winter precipitation minimum (January-February) and an early summer maximum (June-July). Both the continental and oceanic areas are characterized by the summer monsoon rains, which end earlier in the east.

AVERAGE YEARLY PRECIPITATION IN SOME EAST CENTRAL EUROPEAN REGIONS

Area	Precipitation (inches)
North Bay of Kotor	over 160
Dinaric Ranges	over 120
Northeastern Carpathians	over 80
Most mountain regions	32-40
Carpathian Basin, Wallachian Plain, Moldavia, and Polish Uplands	20-30
Areas around Prague, Hortobágy, Silver Coast, and Dobruja	16-20
Danube Delta and Masovia	below 16

Natural Vegetation, Soils, and Animal Life

Natural Vegetation. The flora of East Central Europe reflects the climate. The climatic-conditioned floral regions have had an exceedingly important influence on the settlement and migration of peoples.

Oceanic climate is represented by the heather (*Calluna vulgaris*), wood anemone (*Anemone nemorosa*), and small leaved linden (*Tilia cordata*), English oak (*Quercus robur*), European beech, and European hornbeam (*Carpinus betulus*). Although the areal extension of the individual plants is different (Figure 127), all six occur in Bohemia, Poland, the outer Carpathian arc, the Bihor, and in Slovenia. Five are represented in the Carpathian Basin's lower mountains and in the northern Dinaric and Central Highlands, four in Macedonia and the Rhodope, three in Wallachia, southern Moldavia, and Albania, and two on the Silver Coast. In the Rumelian Basin and the Little and Great Alföld, beech is lacking. The oceanic floral region coincides with the migration and settlement of the Germanic peoples.

The long cold winter (continental) climate is represented by the green flowered wintergreen (*Pirola chlorantha*), white birch (*Betula verucosa s. alba*), speedwell (*Veronica longifolia*), dwarf cherry (*Prunus fruticosa*), Tartar maple (*Acer tataricum*), Russian almond (*Prunus nana*), and licorice (*Glycyrrhiza echinata*). All seven are present in the Danube delta, Dobruja, and in a broad belt along the Danube including the Great Alföld. This belt extends as far as the southern Urals, and was the route of all Asiatic peoples migrating into Europe (Figure 127). Five or six of these plants appear in the rest of the Carpathian Basin, northern Dinaric Mountains, the Rhodope, the Balkan Ranges, and Moldavia; four in Slovenia, Transylvania, the Polish Upland, Bohemia, and the Glacial Valley region; only three in Albania, Thrace, and the Baltic Moraine Zone.

The boreal flora includes Norway spruce (*Picea excelsa*), Scotch pine (*Pinus silvestris*), and dwarf birch (*Betula nana*). The third is lacking entirely in the area; the other two appear in all mountain areas, but only as far south as a line drawn between Trieste and Constanta. The silver fir (*Abies alba*) typical of the mountain climate is present in all high regions except the Eastern Balkan.

The Mediterranean climate group is represented by vine (*Vitis vinifera*), corn, chestnut (*Castanea sativa*), olive tree (*Olea europea*), orange (*Citrus aureus*), and the macchia scrub. All are found along the Adriatic coast; five around Lake Scutari; four in

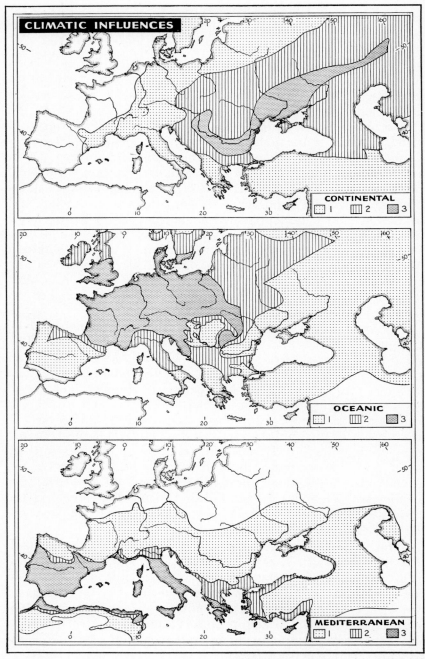

FIGURE 127. Continental, oceanic, and Mediterranean climatic influences, as represented by the presence of characteristic plants. (*Explanation on opposite page.*)

526

Macedonia; three in Slovenia and the Istrian Peninsula; two farther north of a line drawn from the Carpathians toward Jassy and one in Bohemia, northern Moldavia, and Ruthenia.

With the exception of the bogs in the Baltic Moraine Zone, forests were once distributed throughout East Central Europe. Today, only 30 per cent of the entire area remains wooded, with a natural maximum in the mountain regions. Conifers dominate in the high altitudes, especially Bohemia, the Carpathian arc, the Bihor, and the Slovenian Alps. Depending on the latitude, relief, and local climate, deciduous forests prevail in lower altitudes. Areas of moderate temperature and high precipitation are favored by the beech, while oak prevails in regions of warmer climate. Only the lower Danube region and the Great Alföld are almost bare; here the steppe often predominates.

Soils. The character of the soil is closely related to climate, vegetation, relief, and drainage. Concentrically around the brown and chestnut colored steppe soils of the basins lies first humus-poor, then deep humus-rich chernozem. Spots of blown sand and saline soil are present in the plains. On the hills and foothills first the brown, then the bleached, forest and heath soil appears, which also occupies most of the northern areas. In still higher altitudes, the mountain soil prevails, most extensively on the Balkan Peninsula. Bleached soils are dominant in the *polja* of the karst regions. Peaty soils, podsols mingled with sand, and sandy soils are prevalent in the Glacial Valley and Northern Moraine zones. Alluvial soils are present along all main rivers, occupying huge areas in the Little Alföld, the Great Alföld, and the Wallachian plains, as well as the Danube delta region and the Vistula estuary.

Animal Life. An abundance of game is characteristic of East Central Europe. Deer of various kinds, roe, and wild boar are widely distributed, while in the Carpathians, the Rhodope, and Balkan ranges the brown bear and the lynx occur frequently. Wolves are common in Moldavia and the Eastern Carpathians,

---

← (EXPLANATION FOR FIGURE 127) *Continental*: (1) one to three plants; (2) four to six plants; (3) seven plants. *Oceanic*: (1) one to three plants; (2) four to five plants; (3) six plants. *Mediterranean*: (1) one to three plants; (2) four to five plants; (3) six to seven plants. There is a remarkable coincidence between the type of plants and the migration of peoples. The darkest "Continental" shading coincides with the northern migration route and settlement areas of peoples entering Europe from Asia (Huns, Avars, Bulgars, Magyars, Ural-Turks, and Tatars; the darkest "Oceanic" shading shows the expansion of Germanic peoples from the North Sea region (Franks, Anglo-Saxons, Danes, and the many Germanic tribes; the darkest "Mediterranean" shading is approximately the area of the ancient world's colonization (Greeks, Phoenicians and early Romans).

and may enter even Wallachia and the northeastern portions of the Great Alföld. The wild goat still climbs the rocks of the Carpathians. Foxes and hares are very numerous on the open fields and in wooded waste land. Beaver and muskrat can be seen and sometimes also the mink and the otter will appear in northern regions. The bird life is also extremely rich. We mention only that partridge and quail are common, and that wild ducks and geese are the most common migrating birds. Cranes and the sacred stork, which is never hunted, live in all parts of the area, and likewise the lark, thrush, and the nightingale. Various kinds of pigeon are as common as the predatory falcons, hawks, owls, and in the mountain regions, the eagle. Sparrows and black crows are a nuisance, feared by the farmer and by townspeople.

Flies are a constant plague; mosquitoes are common everywhere, and may carry malaria in Mediterranean areas. Wild bees, wasps, and hornets are as common as the butterflies, grasshoppers, and crickets of the flowering meadows, and fleas, bugs, lice, and cockroaches are fought by all who struggle for healthful surroundings.

The Cultural and Social Background

It is impossible to describe all the changes in peoples, settlements, and states which have occurred in East Central Europe since the dawn of European history. Nevertheless, the main trend can be delineated, because it was dependent upon the interrelation of the physiographic factors with the inherent characteristics and cultural behavior of the peoples concerned. Thus, one may ask: "Who were the races and peoples of East Central Europe and whence did they come?"

The larger groups competing for the area have been the Mediterranean or Helleno-Roman and related peoples, the Germanic, the Slavic, and the Turanian, including Ugrian and Turkic. The Turkic peoples are nomadic steppe warriors, while the Ugrians are seminomadic and rural in habit. The Slavs are land tillers and fishermen, adapting themselves to the surroundings, but moving mainly into lowlands and valleys to follow the forest-grassland-belt way of life. The Germanic peoples, who move along foothills or great streams to reach hill lands and forested areas with an oceanic climate, are primarily settlers who alter their surroundings, organizing communities and building towns.

The Mediterranean group can be divided into subtypes: the coastal traders and town developers, like the Hellenes; the land tillers and practical organizers, the route and fort builders, like the Romans; and the pastoral mountain folk, like the Albano-Vlachs, who are found characteristically in mountain climates, wandering along ridges or upland pasture areas. All these groups are shaped by the relief and surroundings in which they move voluntarily or involuntarily, as conquerors or settlers, as free men or slaves. Depending on the physiographic scene to which they must adapt themselves, they develop their own special cultures and civilizations.

Thus the nature of shelter and the building of houses depend on the material present. In addition to the tent dwellings of nomads, East Central Europe had clay houses in the Little Alföld, the Great Alföld, Transdanubia, Wallachia, and Eastern Moldavia; wood houses in the Carpathians, in the Transylvanian mountain regions, and the Slovenian Alps; stone houses in Albania, Macedonia, and Rumelia; other areas offer combinations of wood and stone. Long, narrow buildings were typical in the lowlands, and high quadrangular structures in the mountains, especially for Germanic settlers. The houses may also enclose a sizable court or yard for household and animals, and very often a well. This type of dwelling, though no longer needed for defense, is still characteristic of East Central Europe. Village communities developed mainly to extend control over crop lands and to increase protection against marauding horsemen. Urbanization is a fairly recent development, mainly of the nineteenth century.

The peoples composing the present nations of East Central Europe were, by the fourteenth century, all settled in their natural regions. Penetration by German settlers changed the rudimentary economy and trade of the Slavs and Magyars. The ring-fence dwellings and dispersed homesteads gave place to the first nucleated settlements, to trade centers, and markets. Virgin forest land was turned into crop fields, while moorland and marshes were reclaimed. Vineyards were developed by the Catholic Church. Trading of furs, wax, honey, fish, amber, hemp, flax, Hungarian cattle, and horses was developed. Minerals of the Erz Gebirge were exploited and the mines of the Carpathians and Transylvania were revived and enlarged. The main route of Germanic colonization toward the Baltic lands passed through Poznan (Posen) and Torun (Thorn) into the East Prussian area. In the thirteenth and fourteenth centuries the Hanseatic league developed trade with and through the Polish lands, and even such inland towns as Wroclaw (Breslau) joined the league. The order of Teutonic Knights undertook the conquest of the territories inhabited by the Prussian Balts.

The Bohemian, Hungarian, and Polish kingdoms developed their own towns and capitals. The capitals changed often, depending upon the political situation, the descent of the ruler, or the best site. Cracow (Kraków) was the residence of the Polish kings and lost its importance only in 1596 when Warsaw, the strategic fortress city built in the ninth century on the left bank of the Vistula, was made the capital of Poland. Esztergom and Székesfehérvár were seats of the Hungarian kings, and Budapest rose to the rank of a capital only in the fifteenth century.

Many universities and theological institutions were founded by clergy, kings, and princes: Pannonhalma (1001), Prague (1348), Cracow (1364), Pécs (1367), and Wroclaw (1506). The "Golden Bull" of Hungary (1222) and the "Statute of Wislica" (1347) of Poland were codes of law affecting administrative boundaries and the life of the free royal towns. These mining, manufacturing, and trade centers showed the rising power of their citizens and their detachment from the rural communities.

Entirely different was the evolution of the Balkan Peninsula. Its peoples fought repeated wars of independence with the Byzantine Empire, Venice, and Hungary. The Serbian culture derived its strength from exploiting the rich humus of the *polja*, as well as from the forest harvests and seasonal pasturage. Cattle, pigs and horses were raised, and honey and wax collected, supplemented by hunting and fishing. Trade was developed by selling timber and gold or silver from the mines of the Southern Highlands, worked mainly by Saxon and Hungarian settlers. The houses were small and generally flat roofed. Much the same conditions were characteristic of the region inhabited by the Bulgars. Byzantine influences were great, however, because Bulgaria formed a patriarchate of the Orthodox Church with a see at Preslav and later at Silistria. Trading towns were Anchialis and Develtus.

The five centuries before the two World Wars brought tremendous changes to the populations and landscapes of East Central Europe. During the Turkish occupation, Hungary's five million inhabitants were reduced to two and one-half million. Poland's population was decimated twice in the eighteenth century and a similar though less severe decrease took place in the Balkans. As a result colonization was intensified, especially in the southern half of the Great Alföld, where Slovaks and Germans were settled, and in Silesia, where the Prussian reorganization crowded the new towns with Germans. In the plains of Hungary the Turkish occupation and constant pillaging caused people to concentrate in large "peasant towns" (see upper map of Figure 128), while the small settle-

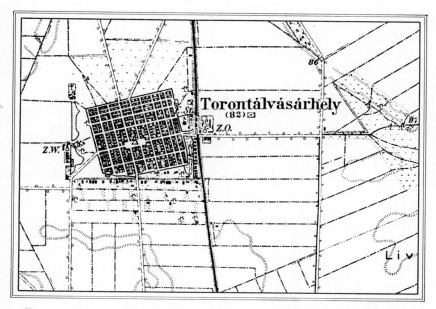

FIGURE 128. Two characteristic settlement types of the Carpathian Basin: (*top*) a circular-shaped rural town established in the Middle Ages, for defensive purposes; (*bottom*) a square-shaped modern village laid out by engineers.

ments were destroyed. In summer or for the harvest this semitown population moved to the crop fields and to little hamlets (*tanyas*), which were only seldom inhabited in winter. The population of such towns or village agglomerations varied between five and twenty thousand inhabitants. In Montenegro, which fought a long-term war of independence, scattered hamlets built of stone developed on difficult terrain.

The general appearance of settlements showed closely patterned nucleated villages (often square in shape) for agricultural regions. Sometimes such units grew up near mines, at wells or springs in regions where water was scarce, as well as around fortresses and clerical or cultural centers. Typical round-patterned settlements were the forest dwellings where deforestation made possible the expansion of agriculture. Dispersed settlements were typical in the lumbering areas, in mountain pasture lands, in areas of poor, gravelly soil, and in sections with plenty of good ground water. In East Central Europe, the size of a settlement does not necessarily determine its type. There are closely patterned villages with ten to thirty thousand rural inhabitants, as in Hungary (Figure 129), northern Yugoslavia, and Poland. There are also towns or cities below ten and even below five thousand in size. This is quite typical of the Dalmatian coastal towns and ports, and of mining communities in the Carpathians, Transylvania, and Bohemia.

A good example is Transylvania, where the Saxon settlements show all the town characteristics of high houses, orderly streets, central administrative buildings, and a market place, while the Magyar towns are more open toward the edges, with closely built up centers. And even though more than half of the population is Romanian, there are no towns of Romanian foundation in Transylvania. The rural aspect did not change much up to the nineteenth century. Because of the need for defense, more and more people concentrated in towns. Most towns were self-sufficient and, having their own fields, did not depend on the rural food producing areas.

Thus, at the end of the eighteenth century, East Central Europe was a region of rural settlements. Agriculture, with the open-field system and a three-year crop rotation followed by one-year fallow, was prevalent. Most of the improvement in agricultural conditions was confined to Prussian and Austrian territories, especially Silesia and Bohemia. Huge marsh areas were canalized and regained for crop fields. Beginning with the 1830's, conditions began to change for the better. By this time East Central Europe had two cities with over 100,000 inhabitants: Budapest and Warsaw. Both were commercial and strategic centers with increasing cultural importance. The first railways were built, linking Olomouc and Györ to Vienna, and the Iron Gate was opened to navigation.

FIGURE 129. A typical eighteenth-century street. Sopron, Hungary.

But only about 1870 was real progress achieved, as a result of political consolidation and expanding liberalism. At this time the coal mines of Silesia were opened. A cotton industry had been developed in Bohemia and in Lodz, the "Polish Manchester."

Thousands of the rural population became seasonal emigrants to surrounding countries, and hundreds of thousands became workers in the rapidly growing industries of the towns. The surplus population emigrated, chiefly to North America.

In 1890 the following cities had over 100,000 inhabitants: Warsaw, Lodz, Breslau, Prague, and Bucharest; Budapest had over half a million. Industrialized areas were Bohemia, Moravia, Silesia, Western Pomerania, and the Lodz region. Textile and heavy industry, blast furnaces, and optical works were concentrated here; sugar plants and mills were founded in the lowlands of Hungary, shipbuilding on the Adriatic, leather works and paper mills in the Polish areas, Bohemia, and Transylvania.

Industrialization had not yet reached the newly formed kingdoms of Serbia and Romania. Bulgaria remained a rural state, and Montenegro was not much more than a pastoral state. The sudden outbreak of World War I halted this healthy and peaceful evolution, with its self determination of peoples and reasonable economic structure. Poland emerged independent, with an area of 150,000 square miles, including Russian and German minorities. Danzig was made a free city, and the Polish Republic built the new Baltic harbor of Gdynia. Czechoslovakia emerged as a new state, with a minority population of more than four million, mainly German and Hungarian. Romania gained Bessarabia, Transylvania, and a huge part of the Great Alföld with a great number of minorities. Yugoslavia was formed of the different Slavic states and groups and Hungary was shorn of territory on every side, losing her mountain areas, mines, forests, and water power. Bulgaria was cut off from the Aegean Sea.

The migration of expelled minorities, the newly formed "customs walls," and the unreasonable fragmentation of the railway and highway systems, hampered economic development between the two world wars. Minorities increased the sense of chauvinism, and politics ruled the trend of life for all countries in East Central Europe. Every state wished to be self sufficient; land reforms were carried out on a political basis with little regard to economic conditions. Attracted by new industries, the surplus population of the pauperized countryside moved into the towns, especially into the capitals.

By 1930, Warsaw and Budapest had grown to cities of over one million inhabitants, Prague to 850,000, Breslau and Bucharest to over half a million, and 22 other towns had populations of 100,000 or more. Industrial and commercial life concentrated in these towns, most of which were also administrative and cultural centers.

Out of World War II the countries emerged with new frontiers. Poland was shifted westward to the Oder-Neisse line; lost were equivalent territories east of the Curzon line, which roughly defined the new boundary between Poland and the Soviet Union. Czechoslovakia had to cede Ruthenia to the U.S.S.R., Romania yielded Bessarabia to the Soviet Union, as well as southern Dobruja to Bulgaria. Yugoslavia, by contrast, gained Istria and a part of Venezia Giulia.

The Geographic Basis of Economic and Political Life

Albania

Albania was overrun during the years 1939–40, first by Italian and later by German forces. In 1945, at the close of World War II, Communists gained control and proclaimed Albania a Peoples' Republic. It is presently divided into 26 districts (rreth), with its capital at Tirana.

In an area of 10,629 square miles live approximately 1.2 million people of two main ethnic groups: the Gheg tribes north of the Shkumbi River, and the Tosk people to the south. In addition, many Vlachs occupy the highland pasture regions, and a considerable Hellenic population is found along the Greek boundary. Many of the Albanian tribes who voted in 1913 for Serbian citizenship live in Yugoslavia. Gypsies are seen frequently in the towns, and Bulgarians or Turks in the rural sections. The Albanian language has several dialects, supposedly derived from the ancient Illyrian or Phrygo-Thracian, with many similarities to Romanian (Vlach). Two thirds of the people are Moslems; of the remaining third, the great majority are Orthodox and the rest Catholic. Although birth and death rates are estimated, they appear to be high, as is illiteracy.

Compared with her neighbors, Albania is sparsely populated, having an average density of only 113 people per square mile. The population increases slowly; and only a few fertile regions have high densities. Over 250 people per square mile are found only south of Lake Scutari, while around Korcë, southwest of Lake Prespa and the coastal alluvial lowlands, the density is over 200 per square mile. In mountainous northern Albania the density is still lower. Emigration has been heavy, and even in Sicily there are approximately 100,000 Albanians.

The industrial population is significant, and is involved in the agricultural industry of the few towns. Only seven of these have a population of more than 10,000 people; Tirana, the capital and Scutari have close to 40,000. The alluvial coast does not provide good ports, and consequently sea trade cannot develop. The two ports of any importance, Durrës (Durazzo) and Vlona (Valona) are not much more than large villages. Three of the more impor-

FIGURE 130. Krujë, an old Albanian cultural center north of Tirana. Note the karstic limestone mountains, the Moslem minaret, and the flat-roofed houses built of stone.

tant centers, Berat, Elbasan, and Gjinokaster, lie in the foothills between the coastal plain and the highland (Figure 130). Except for some modern buildings in Tirana and other towns, the houses are small and low, generally built of stone. Fortified houses are occasionally found in the mountains. Despite the authoritarian character of the Albanian government, tribal autonomy is strong and feuds survive.

Albania is predominantly an agricultural country, over 91 per cent of its population being farmers, two thirds of them in animal husbandry (Figure 131). Economically, Albania is backward and even primitive, as a consequence of her rough topography. Close

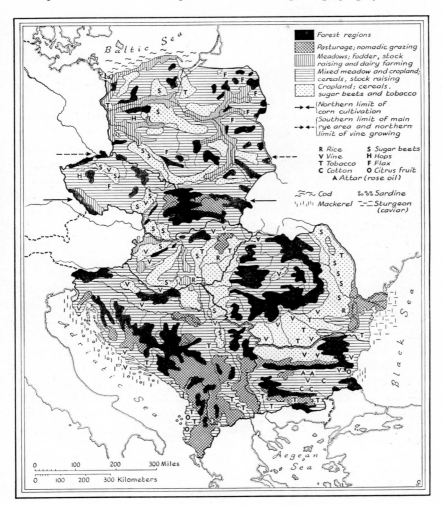

FIGURE 131. Land utilization in East Central Europe.

to a third of the country is covered with forests; close to a third of its area is in pastures and meadows. The area under cultivation amounts to less than one tenth of Albania's total area and is limited to the fertile lowlands and larger valleys. Improvement in protection from sudden and extensive floods has proceeded slowly.

The main foods are ground corn, unleavened bread cakes, beans, lentils, vegetables, rice, cheese, and eggs. Coffee drinking is as common as in Turkey. Corn is the chief crop, serving as the staple food of the peasants, and as fodder for cattle. Wheat is second in importance, followed by barley, oats, and rye. Rice cultivation is increasing around Tirana, Elbasan, Berat, and Vlona. Sugar beets and sugar cane are grown in small quantities, and beans, lentils, potatoes, and vegetables are cultivated for local consumption. Citrus fruits, figs, apples, and grapes are the main crops of the fruit-growing regions of Vlona and Elbasan; of the nut crops, walnuts alone have export value.

Extensive cultivation of olive trees along the coast is centered between the Sarandë and Seman rivers, and olives in great quantity were exported to Italy before World War II. Cotton has been planted in the Shkumbi Valley and flax and hemp are manufactured for homespun clothing. Tobacco is grown around Shkodër, Elbasan, and Durrës. Fish are caught principally for export, although the domestic consumption has been rising. Grey millet, mullet-roe, dory, bass, and eels are the chief catch.

Stock raising is the traditional occupation of the people. Cattle are concentrated in the lowlands where, together with the water buffalo, they are the main draft animals of primitive farming. The once-famous Albanian horses have degenerated, mules and donkeys now being commonly used for transport. Despite the Moslem faith, pigs are raised and eaten everywhere. Most important are sheep and goats, raised by mountain nomads. Over 1.5 million sheep and close to a million goats are raised, chiefly for milk, cheese, soft cheese, and wool. Transhumance is practiced in the mountain pastures, which have dense forest cover containing excellent timber. Almost half of the woodland, which is richest in the north, is composed of oak varieties, with beech and conifers each representing about 20 per cent of the total. Vast tracts of walnut and chestnut trees are of great value.

Albania's mineral wealth is only slightly exploited. Petroleum is found in two fields, one around Patos, and a more important one at Stalin (Figure 133). A pipeline connects the wells with the port at Vlona. Reserves are estimated at 70 million barrels and about 1.5 million barrels are produced yearly. Some natural gas and asphalt are produced at Selenicë on the Vijosë River. Copper is mined south of the Drin, and many copper-bearing seams have been explored in the northern mountains. Chrome ores are mined near Lake Ochrida. Minor deposits of pyrite, arsenic ore, mercury, lead, zinc, and a little bauxite are worked, while some gypsum is mined at Vlona. A very rich iron ore reserve with good quality hematites lies at Lake Ochrida.

As we mentioned above, the meager industry of Albania is almost entirely based on its agriculture and is concentrated in few towns, all of which have flour mills. The main industrial center is Shkodër, which has Portland cement works, soap, cigarette, and fish-preserving factories, and a distillery. Oil refining is done in Vlonë, and Tirana has a cotton-textile mill, a wagon factory, and brick works. Olive oil and cheeses are made in the main towns as well as along the coast. The first hydroelectric plant was started in 1947 at Selita.

Communications have steadily improved, although there is only one narrow-gauge railway from Vlona to the Selenicë asphalt mine, and two main standard-gauge lines: Durrës-Pequin-Elbasan and Durrës-Tirana. A few short lines are under construction. The few main roads are good and tarmac surfaced. In the northern mountains, mere trails provide passage by mule and horse only.

Since 1945, there has been little foreign trade other than with the Cominform states. Copper and chrome ore, asphalt, wool, and hides are exported in exchange for aluminum goods, electrical and technical equipment, textiles, and drugs. Because of her strained relations with Yugoslavia, Greece, and Italy, Albania's coastwise trade is restricted to her own ports. Geopolitically, these small ports, together with fortified Saseno island, are of importance in that they are strategic points of Soviet power in the Adriatic, controlling the Strait of Otranto between the Adriatic and Mediterranean seas.

Yugoslavia

Out of World War I emerged a state called the Kingdom of Serbs, Croats, and Slovenes. Not until 1929 was the name Yugoslavia introduced. Since that time Croat separatism has grown strongly; nevertheless, after World War II Yugoslavia was restored, in accordance with communist wishes, as a Federated Peoples' Republic. It is composed of six autonomous republics: Serbia (Srbija), Croatia (Hrvatska), Slovenia, Bosnia-Herzegovina, Montenegro (Crna Gora), Macedonia, and two autonomous provinces, Vojvodina and Kosovo-Metohija. The revived state has expanded only slightly in area, to gain from Italy Istria, the Julian March, Rijeka (Fiume), Zadar (Zara), and some Dalmatian islands. In addition, Zone B of the Free Territory of Trieste has been virtually incorporated into the Yugoslavian state. The federal capital is Belgrade.

Almost 16 million people live in an area of 95,500 square miles. The majority are concentrated in the nucleated settlements of the fertile main valley plains along the Danube, Drava, Sava, Tisza, and in the Morava corridor. The Rhodope and Dinaric karstlands contain small, dispersed settlements with low population density. Only four of the capitals of the autonomous republics and provinces have more than 100,000 inhabitants (Belgrade, Zagreb, Ljubljana, and Sarajevo), and of the other important towns only the market center of Subotica exceeds this number. Rijeka (including Sušak), the main port on the Adriatic, is a trading agglomeration.

The boundaries of the republics and provinces represent the main ethnic groupings. Nevertheless, large minorities are included in the different groups. The Jews have disappeared, as have most of the former Germans of the Banat and Syrmia (Srem) regions. There are half a million Hungarians grouped compactly on the Hungarian frontier in the Bačka and the Banat. Romanians (Vlachs) of the Banat, the Timok area, Macedonia, and Istria form another important minority of about a quarter of a million persons, while nearly half a million Albanians are concentrated close to Albania's boundary. Turks are numerous east of the Vardar River, whereas the Italians who once lived in Istria and Dalmatia have been expatriated.

Yugoslavia's Slovenians, Croatians, and Hungarians are Catholic; Serbians and Romanians belong to two different branches of the Orthodox Church, which has also many adherents in Bosnia-Herzegovina and Montenegro. The Turks and most of the Albanians are Moslems, while the disappearance of Germans has almost eliminated Protestant churches. The boundary between the Catholic and Orthodox faiths is an old cultural one. West of this line, including parts of Bosnia, the people live in nucleated villages or traditional, well-built towns with orderly streets and houses. The percentage of illiterates in the Catholic area is low as compared with the Orthodox eastern sector, where the standard of living is also low, and the towns and settlements are more dispersed (Figure 132). The habits, customs, and ways of thinking also are different on the two sides of the boundary. The cultural level of Zagreb is higher than that of Belgrade.

Not counting war losses, the average natural increase of population is about one per cent per year for the whole country. The rate is higher in the eastern part, where the birth and death rates, the proportion of illiterates, and the percentage of agricultural popu-

FIGURE 132. A typical village street in Macedonia. Note its narrowness and the open sewage canal.

lation exceed those of the West. The small number in the 25-to-40-year age group is due to a low birth rate during World War I, and to the fact that this same age group carried the burden of World War II.

About three quarters of the population are occupied in agriculture, forestry, and fishing, and a large number labor in the mines. As a consequence of the five-year plan of 1947, the industrial population has tripled since 1931, and now includes close to a million workers. The number of people in trade, commerce, and finance is still very low, but comparatively more are in military and police services. The per cent of agricultural population is greatest in Bosnia and Serbia. In comparison with the acreage of arable land, however, the karst regions of the Dinaric Ranges excel in agricultural population, while the rich soils of the Vojvodina show the lowest density. Many of the Yugoslavian towns are inhabited by a majority of agricultural people, though the general insecurity in rural districts and the war damage have both contributed to rapid urbanization in the last decade.

The natural and social environment defines the problems of the state. Yugoslavia is a predominantly agricultural country (Figure 131). After World War I not more than one out of ten farms was larger than 25 acres, and two thirds were less than half that size. In 1945 a new land reform redistributed 2 million acres, and cooperatives were established. In 1950 almost a third of the 18 million acres representing arable land were state owned or transformed to cooperatives, especially in the Vojvodina with its rich chernozem soils.

Flood control of the Danube and Sava lowlands, and the reclamation of the Yugoslavian part of Lake Scutari, under the five-year plan, will increase the arable acreage. Close to one third of the total surface is arable, one third forests, one quarter pasture and meadows, and the rest waste land. Although the arable area, with its semi-intensive type of farming, will not support the needs of the population, the forests and pastures make possible a well-balanced agricultural economy.

Wheat and corn, the main crops, are predominately grown in the northern lowlands, though corn occupies most of the arable area all over the country. Rye, barley, and oats are of minor significance, chiefly as fodder crops. Rice growing has been improved, but is confined to the Bačka and Banat. Potatoes are important in Slovenia, Croatia, and on the sandy soils of the Vojvodina, while vegetable growing and gardening are concentrated around cities and in the karst lands.

Fruit is widely cultivated, but poor transport limits distribution. Figs, citrus fruits, and almonds are confined to the mild climate of the southern Adriatic Coast. Millions of plum trees in northern Serbia provide the new industries with the basic ingredients for jam and the well-known Serbian drink *slivovitz*. Walnut, apple, pear, and cherry trees are grown everywhere, including the "marasca" cherries from which the maraschino liquor is made.

Viticulture occupies over half a million acres, but is of commercial importance only along the Dalmatian coast and in the Danube-Morava corner. Tobacco is the outstanding cash crop, being grown mainly in Macedonia and in Herzegovina. Sugar beets, presumably enough for domestic needs, are grown in the Vojvodina and Syrmia, where hemp and oil seeds are also grown intensively. Although much enlarged after World War II, the cotton area is confined climatically to southern Macedonia. Medicinal plants are of great export value, and opium is an important product of Macedonia.

In the mountainous areas only the basins and flat *polja* are cultivated. The meadows of Slovenia supply excellent fodder, whereas the southern highlands provide extensive pasture of poorer quality. The richest pasture regions are those inhabited by the Albanian minority.

Slovenia and Bosnia have the thickest forests, though only a small percentage of Yugoslavia's timber is scientifically managed. Roughly two thirds of the 20 million acres of forest is deciduous, about 12 per cent coniferous, and the rest mixed. Conifers of Slovenia, Croatia, or Bosnia, and the deciduous pedunculate oak are important timber raw material for construction and export. Beech, less valuable for industrial purposes, is the main domestic firewood. Deforestation exceeds the natural growth. The five-year plan, extended in 1951 into a six-year plan, included a reforestation program of 240,000 acres, especially in the karst regions where medieval Venetian shipbuilding, as well as goat and sheep grazing more recently, have pretty well destroyed the originally dense forest cover.

Fishing is of some importance, despite the fact that the Adriatic submergent coasts, with their many islands, deep channels, strong currents, and the sudden *bora* winds, do not constitute good fishing grounds. Mackerel and sardines are the chief catch, though various kinds of mollusks, crayfish, and lobsters are a constant food of the Dalmatians. Autumn and spring are the seasons for the migrating fish, and the catch has been increased in late years by modern equipment.

The serious war losses in livestock have not yet been made good. Cattle, evenly distributed over the country, are raised mainly as draft animals and for beef. Grazing from mountain pasture in summer to lowlands in winter is common in all mountainous areas. Horses, for the most part draft animals, show high density in the Vojvodina and between the Drava and Sava rivers. Swine, raised for fats, are concentrated in the corn area of the Bačka and northwestern Serbia. In the Dinaric regions, the Central Highlands, and the Rhodope, sheep and goats are raised. Slovenia and northwest Croatia raise very few sheep. Goats are very common, and only Bulgaria and Albania raise more per capita in East Central Europe. In general, the quality of animal stock is low. The actual deficiency in meat is due largely to war damage.

Yugoslavia's mining and manufacturing industries have developed rapidly since 1945, with light industry favored. A serious problem is the lack of coking coal and transportation facilities. Lignite and bituminous coal are mined, the most important lignite-producing areas being the Sarajevo region east of the Bosna River and the mines near Ljubljana and in Istria. Bituminous coal is mined in the Timok Valley areas (Figure 133). The iron ore production of a million tons comes mainly from mines at Ljubija and Vares, which also include the most extensive reserves of Yugoslavia. Some petroleum and natural gas occur near the Mura River.

Of the nonferrous metals, the copper ores of Bor in northeast Serbia are famous, while lead and zinc ores are found in the Kopaonik Mountains, with some also in the Karawanken Mountains and in the Drina Valley. The chrome ores of the Skoplje region and north Serbia, as well as the bauxites of the Dinaric karst and Istria are almost equally important. Mercury, in the Julian Alps, should also be mentioned. The production of magnesite, manganese, pyrites, antimony, rock salt, asbestos, and molybdenite is of minor significance, although the first two have been developed considerably. Salt is obtained by pan evaporation on the Adriatic coast. About 20 per cent of the estimated three million hp. water power potential has been converted into electricity.

Compared with her rich natural resources, Yugoslavia's prewar industry was small. Even the few industrial centers suffered war damage, especially the textile, metallurgical, and chemical plants. Belgrade is the main industrial center, where iron and steel, processed food, tobacco, leather, chemicals, machinery and tools, textiles, electrical equipment, and aircraft are produced (Figure 134). The chief heavy industry base is the Vares-Zenica region near Sarajevo; another is situated along the Kulpa River (Karlovac and

Sisak). The deficiency in coking coal, formerly imported from Poland, is a serious handicap to Yugoslavia's industrial development.

FIGURE 133. Distribution of mining in East Central Europe.

Copper refineries are situated at Bor and railway material and wagon works in many of the towns. Shipbuilding is carried on at Split, Pula, and Rijeka. A sheet metal rolling mill (Jesenice), as well as steel manufacturing in Slovenia (Gustanj), deserve mention. Another highly important industrial concentration is around Zagreb, with wool, silk, leather, furniture, tobacco, food processing, ceramics and china, glass, chemical and electro-technical plants. Ljubljana produces woolen goods, electrical machinery and turbines, and rolled aluminum.

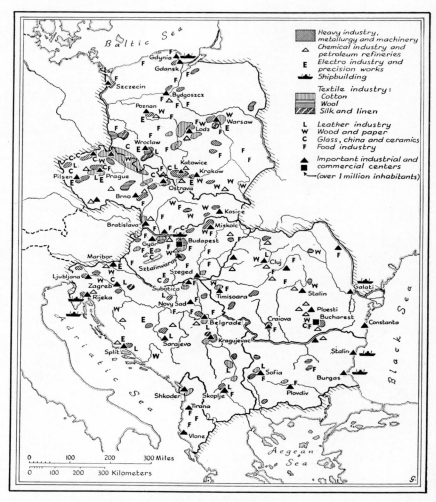

FIGURE 134. Distribution of the main industrial regions and more important industrial and commercial centers of East Central Europe.

The regions of Sibenik and Omiš on the Adriatic coast are important for electro and chemical industry, aluminum, and ferrochrome plants. Nylon is made in Split. The largest brickworks are in the Banat region. Subotica and many other towns have improved their food-processing and agricultural industries. Forest products are of great importance in Slovenia and Croatia, the cellulose of Drvar being well known. Sugar factories are distributed widely in Yugoslavia, and breweries are found in every large town. Tobacco factories, cement works, and paper mills are worth mentioning.

Communications and transportation are grave twin problems in Yugoslavia. Telephone and telegraph lines serve only the main centers and towns. The repair of war damages has hampered the building of new roads and railways, and the existing roads are still poor compared to American highways. The main artery is the standard-gauge railway along the Sava-Danube-Morava-Vardar corridor. Belgrade is connected through Subotica to Budapest, and from Niš the Orient express runs toward Sofia. Ljubljana is connected with Italy through Trieste and Tarvisio, and Zagreb to Graz and Vienna. The Dinaric region has only a few narrow-gauge railways winding along the valleys around Sarajevo.

The main navigable waterways are the Danube, the Tisza and their connecting canals in the Bačka, and the Sava (Figure 135). Large vessels can navigate only on the Danube, which was an important prewar outlet for Yugoslavia's trade toward the Black Sea. With the exception of Dubrovnik, Rijeka, and the naval harbor of Pula, the Adriatic ports are only of local importance.

An economic analysis of Yugoslavia shows that the highly productive agricultural regions lie in the northern plains, with the most important industrial regions along the Sava Valley. Even the communication pattern is developed only in these highly productive, densely populated regions. The relief affects the economic development considerably. The Dinaric Ranges wall off the natural outlet for trade and commerce toward the Adriatic, and even Rijeka can be reached only on a long, winding railway. Yugoslavia's natural connections and trade to Soviet-ruled lands are now cut and the Danube outlet is likewise barred. The Vardar Valley opens only to the much-desired Greek port of Salonika. Railways and routes lead mainly toward Austria and Italy, from which Yugoslavia claims minor territories, with resulting poor economic relations.

Such circumstances determine the trade of Yugoslavia. Her exports, mainly of forest products, minerals, and since the war food products, are exchanged for machinery, tools, armaments, consumer goods, and even basic foods. In prewar years, Yugoslavia's commerce was chiefly with Austria, Czechoslovakia, Italy, and Germany, but since 1949 the United Kingdom, the United States, Austria, Italy, and Western Germany rank as the best cus-

FIGURE 135. Navigable waterways and main railway lines.

Bulgaria

tomers for Yugoslavia's exports as well as the chief sources of her imports.

In 1940 Bulgaria regained the southern Dobruja from Romania. The Soviet Union declared war on Bulgaria only in 1945, occupied the country, and forced the establishment of a "People's Republic" in 1946. After the liquidation of democratic elements, Bulgaria was transformed into a Soviet strategic fortress against Greece and

Turkey, and, after the defection of Yugoslavia, toward that country as well. The country is divided into 14 large districts (*okresi*), with the capital city of Sofia (Sofiya) forming a separate unit.

Bulgaria's population of roughly seven million people lives in an area of 42,796 square miles, the average density of population being 169 per square mile. While mountainous regions still have no more than a hundred inhabitants per square mile, the more densely inhabitated regions include the area around Vidin in the northern corner, the basin of Sofia, Rumelia, Danubian Bulgaria, and the Black Sea coast basin of Stalin (Varna). Densities along the Turkish boundary and in the Rila Mountains are low.

Towns of over 100,000 are Sofia and Plovdiv; Stalin and Ruse have only 50,000 inhabitants, and other towns are even smaller. The nation is predominately rural in its way of life: over four fifths of the population live in dispersed villages of less than 2,000 persons, and even town inhabitants are more of the agricultural than the urban type. Since 1880, the country has trebled its population.

Non-Bulgar nationalities are few, due in part to the Greco-Bulgarian population exchange after World War I. Many Turks who lived in southeastern Bulgaria and in compact groups around Ruse have been expelled. Bulgarian minorities live in Macedonia, where they are the constant source of frontier disputes between Yugoslavia and Bulgaria, while some others live in Greece (Figure 136). Romanians are found in the southern Dobruja, but are more than outnumbered by the Bulgarians who live in Romanian northern Dobruja. Bulgarians are predominantly of Greek Orthodox faith, but the so-called "Pomaks" are Islamized Bulgarians.

Three quarters of the population are occupied in agriculture, and about one tenth in mining and industry; the rest are engaged in administration, military service, commerce, or trade. In percentage of the total population, the agricultural population is high everywhere except around Sofia, Plovdiv, Stalin, and Burgas. The population density, however, is close to 300 per cultivable square mile, higher than that of Yugoslavia or Romania. Industrial population is high in Sofia, in the coal mining areas of the central Balkans, and on the northern edge of the Rumelian basin. Trade is concentrated in Sofia, Stalin, and Burgas, while administration is centered in the capital. Illiteracy is comparatively low except among the Romanian minority. The prevailing and state language is Bulgarian, a combination of Slavic and Turkic.

Notable is the great number of old people and the tendency to long life, which may be caused by the fair climate, good health conditions, and the slow progress of industrialization. But, as in every East Central European country, the middle age group is poorly represented: a consequence of World War I and the communist persecution of the present era. Another salient fact is that, alone among the East Central European states, Bulgaria is the only one in which males exceed females in the population.

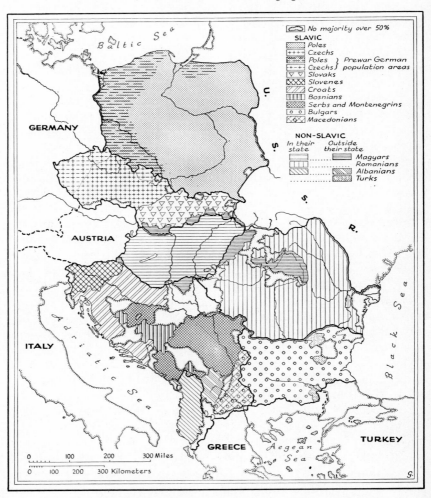

FIGURE 136. Ethnographic pattern of East Central Europe. Majorities over 50 per cent are represented, on the basis of censuses taken since 1919 and unofficial data concerning German resettlement.

World War II did not harm Bulgaria seriously. The only damage was done by the struggles of 1945 and by the Russian occupation troops. After the political and economic difficulties of 1946, the two-year plan of 1947 was introduced for reconstruction and socioeconomic changes. Then followed the five-year plan of 1949, which was designed to socialize Bulgaria and improve her industrial output.

Bulgaria remains, however, predominantly an agricultural country. Of a total of 25 million acres, nearly two fifths are arable, 3 per cent are in meadow and pasture, and a third is covered with forest. Almost a fifth of the area is waste land, the highest proportion among the East Central European countries (see Figure 131). Most of the arable land is confined to the Danube Valley, the southern Dobruja, and the central areas of the Rumelian Basin, which has the richest soils and a good central position between Sofia and the port of Burgas.

Meadows rank high in the percentage of total area for the western districts of Sofia, Vratsa, and northern Plovdiv. Pastures are frequent in the mountain districts of the west, in the Central Balkan ranges, and in the coastal lands south of Burgas. Yet the rental value of meadows and pastures is very low and therefore grazing prevails. Four forest types are present: the richest and most dense, often virgin, forests of the Rila and Rhodope mountains are coniferous; the Eastern Balkan and the area south of Burgas are covered with oakwoods. The remaining Balkan ranges have deciduous and mixed forests, while scrub growths are prevalent in the hill lands.

The chief agricultural crops are wheat and corn. Both are grown in Danubian Bulgaria, southern Dobruja, and Rumelia, and both have their highest acreage and yields along the Danube sections of the Vratsa district. But yields in general are low, due to primitive methods of tilling the soil and the growing resistance to cooperatives. Although rye, barley, and oats are grown in the same regions, their main cultivation is concentrated in southern Dobruja. Potatoes and sugar beets must still be considered as minor crops, although the acreage planted to them has been increased in recent years.

Besides a variety of vegetables (especially tomatoes, eggplants, and pumpkins, so important in the diet of the population), rape, sunflower seeds in the Danube area, and peanuts are grown. Olive trees also are gaining in the southern coastal regions. Sesame and poppy are other widely grown oleaginous plants. Flax and hemp cultivation is practiced only on a small scale, but cotton production is increasing rapidly in Rumelia and may even yield a surplus for export. Leguminous plants such as beans and peas are raised widely for local consumption.

Highly important is the cultivation of tobacco plants on 1.5 per cent of the total usable area, mainly the Arda Basin and the southern slopes of the Rhodope Mountains. Both the yearly production of 35,000 to 40,000 metric tons and the quality are outstanding. The mountain (*jebel*) variety, very suitable for blending and mixing, is exported in huge amounts. Another very important product is rose oil (*attar*), of which Bulgaria is the leading world producer (Figure 137). The production is a state monopoly, and the cultivation centers in the Anti-Balkan area. The cultivation of wine grapes and fruits is also important. Apples in the Sofia district, lemons on the southern Black Sea coast, peaches, apricots, figs, pomegranates, almonds, and walnuts are raised; plum trees occupy nearly half of the orchard area.

FIGURE 137. Rose cultivation at Kalofer, Bulgaria.

Animal raising is almost as important as cropping. Ten million sheep and a million goats constitute the main wealth of the rural population. They are grazed mainly in the Central Balkan Mountains, in the region between Sofia and Plovdiv, on the coastal lands, and in the regions southeast of Burgas. Pigs are concentrated in the oakwoods south of Burgas and in the corn region of the Vratsa district. Close to two million cattle are equally distributed, being kept for their dairy products and as draft animals; in the lowlands the chief draft animal is the horse, numbering over half a million. The many asses and mules in the southern districts are used for transport. Poultry are common, mainly chickens. Fishing is insignificant, but honey production is well developed and Bulgarian silk cocoons have a good reputation.

The development of Bulgaria's mining and industry has occurred only since the 1920's, and has been bolstered anew by the five-year plan, with the intention of strengthening the industrial workers' organizations, the basic power resource of Communism. Mining and industry are nationalized and a ministerial decree forbids workers to change jobs.

Bituminous coal is mined near Sofia. Iron ore is scarce, being found principally in the Rila Mountains. Bulgaria's other minerals are of little importance, although manganese deposits north of Sofia and near Stalin are increasingly mined, as are the copper-gold-lead-zinc ores and pyrites at the headwaters of the Isker River, the lead-zinc ores and pyrite southwest of Ruse, some bauxite, and small quantities of kaolin, gypsum, and serpentine (Figure 133).

Salt is obtained by evaporation of salt springs at Provadia and from the sea water on the Black Sea coast. Five per cent of the water power resources have been developed and furnish about half of the electrical power of Bulgaria.

Although 10 per cent of the population is industrially occupied, not even a third is involved in true industry. The majority of the industrial workers are engaged mainly in handicrafts, home industries, and manufacture on a small scale, subordinated to agricultural life. Such "home manufactures," distributed all over the country, include small flour mills, tanneries, distilleries, shoe, slipper, cloth, rug or furniture manufactures, and copper-, silver-, gold-, and swordsmiths.

Heavy industry is represented by the iron, steel, and metalworks of Plovdiv, Sofia, Nevrokop, and Stalin. Stalin and Burgas are shipbuilding centers (see Figure 134). The chemical industry is located in Plovdiv, and Stalin, and the center of leather industry is in Sofia. Various textiles are made in Karlovo and Sofia; the wool industry center is in Trnovo and cotton mills center at Stalin. Plovdiv also has a silk factory. As a consequence of socialization, sugar refineries, large flour mills, and tobacco factories are developing rapidly, in addition to distilleries, and canning. The wood industry is based on small local sawmills. Bulgaria's main industrialized area is that of the west-east axis of the country between Sofia, Plovdiv, and Burgas, which is equally the country's chief commercial artery.

Communications are sufficient, although meager in comparison with the countries of northwestern Europe. Something over 2,000 miles of standard gauge, 300 miles of narrow-gauge railways, and 20,000 miles of road (of which about one fifth are "highways" in the Balkan sense) connect the various urban centers. The main roads generally follow the railway pattern. The main railway artery of Bulgaria is the line from Niš (Yugoslavia) via Sofia, Plovdiv, and Slivengrad to Adrianople (Edirne, in Turkey). The single navigable waterway is the Danube, which has one crossing (by railway ferry at Ruse) to Romania. Telegraph and telephone lines are few.

Inland commerce focuses on Sofia, the capital, and on Plovdiv. The two Black Sea ports, Stalin and Burgas, and the Danube ports of Vidin, Lom, and Ruse are at present the main inlets and outlets of foreign trade. Metals, textiles, mineral oils, machinery, vehicles, chemicals, paperware, and cereals are the main import goods. Exports are headed by tobacco, wine, attar, lead, lamb hides, and tomato pulp. Corn, wheat, flour, barley, live animals, fruit, and eggs, which were important prewar exports, have almost disappeared from the list. Prewar exports went chiefly to Germany, Great Britain, Poland, Czechoslovakia, and Austria; today, almost three fourths of Bulgaria's exports go to the Soviet Union, followed by Czechoslovakia and Poland. Prewar imports came mainly from Germany, plus small amounts from Czechoslovakia and Poland. Three fourths of the imports now come from the Soviet Union and a large volume from Czechoslovakia. Bulgaria's neighbors are either unfriendly to her or have the same surplus goods.

As a strategic outpost of the Soviet Union's Aegean aspirations and desire to control the Straits, Bulgaria is also a threat to Yugoslavia's southern railway outlet. But the Balkan ranges are an important defense line for Wallachia and the Ukrainian lowlands, while Rumelia, the center of economic life, is open to the southeast.

Romania

In August, 1944, almost at the end of World War II, Romania changed sides and joined the Allied Powers. Northern Bucovina and Bessarabia were annexed by the Soviet Union, while the 1940 cessation of southern Dobruja to Bulgaria remained in force. Occupied by the Red Army, the country was gradually forced under communist leadership and, in 1947, was transformed into a "People's Republic," divided (according to the constitution of 1952) into 17 administrative regions (regiune) and an antonomous region in Transylvania. The capital is Bucharest (Bucureşti).

Romania's urge to extend her national boundaries even further than those of 1920, combined with ruthless anti-minority policies, have produced unfriendly neighbors. The common boundaries with Czechoslovakia and Poland no longer exist and therefore Romania's precarious strategic position between the Balkan states and the Soviet Union is even more accentuated. Bessarabia, north Bucovina, and the southern Dobruja have been lost. In July, 1952, the Székelyland [4] was made an "Autonomous Hungarian Territory." The Transylvanian problem is a territorial dispute between Romanians and Magyars. The idea of an autonomous or independent Transylvania is being fostered increasingly because it might balance and appease the political differences between Romania and Hungary, thus facilitating the economic development of the whole cultural and geographic unit.

Romania has over sixteen million inhabitants in its 91,584 square miles of territory, an average density of 176 per square mile. Densely populated regions include the Wallachian Plain, the Siret Valley, and the center of the Transylvanian Basin, but concentrations of over 300 are found only around Bucharest, the oil fields of Ploești, in the district of Galați, and in the little basins of Cluj and Târgu-Mureș in Transylvania. The Carpathian ranges have a very low population density, in many parts not over two inhabitants per square mile. From these regions, however, there is a constant emigration to the lowlands.

Although one quarter of the population is called "urban" in the statistics, these figures give in general an incorrect picture, because many of the towns are merely huge villages with a high quota of rural people. Four fifths of the people live in communities of fewer than 10,000 inhabitants. This suggests that in the occupational distribution, the agricultural population is predominant. Despite its population of just over a million (six per cent of the total population), even Greater Bucharest is a huge rural town, with many small houses and unpaved, irregular streets. Only two other cities have more than 100,000 inhabitants: Cluj in Transylvania, and Timisoara in the Banat. They are both towns with a large minority, chiefly Magyars.

Three other important centers are Jassy (Iași), Ploești, and Galați, which before the war had over 100,000 people, but has now dropped below this number. The decreased population of other towns has resulted in part from the extirpation of Jews and in part from emigration. The birth rate is very high, but the death rate is also excessive in comparison with that of western states. Therefore, the net increase is only about 1.4 per cent, close to that of Yugoslavia.

[4] The inhabitants of this region are called Székely ("Szeklers" in German, and "Siculs" in Romanian). They form a compact group of roughly 600,000 people. Their language as well as their nationality is Magyar.

Of the sixteen million people, roughly four fifths are enumerated as Romanians, who speak a complex near-Romance language. The Magyar minority is 10 per cent of the total population; 2 per cent are Germans, while Serbs, Slovaks, Ruthenes, Ukrainians, Poles, Gypsies, Bulgarians, Jews, Turks, Greeks, and Armenians are represented by small groups (see Figure 136). Both Magyars and Germans live in compact blocks in Transylvania, where they also form huge groups in the towns. The Székelyland is about 85 per cent Magyar, and Magyars are also found along the Hungarian frontier, in and around Cluj, and in many regions of northern Transylvania (Figure 138). The Germans are concentrated in and

FIGURE 138. Székely village house, with hand-carved gate, in Transylvania.

around the two towns of Sibiu and Bistriţa. There are, however, no reliable indications as to whether the thousands of people in the forced labor camps, mainly belonging to minority groups, are counted in the census or not. Almost 75 per cent of the population belong to the Romanian Orthodox Church, another 8 per cent are Greek Catholics. These two groups compose the Romanian ethnic unit, while Magyars are Roman Catholic or Protestant. The Germans (called Saxons) are mainly Protestants. Jews have diminished from 4 to 1 per cent. The Protestant and Catholic (including Greek Catholic) population lives almost entirely in Transylvania.

Illiteracy is highest in the pure Romanian regions, and lowest in the districts with German or Magyar minorities. The high rates of illiteracy are also common to the areas with Orthodox faith. Owing to two world wars, Romania has a serious lack of men in the 25-to-40-year age group.

Because of the stress laid on the production of raw and semi-finished material for export to the U.S.S.R. and Czechoslovakia, the number of men involved in mining and industry increases every year. But three quarters of Romania's population are still occupied in agriculture, which in percentage of total population numbers highest in the Danube and Siret valleys, and central and eastern Transylvania (Figure 139). Compared to the acreage of arable land, on the other hand, high density appears in the southern foot-hills of the Carpathians and in the Székelyland. Trade, now taken over mainly by the state, is responsible for the concentration of people in the towns of Bucharest, Stalin (Brașov), Cluj, Oradea, Timișoara, Jassy, and Galați.

FIGURE 139. Romanian shepherds in the eastern Carpathian Mountains.

One half of the total area of Romania is occupied by cropland, almost one quarter by woodland, and one sixth by meadows and pastures; the remainder is wasteland (see Figure 131). The percentage of arable land as compared to the total area is proportionately high in the Danube districts, low in Transylvania, and almost nonexistent in the Carpathians, which are occupied by forests, pasture land, and meadows. Cereals occupy four fifths of the arable land, corn ranking first, both in acreage and in crop size. Wheat ranks next. Agriculture still is of the extensive type and yields per acre are low.

The main corn-growing region is the Wallachian Plain, followed by Moldavia and the Banat. In the Banat and in Transylvania, an intelligent, literate populace and a favorable climate produce high yields compared with other regions of the country. Almost the same circumstances prevail for wheat, with the slight difference that the center of the Transylvanian Basin produces much of this cereal. Rye is unimportant and is chiefly grown in the Saxon and Székely areas, while barley is the main crop of the low Balta region and the steppe plateau of the Dobruja. Oats are grown all over the country except the mountains and the Danube Valley proper. Millet cultivation is increasing, but rice is still unimportant.

Because the main food of Romanians is a corn meal, called *mamaliga* (*puliszka* in Transylvania), the growth of potatoes is neglected. In the Székely and Saxon regions, however, potatoes occupy a large acreage, and are consumed chiefly by the local population. Because of the primitive methods of farming and the great amounts which go to the U.S.S.R., there is a considerable shortage in cereals, especially in Moldavia and Transylvania. Sugar beets are raised mainly in the western lowlands. Tobacco is cultivated extensively, but is of low quality.

Large acreages of beans and peas are grown, often between the rows of corn; although average yields are low, more is produced in Romania than in any other East Central European state. Sunflowers, grown everywhere in large quantities, and rape, which is increasingly being cultivated in Wallachia, are the basic plants for vegetable oil. Prewar Romania was the only East Central European country with an active foreign trade in linseed and soybeans, which are cultivated to a large extent in the lowlands.

Romania also produces a great quantity of grapes, which are grown in the regions of the Upper Mureş and the two Târnava rivers in Transylvania, the southward foothills of the Southern Carpathians, and in the Dobruja. Fruit growing has been widely expanded, the apples and pears of Baia Mare and the plums of Bistriţa being famous for their quality.

Animal breeding is generally seminomadic. Transhumance is common between the lowlands in winter and mountain pastures in summer. Fodder is not cropped but is mainly grazed by the large sheep herds, which in bad years descend into the lowlands, grazing even crop fields. Long-wooled sheep, called *raţca* and *ţigaja*, make up the herds of the originally pastoral Romanians, and are raised mainly for milk, cheese, and wool. Wallachia, Moldavia, the Dobruja, and the Bihor are the regions of highest sheep density. The distribution of horses shows the highest densities in Moldavia, the Dobruja, and the Banat, while cattle are represented everywhere by different types, such as the white Hungarian, the dark-brown Bessarabian, and the well-known Swiss. The many water buffaloes are characteristic of Transylvania. Pigs are raised all over the country for fat and meat, and the Banat is noted for the number of Yorkshire and other types.

Fish are plentiful, caught mainly in the Danube delta region, the Balta, and the marshy lagoons of the Black Sea coast. Trout from the Carpathian creeks are famous, and carp, perch, shad, and pike are common. Sea fish like sturgeon, salmon, and mackerel are consumed widely, and grey caviar is well known and even exported. Poultry are raised in great numbers, increasingly since 1946 because of the meat shortage resulting from extensive exports to the U.S.S.R.

The mineral wealth of Romania, centered around the rich oil fields near Ploeşti and some wells east of Bacău, produced under Russian control approximately five million metric tons of crude oil in 1950. Some pyrites and copper are found in the Dobruja, but the richest mining area is the Transylvanian basin. The periphery of the basin contains rock salt, while the center produces much methane gas.

Bituminous coal is scarce, and the only valuable mines are at Reşiţa in the Banat Mountains, and north of the Iron Gate. Lignite is mined in the upper Jiu Valley, and mining of the Jiu Valley coal has been increased in the last five years. The production of iron ore in the Banat mountains, as well as in the Pojana Ruska, has been considerably increased by the communist regime. Phosphates in Transylvania (near Lugoj) are also important. The Transylvanian Ore Mountains with their rich gold mines, which also produce silver and copper, are most valuable.

Although the bauxites of the Bihor are nearly exhausted, some manganese ore is still mined. In the north, the district of Baia Mare-Cavnic produces gold, lead, and zinc, plus sulphur and sulphuric acid. From Baia Mare as far as the Alps of Rodna, pyrites are extracted in several mines. Control of the gold mines has changed hands often as a consequence of alteration in political life. At present, all natural mineral resources, together with the key industries, are nationalized.

Heavy industry is concentrated at Reșița, though some machinery, tool, and precision works are found in Bucharest and in a few other towns of Transylvania (see Figure 134). Ships are built in Galați and railway equipment in Cluj. Oil refineries are located at many places, but the main plants are concentrated in and around Ploești, whence a pipeline runs to the port of Constanța and another via Bucharest to the Danube. The chemical industry is located in Bucharest, Baia Mare, and in the central part of Transylvania.

More importance must be attached to the agricultural industries such as flour mills, breweries, and distilling plants, which are located in the cities and towns of the lowlands. Various textiles are fabricated in Arad, Timișoara, and Bucharest, and there are many small woolen industries in the Székelyland. Linen is manufactured in Jassy, leather goods and drugs in Cluj. The rich water-power resources are only slightly developed (7 per cent of the potential), but a new hydroelectric plant in the Eastern Carpathians will increase the percentage. Large Portland cement plants are working in Transylvania and Wallachia. Timber and wood products are important to Romania's economy, and this industry is widely followed, especially in the Eastern Carpathians. The industrial pattern gives predominance to Transylvania and the western lowlands of the Carpathian basin.

The five-year plan of 1950 was intended to increase output, but the reprisals required to enforce various orders concerned with industrial progress reflect serious trouble in manpower and output, and goods have not been delivered to the Soviet Union as scheduled. The supply situation is especially bad for oil, coal, timber, leather, textiles, and construction products. Romania's small prewar industry has been improved, but is still underdeveloped.

Like industry, communications are also underdeveloped. There are barely 6,000 miles of railways and 43,000 miles of roads, of which only 7,500 are in fair condition. Since November, 1944, a broad-gauge railway line has been put into operation from Ploești to the Soviet Union. Two main lines coming from Hungary cross Transylvania. Both meet at Stalin, whence the tracks run through Ploești to Bucharest, being met there by the line crossing the Wallachian Plain. From the capital a main railway runs to Cernavoda on the Danube, and crosses the longest bridge of East Central Europe to reach the port of Constanța. Another important line runs from Ploești north along the outer slopes of the Carpathian arc.

The main roads follow these railway lines, except for a good connection from Craiova through the Turnu Roșu pass into Transylvania. The only navigable waterway at present is the Danube, the most important outlet of Romanian trade to the seas. A new Danube-Black Sea canal links Cernavoda and Midia north of Constanţa. Brăila and Galaţi are both important Danube ports, while on the Black Sea the only port of real commercial importance is Constanţa.

The chief export goods of the prewar period were wheat, flour, petroleum, timber, and live animals, while imports included cotton and cottonware, iron and machinery, leather, woolen goods, and chemicals. The foreign trade list of states for both exports and imports was headed by Germany, followed by Great Britain, Austria, and Czechoslovakia. At present the Soviet Union heads the list, followed by Czechoslovakia and Poland.

Hungary

The Peace Treaty of 1920 reduced Hungary from more than 125,000 square miles to 35,926, giving land to Romania, Yugoslavia, Czechoslovakia, Austria, Poland, and Italy. The state persisted, however, as a kingdom, represented by the Holy Crown and ruled by a regent assisted by the two houses of parliament. In 1946, under Soviet pressure, Hungary became a republic and ceded 24 square miles of territory opposite Bratislava to Czechoslovakia. In 1949 the state title was changed to "People's Republic" with 19 counties (megye) as administrative areas, and "Budapest Capital City" as the governmental center.

Over nine million people live on the 35,902 square miles in the center of the Carpathian Basin. The population density of 259 per square mile is the highest of the East Central European countries, exceeding even that of highly industrialized Czechoslovakia. The greatest density is found around Budapest, in the Miskolc industrial region, around Pécs, Szeged, and Debrecen, while densities below 200 per square mile occur only in southern Transdanubia and in the Hortobágy steppe. The rural density is highest in the southeastern corner of the country, where the soil is richest, but the prewar densely populated areas along the Austrian frontier are today depopulated because of a Russian security zone formed since 1946.

Because of the shifting of population in accordance with Soviet political and military requirements, some regions, like the industrial centers, are overpopulated. Many concentration camps and forced labor battalions, imprisoning thousands of people, have been shifted back and forth, and the constant deportation of other thousands makes the accuracy of population estimates doubtful. This holds true for all Iron Curtain countries.

After World War I, Hungary became an ethnically compact state, 96 per cent Magyar, with a very strong national consciousness. Of the minorities, only the German is notable. Jews are not counted separately if they do not wish to declare themselves as such. Two and a half million Magyars also live in Czechoslovakia, Romania, and Yugoslavia, most of them along the Hungarian boundary (Figure 136).

FIGURE 140. National costumes of the rural population. These are Hungarian, but such costumes are still very common all over East Central Europe.

The natural rate of population increase is highest in the northeastern corner of Hungary, lowest in southern Transdanubia. Two fifths of the population lives in localities of less than 10,000 inhabitants (Figure 140), nearly two fifths in towns of 10,000 to 100,000, approximately 400,000 in Debrecen, Szeged, and Miskolc, and one fifth in Budapest with its suburbs. The lack of the 25-to-35-year-old men is due to the two world wars. The natural increase on a thirty-year average is low (about 7 per thousand) and, among the seven nations of East Central Europe, only Czechoslovakia has a lower rate of increase.

The language, called Magyar, is spoken throughout Hungary. It belongs to the Finno-Ugrian family, but according to some authorities is related to Sumerian and Turkic. Idioms vary in different parts of the Carpathian Basin, and there are only slight deviations from the standard. The study of Russian is now compulsory—an attempt to Slavify the Magyars, who geographically divide the northern and southern Slavic peoples. Illiteracy is low, being highest among the peasants in the Great Alföld.

The bulk of the population, about two thirds, are Roman Catholic, especially west of the Danube. East of the Tisza River, however, there is a Calvinist center around Debrecen and Sárospatak, and of Lutherans around Miskolc. Jews concentrate in Budapest.

Before World War II, 53 per cent of the total population of Hungary was occupied in agriculture. Today it has fallen below 50 per cent, due partly to the forced increase of mining. Because of abolition of private enterprise, the population occupied in trade and commerce has shown a marked decrease while administration has absorbed a large number. As a result of the new form of life, involuntary urbanization has brought a concentration in the main towns and industrial centers. Szeged and Debrecen, which are marketing, administrative, and cultural centers of the Great Alföld, have not grown much in recent years, while Miskolc, an industrial and mining center in the market belt, has doubled its population in the last two decades. This may also be said of the smaller Pécs in southern Transdanubia, while the other towns of this region and the huge "village-towns" of the Great Alföld are stagnating. In the Little Alföld only Györ, the heavy-industry center, has shown rapid expansion.

The 1920 Peace Treaty left Hungary with lowlands and hill lands but deprived it of mountains, timber, mines, and upper river courses needed for water power, irrigation, and flood control. The railway and road pattern was crossed by new frontiers, with artificial customs walls. As a consequence, the economic unity of the Carpathian Basin was abolished and the new frontiers were unable to achieve a stable economy in East Central Europe. Hungary's best industrial regions went to Czechoslovakia, her best croplands to Yugoslavia, and mines and woods to Romania. What remained for Hungary was entirely agricultural, producing chiefly wheat and corn. Two thirds of the land are crop land and vineyards, one sixth meadow and pasture, and a tenth forest, predominantly beech and oak. The remaining area is occupied by settlements, roads, and waste land (see Figure 131).

Most of the world-famous hard wheat is grown in the Transtisia region. Rye is mainly raised in the Danube-Tisza mesopotamian region, in the eastern corner of the country, and also in Transdanubia. Barley and oats are grown everywhere, but the main center for barley is the Little Alföld. Corn, though common throughout Hungary, yields best in the Sárköz (between the Sió Canal and the Danube) and in the southern and southeastern areas. Since the introduction of cooperatives and the communist planned economy, grain yields have dropped.

This is also true for potatoes, with their intensive culture on the sandy soils in the eastern corner of the country and in the regions close to the Austrian boundary. Sugar-beet cultivation is well represented in Transdanubia and the Little Alföld, and leguminous plants, like beans, peas, and lentils are common. Vegetables and fruits such as apples, pears, cherries, plums, grapes, peaches, apricots, and melons are grown both in small gardens and on large plantations; most are consumed locally or marketed in Budapest or Kecskemét.

Owing to the high number of hours of sunshine per year and to the variability of the climate, the vegetables and fruits have the highest vitamin content (especially vitamin C) in Europe. One of the most important crops with significant export value is paprika, a common food of Magyars. It is eaten "green" (fresh) or is dried and ground as a spice. The market center is Szeged. Vitamin C is also produced from paprika in great amounts. Because Hungary's meadows and pastures have a low capacity for efficient animal husbandry, fodder plants, especially turnips, are cultivated. Flax is an important crop for export, and cotton growing has been started in the Transtisia region, while hemp cultivation is declining. Oleaginous seeds are a common crop and rice is grown on many of the former depressions, which were reclaimed between the two wars by intensive canalization and irrigation. Rice fields in the Hortobágy plain have been increased considerably since 1946.

The main marketing centers of the Great Alföld are Debrecen, Szeged, Szolnok, and Kecskemét. Vineyards are widely distributed, the chief wine grape growing regions being Tokaj and around Lake Balaton, but wine production has fallen considerably as a consequence of the 1945-46 land reform. Tobacco, another important crop, grown chiefly in eastern Hungary, is manufactured into cigarettes and cigars by the state.

The number of animals decreased during the German occupation of Hungary in 1944, and suffered further depletion under the pillaging of the Soviet occupation army. The prewar number of pigs was restored in three years, but there is still a deficiency of cattle and horses and their quality is inferior. Seminomadic cattle and horse raising is still common to regions like the Hortobágy or the *puszta* (grass steppe) of Bugac near Kecskemét, but can be seen also in other regions east of the Danube. For the most part, the cattle are the white, long-horned Hungarian type (Figure 141), which were an important export to western countries before World War I. Pigs are raised chiefly in the southern corn areas and the Little Alföld, while sheep are concentrated in the northern highlands, in eastern Hungary, and in southern Transdanubia. Goats have increased in number since 1945.

FIGURE 141. Animal husbandry in the Great Alföld. Long-horned white Hungarian cattle at a *gémes kút* (crane-shaped well) in the Hortobágy.

Poultry are raised by millions all over the country. The most valuable are geese, because of their feathers, downs, liver, and fat, used now instead of lard, which is exported. Because of the lack of equipment after the 1945 land reform, the small farms of 5 to 20 acres were unable to produce enough. As a consequence, cooperatives were formed and much land was taken over by state-owned and state-directed cooperatives. But the nationalization of the land has made slow progress.

Hungary's economic weakness is her lack of minerals. Only the coal mines near Pécs in the Mecsek produce some coking coal; the large mines of Transdanubia, as well as the northern mines of Salgótarján and the Mátra foothills have lignite reserves (see Figure 133). Without rivers suitable for the development of water power, the electric plants depend entirely on the low-grade coal.

Petroleum and natural gas are produced from wells around Lispe in the southwestern corner of the country and pipelines connect the fields with the Budapest refineries. The 850,000 metric ton production of 1943 has dropped as a result of Soviet control and too hasty exploitation. Iron ore is mined near Miskolc and production has increased by great strides in the last few years. Of the nonferrous metals, only bauxite is of great importance. Hungary is today one of the world's largest bauxite producers. The chief mines are near Székesfehérvár, close to large coal mines. Manganese ore is mined in the Bakony, and some copper, arsenite, pyrites, gold, silver, and lead in the Mátra mountains. Of special significance are the many artesian warm-water wells of Budapest, which have made the capital a well-known spa.

After World War I, industry had to be redeveloped in Hungary because of the lost industrial regions. Thus capital needed for land reform had to be used for construction. After World War II, a socialist planned economy was introduced, but the three-year plan of 1947 was apparently a failure, and the five-year plan of 1950 a questionable success. Whereas statistics show that the total quantity of manufactured goods increased, much was of low quality. Also, military preparation and armaments represent two fifths of the national expenditure.

Hungary has three main industrial regions. The first consists of Budapest and its environs (flour mills, tobacco and sugar works, distilleries and breweries, paper and textile mills, machine and tool factories, metallurgical plants, electric power plants, and plants producing various consumer goods). Airplanes and armaments are produced at Csepel. The second industrial region is northeast Transdanubia. The region includes the towns of Györ (textile plants and wagon works), Ajka (coal mines, electric power plants, glass works), Sztálinváros (metallurgical plants), and Dorog (coal mines and electric power plants). The region also includes the petroleum refineries at Szöny and Almásfüzitö, the huge electric power plant and cement works of the Tatabánya coal region, the chemicals plant at Pét, and the china factory at Herend. This second region is notable for producing most of Hungary's coal, manganese, bauxite, and a third of its electric power.

The third region is the highly important chemical-metallurgical complex centering around Salgótarjan, Ózd, Diósgyör, and Miskolc in the Mátra-Bükk Mountains. Its output is almost entirely geared into the Soviet economy. Here iron ore from Slovakia, domestic iron ore and coal, plus iron ore imported from Krivoi Rog in the U.S.S.R. are transformed into machinery, tools, and armaments.

Textile and flour mills, sugar refineries, breweries, tobacco factories, and food industries are scattered over the entire country. Petroleum refineries have been expanded since 1946 and an irrigation dam and power plant has been built on the Tisza River (at Tiszalök).

The communications pattern is dense and centers around Budapest, whence radiate the railways, all standard gauge, in every direction (Figure 135). These lines are also paralleled by the main highways. The heaviest traffic is on the Vienna-Györ-Budapest-Szolnok-Békéscsaba railway line to Romania and on the two lines to the U.S.S.R. by the Szolnok-Debrecen line and the newer line from Budapest to Miskolc and Cop. Roughly 3,500 miles of railways and 18,500 miles of roads crisscross the almost flat country. A little over 1,000 miles of waterways are navigable, including the entire Hungarian section of the Danube, the Tisza as far north as Tokaj, the Dráva up to Barcs, and the Körös up to Békés (Figure 135). Budapest can be entered by Danube River vessels of 2,300 dead-weight tons. A Danube-Tisza canal is being built, and navigation on Lake Balaton is intensive.

Like industry, trade and commerce are now controlled by the state. Business centers are in the main cities, from which distances to the producing areas are small. Most of the internal commerce is concentrated in Budapest. Whereas in prewar times exports were mainly agricultural goods, the important postwar exports include important bauxite, leather, textiles, drugs, electrical equipment, and machinery. The main imports are wood, lumber, cotton and cotton goods, paper, crude metals, petroleum, coal, coke, and leather goods. Germany's prewar first place in trade has been taken by the Soviet Union. Before the war Austria, Romania, Czechoslovakia, and the United Kingdom came next, followed by Italy and the United States. Today the United Kingdom is second, followed by Czechoslovakia, Austria, Germany (mainly eastern), and Poland.

Strategically, Hungary is open on every side. Almost everything is concentrated in Budapest, which lies close to the Slovakian lands. In population, economics, communications, strategic aspects, and cultural life the capital is the heart of Hungary.

Czechoslovakia

Although based on the traditional evolution of Bohemia, the Czechoslovak Republic was the least natural state created after World War I. Bohemia, Moravia, Slovakia, and Ruthenia formed the parts of a long, unnatural, composite area, with varied relief.

peoples, communications, and economic development. Not satisfied with Czech domination, the Slovaks formed an independent state when Germany occupied Bohemia-Moravia in World War II, and also became the ardent supporter of Nazi imperialism. After World War II, the Soviet Union forced the Republic—its ally—to cede Ruthenia to her.

As a consequence of the new belief in international politics that frontiers do not have to be adjusted to nations or nationalities but peoples fitted to the existing boundaries, three million Sudeten Germans and many thousands of Magyars were expelled. Yet Slovak separatism and anti-Czech feelings have strengthened, and are kept down only by the Soviet Union's power, which makes all states behind the Iron Curtain uniform for the sake of security. As a result, victors and vanquished now share the same fate. Instead of its prewar regional units the Republic now has two provinces, the Czech Provinces and Slovakia, subdivided into districts (krajs), with local administration centers. The capital is Prague (Praha), center of all political, administrative and cultural life, while Brno and Bratislava have been demoted to secondary roles.

A little more than twelve million people live in an area of 49,358 square miles; the decrease of two million people from prewar figures is due to the expulsion of minorities. As a consequence, the prewar average population density of 267 has dropped to 252 per square mile. Over 500 people per square mile live in the industrial regions of Ostrava, and around Prague and Plzeň (Pilsen). The Bohemian Forest, the Czecho-Moravian Upland, and the Carpathian ranges show densities below 150, and in the Tatras even lower than 70 per square mile. Kosice and its environs is a little island of high density.

Half of the dominantly rural population lives in localities with 500 to 5,000 inhabitants, while one fifth lives in even smaller places. Only 1.7 million people inhabit cities of over 100,000, Prague alone accounting for almost a million. Birth rates are increasing and the death rates decreasing; the natural increase therefore has been high since 1946. It is highest in the Eastern Slovakian mountain regions (where illiteracy is prevalent), followed by the Danube lowland and Moravia, and is lowest in the Bohemian Basin.

West of the Carpathians the Czecho-Moravians form an almost pure ethnic group, and only a few Germans in the Erz Gebirge and some Poles in the northern Moravian lands remain as minorities (Figure 136). There are few Czechs in the Carpathian lands, which are ethnically almost solidly Slovakian, although half a million Magyars occupy a compact strip along the southern boundary with Hungary. Several thousands of these Magyars were expelled and others forcibly settled in the former German areas of Bohemia.

The population is predominantly Roman Catholic, especially in Bohemia, Moravia, and western Slovakia; only about 25 per cent of the people belong to other religious groups like the Protestant churches. About a million persons are without church affiliations.

The occupational distribution has a remarkably regional character. Of the total population, a little over a third is occupied in agriculture, and almost two fifths are miners and industrial workers. The bulk of the industrial workers are concentrated in Bohemia, northern Moravia, and the mining districts of central Slovakia. In contrast, the densest areas of agricultural population are the Slovakian part of the Danube lowland and the northeastern section of the Carpathians. The way of life is also different in these two main regions, Bohemia-Moravia and Slovakia, which have related yet separate languages and yet have divergent cultures, traditions, and ways of thinking. By governing the Slovakians more than taking them as partners, the Czechs caused Slovak separatism to grow and intensify. At present the difference is overcome by communist dictatorship, yet is strong under the surface. Trade and the free occupations have diminished, and industrial population is expanding rapidly, as are the administrative and military forces. Prague and the smaller cities increase rapidly in size, not only because of the accelerated industrial production but also because many people find more security in the larger urban units.

After the failure of the two-year plan of 1947, the Czechoslovak five-year plan of 1949 proposed a reorientation of the economy from finished goods industries to engineering and heavy industry. Most of the industrialization program is centered in Bohemia, while Slovakia remains chiefly agricultural. Yet agriculture is more intensive in Bohemia, and is of minor importance only in comparison to its industry; over four fifths of the cultivable area is crop land, close to one third forests, and about a seventh meadow or pasture. But even this proportion of crop land cannot support the needs of the people (see Figure 131).

About half of the forests are coniferous, 20 per cent are mixed, and 30 per cent are deciduous. Lumbering is widely distributed and is a basic source of revenue for the state. Agricultural life is most intensive in the northern sections of the Bohemian Basin, the Moravian Depression and the Slovakian part of the Little Alföld, while the Carpathians are the pasturing center, and also produce the best cheese. Wheat, rye, barley, and oats are the main cereals; because of unfavorable climatic conditions, corn is only cultivated in the Slovakian lowlands and a little in southern Moravia. These areas, together with the Bohemian Basin, are also the main wheat producers. Rye is cultivated all over the country, and is scarce only in the Carpathians. Barley is grown in the Danube lowlands, the Moravian lowlands, the Labe (Elbe), and the lower Ohře valleys, while oats are grown chiefly in the Czecho-Moravian Uplands and the central region of the Bohemian Basin. Potatoes are highly favored and cultivated in all parts of Czechoslovakia; the densest acreage is found in the low and hilly lands of Moravia, with the heaviest yields coming from southeastern Bohemia and eastern Slovakia.

As a consequence of skilled farmers and a balanced climate, the highest crop yields are obtained in Bohemia and northern Moravia. Because of the dense population, however, there is a deficiency of cereals and potatoes in the country, with only eastern Slovakia showing a slight excess.

A very important industrial crop is sugar beets, which supply the highly developed sugar industry of the country. The chief cultivation areas are southwestern Slovakia, the Morava Basin, and the Labe Valley. These regions also raise grapes, while an important crop for the beer industry is hops from the Ohře Valley and the Moravian Basin. Tobacco is grown along the Danube and the lower Morava. The best yields of fodder crops in all East Central Europe are found in Czechoslovakia. Turnips, alfalfa, and clover are all cultivated intensively because of the poor pastures and meadows. Flax and hemp are grown in the southeastern Bohemian Forest, in the Czecho-Moravian Upland, and the northern mountain belt. Rape and poppy are of minor importance.

As for livestock, Czechoslovakia has close to four million cattle, of which the greatest number are in Bohemia and Moravia. Half a million horses are fairly well distributed over the country, and so are three million pigs, with the highest density in the lowlands and valleys. Sheep are numerous in the Slovakian Carpathians and goats are also important there, as well as in the northwestern mountain districts. Poultry raising is common.

Mining is highly developed and is a traditional occupation of the country. The main mineral wealth is represented by the anthracite and bituminous coal of the Upper Silesian coal basin around Ostrava (see Figure 133). The yearly production is now about 18 million tons. Bohemia has many other minor yet important bituminous coal mines, while lignites are extracted mainly in the

Teplice-Šanov-Chomutov coal district. Slovakia has only one lignite mine of importance, in the upper Nitra Valley. The production of petroleum is insignificant. The mining of graphite north
of Plzeň and Brno is very important as the basis for the pencil
industry.

Bohemia produces great quantities of iron ore from the mines
southwest of Prague and in the Erz Gebirge, while Slovakia's rich
mines are located in the Slovakian Ore Mountains. Of the iron-
alloy metals, manganese is of greatest importance. Also of great
importance are the wolframite and pitchblende from Jáchymov in
the Erz Gebirge. Uranium extracted from these ores is the basic
material for the Soviet Union's atomic-energy projects. Mining
has been speeded up by using forced labor, though the reserves
are poor and possibly near exhaustion. Other metal ores of
value are antimony and magnesite from the Slovakian Ore Mountains, as well as mercury in the Topla Valley, lead and zinc ores of
Příbram, and some pyrite, copper, and gold or silver ores. Since
the loss of Ruthenia, salt mining has decreased considerably, and
only one rock salt mine in eastern Slovakia furnishes small quantities for the chemical industry and domestic use.

An account of Czechoslovakia's mineral wealth would be incomplete without mentioning her high-quality kaolin, so important to
the china industry, and the good raw materials for glass in Bohemia.
Water-power resources are about a million hp., of which over 15
per cent is exploited. Of special value are the many mineral springs
and spas, of which Karlovy Vary (Karlsbad) is best known.

By far the most important feature of the Czechoslovak economy
is the highly developed industry (see Figure 134). The Soviet-
inspired reorganization of the formerly strong capitalist industry
has brought about nationalization of the plants. Industrial life is
completely in the hands of the government. The two outstanding industries are heavy machinery and metals, with close to
500,000 workers, and textiles, which has more than 200,000. Next
in importance are the glass, china, and stone industries, with
over 100,000 workers, followed by the food and wood industries.
The more than 13,000 industrial plants of Czechoslovakia equal the
combined total of those in Hungary, Romania, Yugoslavia, Bulgaria, and Albania.

Heavy industry shows two chief concentrations, one in the coal
area around Ostrava, the other in the Prague-Kladno-Plzeň triangle.
A third and minor one is in the Erz Gebirge. Prague and Plzeň
also have factories producing tools, machinery, automobiles, airplanes, precision tools and machines, electrotechnical equipment,

armament, locomotives, and railway equipment. Additional heavy industry and machinery plants are located in Bratislava, where dynamite is produced, in Brno, and other cities.

The chemical and drug industry, including the production of fertilizers, has many plants, situated mainly in Bohemia; the largest chemical plant is Ústi on the Labe. Several refineries use imported petroleum. Textiles are the most developed industry in Bohemia. Cotton mills and linen production are concentrated in the north around Liberec, while the center of the wool industry is Brno. Notable for wood products are the furniture factories in Prague and Brno. Wood-pulp mills are concentrated in northeastern Bohemia, while sawmills are important in Prague. Musical instruments, toys, jewelry, lace, rubber, and various other products for consumption also help to make Bohemia an industrial stronghold of East Central Europe.

The agricultural and food industries are also highly developed. Sugar and flour mills are located in every large town of the Danube lowland, the Morava Valley, and the Labe-Ohře Valley. In Moravia and Slovakia the dairy industry, the production of starch, dextrin, and glucose, the malt factories of Moravia, and world-famous breweries are located at Plzeň and Česke-Budějovice (Budweis). The tobacco factories of Prague and Bratislava produce for domestic consumption, chiefly with imported tobacco.

The communications pattern is very dense in Bohemia and Moravia, whereas the mountains of Slovakia form a great hindrance to transportation. Yet all roads are excellent and the main-line railways are double tracked. Close to 10,000 miles of standard-gauge railways, and about 40,000 miles of road, of which close to 6,000 are first class, crisscross the country. All important towns are connected by railways. From the railway center of Prague, lines fan out westward to Plzeň and Cheb, northward along the Labe River, eastward to Olomouc and Ostrava, and southward to Brno and Bratislava, which is the western railway terminus of Slovakia. Two west-east lines cross Slovakia. Roughly 300 miles of navigable waterways are limited to the Danube (with Bratislava and Komárno as ports), the Labe, and the Vltava as far south as Prague.

Czechoslovakia's foreign trade and commerce are very extensive. The main exports are textiles, machinery and tools, ironware, leather goods, sugar, glass and china, flour, coal, wood and timber, flax and hemp. The imports include cotton and cotton goods, wool, live animals, cereals and flour, silk and silk goods, chemicals, ores and ironware. The prewar exports went chiefly to Germany, Great Britain, Austria, and the United States, while imports came from Germany, Great Britain, the surrounding agricultural countries, and the United States. At present the Soviet Union ranks first both as a customer for Czechoslovakia's exports (mainly armaments and machinery) and as a supplier of her imports. In exports Poland, the Netherlands, Germany, Sweden, Switzerland, and Great Britain follow, while the imports come from the Netherlands, Great Britain, Poland, Sweden, Belgium, the United States, and France. As a result of Czechoslovakia's political reorientation, trade with the west has much decreased.

Poland

An old European kingdom re-emerged as a republic from the ruins of World War I. The "new" Poland, a buffer state between Germany and the Soviet Union, was inhabited by a composite national population of 35 millions and had an area of 150,000 square miles. Partitioned between Germany and the Soviet Union in World War II, Poland was transformed after the war into a communist-ruled Polish Republic. Its eastern lands were taken by the U.S.S.R., and as compensation Poland was allowed at the expense of Germany a part of East Prussia, Danzig, Silesia, and Pomerania—the German lands as far west as the Oder-Neisse line. Poles who lived in the territory absorbed by the U.S.S.R. were resettled in the newly acquired western and northern territories, from which all Germans were expelled. In May, 1951, the Soviet Union ceded an area of 300 square miles south-southwest of Przemyśl to Poland and received in return an equal area in the angle of the Western Bug and Solokija rivers. By these changes the country became smaller by one fifth, but more compact and unified in nationality and language. The Republic is divided into 19 administrative districts. Its capital is Warsaw (Warszawa) on the Vistula River.

Twenty-four million people occupy an area which now totals 121,131 square miles. Despite the millions of Polish lives lost during World War II, this gives an average density of 206 per square mile. A densely inhabited belt, with over 250 people per square mile, runs along the Silesian Plain, over the Silesian coal fields, and across the Carpathian foreland of the Upper Vistula and San valleys. Very dense agglomerations exist around Wroclaw and the industrial coal region. Other closely settled regions are found in the vicinity of Czestochowa, Lublin, Warsaw, Poznan (Posen), Bydgoszcz, Szczecin, and Gdansk. Warsaw and Lodz have just over 600,000 inhabitants, and twelve other cities have exceeded the 100,000 mark. In contrast, Szczecin, the former German port of Stettin which had a population of 383,000 people, has decreased to about 80,000 inhabitants.

The present population is almost uniformly Polish. Some Balts, a few Belorussians, Ukrainians, and Czechs make up small, dispersed minority groups. A striking feature of Poland is the great number of old and very young people. The middle-age group between 25 and 45 years of age is comparatively small, as a direct consequence of war and postwar developments. Postwar birth rates have dropped, but death rates grow constantly because of increasing resistance to the Communists. Thus the natural increase in population is estimated at about 0.9 per cent per year. Polish is the only language spoken, although Russian is taught in schools and in the universities. The great majority of the population is Roman Catholic, but many may be without religion or faith.

Because Poland and Czechoslovakia are the two industrial strongholds of the Soviet Union in East Central Europe, the occupational distribution of Poland has changed in the last few years. The agricultural population, 65 per cent in 1937, has since dropped to an even 50 per cent, and the industrial population has risen to over 30 per cent. The main industrial agglomeration is Silesia's rich coal district, while trade and commerce show a high occupational density in the capital, in Lodz, and in the three Baltic ports of Gdansk, Gdynia, and Szczecin. Free occupations have decreased rapidly, and military forces show a steady growth. The densest region of rural population is in southeastern Poland, densities of over 250 persons per square mile occurring in the Carpathian foreland, the Silesian plateau, and the districts around Czestochowa, Kielce, and Warsaw. Two other dense rural districts are located at Gdynia and Szczecin. The western regions taken from Germany and resettled with Poles are still underpopulated, in spite of their balanced climate and fair soil. Mazuria, on the other hand, is inhospitable, and here the small villages are sparsely distributed.

Whereas prewar Poland was predominantly agricultural, the addition of highly industrialized German Silesia has produced a balance of agriculture and industry. After completion of the three-year reconstruction plan of 1947, the six-year plan of 1950 stressed industrial expansion. The reason may be found in the increasing military preparations and its close ties with similar developments in the U.S.S.R.

A little over half of present-day Poland is arable. Meadows and pastures represent over a tenth, and almost a quarter is woodland (see Figure 131). The best croplands are the central Glacial Valley plains and the southern river valleys. The Glacial Valley Zone and Silesia contain the highest percentages of arable land (Figure 142), while the best meadows and pastures are found in the east and south. Of the 8.5 million acres under cultivation, rye occupies five million, wheat one million, and potatoes two and a half million. Rye, the most important cereal and prewar export crop, is grown all over the country, but occupies most of the arable land in the northwest and on the Carpathian slopes. The most important wheat areas, with the greatest production, are the Silesian Plain, the vicinity of Lublin and Cracow, and the lower Vistula Valley from Bydgoszcz to the Baltic estuary. Potatoes, the chief item of

FIGURE 142. Harvesting in Polish Silesia. Such simple methods are still very common in East Central Europe.

the Polish diet, are also a general crop of all regions. The lowest acreages are found in the southern wheat and rye regions, while they predominate in the Baltic Moraine Zone. Five to six million metric tons of rye, and 25 to 30 million metric tons of potatoes constitute the main agricultural wealth of Poland. Oats, cultivated on almost two million acres, and barley, with an acreage of a little less than one million, are not so important although they are grown everywhere. Most of the barley is grown in Silesia and the Polish Upland, while oats predominate south and east of Cracow.

Sugar beets are grown on over 200,000 acres, and yield from 3 to 4 million metric tons a year. The richest sugar beet area is the Silesian Plain. An important industrial crop is flax, grown mainly in the Baltic Moraine Zone. Hemp, hops, and chicory are widely grown, mainly in the southern regions.

Climatic conditions make rice growing impossible and corn and vine grapes are rare. Although Poland's climate is not overly favorable to tobacco, the area devoted to its cultivation has been increased by 400 per cent, compared to prewar conditions, chiefly in the southwest. Other important products are rape seed, linseed, hempseed, and hemp. Fruit growing is chiefly concentrated in former German areas.

The losses in animal stock during the war were almost as great as in Hungary, amounting to more than half of the cattle, one third of the pigs, and about half of the horses. The pig population, close to 5 million, has been restored, whereas only a part of the horses and cattle has been replaced. About five million sheep and close to a million goats add to the national wealth.

Horses are fairly evenly distributed in the country, the highest number being found around Lublin and Lodz. Cattle prevail in the central parts of Poland, while the Glacial Valley Zone is the chief swine-raising region. Sheep are prevalent around Bialystok and Bydgoszcz, which are also the best centers for fodder crops, except for the Carpathian mountain regions, where sheep and goats are very common in the higher pastures. Poultry are found in great numbers in the southern and central areas. Fishing is an important occupation. Besides the cod and mackerel of the Baltic, river fish are also caught, with carp, perch, and pike the main varieties.

Although many forests were devastated in the war, forests still cover almost a quarter of Poland's area. On limy soils, mixed and deciduous forests prevail, while in the north the pine offsets its low quality by its rapid growth. Fir, the most valuable timber material, is confined to the Carpathian regions. The densest forest regions are the former German lands, where reforestation was systematic, and the southern hills and mountains.

The outstanding mineral wealth of Poland is the good anthracite of the Silesian coal basin (Figure 143). The acquisition of the former German coal mines has had a sharply favorable affect on Polish coal production, which is now over 80 million metric tons a year. The main bituminous mines are around Katowice (see Figure 133), but others are important in the same area. Good coking coal constitutes not more than 20 per cent of the total output. Another important coal district (also formerly German) with good coking coal is Žaclér (Schatzlar), southwest of Wroclaw, close to the Czech frontier. Lignites are mined along the right bank of the Nisa (Neisse) River on the German frontier, and the mining of lignite reserves between the Warta and Odra rivers, and those south of Lublin, are a part of the six-year plan.

Poland's main pre-World War II oil field (Drohobycz-Boryslaw) has now been incorporated into the Ukrainian S.S.R., so her petroleum output is now limited to the Jaslo wells southeast of Tarnów in the Carpathian foreland. Natural gas from this region is carried by pipeline to the Kielce and Katowice mining districts and to Cracow. The enormous water power resources of the Carpathian rivers have not yet been developed.

FIGURE 143. General view of the industrial and coal-mining district of Walbrzych, Silesia. (Polish Information Bureau.)

Iron ores are of low quality, but the mining has been improved in the Polish Uplands around Częstochowa and Kielce. The iron ores of Upper Silesia have been almost entirely exploited. Thus, Poland's heavy industry remains dependent upon imports of iron ore, crude iron, and alloys, of which she has little or none. As for other metal ores, zinc, accompanied by small amounts of lead, silver, and cadmium, is very important in Silesia. Arsenite ores with a little gold, found south of Wroclaw, have some significance.

The important pre-World War II potash mines have also fallen to the Soviet Union, but some phosphates are available west of Lublin. The enormous deposits of rock salt located at the confluence of the Vistula and Dunajec rivers, are mined chiefly at Wieliczka and Bochnia. The Glacial Valley and the Northern Moraine zones are almost bare of mineral raw materials, but a valuable article is amber, washed out of the sand along the Baltic.

Poland's industrial development since 1920 has been rapid, due chiefly to the double acquisition after the two world wars of highly industrialized areas which were formerly German (see Figure 134). Textile and metallurgical industries are predominant. Huge textile works are operated, using imported cotton, flax, hemp, jute, and wool. Lodz, called "the Polish Manchester," is the textile center. Owing to its central location, it is an outstanding industrial and commercial city, with metallurgical, chemical, food preserving, electrotechnical, and printing industries.

The wool-weaving industry is outstanding only in Bialystok and Bydgoszcz, while textile and clothing plants are also located in central Poland and Silesia. Heavy industry is well represented and has its center in the Silesian coal basin (Bytom, Katowice, and others). Blast furnaces and steel rolling mills operate predominantly with ores imported from Czechoslovakia and the Soviet Union, but machinery and tools are manufactured in many other towns. The two largest water power plants are located at Laskowice on the Czarna Woda River north of Bydgoszcz, and at Roznów on the Dunajec River.

Shipbuilding is located in Gdansk, Gdynia, and Szczecin. The largest concrete plants are in Szczecin and Sosnowiec, while glass and ceramic manufacturing is densest in Silesia and around Warsaw. Flour mills, breweries, distilleries, sugar refineries, and plants for food canning or preservation are the most widely developed in the area limited by a line drawn from Bydgoszcz to Poznan, Lodz and Warsaw, and with a secondary concentration in central Silesia. Chorzow is an important timber industry center, while semifinished and finished woodwork plants are concentrated in many of the cities of central and southern Poland. Paper mills are found in western Silesia and in the Silesian coal basin.

Communications, to a large extent destroyed during the war, have been almost entirely restored. But the 14,500 miles of standard-gauge railways and the 60,000 miles of hard-surfaced roads are in reality a scanty network for the large country. The 2,500 miles of narrow-gauge railways help traffic and transport. The densest part of the network is found in the west and north, where the Poles have fallen heir to railways built by German skill and energy. The main railways are the Gdansk-Bydgoszcz-Lodz-Katowice line and the line from Szczecin and Poznan to Warsaw. These are the routes of heaviest traffic and largest transport between the outlets on the Baltic Sea and the industrial regions.

The telephone and telegraph network is well developed, but again, most of the lines are in the western half of the country. Of the waterways, 2,500 miles are navigable and have a good distribution for transport. The Oder is usable from the Baltic to Wroclaw, and is canalized southward and connected by a canal to Katowice. The Vistula is navigable from the Silesian coal basin to its two estuaries, and is linked by the Vistula-Notec Canal to the Warta and Oder rivers. Poznan's navigable river is the Warta, while Warsaw has another connection with the Baltic via the Bug and Narew; in addition, a canal links the latter with the Pregel River, which flows into the Baltic Sea. The chief ports of Poland are Gdansk, Gdynia, and Szczecin. The annual turnover of goods for the first two exceeds 12 million metric tons, and Szczecin handles from 2 to 3 million metric tons a year.

Poland's prewar foreign trade was carried on chiefly with Great Britain, Germany, and the United States, followed by Czechoslovakia and Austria. Today the Soviet Union heads the list, followed by Great Britain, Denmark, and the neighboring Cominform states, trade with the latter being much increased in volume. The main export goods are coal, coke, metals (headed by zinc and zinc plate), machinery, textiles, timber, and foodstuffs (barley, sugar, meat, butter, eggs, and pigs), and the many armament products which are transported to the Soviet Union. Imports are mainly ores, semicrude metals, machinery, cars, and trucks, cotton and textiles, rubber, corn, rice, tobacco, leather, and chemicals. The inland commerce centers on the chief cities. Trade is controlled by communist-directed commercial cooperatives.

The Most Urgent Problems Facing the Countries of East Central Europe

The problems faced by the nations of East Central Europe are thoroughly related to their geographical situation. The diverse physiography has resulted in an equally great diversity of climate and vegetation. As a result the "corridor" character of the area—the varying peoples, languages, and customs—only a few states of East Central Europe have been able to maintain stability and fairly permanent boundaries throughout the centuries.

The peace treaties of 1919-20 brought three main problems after a long period of evolution: all arose from the new territorial distribution, the new state pattern. First they posed a pressing problem of administrative reorganization; second, they revived, in new ways, the minority question; and third, but not least, they introduced a new series of economic problems. These problems, and their interactions, produced a zone of insecurity in Central Europe.

These problems were not resolved by World War II. Three million Magyars and half a million Albanians are the two largest minorities outside their national boundaries. The eccentricity of the capitals, close to the boundaries of neighbor states, the railways more or less centering on a few cities, the many customs frontiers on the most important exchange lines, all hinder the economic unification of larger territories. A special and serious problem of the Carpathian Basin arises from the fact that the drainage pattern is cut by many national boundaries. The upper courses of rivers which could provide the water needed to irrigate the dry lowlands, as well as to furnish water power for electricity (especially for Hungary, which is short of coal), are in neighboring states which show no interest in improvements. As a result, the water power of the Carpathian Basin is not used to raise the standard of life. A Danubian TVA, while often proposed, has not been attempted mainly because of political reasons.

To these problems, which are only partly overcome by the newly formed cooperation of the communist governments (with the exception of Yugoslavia), some others have been added after World War II. Again new boundaries were set. Poland was shifted westward, and Ruthenia was incorporated into the Soviet Union, which thus entered the Carpathian Basin for the first time. Yugoslavia received Istria, a part of the Dobruja went to Bulgaria (during the war), and Bessarabia and northern Bucovina were attached to the Soviet Union. To conform to these territorial changes populations were exchanged or expelled from different countries: Germans, Poles, Romanians, Russians (including Ukrainians), Hungarians, Slovaks, Turks, Italians, as well as Jews migrated by the thousands or millions. Over a million nationals of present East Central European states fled their countries and migrated to the United States, Canada, Australia, Argentina, India, Union of South Africa, Israel, and various other countries.

The exodus of Germans from Czechoslovakia produced not only a lack of skilled manpower in that country but also a decrease of the total population and thus of the population density. As a result, industrial Czechoslovakia has fewer inhabitants per square mile than agricultural Hungary. The exodus of the Jewish people created a dearth of trained bankers, economists, and traders in many countries, and produced a setback of commerce and trade. The resettlement of Poles from pre-World War II eastern Poland into present western Poland held back the production of these latter regions for a few years. All these resettlements caused a problem to governments and local administration and resulted in an increase of administrative employees all over the area.

All East Central European countries now have communist-type planned economies. Various three-, five-, or six-year plans, and their accompanying land reforms have completely changed the economic structure. Cooperative farms are spreading constantly, although the resistance of peasants does not allow rapid progress. The agriculture statistics which have been released show a constant increase in production, but all news coming from behind the "Iron Curtain" shows that people have less food than in pre-World War II years.

The industrial development has been rapid. Stress is laid on armament and heavy industry as well as on mining. Communications, especially waterways (new canals) have been improved. As a result, the production of consumer goods has decreased or is of poorer quality and there are considerable shortages. This situation is one of the most pressing problems of the entire area because it produces dissatisfaction not only in the communist-attacked "old reactionary classes" but also among the working people who form the base on which communist "People's Democracies" are founded.

As for the future, the problems it will bring appear to be equally complicated. If things remain as they are for a long time, a new generation will grow up with a different way of life than that of the Western World. If East Central Europe should be forcibly freed by the West, the area would be so devastated that rehabilitation would take many years. New minority problems will arise; possibly western Poland would become an area of friction between Germans and Poles. The lack of a well-trained and educated middle class, which has been systematically destroyed, would certainly hamper reconstruction.

One solution may be some kind of federation depending on: (1) self-determination of traditional regions and peoples, (2) the possibility of free migration and settlement, (3) the abolition of nationalistic economic barriers, (4) a common economic planning of power, communications, and key industries, (5) a return to private property, without the motto of "everything back to the former owners," but a sound and organized reconstruction based on law and justice all over the area, and (6) cultural cooperation, initiated by the countries concerned.

There is no doubt that, in a free world, East Central Europe could form a progressive unit. Its raw materials, good soil, fair climate, and not too dense population give it every chance almost to double its population, without serious economic setbacks. But whereas today heavy industry and armament works are the main emphasis—under Soviet leadership—the future may very well hold better opportunities for the developing of industry in conformity with a strong agricultural economy.

BIBLIOGRAPHY

A. Books in English

Barker, Elizabeth. *Macedonia: Its Place in Balkan Politics.* New York: Royal Institute of International Affairs, 1950.
Betts, R. R. *Central and Southeast Europe, 1945-1948.* London: Royal Institute of International Affairs, 1950.
Boyd, Louise A. *Polish Countrysides.* New York: American Geographical Society, 1937.
Hertz, F. *The Economic Problem of the Danubian States.* London: Victor Gollancz, Ltd., 1947.
Kerner, Robert J. (ed.). *Czechoslovakia.* Berkeley: University of California Press, 1940.
Macartney, Carlile Aylmer. *Problems of the Danube Basin.* London: Cambridge University Press, 1942.
Roberts, Henry L. *Rumania.* New Haven: Yale University Press, 1951.
Schmitt, Bernadotte (ed.). *Poland.* Berkeley: University of California Press, 1945.
Seton-Watson, Hugh. *Eastern Europe Between the Wars, 1918-1941.* London: Cambridge University Press, 1945.
Teleki, Count Paul. *The Evolution of Hungary and its Place in European History.* New York: The Macmillan Co., 1923.
Warriner, Doreen. *The Economics of Peasant Farming.* London: Oxford University Press, 1939.
Wszelaki, Jan. *Fuel and Power in Captive Middle Europe.* New York: The National Committee for a Free Europe, 1952.

B. Books in Foreign Languages

Bulla, B., and Mende, T. *A Kárpátmedence földrajza* (The Geography of the Carpathian Basin). Budapest: Egyetemi Nyomda, 1947.
Encyclopedia Romaniei, 3 vols. Bucharest: Imprimeria Nationala, 1936-1940.
Hassinger, Hugo. *Die Tschechoslowakei* (Czechoslovakia). Vienna: Rikola Verlag, 1925.
Kündig-Steiner, Werner. *Nord-Dobrudscha* (Northern Dobruja). Zürich: Aschmann & Schiller, 1946.
Novak, Vlad J. *Zeměpis Ceskoslovenska* (Geography of Czechoslovakia). Prague: Melantrich, 1947.
Siebenbürgen (Transylvania). Budapest: Ungarische Historische Gesellschaft, 1940.

C. Articles

Almagià, Roberto. "Modern Albania: A Review," *Geographical Review*, XXII (1932), 464-73.
Beynon, E. D. "Budapest: An Ecological Study," *Geographical Review*, XXXIII (1943), 256-75.

GABENSKY, IVANKO. *Bulgarian Economy*. New York: National Committee for Free Europe, 1952.

HALICKA, H. "Zmiany w zaludnieniu Polski w latach 1931/33-1946" (Population changes in Poland 1931/33-46). *Czasopismo Geograficzne*, XVII (1939-46), 123-33. (Contains English excerpt.)

HARTSHORNE, RICHARD. "The Upper Silesian Industrial District," *Geographical Review*, XXIV (1934), 423-38.

HOFFMAN, GEORGE W. "The Shatter Belt in Relation to the East-West Conflict," *Journal of Geography*, LI (1952), 266-75.

KISH, GEORGE. "TVA on the Danube," *Geographical Review*, XXXVII (1947), 274-302.

——. "Yugoslavia," *Focus*, I (March 15, 1951).

KOSTANICK, H. LOUIS. "Postwar Yugoslavia," *Geographical Review*, XLI (1951), 494-97.

LE LANNOU, MAURICE. "La Venétie Julienne, étude de géographie politique" (The Julian March, a study in Political Geography). *Annales de Géographie*, LVI (1947), 13-35.

LESCZYNSKI, STANISLAW. "The Geographical Bases of Poland," *Journal of Central European Affairs*, VII (1948), 357-73.

MENDE, TIBOR. "Magyarország közlekédési földrajza" (The Geography of Communications in Hungary). *Földrajzi Zsebkönyv* (1947), 48-55.

MOSCHELES, JULIE. "Natural Regions of Czechoslovakia," *Geographical Review*, XIV (1924), 561-75.

RÓNAI, ANDREW. "Population conditions in Transylvania," *Journal de la Société Hongroise de Statistique*, XVII (1939), 56-80.

SCHECHTMAN, JOSEF B. "The Elimination of German Minorities in Southeastern Europe," *Journal of Central European Affairs*, VI (1946), 152-66.

SHUTE, JOHN. "Czechoslovakia's Territorial and Population Changes," *Economic Geography*, XXIV (1948), 35-44.

STEERS, J. A. "The Middle People: Resettlement in Czechoslovakia," *The Geographical Journal*, CXII (1948), 28-42.

chapter 9

EASTERN EUROPE

I<small>N CONTRAST</small> to the maritime and peninsular characteristics of Western Europe, a broad continuity, massiveness, and continentality are the essential features of the eastern part of Europe. No longer is the continent dissected by long arms of the sea into great tongues of land. Instead, one finds Europe, at its widest extent, forming a bridge to Asia. This entire transition area falls within the confines of the Union of Soviet Socialist Republics (U.S.S.R.), more commonly called the Soviet Union.

Physiographic Basis of Cultural Forms

Location and Boundaries

The European U.S.S.R. occupies roughly the eastern half, or 2,000,000 square miles, of the European continent. Vast as this area is—corresponding to two thirds of the continental United States—it represents only one fourth of the total area of the U.S.S.R. The remainder of the country—Siberia, Kazakhstan, and Central Asia—covers the northern third of Asia.

With a total area of eight and one half million square miles, the Soviet Union is the largest continuous political unit in the world, exceeded in area only by the British Commonwealth of Nations, and is nearly three times as large as the United States without its territories and dependencies.

From the extreme western point of the U.S.S.R., at 20° E., in former East Prussia near Kaliningrad (Königsberg), it is 170° of longitude to Cape Dezhnev (170° W.) on the Bering Strait opposite Alaska, or almost halfway around the world. This vast east-west span is matched by a spectacular north-south extent. Taking the northernmost point at Cape Chelyuskin (77° 44′ N.) on the

Arctic Ocean, a latitude corresponding to that of Spitsbergen (Svalbard), the continental U.S.S.R. extends nearly 3,000 miles south
to Kushka (35° N.) on the Afghanistan frontier, at the latitude of
Crete. It should be noted, however, that in addition to the Arctic
island groups of Franz Josef Land and Severnaya Zemlya (North
Land), the U.S.S.R. lays claim to the entire polar sector between
the meridians of Murmansk (32° E.) and of the Bering Strait
(168° 45′ E.) and as far north as the North Pole. In addition to
its outlying island dependencies, the U.S.S.R. controls, since World
War II, the leased naval base districts of Porkkala, on Finland's south coast west of Helsinki, and Port Arthur, which is
located at the tip of the Liaotung Peninsula of southern
Manchuria.

The continental U.S.S.R. proper is bounded by the sea in the
north and east, and by land in the west and south. In the north it
fronts on several seas of the Arctic Ocean—the Barents Sea, Kara
Sea, Laptev Sea, and the East Siberian Sea. In the east it borders
on seas of the Pacific Ocean—the Bering Sea, the Sea of Okhotsk,
and the Sea of Japan. Along its western (European) land frontier,
the Soviet Union adjoins, from north to south, Norway, Finland,
Poland, Czechoslovakia, Hungary, and Romania. In the south, its
Asian neighbors are Turkey, Iran, Afghanistan, China's Sinkiang
Province, the Mongolian People's Republic (Outer Mongolia),
China's Manchuria, and Korea.

As a result of the first and second world wars, Russia (later the
Soviet Union) underwent extensive territorial transfers along its
periphery, particularly so in Europe. The complexity of these
changes and their far-reaching political import justify a more detailed examination at this point.

Finland, which had become independent of Russia following
World War I, was by the Treaty of Moscow in 1940 obliged to
cede to the Soviet Union her share of Karelia, including the cities
of Viipuri (Vyborg) and Sortavala. By the same treaty, which
ended the Soviet-Finnish War (1939-40), the U.S.S.R. also obtained a lease on the Hanko (Hangö) Peninsula, at the entrance to
the Gulf of Finland. After World War II, following Finland's
participation on the side of Germany, the U.S.S.R. acquired the
Petsamo (Pechenga) district of northern Finland, which thus lost
her exit to the Arctic Ocean. With the acquisition of Petsamo,
which had been ceded by Russia to Finland in 1920, the Soviet
Union re-established its common frontier with Norway. At the
same time, the U.S.S.R. surrendered the Hanko base in exchange
for the Porkkala leased naval base area.

The Baltic states of Estonia, Latvia, and Lithuania, which had been part of Russia until World War I, obtained their independence in 1920. Twenty years later, in 1940, they were incorporated into the U.S.S.R., an act that has not been recognized by the United States.

In 1945, as a result of the Potsdam Conference of the Big Three, the U.S.S.R. obtained control for the first time of the northern part of East Prussia, including the city of Kaliningrad, which was organized in 1946 as an integral part of the U.S.S.R. In January, 1945, the Memel Territory had already been occupied by Soviet troops and reincorporated into Lithuania, by then part of the U.S.S.R.

Poland was formed after World War I out of territory lost by Russia, Germany, and Austria-Hungary, the line with the Soviet Union having been set by the Treaty of Riga (1921). At the outbreak of World War II in 1939, Poland was partitioned between Germany and the U.S.S.R., but the agreed demarcation line was violated in 1941 by the German attack on the Soviet Union. After the war, the present Soviet-Polish border was agreed to in 1945, roughly along the 1939 demarcation line, but with the return of the Bialystok area to Poland. The frontier now corresponds nearly to the Curzon Line, which had been first proposed as a Russo-Polish boundary after World War I. As a result of the territorial transfers on the Polish frontier, the Soviet Union reacquired territory lost to Poland in 1921, but also for the first time annexed Galicia, which had been part of Austria-Hungary prior to World War I.

Similarly, the Soviet Union acquired territory from Czechoslovakia that had never been held by Russia before. The transfer (1945) of the Carpatho-Ukraine (Ruthenia) from Czechoslovakia to the U.S.S.R. placed Soviet territory for the first time across the Carpathians into the northeastern corner of the Tisza-Danube Basin. Consequently, the Soviet Union obtained a common border not only with Czechoslovakia but also with Hungary.

Bessarabia, an area neatly delineated by the Dniester and Prut rivers, had long been a territorial bone of contention between the U.S.S.R. and Romania. Included in Russia after 1878, Bessarabia was occupied by Romania in 1918. Its incorporation into Romania, though agreed to by the Western Allies in 1920, was never fully accepted by the Soviet Union, which retook the territory in 1940. At the same time it occupied northern Bukovina, which Romania had acquired in 1919 from Austria-Hungary.

Although as a result of the last two wars the aggregate of the territorial losses and gains of the U.S.S.R. may appear small—of the order of 300,000 to 400,000 square miles—when compared with the total area of the country, the affected areas, apart from their great economic and strategic value, are of considerable size when considered on a European scale.

The U.S.S.R. is clearly a unit, one of the most strongly unified political units of the world, and should normally be treated as such. The general scope of the present volume necessitates, however, that this chapter be limited to the European section. The European U.S.S.R. will thus receive most of our attention in this chapter. However, major facts of the geography of the Asiatic section will be brought in where they are of exceptional magnitude in relation to the entire country or where they bear more or less directly on a particular aspect of the European U.S.S.R.

Because of the general lack of agreement between political and natural boundaries, various dividing lines have been used in the past to separate Europe and Asia. For purposes of the present volume, it was not found advisable to adopt the strictly physical dividing line of conventional geography, i.e., the crest of the Urals, the Ural River, and the crest of the Greater Caucasus. Instead, the author has used internal political boundaries of the U.S.S.R. in order to be able to use statistics organized by political units.

Any such division is arbitrary and in this particular case the eastern boundary of Europe was chosen in order to maximize the territory under consideration. As a result, the present chapter includes the economic region of the Urals, as well as Transcaucasia, within the confines of the European U.S.S.R., excluding the part of the Ural River falling within the Soviet republic of Kazakhstan.

Landforms and Geologic Structure

The U.S.S.R. consists, essentially, of a vast lowland lying north of the high mountain and plateau belt that extends east and west across the heart of the Eurasian land mass. The major divisions of this lowland are the East European Plain, west of the Ural Mountains; the West Siberian Plain, east of the Urals, which is continued south by the Turan Lowland, east of the Caspian Sea; and the Central Siberian Plateau. These major lowland areas are bounded in the south, roughly along the U.S.S.R. frontier, by the highlands of the Caucasus, the Kopet Dagh, the Tien Shan and Pamirs, the Altai and Sayan mountains, and the East Siberian highlands.

By far the dominant feature of the U.S.S.R. in Europe is the East European, or Great Russian, Plain. Representing an eastward broadening of the North German Plain, this lowland rises almost imperceptibly toward the Urals in the east. Geologically it coincides with the East European platform of Pre-Cambrian [1] crystalline rocks, overlain by younger sedimentary deposits that have remained largely undisturbed in horizontal strata. At the northwestern and southwestern rims of the platform, the Pre-Cambrian formations appear as surface outcrops in the form of crystalline shields or blocks. In the northwest, the Fenno-Scandian shield includes Karelia and the Kola Peninsula, while in the southwest the Azov-Podolian shield extends through the Ukraine, forming the Volhyno-Podolian Upland (Figure 144).

In addition to these emergences of the crystalline base, further relief has been added to the plain by occasional downfaulting, as in the Donets Basin where major coal deposits of the Carboniferous period have been preserved, and by upthrusting, as in the Kursk-Voronezh horst, which forms the southern section of the Central Russian Upland. Other eroded remains of uplifting actions are the Volga Upland (with the Zhiguli Mountains) along the right bank of the river's middle course, the horst of the Ufa Plateau at the western foot of the central Urals, and the Stavropol Plateau at the northern edge of the Caucasus. Thus, while it would be incorrect to exaggerate the rigidity of the crystalline platform, which experienced warping and faulting at several geologic periods, the fact remains that rolling lowland topography extending over an area 1,500 miles broad never rises above 1,300 feet.

Although the main relief features of the East European Plain are due to tectonic action, the detailed topography has been largely the result of the Pleistocene ice sheet that covered the northern part of the plain and of recent marine transgressions in the extreme north and the southeast.

As in the North German Lowlands, ice radiating from the Scandinavian glaciation focus covered the northwestern and middle portions of Eastern Europe. A lesser center of ice expansion was located on Novaya Zemlya and in the northern Urals. The maximum penetration was reached during the second stage or Riss glaciation, which largely obscured the work of the first (Mindel) stage. The southern boundary of this most extensive glaciation extended to the edge of the Volhyno-Podolian and Central Russian uplands, but formed two tongues in the Dnieper and Oka-Don lowlands. The maximum limit then followed the foot of the Volga Upland and continued along the 60th parallel to the central Urals. While the greatest area was thus covered in the Riss stage, it is the latest or Würm glaciation that has left behind most of the

[1] For geologic terms see Appendix I.

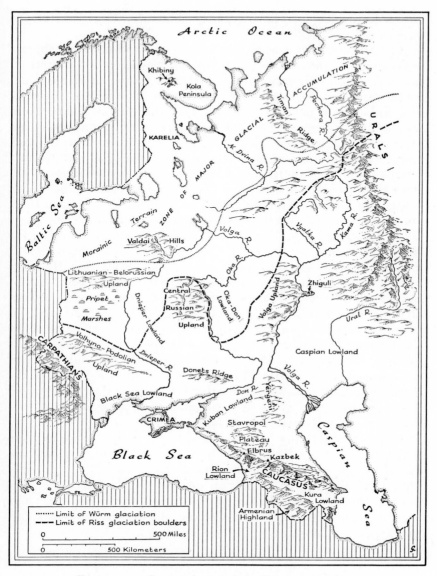

FIGURE 144. Structural map of the European U.S.S.R.

589

effects of the Ice Age, having partly obliterated the marks of the Riss period.

The advancing and retreating ice scoured and denuded the ancient rocks of the Kola-Karelian shield, leaving a topography of bare crystalline outcrops and glacial lake basins similar to that found in Finland. Most of the deposition of morainic materials, such as boulders, pebbles, sand, and clay, occurred in the northern section of the East European Plain. Here terminal moraines, arrayed in several festoons, present a conspicuous feature of the landscape. The most important morainic ridge remains as a continental watershed, separating the Baltic-Arctic drainage system in the north from the Black Sea and Caspian basins in the south. This divide consists of the Lithuanian-Belorussian Upland, the Valdai Hills, and a series of low ridges extending toward the Urals.

Although not directly covered by the continental ice sheet, the southern portion of the East European Plain has been greatly affected by the phenomenon of glaciation. Following the final retreat of the ice, finely ground clay and sand were washed out by the water and later spread by the wind over vast areas of unglaciated territory, forming a mantle of fine-grained, dustlike loess. It is this easily eroded loess cover that has been partly responsible for the characteristic ravine and gully relief of large sections of the southern European U.S.S.R. Coarser deposits of sand and clay were also carried from the retreating ice south to the valleys of the Pripet, Dnieper, Oka, and Tsna rivers, where they were deposited as outwash plains. These appear today as swampy, forested lowlands, known in Russian as *polesye*.

On its southern and eastern margins, the East European Plain is bounded by the Carpathians, the Crimean Mountains, the Caucasus and the Urals. These mountain ranges, except for the Urals, date from the Alpine revolution of the mid-Tertiary geological period. The Urals, in the east, were formed during the Hercynian orogenesis in the Carboniferous period and passed through subsequent peneplanation and rejuvenation stages.

Hydrography

Although the U.S.S.R. has the longest coast line of any country in the world, its littoral has been rendered largely useless by the presence of frozen seas and low, marshy shores. The greater section of the coasts lies in sparsely settled or totally uninhabited regions along the seas of the Arctic Ocean. Where the coastal density of population is somewhat higher, closed or nearly closed seas make access difficult, as in the Baltic, Black, and Caspian seas. Only a few rocky shores provide the country with good natural ports, and the year-round direct access to the open sea is offered only by the Murman coast, in the extreme northeast, on the Barents Sea.

The Barents Sea is the westernmost of the Arctic seas along the U.S.S.R.'s coast. It is bordered in the east by Novaya Zemlya, a group of two main islands, separating the Barents Sea from the Kara Sea. These two seas are linked by the strait of Matochkin Shar, between the north and south islands of Novaya Zemlya, as well as by the Kara Gates, between Novaya Zemlya and the mainland. Toward the west, the Barents Sea opens onto the Norwegian Sea between North Cape and Spitsbergen. Through this passage the Gulf Stream penetrates into the southwestern reaches of the Barents Sea, rendering ice conditions far more favorable to navigation than is the case in the other Arctic seas along the U.S.S.R. coast. Fish and seal herds abound along the rocky, fjord-indented shore of the Murman coast, where the port of Murmansk is accessible throughout the year.

At the other extreme of the favorable situation in the Barents Sea is the White Sea. It constitutes a southern appendage of the Barents Sea and is connected with it by a 30-mile wide neck, known as *gorlo* in Russian. A shallow body of water, reaching a depth of 1,000 feet only in northwestern Kandalaksha Bay, the White Sea is generally frozen from November until May, though frequent storms prevent the formation of a solid ice cover in its center. During its open season, now extended by the use of icebreakers, the White Sea is of great importance to navigation as the northern outlet of the Baltic-White Sea Canal and the access route to the port of Archangel (Arkhangelsk), one of the leading Soviet lumber-shipping centers.

Of considerably greater usefulness is the Baltic Sea, which represents the shortest route between the U.S.S.R. and the countries of Western Europe and the Atlantic Ocean. Between the two world wars, the Soviet share of the Baltic littoral had been restricted to the easternmost part of the Gulf of Finland around Leningrad, a section that is icebound from November until April. With the acquisition of the Baltic States (1940) and northern East Prussia (1945), the U.S.S.R. obtained access to the central Baltic where the ports of Liepaja (Liepaya) and Kaliningrad are ice-free almost the year round. Long stretches of the Baltic littoral are lined with dunes, up to 200 feet high, which frequently form narrow sandspits (German *Nehrungen*), closing off lagoons (German *Haffe*), char-

acteristic of this part of the Baltic coast. Unlike the other seas
of the U.S.S.R., the Baltic is relatively poor in fish.

The Black Sea bounds the East European Plain in the south.
It consists of a shallow section in the north, where the quadrangular
Crimean Peninsula nearly shuts off the Sea of Azov; and a deep
basin in the south, where the depth generally exceeds 7,000 feet.
The northern coast is low and characterized by the so-called *limans*,
flooded river estuaries that now constitute shallow lagoons sheltered
by sand bars. The deep-water section is stratified into an aerated
layer of low salinity (to a depth of 600 feet) and a stratum of 6,000
feet of high salinity, which receives no oxygen and is extensively
polluted by hydrogen sulphide produced by decaying microorganisms. The shallow water abounds in fish; dolphins are caught along
the rocky southeast coast, and iodine is processed from seaweed.
Since there is only a thin two-month ice cover in the north, the
Black Sea is open to navigation throughout the year. Its usefulness
from the Soviet point of view, however, is handicapped by the fact
that Turkey controls the straits leading to the Mediterranean and
hence to the Atlantic Ocean. The principal ports are Odessa, the
naval base of Sevastopol, Novorossisk, Poti, and Batumi.

The Sea of Azov is a shallow inlet reached through the four-mile
wide Kerch Strait. Its depth, about fifty feet, is gradually decreasing as a result of sedimentation by the Don River. Prevailing
northeasterly winds have caused the formation of characteristic
sandspits along the low north shore. Apart from Rostov on the
lower Don, the main ports are Taganrog, Zhdanov, Osipenko, and
Yeisk.

The Caspian Sea on the southeastern margins of the European
U.S.S.R. is the largest inland sea in the world, having an area of
163,800 square miles. During the 1940's, investigation disclosed
a seven-foot drop in level, from 85 feet to 92 feet below sea level,
which also brought about a reduction in area from the former
169,100 square miles. This level change was only the latest in a
series of fluctuations that began in recent geologic times when the
Caspian was joined with the Black Sea by the Manych depression
and with the Aral Sea by an arm of the river Amu Darya. The
750-mile long sea consists of a shallow northern part and two deeper
sections (to 3,200 feet) in the south. The shallow reaches in the
vicinity of the Volga delta have an average depth of 15 feet. This
section, which is gradually being filled by Volga River sediments,
is icebound two to three months. Its low salinity, shallowness, and
the abundance of microorganisms (discharged by the Volga) have
turned this part of the Caspian into the richest fishing grounds of

the U.S.S.R., furnishing 35 per cent of the total catch. Salinity increases from north to south and reaches a maximum of 16 to 18 per cent in the natural evaporating basin of the Kara-Bogaz-Gol. This vast salt reservoir, situated on the Asiatic shore of the Caspian, precipitates under winter temperatures great quantities of Glauber salt, furnishing the basis of an important local chemical industry.

From the shipping standpoint, the use of the Caspian was long restricted to inland navigation until the completion of the Volga-Don Canal in mid-1952 made a direct link with the Sea of Azov and the Black Sea. The leading ports, among the busiest in the U.S.S.R., are Baku and Astrakhan, Guryev, Makhachkala and Krasnovodsk.

In spite of the rigorous climate, which freezes the rivers up to eight and nine months a year, and the accident of relief, which orients over one half of the drainage area of the entire U.S.S.R. toward the Arctic Ocean (though only one quarter of the European part), the river systems of the country have long played a vital role in its history and its economy. From the earliest times, they have served as routes across the steppes as well as the forests. Low, short portages, later partly replaced by canals, have welded the systems together, particularly in the European U.S.S.R. The conquest of the outlying sections of European Russia and, especially, the drive through Siberia in the sixteenth and seventeenth centuries were effected by means of these interconnecting water routes. The railroad era of the nineteenth century brought the waterways into partial decline. Recent developments, such as the use of hydroelectric power, the construction of new canals and the modernization of older ones, have given the waterways of the U.S.S.R. a new and important role in its economy.

The rivers of the East European Plain are generally characterized by an insignificant gradient and a consequent slow and winding course. This is a direct result of the low elevation of the main morainic divide, which constitutes the Lithuanian-Belorussian and Valdai hills, and reaches the highest point in the Valdai section with 1,053 feet. The streams rising on the northern slope of the divide, which trends generally WSW-ENE, flow to the Baltic Sea and the Barents Sea of the Arctic. Drainage south of this main divide is into the Black and Caspian seas.

One of the leading factors affecting the regime of the rivers in the European U.S.S.R. is the duration of the ice cover. The streams freeze in the winter for a period varying from two to three months in the extreme southwest (Dniester River, lower Dnieper River). The frozen period increases gradually toward the northeast, reaching an extreme of seven months in the lower Pechora River near the Barents Sea. As a rule, thawing is followed by a high-water stage in the spring and a lower water level through the summer, autumn, and winter. Because of the relatively greater precipitation, reduced evaporation, and the presence of forests, the northern rivers have a greater volume than those of the south. In areas of resistant crystalline outcrops, rapids are formed along the river courses, particularly in the Kola Peninsula and Karelia and in the Ukraine. Many of the obstructions have been utilized for the production of hydroelectric power.

In the semiarid conditions of the southeastern part of the European U.S.S.R. the river network is poorly developed, the minor streams have a very reduced or even intermittent flow in the low-water season, and major rivers, such as the Volga and the Ural, are devoid of tributaries in their lower courses. This hydrological problem is particularly serious in this area, where drought conditions in agriculture would normally necessitate an abundant water supply for irrigation.

The most important rivers of the East European Plain are the Pechora and the Northern Dvina, which flow respectively to the Barents and White seas of the Arctic Ocean; the short, but abundant Neva, the Western Dvina, and the Neman (Niemen), which drain into the Baltic Sea; the Dnieper, Don and Kuban rivers, which enter the Black Sea and its satellite, the Sea of Azov; and the Volga, Ural, and Terek rivers, which flow into the Caspian Sea.

Of all these streams it is the Volga that has the greatest economic significance for the European U.S.S.R., in spite of its great handicap of entering the Caspian, a closed sea. With a course of 2,290 miles, the Volga is Europe's longest river and, with its far-flung tributaries, drains one third of the European U.S.S.R. It is the country's leading waterway, connected by canals with all the bordering seas of the U.S.S.R. These canal systems are the Moscow Canal, linking the upper Volga with Moscow, the Mariinsk canal system between the Rybinsk Reservoir of the Volga and the Baltic Sea at Leningrad, the Baltic-White Sea Canal, and the Volga-Don Canal, which constituted the last missing link with the Black Sea. As a result of these connections, the focal Volga route accounts for more than half of the freight carried on the waterways of the whole Union.

In addition to the importance of navigation, as exemplified by the Volga, the rivers of the U.S.S.R. play a major role as timber-floating routes, particularly the Pechora and the Northern Dvina in the northern forest belt, as producers of hydroelectricity (Volga and Dnieper), and for irrigation of the drought-ridden southeast. Major projects have been initiated by the U.S.S.R. for the early 1950's, calling for the vastly increased exploitation of the hydro-electric and irrigation potential of the Volga and Dnieper rivers.

Unlike the streams of the East European Plain, the rivers of the Caucasus are not navigable, except in their lower reaches. Their regime is characterized by two high-water stages, one in spring caused by the melting of snow, the other in the summer caused by the melting of glacier ice in the higher altitudes. The Caucasian rivers play a very important role, however, in the production of water power and in the irrigation of the dry lowlands at the foot of the mountains. The most important rivers in this region are the Kuban, Terek, and Kuma, on the northern slopes of the Caucasus, and the rivers of Transcaucasia—the Rion, Kura, and Aras— which do not freeze during the winter season.

The European U.S.S.R. is rich in lakes, particularly in the glaciated northwestern and western reaches. Here are the lakes Ladoga and Onega, the largest fresh-water bodies in Europe; Lake Peipus, Lake Beloye (white lake), and Lake Ilmen. Some of these lakes are remnants of a former sea strait. Others were formed through faulting of the earth's crust, as along the northern shores of Ladoga and Onega, or through the obstruction of streams by glacial debris. While the European lakes are relatively shallow, with Lake Ladoga reaching a depth of 732 feet, the U.S.S.R. also contains the deepest (5,712 feet) inland body of water in the world in Lake Baikal, in Eastern Siberia.

Climate

Except for the small Mediterranean region of the southern Crimea, the humid subtropical parts of Transcaucasia, and the monsoon region of the Soviet Far East, the U.S.S.R. has a continental climate *par excellence*, with the continentality increasing from west to east. This continental quality of the Soviet climate is marked by the weakness of moderating maritime influences, low precipitation, most of which occurs in the summer, a great annual temperature range, long winters, and brief spring and autumn seasons.[2]

The U.S.S.R. is situated in latitudes where the Eurasian land mass reaches its greatest east-west extent, at great distances from the moderating effects of the Atlantic and Pacific oceans. Particularly does most of the U.S.S.R. find itself far to the east of the

[2] See climatic graphs, Appendix II.

humidity-laden westerly winds blowing from the Atlantic. Instead, situated on the shores of the Arctic Ocean and devoid of any major mountain ranges extending in an east-west direction, the U.S.S.R. is exposed to the invasions of Arctic and polar air, while the high mountain and plateau belt of Central Asia bars the access of warmer air masses from the Indian Ocean.

A key factor in determining the average climatic conditions of the U.S.S.R. is the great continental high-pressure ridge, especially well defined during the winter, that extends in a continuation of the Azores High, past Kharkov, Saratov, and Uralsk, toward the world's cold pole of Verkhoyansk-Oimyakon in Eastern Siberia. This anticyclonic ridge governs the wind regime of the European U.S.S.R., particularly during the cold season. Then, on the northern side of the high-pressure area, west and southwest winds bring warm, humid Atlantic air to the East European Plain, making for generally milder winters in the northwest. South of the ridge, prevailing north and northeast winds produce drier and colder winters.

During the summer, the anticyclonic ridge in Siberia is replaced by a low-pressure system which plays a vital role in the monsoon exchange of the Far East. In the European U.S.S.R., the high-pressure area maintains itself somewhat even in the summer, primarily owing to the permanence of the Azores High. Consequently, the moderating Atlantic influence continues, though in weakened form, producing cool, humid summers in the north. In the south, on the other hand, warm, dry summers are the rule.

This combined effect in winter of the moderating Atlantic influence and the cooling of the Eurasian interior produces a nearly north-south alignment of the January isotherms. During the summer, the Arctic Ocean acts on the northern U.S.S.R. as a cooling agent and the July isotherms are reoriented in an east-west direction.

Precipitation in the East European Plain, largely of Atlantic origin, decreases from the west toward the northeast and southeast. It is highest in the region of the upper Dnieper (26 inches) and lowest in the Caspian lowland (8 inches) and the Pechora tundra (12 inches). In the north, rainfall is distributed evenly through the summer months and the snow cover, during the winter, reaches mean depths of 25 to 30 inches. In the south, half the precipitation occurs in late spring and early summer and snowfall is quite light.

The arid regions of the European U.S.S.R. are further characterized by the presence of permafrost (Russian *merzlota*), in the northeast, and scorching winds (*sukhovei*), in the southeast.

While permanently frozen soil covers about 45 per cent of the total area of the Soviet Union, particularly in Eastern Siberia, only a relatively minor wedge extends into the extreme northeastern section of the European U.S.S.R. Because the top layers of soil thaw and become waterlogged under permafrost conditions, allowance has to be made for the settling of buildings and other installations in far northern construction projects.

The *sukhovei* winds are particularly harmful to agriculture in the arid southeast and have frequently led to crop failure. Among the measures that have been taken to lessen the effect of these dry, hot southeasterlies are the planting of shelter belts, a program of snow retention, and several irrigation projects.

The special climatic province of the southern Crimea, sheltered against northern influences by the Crimean Mountains, is of the Mediterranean type. It has a winter rainfall of 20 to 25 inches and a hot, dry summer.

Another separate climatic region is formed by the humid subtropical Black Sea littoral of Transcaucasia. Precipitation here, among the highest in the U.S.S.R., occurs all year round and averages between 40 and 100 inches. A similar type of climate is found in the Lenkoran lowland in eastern Transcaucasia, on the shore of the Caspian Sea.

Soils and Vegetation

Largely as the result of the predominantly lowland topography and the climate, particularly the east-west trend of the summer isotherms, the entire territory of the U.S.S.R. falls into a number of broad latitudinal soil and vegetation belts, which also have their characteristic fauna. Beginning at the shores of the Arctic Ocean, these belts are, from north to south, the tundra zone, the forest zone, the steppe zone, the semidesert and desert zone around the Caspian and Aral seas, and the subtropical zone. Highland vegetation is considered apart (Figure 145).

With the exception of the subtropical zone, these vegetation belts developed after the retreat of the last Quaternary ice sheet. While the tundra zone remained along the margins of the ice, the remainder of the freed territory was invaded by deciduous trees from Western Europe and by conifers from Mongolia, as well as by steppe and desert from the foothills of the Altai and Caucasus mountains. The scattered sections of subtropical vegetation, on the other hand, represent relic forms of the luxuriant flora that prevailed in the U.S.S.R. during the Tertiary period.

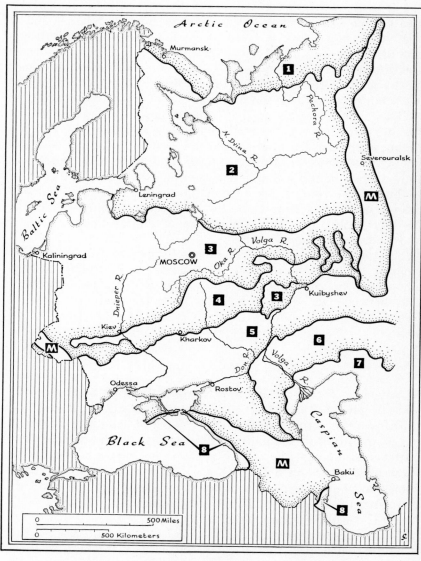

FIGURE 145. Vegetation belts of the European U.S.S.R.

1. Tundra
2. Coniferous taiga
3. Mixed and deciduous
   forest
4. Forest-steppe
5. Steppe
6. Semidesert
7. Desert
8. Subtropical
M. Mountain vegetation

The tundra zone occupies most of the area north of the Arctic Circle or over 10 per cent of the total territory of the U.S.S.R., but less than 5 per cent of the European part. The width of the belt varies from about 50 miles on the north shore of the Kola Peninsula to over 800 miles in northeastern Siberia. Winters are long and severe, summers short and cool, the annual mean temperature remaining below freezing. Precipitation varies from 12 inches in the west to 8 inches in the east. The snow cover, up to 280 days in duration, is relatively thin due to the reduced precipitation and strong winds. Vegetation is marked by the absence of trees, though dwarf birch (*Betula nana*) and shrub willow (*Salix glauca*) are found in sheltered spots. Lichens and berry shrubs grow in stony and dry, sandy areas, while moss and sedge occur in damper, low-lying sites. During the brief summer, small multicolored flowers come to life on south-facing slopes. The slow decomposition of vegetable matter under the existing climate produces only a thin layer of topsoil above the permanently frozen subsoil and leads to the formation of peat and bog-type soils. Tree growth is favored toward the south where the so-called forest-tundra forms a transition to the true forest belt.

Typical animals of the tundra are the widely domesticated reindeer which supplies the local population with food, leather, and bone; rodents, such as the lemming and the Arctic hare; the Arctic fox and the ermine, valued for their fur. Characteristic birds are the snowy owl and the ptarmigan. During the summer, swarms of waterfowl nest on rocky ledges along the coastal cliffs. After warm weather sets in mosquitoes also appear, constituting a real hardship for the reindeer, which then seek relief along the sea coast.

The glaciated Arctic islands—Franz Josef Land and northern Novaya Zemlya—are sometimes regarded as a separate zone. Here the polar bear, walrus, and seal are found, and, among the birds, the little auk, the guillemot, and the kittiwake, which nest in colonies (bazaars) along the rocky west shore of Novaya Zemlya.

South of the tundra lies the vast forest zone, which occupies more than half of the total area of the U.S.S.R. This broad belt is commonly divided into two main subzones: the coniferous taiga and the mixed forests, with an admixture of deciduous trees. A narrow belt of purely deciduous trees forms the southern limit of the forest zone, adjoining to or intermingled with the forest-steppe.

Light gray podsolized soils are typical of the forest zone. This soil consists of three layers, which in cross section present a striking three-colored profile; they are the grayish topsoil, three to six inches thick, containing about 2 per cent of humus; the middle ash-colored horizon of podsol proper (Russian *zola* means ash), which has given its name to the soil type; and the lowest layer, a yellowish-brown zone, colored by iron compounds. Podsolization is a complex leaching process in which soil waters carry aluminum and iron oxides from the upper podsol horizon, about 12 inches thick, to the lower layers where they are precipitated. This process leaves only fine-grained silica in the podsol proper, leading to its predominantly sandy character. The podsol-forming process is speeded on an impermeable clay basis, which retains the water, and in sandy soils, out of which the salts are easily washed. The process, which is particularly developed in depressed sites, leaves a soil of reduced fertility, but one that can be made very productive by the application of mineral fertilizer.

The coniferous forest (taiga), which succeeds the forest-tundra zone, constitutes nearly the entire forested area in the Asiatic U.S.S.R. In the European section only somewhat more than half the forested area or about 25 per cent of the total area belongs to the taiga type, which, however, dips much farther south than in Central or Western Europe. The southern margins run along the line Leningrad-Gorki-Sverdlovsk to about 57° N. The taiga still has a six- to seven-month winter and a correspondingly short growing season, but average summer temperatures are fairly high (60° to 65° F.). In the European taiga Norway spruce and pine are the most common species, merging in the northeast with the Siberian spruce (*Picea obovata*), fir (*Abies sibirica*), and stone pine (*Pinus sibirica*). Deciduous species—birch, aspen, alder—are of secondary importance.

The mixed-forest subzone in the European U.S.S.R. forms a triangular wedge some 600 miles wide in the west. Occupying about 20 per cent of the total area, this is the heartland of the European U.S.S.R., from which the Russians have advanced into the northern taiga and the southern steppe. In the mixed forests, the growing season is somewhat longer than in the taiga, though four to five months still have mean temperatures below freezing. Summer temperatures, on the other hand, are above 65° F. in the average. In this zone deciduous species—linden, oak, elm, and maple (*Acer platanoides*)—appear together with the conifers. In the southwest, beech and hornbeam are more numerous. The linden extends farthest north of all the broad-leaf types, beyond 60° N. Large sections of the forest zone contain marshes and peat bogs, particularly where precipitation is fairly high and the watershed area at a very low altitude. Finally, in the purely deciduous forests, oak is the predominant tree, associated with hornbeam in the southwest.

Animal life is fairly uniform throughout the forest zone. Among the large mammals are the elk and reindeer, predominantly in the northern coniferous forest, and the roebuck, red deer, and wild boar in the mixed and deciduous forests. The brown bear and the rare lynx are the principal carnivores, while rodents such as the squirrel, the flying squirrel, and the common hare are also widespread. Typical birds are the capercaillie (a large European grouse), the hazel grouse, and the woodpecker.

South of the pure deciduous forest belt, the last component of the forest zone, extends the steppe, which constitutes about 12 per cent of the total area of the U.S.S.R., but 35 per cent of the European part. Largely characterized by grassy vegetation, its limited tree growth diminishes southward from the transitional forest-steppe, where it occurs in small, noncontiguous, frequently oval-shaped wooded islands. Precipitation varies from 16 inches in the north to 10 inches in the south, with a maximum in spring and early summer. Summer temperatures are high (70° to 75° F.) and evaporation then exceeds precipitation.

The steppe corresponds to a large extent with the distribution of the chernozem (black earth), one of the most productive soils in the world, which accounts for two thirds of the arable land of the U.S.S.R. The chernozem develops generally on loess or loess-like clays. Its color varies from black to chocolate brown, and the thickness of the layer from three to five feet. The rich grass vegetation of the steppe is conducive to the formation of humus which, as a result of the dry climate, is not leached from the soil, but remains on the loess base. The humus content varies between 5 and 10 per cent and even reaches 20 per cent in some areas. It is to this high humus content, as well as to its soluble mineral constituents, that the chernozem owes its great productivity.

The absence of tree growth in the steppe zone is believed to be the result primarily of climatic factors. The insufficient moisture in summer and the high rate of evaporation are conditions unfavorable to the development of forests. It has also been suggested that grass fires, started by lightning or by man, which swept the steppe destroyed the young trees as rapidly as they were produced. At the present time most of the steppe and forest-steppe has been brought under cultivation, however, and the original tall-grass vegetation has been destroyed.

The native fauna of the steppe includes the saiga antelope, and rodents such as the suslik, jerbos, and hamster. The bustard and the steppe eagle are representative birds. In the few remaining virgin steppe areas, the grass vegetation is of the broad-leaved meadow type in the northern wooded steppe and of the narrow-leaved feather (*Stipa*) and fescue (*Festuca*) grass in the drier south.

Toward the southeast the steppe is succeeded by the semidesert and desert zones, where vegetation is limited or wholly absent. Only the extreme southern European U.S.S.R., or 5 per cent of the European part adjoining the Caspian Sea, falls within this zone. It reaches its widest extent in the arid areas of Kazakhstan and Central Asia east of the Caspian Sea. Limited precipitation (less than eight inches yearly) and high summer temperatures are the rule in this zone. The semidesert is a transition zone toward the true desert. The climate becomes progressively drier and bare areas begin to appear amid the grass vegetation. The humus content of the predominantly chestnut-brown soils decreases, while soil salinity increases. Vegetation in the semidesert is usually of the wormwood-grass type and, in salt-impregnated areas, salt-loving plants (halophytes). Rodents, the saiga antelope, and the corsac fox are characteristic of the semidesert, while a great variety of birds is found in the flood plains and deltas of large rivers.

Subtropical vegetation is found in Transcaucasia along the Black Sea littoral and in the Lenkoran lowland on the Caspian Sea, as well as on the south coast of the Crimea. Here the lateritic yellow and red soils and the luxuriant plant life are vestiges of the Tertiary period. Forests are a mixture of deciduous trees (oak, hornbeam, beech) and relic forms from the Tertiary period, such as the Caucasian wing nut (*Pterocarya*) and the zelkova of the elm family, with an undergrowth of the common box, rhododendron, and laurel cherry (*Prunus laurocerasus*). In the Lenkoran lowland, the Persian parrotia, noted for its hard wood, and the chestnut-leaf oak (*Quercus castaneaefolia*) are endemic species.

Highland vegetation in the European U.S.S.R. is restricted to the Carpathians, the Crimean Mountains, the Caucasus, and the northern Urals, where the latitudinal belts are replaced by a vertical distribution. The upper reaches of these highlands, beyond the timber line, are covered with so-called alpine meadows or, as in the northern Urals, by tundra. The limits of the meadow belt vary with the latitude and the local climate. In the Caucasus, for example, tall-grass subalpine meadows begin at the elevation of 6,000 feet, while the short-grass alpine meadows lie above an altitude of 8,000 to 10,000 feet.

Historical Geography

Early Russian history has been shaped to a very large extent by the nation's forests and rivers. It was in the forests that early Slav settlement took place, in relative seclusion from the nomadic or seminomadic Asiatic tribes that roamed the southern steppes. And it was the extensive river system of the East European Plain that was instrumental in the rise of the Muscovite state and ultimately brought about the unity of the Russian lands (Figure 146).

At the beginning of our era, Slav tribes first mentioned in the first century A.D., inhabited the west central reaches of the vast Russian lowland, on either side of the north-south river axis formed by the Volkhov, Lovat, and Dnieper rivers. This was the zone of the mixed forests, in which the primitive population engaged in rudimentary agriculture, beekeeping, and trapping.

Along the Black Sea coast, Greek colonies had been established at river mouths and in the Crimea as early as the seventh and sixth centuries B.C. These settlements, some of which had probably been based on earlier Phoenician sites, were Tyras at the mouth of the Dniester, Olbia near the Dnieper estuary, and Tanais on the Don delta. On the Crimean coast were the colonies of the Heraclean Chersonese (the modern Sevastopol), Theodosia (the modern Feodosiya), and Panticapaeum (the modern Kerch).

Between these two settled belts, the forests and the littoral, extended the steppe, dominated since earliest times by warlike horsemen from Asia. The earliest reference is to the Cimmerians, who are believed to have occupied the area between the Dniester and the Don from the tenth to the eighth century B.C. and are mentioned by Homer. They were followed by the Scythians, who, according to Herodotus, occupied these open spaces until displaced in the third century B.C. by the Sarmatians. During the first millennium of the Christian era many peoples passed here in the great migration: the Goths, who in this very steppe split (about A.D. 200) into the west and east wings—the Visigoths and the Ostrogoths; the Huns under Attila, who swept through in the late fourth century; the Avars, on their way to the Balkans; the Bulgars, who also divided here (about A.D. 500), one branch taking the route to modern Bulgaria and the other moving into the middle reaches of the Volga River. Finally, following the passage of the Magyars (about A.D. 800) a certain stability returned to the steppe with the formation of the Khazar domain in the Don-Volga area, with its headquarters at Itil on the site of modern Astrakhan.

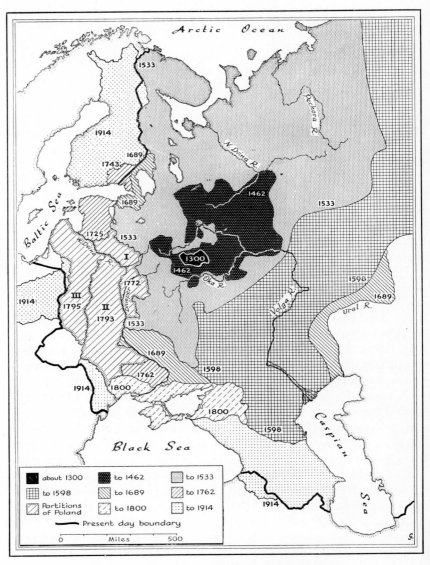

FIGURE 146. Growth of the Russian Empire in Europe.

In the meantime, intruders from Scandinavia had also appeared in the secluded forest, beginning in the early ninth century. These were the Varangians or Northmen who, in search of a trade route to Constantinople, had made their way south along the Volkhov-Dnieper river axis. They settled at trading sites that already had been occupied by the Slavs: Novgorod, Pskov, Smolensk, Chernigov, and Kiev. Moved by their common interest in trade and their need for defense against the steppe peoples, the Slav tribes gradually consolidated under Varangian leadership into what became known as Rus (or Russia), a name of uncertain origin. Originally centered on Novgorod, this early Russian state moved its capital to Kiev in 882 and is therefore known today as Kievan Russia.

Kievan Russia, one of the leading states of the early medieval Europe, was essentially a loose confederation of principalities, each centered on a trading town, united under the rule of a senior prince. The Varangian trade route along the Volkhov and Dnieper rivers was its life line and as long as the perilous Dnieper rapids and the threat of the steppe peoples could be overcome, Kiev prospered. Commerce was primarily with Constantinople. The Slavs sent furs, honey, and slaves, and imported silks, wine, fruit, and gold. Trade, however, also moved along the Volga, in whose upper reaches stood the remote Slav towns of Rostov, Suzdal, and Murom. The Volga was the direct link with Central Asia, serving en route the domain of the Volga Bulgars, whose capital was at Bulgar, near the Kama mouth, and Itil, the Khazar headquarters.

The Kievan state was to be short-lived. In the tenth century, warlike nomad tribes appeared in the steppe, ending the relatively stable rule of the Khazars and making the Dnieper route more and more difficult to use. Raids by these nomads began to threaten Kiev and led to its gradual decline in the twelfth century. A shift in the political center of gravity of the Slav domain followed. One new power nucleus formed in the southwestern principalities of Galicia and Volhynia, which was shortly to be absorbed by the expanding Polish and Lithuanian states.

The major movement from the Kievan area was, however, to the northeast, into the remote forests in the upper reaches of the Volga. A period of intensive colonization began in the watershed area between the upper Volga and Oka rivers. This mesopotamia, or *mezhdurechye* as the Russians know it, had already been sparsely settled by Slavs and Finnic tribes. The influx of refugees from the southern forest margins resulted in a great increase in population and the consequent political rise of the principality of Suzdal-Rostov, later known as Vladimir-Suzdal, or simply Vladimir, as the ruling power shifted from city to city.

The central watershed in the midst of the East European Plain was the nucleus of the future Russian state. It was relatively less exposed to attack by the sheer factor of distance, and was also protected by the river lines of the Volga and Oka and by the surrounding forests. Agricultural conditions were difficult in the forest clearings, and a good part of the population turned to handicraft industries as a livelihood. Linen, leather, woolen cloth, wood and metal goods were produced. Trade was with Kiev by the Dnieper route, with the Caspian area via the Volga, and with western Europe through the trade centers of Pskov and Novgorod. Goods were also traded with the Genoese ports in the Crimea, notably Kaffa, the modern Feodosiya.

Novgorod itself had built an empire of its own following the decline of Kiev. Situated on the direct route between the Volga valley and the Baltic Sea, Novgorod became one of the chief trading depots of the Hanseatic League. Merchants extended Novgorod's power throughout northern European Russia to the Arctic shores and across the northern Urals, levying fur tribute and founding colonies.

During the thirteenth century, the nascent Russian domain was closely threatened by foreign incursions. Tatars under Mongol leadership established the Golden Horde on the southeastern margins, following devastating raids through the Russian towns in 1237-40. In the northeast, the Novgorod empire, under the leadership of Alexander Nevski, defeated the Swedes (1240) and the Teutonic and Livonian Knights (1242), but the rising Lithuanian state annexed all the southwestern Russian principalities in the fourteenth century.

Ringed by the Tatars in the east and by the Lithuanians in the west, the Russian state proceeded to consolidate its holdings. Political leadership had passed to the small principality of Moscow in the early fourteenth century. Its rulers, still tributary to the Tatars, began to be called the grand dukes of Moscow or Muscovy. Spurred by the victory (1380) of Dmitri Donskoi over the Tatars, the Muscovite state expanded through the fifteenth century, absorbing the other Russian principalities and, in 1478, absorbed Novgorod with its vast northern holdings. Under Ivan III, who reigned from 1462 to 1505, Muscovy ceased to pay tribute to the Golden Horde, which had disintegrated into the Tatar khanates of Kazan, Astrakhan, Sibir, and the Crimea, and began to call itself the "Russian" state. Ivan IV (the Terrible), who reigned from 1533 to 1584, was the first to assume the title of tsar (in 1547).

With the consolidation of the Russian state completed, Ivan embarked upon the initial conquests of non-Russian territory. The weakened Tatar khanates of Kazan (1552) and Astrakhan (1556) fell and the Volga became for the first time an all-Russian river. Samara (the present Kuibyshev) in 1586, Tsaritsyn (the present Stalingrad) in 1589, and Saratov in 1590 were founded in rapid succession as the first Russian outposts on the lower Volga.

On the western slopes of the Urals, the Stroganovs, a landed family of salt and fur merchants, eyed with envy the reputed riches beyond the Urals. On their initiative, the Cossack Yermak and his band crossed the Urals in 1581 and subdued the Tatar khanate of Sibir, on the lower Irtysh River. Other Cossacks followed, penetrated rapidly eastward by land and river, building a string of small fortified posts (*ostrogs*) and levying fur tribute from the sparse indigenous population. In less than 60 years, the vast reaches of what came to be known as Siberia were traversed and the Pacific shores reached by 1640.

Following a period of chaos—the Time of Troubles—marked by the appearance of false pretenders (the false Dmitris) and by Swedish and Polish-Lithuanian intervention, Russia rallied again in 1613 under Michael, the first of the Romanovs. In a series of wars against Poland during the seventeenth century, the Russians even succeeded in annexing the left-bank Ukraine and Kiev.

However, the country was still a semi-Oriental state. Medieval in culture and outlook, it was not regarded as a member of the European community of nations. In its economic development Russia was far behind the European West, and its distrust of foreign ways and innovations kept it ignorant and isolated. Whatever industry had been developed, was concentrated in the Moscow region. There were a number of ironworks based on Tula ore, linen, leather and other handicrafts. Salt, obtained at Solikamsk on the Kama River and Solvychegodsk on the Vychegda River, was an important article of trade. Grain and flax were the leading agricultural products; fur-bearing animals were hunted in the northeast and in Siberia, while grazing was the main economic activity in the southeastern steppe adjoining the lower Volga. Except for Astrakhan, on the closed-in Caspian Sea, the only maritime outlet was Archangel, through which English merchants had established trade links in the late sixteenth century.

It remained for Peter I (the Great), who reigned from 1689 to 1725, to revolutionize Russia politically, economically, and culturally. Peter, who was the first to assume the title of emperor, westernized Russia by a series of reforms that were imposed on the people by the most stringent measures. He created the Russian navy, modernized the army, founded the first major industries, and recast the administrative organization of the country. Moved by the desire to make Russia a maritime European power, Peter directed his efforts at territorial expansion toward the Baltic Sea. In the Northern War, he wrested Estonia and Livonia from Sweden and shifted the Russian capital from Moscow to his newly founded St. Petersburg, the "window on Europe." He also began the push toward the Black Sea and succeeded in briefly winning (1696-1711) the fortress of Azov from the Crimean Tatars, but it remained for his successors to reach the Black Sea on a broad front. Peter the Great also temporarily gained hold (1723-32) of Baku from Persia.

However, it was particularly in the economic sphere that Peter's achievements were remarkable from the geographical point of view. He began the industrialization of the Urals, establishing a number of copper and iron smelters and arms factories to supply his troops. Yekaterinburg (the present Sverdlovsk) in 1723, Yegoshikha (the later Perm and present Molotov) in 1722, and Nizhni Tagil in 1725 were founded at this time. A Russian shipbuilding industry was developed, with yards at St. Petersburg and Archangel, as well as at Voronezh (on the Don) and Kazan (on the Volga), while the Vyshnevolotsk Canal, the first to link the upper Volga with the Baltic Sea, was built from 1709 to 1722. The reorientation of western European trade, which began to flow predominantly through St. Petersburg, led to the gradual decline of Archangel in the north.

Following Peter's death, a number of inferior rulers kept Russian achievements static, but the country soon became a leading European power under Catherine II (the Great). Under her "enlightened despotism," Russia secured the lion's share in the successive partitions of Poland (1772, 1793, 1795), reaching approximately the present Soviet boundary, with the exception of Galicia, Bessarabia, and East Prussia. Catherine's wars against Turkey were equally successful, and by the treaties of Kutchuk-Kainardji (1774), the surrender of the Crimean khanate (1783), and the treaty of Jassy (1791), Russia reached the Black Sea between the lower Kuban River and the Dniester. The Russian colonization of Alaska also dates from Catherine's reign.

Under Catherine's successors, Russia became involved in the French Revolutionary, later Napoleonic, wars which culminated in Napoleon's disastrous march on Moscow. Among the territorial acquisitions in the early nineteenth century were the greater part of the Caucasus (1801-13), Finland (1809), Bessarabia (1812), and, following the Congress of Vienna (1815), the Grand Duchy of Warsaw (Russian Poland). Except for minor changes, Russia's European frontiers were to remain unaltered until the First World War.

Economically, Russia underwent a great transformation in the nineteenth century. In the beginning, the agricultural frontier was greatly expanded with the settlement of the rich chernozem zone, which began to yield hard-grained export wheat and sugar beets. With the construction of ports along the nearby Black Sea (Odessa, Nikolayev, Mariupol, Novorossisk), an active export trade in grains began to develop during the nineteenth century. This flow was greatly speeded after the building of railroads. The first long line linked St. Petersburg and Moscow in the 1850's and a rail net rapidly developed in radial fashion around centrally located Moscow. In addition to the old industrial region of the Urals, other manufacturing complexes developed at St. Petersburg (mainly metal fabricating, based on imported raw materials) and in the Moscow-Ivanovo belt, where a major textile-milling district was supplied first by foreign, later by Central Asian cotton. A major development in the sphere of mining and heavy industry was the decline of the once-flourishing charcoal metallurgy in the Urals and the rapid rise of the Donets Basin and the Krivoi Rog iron-mining district in the Ukraine. In addition to the Black Sea grain ports, Russian foreign trade was handled through the Baltic ports of Libau (Libava), Riga, Reval (Tallin), as well as St. Petersburg. The development of the northern lumbering industry for export also gave new impetus to the port of Archangel.

These were, in very broad terms, the conditions that existed on the eve of the First World War, which Russia entered on the side of the Allies. The territorial adjustments that followed the war and the Russian Revolution of 1917 have been outlined at the beginning of this chapter. The considerable economic transformation that followed the establishment of the Soviet regime is described in the section on the present economic life.

Evolution of the Political-Administrative Structure

We have noted that Peter the Great was the first Russian ruler to introduce (in 1708) a modern administrative structure into the expanding Russian Empire, creating large internal divisions known as governments (*guberniva*). The first such divisions were the governments of Moscow, Ingermanland (renamed St. Petersburg in 1710), Archangel, Kiev, Smolensk, Kazan, Azov, and Siberia. The number of units increased steadily through the eighteenth and nineteenth centuries, in part through the incorporation of new territories, but essentially as the result of the subdivision of originally larger units. The governments were divided into *uyezds*, and these in turn into *volosts*. In 1917, on the eve of the Revolution, the Russian Empire consisted of 101 governments, 812 *uyezds*, and 16,760 *volosts*.

Although the Tsarist system of local government cannot be described as static, the changes in the structure only seldom reflected reorganization for economic-geographical purposes. The creation of new units or the abolition of existing divisions was usually predicated on purely administrative or military criteria. This is especially obvious in view of the later Soviet reorientation of the administrative system on strictly economic grounds. To cite a typical example of the lack of economic dynamism in the Tsarist system, let us consider the case of Ivanovo-Voznesensk (now called simply Ivanovo). This city, a major cotton-milling center northeast of Moscow, had a population of 54,208 according to the census of 1897. Although it was the largest city within the government of Vladimir, it remained relegated administratively to the rank of a minor provincial town within Shuya *uyezd* of the Vladimir government. One of the first administrative measures of the Soviet regime was to create a new government with Ivanovo-Voznesensk as its center.

The profound changes that occurred in Russia following the Revolution of 1917 were closely reflected in the political-administrative structure. The process of territorial changes took place along two parallel lines: (1) the creation of national autonomous units for individual ethnic groups, and (2) reform of the administrative-territorial units along economic lines.

In the late nineteenth century about 100 distinct ethnic groups inhabited the territory of the Russian Empire. According to the 1897 census, out of a total population of 130 millions, only 43 per cent were reported as Great Russians. As a result of this circumstance, the young Soviet regime proclaimed in the very first days of the Revolution the "Declaration of Rights of the Peoples of Russia." This act guaranteed (1) the equality and sovereignty of the peoples of Russia, (2) their right to self-determination, even to the extent of secession and the formation of an independent state, (3) the abolition of all national and national-religious privileges and restrictions, and (4) the free development of national minorities and ethnic groups inhabiting Russian territory. Following this declaration and subsequent legislation, the formation of national autonomous units proceeded rapidly, though it now appears clear how far short of realization all these ideals have been put into practice.

The Russian Soviet Federated Socialist Republic and the Ukrainian Soviet Socialist Republic were first proclaimed in 1917. After an interval of civil war, the Belorussian S.S.R. and the German Volga and Bashkir autonomous republics were organized. In 1922, the Georgian, Armenian, and Azerbaijan republics were joined to form the Transcaucasian S.F.S.R. Finally, in December, 1922, the Russian, Transcaucasian, Ukrainian, and Belorussian republics were joined in the Union of Soviet Socialist Republics. By that time about twenty lesser autonomous units had also been created.

While the formation of the autonomous national units was proceeding during the early years of the Soviet regime, plans were laid for the reform of administrative units within ethnically homogeneous areas. This reform was essentially a reorganization of the existing structure into integrated economic units. Beginning in 1922, at the start of the New Economic Policy of relaxed state control, there began the gradual transition from the former structure of *government-uyezd-volost* to a new territorial system of *oblast-okrug-raion*. By 1930 the last government had been abolished. The *oblast* (or *krai*) was originally intended to be a large economic region, only a limited number of which were to be constituted in the U.S.S.R. Its very large size was soon found to be an obstacle to efficient administration, however, and during the late 1920's smaller first-order divisions began to be formed and the intermediate unit—the administrative *okrug*—was largely suppressed in 1930. As a result of its abolition, the *raions* were subordinated directly to the first-order unit, whether *oblast, krai,* or republic.

The present administrative-territorial structure of the U.S.S.R. has thus evolved along two parallel, though closely integrated patterns: the creation of national autonomous units and the reform of the purely administrative divisions for purposes of economic management (Figure 147).

It is the principle of national autonomy that governs the division of the U.S.S.R. into the so-called union republics, which are the country's primary units. These republics are said to form a volun-

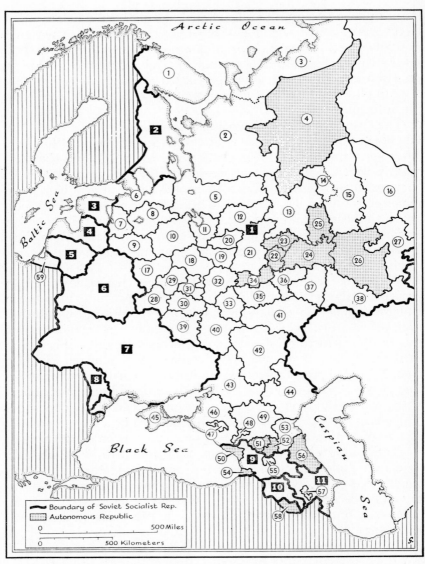

FIGURE 147. Administrative Divisions of the European U.S.S.R.

SOVIET SOCIALIST REPUBLIC

(White numbers in black squares)

1. Russian	5. Lithuanian	9. Georgian
2. Karelo-Finnish	6. Belorussian	10. Armenian
3. Estonian	7. Ukrainian	11. Azerbaijan
4. Latvian	8. Moldavian	

(Continued on opposite page)

tary union of nations and to reserve the right of free secession, according to the Soviet constitutions of 1924 (Article 4) and 1936 (Article 17). Of course, in view of the purely nominal autonomy, no union republic has ever raised or is likely to raise the question of secession in practice. From the original six union republics at the time of the formation of the U.S.S.R., their number increased to eleven at the time of the promulgation of the 1936 constitution, and to sixteen (their present number) in 1940, with the formation of the Karelo-Finnish and Moldavian republics and the accession of the three Baltic states. According to current terminology, all except the Russian S.F.S.R. are known as Soviet Socialist Republics, the form "Socialist Soviet Republic" being no longer in use. The Russian S.F.S.R., which is the leading and most important republic in every respect, is a federation of a number of major nationalities associated with the Russian nation and therefore continues to be known as a Soviet Federated Socialist Republic.

The same principle of national autonomy determines also the formation of lesser units, below the rank of union republic. These are the autonomous republic, commonly abbreviated A.S.S.R., the autonomous *oblast*, the national *okrug*, and, of minor importance, the national *raion* and the national village council. The autonomous republic is subordinated directly to the union republic in which it is located and is formed by ethnic groups that form large

---

← OTHER DIVISIONS IN THE RUSSIAN S.F.S.R. AND TRANSCAUCASIA—See Fig. 147

1. Murmansk
2. Archangel
3. Nenets National Okrug
4. Komi A.S.S.R.
5. Vologda
6. Leningrad
7. Pskov
8. Novgorod
9. Velikiye Luki
10. Kalinin
11. Yaroslavl
12. Kostroma
13. Kirov
14. Komi-Permyak National Okrug
15. Molotov
16. Sverdlovsk
17. Smolensk
18. Moscow
19. Vladimir
20. Ivanovo
21. Gorki
22. Chuvash A.S.S.R.
23. Mari A.S.S.R.
24. Tatar A.S.S.R.
25. Udmurt A.S.S.R.
26. Bashkir A.S.S.R.
27. Chelyabinsk
28. Bryansk
29. Kaluga
30. Orel
31. Tula
32. Ryazan
33. Tambov
34. Mordvinian A.S.S.R.
35. Penza
36. Ulyanovsk
37. Kuibyshev
38. Chkalov
39. Kursk
40. Voronezh
41. Saratov
42. Stalingrad
43. Rostov
44. Astrakhan
45. Crimea
46. Krasnodar Krai
47. Adyge Autonomous Oblast
48. Cherkess Autonomous Oblast
49. Stavropol Krai
50. Abkhaz A.S.S.R.
51. Kabardian A.S.S.R.
52. North Ossetian A.S.S.R.
53. Grozny
54. Adzhar A.S.S.R.
55. South Ossetian Autonomous Oblast
56. Dagestan A.S.S.R.
57. Nagorno-Karabakh Autonomous Oblast
58. Nakhichevan A.S.S.R.
59. Kaliningrad

minorities within a constituent republic. The Russian S.F.S.R., as would be expected, contains the greatest number of autonomous republics—twelve out of a total of sixteen. The autonomous *oblast*, formed by less numerous minorities than the preceding category, is subordinated to a *krai* within the Russian S.F.S.R. and directly to the union republic in the case of the lesser constituent units of the U.S.S.R. Out of a total of nine, six are contained within the Russian S.F.S.R. The national *okrug* is the lowest category of the major types of the autonomous units. It is a type which occurs only in the Russian S.F.S.R. and forms the basis of organization primarily of small Siberian ethnic groups. Finally, the national *raion* and village council are of only local importance and are generally formed on the basis of small isolated minorities.

These various categories of autonomous administrative units form what has been called the "nationalities' ladder." Theoretically, in accordance with the Soviet nationalities' policy, an ethnic group is assigned an autonomous category in accordance with its number of people and its degree of political and cultural development. Then, depending on future growth and development, the group may ascend the rungs of the ladder to higher categories of autonomous units. Four autonomous republics—the Kazakh, Kirghiz, Karelian, and Moldavian units—have been raised to the status of full constituent republic during the three decades of Soviet rule. It has developed in practice that union republics were created only on the periphery of the Russian S.F.S.R.—in order to enable them to secede if they so desired, according to the Soviet view—and only for groups having more than 1,000,000 people. (The Karelo-Finnish S.S.R. with about 600,000 inhabitants is a notable exception, probably the result of political expediency.) As a result of this more practical policy, important ethnic groups within the Russian Federation—such as the Tatar and Bashkir autonomous republics—have little chance of ever achieving the status of union republic, although they number more than three million people.

The greatest number of promotions in autonomous categories has been from autonomous *oblast* to autonomous republic. About ten such transfers took place in the Russian S.F.S.R. during the 1930's. Only in one isolated case—the Kirghiz group—was an advance through two successive categories achieved: the Kirghiz Autonomous Oblast, formed in 1924, became an autonomous republic in 1926 and a full union republic in 1936. However, with the exception of the Karelian and Moldavian groups, no promotion has occurred since the promulgation of the 1936 Constitution, and it would appear that at least the autonomous aspect of the Soviet administrative structure has assumed a certain stability after the early dynamic period of transformation.

It should be noted that the national autonomy in Soviet administration is reflected in the organization of the highest legislative body of the U.S.S.R.—the Supreme Soviet of the U.S.S.R. This body consists of two chambers, the Soviet of Nationalities and the Soviet of the Union. According to the Constitution, members of the Soviet of Nationalities are elected on the basis of the major autonomous divisions—twenty-five for a union republic, eleven for an autonomous republic, five for an autonomous *oblast*, and one for each national *okrug*. In the Soviet of the Union, on the other hand, the election is by union republics, with one deputy for every 300,000 inhabitants. In the union republics and the autonomous republics, the Supreme Soviets are unicameral. There election proceeds on a population basis only, with the size of an electoral constituency varying from 150,000 (Russian S.F.S.R.) to 2,000 (Nakhichevan A.S.S.R.).

Parallel to the autonomous aspect of the Soviet administrative system is the perhaps more real aspect of the economic-administrative unit. Ethnically homogeneous territories are divided into these units, which are delimited in such a manner as to obtain a well-integrated economic region. Ideally, such a region produces one or more commodities for export to other parts of the U.S.S.R., while remaining as self-sufficient as possible in basic consumer goods, construction materials, and similar items. The *oblast* is the largest type of economic unit and is found in most of the union republics. The Russian S.F.S.R. contains in addition the *krai*, which has essentially the same status as an *oblast*. The existence of a *krai* is determined by the fact that it contains an autonomous *oblast*.

Rural local government resides in the *raion*, the village, and other local Soviets, such as nomad headquarters. The *raion*, first formed in 1924, is intended to be a miniature oblast. The same economic principles guide its creation, though on a much reduced scale. All major administrative units, such as *oblasts, krais*, autonomous divisions, and the lesser union republics are divided directly into *raions*. These vary tremendously in area, from nearly 150,000 square miles in the sparsely inhabited Siberian North to less than 100 square miles in the Ukrainian chernozem zone. The village Soviet, and other types of local councils, are the smallest rural administrative units of the U.S.S.R. and comprise one or more villages, hamlets or other populated places.

Urban local government resides in the cities and towns, the latter being called city-type settlements and workers' settlements, to use official Soviet terminology. Just as in the case of the territorial units, economic considerations guide the creation of urban centers. The establishment of an industry or the opening of a mine in a previously rural agricultural community generally leads to the establishment of a workers' settlement or a city-type settlement. In the Russian S.F.S.R., the criterion for the creation of such a town is a minimum population of 400 adults, 65 per cent of which are industrial workers or employees. As the locality grows and its population and production increases, it may be converted into a city, which in turn may be subordinated successively to the *raion*, the *oblast*, or *krai*, or even to the republic. The rise of urban centers is thus an excellent guide to the economic development of the country.

The Demographic Basis

In discussing the national autonomous aspect of the Soviet administrative structure we have already indicated one of the key features of the population of the U.S.S.R.; that is, its multinational aspect. Other characteristics that distinguish the demographic development of the U.S.S.R. from that of other European countries are (a) the high rate of natural increase—1.23 per cent annually between 1926 and 1939, (b) the spectacular urbanization, which went hand in hand with the forced industrialization during the 1930's and 1940's, and (c) the state-controlled internal migration of large segments of the population.

With an estimated population of 201,000,000 at the beginning of 1950, the Soviet Union ranks third in the world, after China (475,000,000)[3] and the Republic of India (350,000,000). Of this total, about 163,000,000 live within the European limits adopted in this chapter and 38,000,000 in Asia.

From the long-range point of view, the most important characteristic of the population has been its rapid natural increase. From the 1897 census to the first Soviet census of 1926, the population of the country (within its 1926 limits) increased from 106,000,000 to 147,000,000, or by 41,000,000 in 30 years. This considerable increase was achieved through the difficult periods of World War I,

---

[3] Estimated population in the *Columbia Lippincott Gazetteer of the World* (New York: Columbia University Press, 1952).

the Russian Revolution, and the subsequent civil war. During the following twelve years until the census of 1939, about 23,000,-000 were added to the Soviet population, which thus reached 170,000,000.

During the years 1939 and 1940, the U.S.S.R. annexed large sections of Eastern Europe, including the Baltic States, eastern Poland, Northern Bucovina, and Bessarabia, with an estimated total population of about 23,000,000 in 1939. This brought the total population of the U.S.S.R. to about 193,000,000 as of 1939. On the basis of the apparent high rate of increase of the preceding years, it has been estimated [4] that the total population of the U.S.S.R. must have been about 200,000,000 at the time of the German invasion in June, 1941.

During the ensuing conflict, in which the German armies swept through territory inhabited by 85,000,000 people or about 43 per cent of the total population, the Soviet Union suffered tremendous losses in manpower unequalled in modern times. These losses included military personnel, excess civilian deaths, a deficit in births, and emigration, forced or voluntary, to the western countries of Europe. In his remarkable analysis of wartime changes in the Soviet population, Frank Lorimer assumes a hypothetical figure of 20 million persons for losses through the effects of war. [5] In projecting the population of the U.S.S.R. on the basis of this hypothesis, he obtains the projected population of 188 millions in 1945 (at the close of the Second World War) and 201 millions in 1950.

Data obtained on the basis of the Union elections of 1946 and 1950 confirm Lorimer's projected population for 1950, but indicate a lower figure (180-185 millions) for the closing year of the war. The number of registered voters, for example, rose from 101,700,000 in 1946 to 111,100,000 in 1950. This increase of nearly 10 millions corresponds to the age group of 18 years and over, less an unknown number of disqualified persons. The proportion of the number of registered voters to the total population of the U.S.S.R. was 55.4 per cent in 1937. Assuming the same ratio for the postwar situation, the total population was about 185 millions in 1946 and 201 millions in 1950. The figure for 1950 is furthermore supported by the creation (in the 1950 election) of 671 election districts, each with an average total population of 300,000, indicating a population of 201,300,000. These figures would tend

[4] Frank Lorimer, *The Population of the Soviet Union: History and Prospects* (Geneva: League of Nations, 1946), pp. 193-94.
[5] *Ibid.*, p. 181.

to indicate not only higher wartime losses (of the order of 25 to 30 millions), but also a higher rate of increase, which now appears to be of the order of 3.5 millions annually.

The Soviet Union's spectacular natural increase has been to some extent the result of the positive population policy inaugurated by the Soviet Government in the middle 1930's. In those years a series of regulations prohibited abortion, except on specific medical grounds, provided for state aid to mothers and children, and discouraged the heretofore easy divorce. The effect of these regulations became evident in a dramatic rise in the birth rate during the late 1930's. This pro-natalist trend was further emphasized in 1944 when state aid to mothers and children was greatly increased, providing particularly allowances and awards to mothers of large families. Mothers of ten or more children began to receive the Order of Mother Heroine, and their names appear periodically with those of other decorated persons in the Soviet journal of laws and decrees.

The effect of wartime emigration has resulted in the DP (displaced persons) problem that has plagued the Western countries during the postwar years and has created a particularly thorny situation in Western Germany. From the over-all point of view of Soviet population, the effect of the loss of, say, two million DP's is small when compared with the annual increase in the population. The loss of DP's was noticeable, however, in the demographic balance of lands with a small population, such as the Baltic States, which furnished a large proportion of the emigrants. For example, the population of Lithuania dropped from a prewar figure of three million to 2,700,000 after the war, that of Latvia from 2,100,000 to 1,800,000, and that of Estonia from 1,200,000 to 1,000,000. Similarly, the Belorussian S.S.R. recorded a loss of population from 9,300,000 to 7,220,000 through the war years.

Although wartime losses, particularly military deaths, have cut sharply into the reproductive age groups, the great youthfulness of the population of the U.S.S.R. will apparently ensure continued rapid growth during the coming decades. In 1939, about 61,500,-000 persons, or 36 per cent of the population, were under fifteen years of age. About 81 millions were in the 15 to 44 age group, representing nearly half of the total, and only 17 per cent were 45 years or older. Frank Lorimer's projections indicate that the young adult group (ages 20 to 44) will continue to form a consistently large proportion (about 40 per cent) of the total population. This factor, ensuring a constant supply of manpower, is surely of tremendous economic and military significance.

Rural and Urban Settlement

The geographical distribution of this great population is extremely irregular, as one would expect from the great variety of climatic and other physical factors. These disparities in density, while particularly marked in the Asiatic part of the U.S.S.R., are evident also in Europe. A dense population wedge with its base on the Leningrad-Odessa line penetrates eastward on the population map, coming to a point in the middle Urals. The densely inhabited heartland of the European U.S.S.R. coincides roughly with the mixed forest zone and the chernozem steppe. The density is generally more than 50 per square mile. Lower densities are found in the coniferous taiga of the European North and in the semidesert of the Caspian lowland in the southeast.

In these sparsely populated areas, rural settlements lie along communication lines, notably rivers and, more recently, railroads. The gravitation of rural population to these routes was dramatized in the early 1940's by the construction of the North Pechora railroad to the coal-mining center of Vorkuta in the European North. This rail line, which cut diagonally across the relatively denser population bands along river routes, in turn became an artery attracting settlement. In the agriculturally important steppe regions of the European South, rural population has settled traditionally in large villages, frequently reaching a population of 15,000 or more in the case of the *stanitsas* of the Kuban Cossacks.

Collectivization of agriculture in the 1930's brought with it a revolution in the rural settlement pattern. In general, the trend was toward the concentration of the population of scattered villages and hamlets in a central collective farm settlement, characterized by a rectilinear main street, orchards and gardens, and administration and recreation buildings of the collective. Actually, the abolition of isolated farmsteads within the territory of a collective farm was begun only in 1939 in the Ukraine. World War II not only brought an abrupt stop to the program of rural settlement consolidation but led to incredible destruction in the zone of military operations.

After the war, following a period of reconstruction (1946-50), another attempt at rural consolidation was made. This time it involved not only the abolition of small hamlets and isolated farmsteads, but the consolidation of small collective farms into larger units. This policy of collective farm merger, begun in 1950, envisaged the creation of central farm settlements of considerable size or veritable "garden cities" (*agrogorod*). While the consolidation phase of the program proceeded rapidly during 1950, with the reduction in the number of farms from 252,000 to 123,000 in one year, the type of settlement intended was slower in developing. The original "garden-city" proposal was criticized within the U.S.S.R. as too ambitious and the term "farm settlement" (*poselok*) was advanced to describe a more modest type of farm center. It remains to be seen how quickly the planned upheaval in Soviet rural settlement will actually take shape. Speculation on the effect of this program on the rural settlement geography of the U.S.S.R. would therefore seem premature.

While the future of Soviet rural settlement patterns is unclear, the trends in urban settlement can be assessed much more precisely. The spectacular drive for industrialization, begun with the first five-year plan, brought about an equally striking rise in the urban population of the country, from 17.9 per cent in 1926 to 32.8 per cent in 1939. The explanation for this phenomenon must be found in a variety of factors. Rural-urban migration to fill the sudden need for industrial manpower was a major factor in the growth of the cities. However, changes in the definition of urban centers led to the reclassification of hundreds of villages into urban communities, in accordance with the Soviet economic concept of the urban center. Moreover, new urban centers developed from nothing through the completion of new industrial installations or the opening of new mines. Some spectacular examples are Karaganda, a village of a few hundred in the late 1920's, which reached 165,937 in 1939 and more than 300,000 in 1950. Equally impressive is the rise of Magnitogorsk, founded in 1931. This prototype of the Soviet industrial boom-town had 145,870 inhabitants in 1939 and also approached 300,000 in 1950.

These urban centers are concentrated primarily in five areas of the Soviet Union. These are the Urals with 100 cities and 175 workers' settlements, the Donets Basin with 50 cities and 175 workers' settlements, the areas of Moscow and Leningrad, with 145 and 75 urban centers, respectively, and in Siberia, the Kuznetsk Basin with 14 cities and 20 workers' settlements. While these regions represent extreme concentration of urban population, other urban centers are scattered throughout the country wherever important mining or industrial activity has caused the formation of such agglomerations. Thus, it can be safely stated that the distribution and concentration of these centers is a fair guide to the distribution and concentration of Soviet industry. The total number of urban centers as of January 1, 1953, was 1,500 cities and 2,250 workers' settlements and city-type settlements.

One of the factors in the rapid urbanization of the U.S.S.R. is the facility with which the Soviet regime has regulated migration within the country in accordance with state policies. The transfer of large numbers of people has been in part compulsory, but has also been effected through higher incentives, such as increased pay and better housing, in areas that had a shortage of industrial labor. Such regions, for example, are the European North and vast sections in Siberia and the Soviet Far East, where the climatic and other physical conditions are extremely inhospitable and do not attract settlement. Another type of compulsory migration occurred during and after World War II, when a number of ethnic groups accused of collaboration with the Germans and of fifth-column activity were forcibly ejected from their historical region and resettled in other parts of the U.S.S.R. These groups were the Volga Germans, the Crimean Tatars, the Kalmyks and, in the Northern Caucasus, the Karachai, Balkar, Chechen, and Ingush peoples. The most recent mass migration, more or less compulsory, was the settling by Russians from densely inhabited regions of the central European U.S.S.R. of the newly annexed areas of northern East Prussia and southern Sakhalin, from which the German and Japanese population had been gradually expelled.

Ethnic Groups

Although the number of ethnic groups in the Soviet Union is generally put at 100 to 150, the so-called multinational character of the population of the U.S.S.R. has to be considered in the proper perspective. In this connection two facts are of the greatest importance. These are the dominant position of the Russian people and the relatively small number of national groups with, say, more than 20,000 persons.

According to Lorimer,[6] no exact figure on the number of nationalities is meaningful. The 1926 census recognized 188 individual groups, but in a few cases numbers were either not reported or only a few individuals were reported for a specific ethnic group. In the incomplete returns of the 1939 census, in which a number of important Siberian peoples were not reported, the total number of nationalities with more than 20,000 persons was forty-nine. When the major missing Siberian groups (Yakuts, Buryat-Mongols, Khanty or Ostyaks, and Evenki or Tungus) and the Tuvinians, who were incorporated into the U.S.S.R. in 1944, are taken into account, the number of ethnic groups with more than 20,000 per-

[6] *Ibid.*, p. 50, n. 1.

sons was fifty-four. Of these, however, six nationalities and one of the Tatar units were deprived of their individual identity as separate ethnic groups as a result of alleged wartime collaboration with the Germans.

The Russians constitute just about half the total population of the U.S.S.R., with the ratio somewhat higher (about 60 per cent) in Asia and somewhat lower in Europe. As would be expected the percentage of Russians is greatest (73 per cent in 1926) within the territory of the Russian S.F.S.R., while in the other union republics and in some of the lesser autonomous units they constitute generally less than 25 per cent of the population. With the Ukrainians and the Belorussians, who form 18 per cent and 4.5 per cent, respectively, of the Soviet population, the Slavic element stands out clearly as the dominant group with nearly 75 per cent of the total number of people within the Soviet Union. Lesser Slavic peoples are the Poles, who are scattered among the Belorussians and the Ukrainians, and the Bulgarians, who live largely in southern Bessarabia.

Of the next two important ethnic families or linguistic groups, the more numerous Turkic peoples (about 8 per cent of total) live largely in Asia, and the Finno-Ugrian peoples (less than 3 per cent) primarily in Europe. The Tatars, the most important European branch of the Turkic family, are concentrated in the Volga region, where they have an autonomous republic, but are also widely dispersed through the rest of the country. The related Crimean Tatars, estimated at 200,000 on the eve of World War II, were among the groups deprived of their cultural identity as the result of collaboration with the Germans. Adjoining the Tatars geographically are the Bashkirs, a Turkic steppe people that settled on the western slopes of the Urals in the tenth century. Like the Volga Tatars, who are descended from the fifteenth-century Kazan khanate, the Bashkirs are organized politically in an autonomous republic. The third major Turkic people in the European U.S.S.R. are the Azerbaijani Turks in Transcaucasia on the Caspian Sea. Although their language is closely related to that of the Osmanli Turks, the Azerbaijanis have acquired their culture and the Shiite Moslem religion from the Persians who dominated the present Soviet Azerbaijan until the early nineteenth century. Of the leading Turkic groups in the Asiatic U.S.S.R., we shall merely mention the Uzbeks, Kazakhs, Kirghiz, and Turkmen in Central Asia, and the Yakuts in Siberia.

Of the Finnic ethnic family, the Volga-Ural division (or the Eastern Finnic branch) is the most numerous. These peoples live on the western slopes of the Urals and along the middle Volga River, in close contact with the Tatars and the Bashkirs. The leading representatives in numbers are concentrated along the Volga. They are the Mordvinians (or Mordvians) and the Chuvash (the latter with considerable Turkic linguistic influence) on the right bank; the Mari (formerly called Cheremiss) and the Udmurt (formerly called Votyak) on the left bank. Finnic primarily from the linguistic point of view, these peoples have acquired a predominantly Russian culture through the centuries of contact with the Slavs, with some survivals from their Finnic ancestors and the ancient Khazars and Volga Bulgars. To the north of this Finnic concentration, along the northern Urals, are the more primitive Komi (formerly Zyryan) and the closely related Komi-Permyaks (or Permian Komi). Along the shore of the Arctic Ocean in the far north of the European U.S.S.R. are the Nentsy (formerly known as Samoyedes), who are distantly related to the Finno-Ugrian family. With the exception of the Nentsy and the Komi-Permyaks who are organized into national *okrugs* (the only such autonomous units in the European U.S.S.R.), the Eastern Finns form autonomous republics within the Soviet administrative scheme.

The Western Finns along the Baltic Region are considerably fewer within the confines of the U.S.S.R. The main group are the Estonians, who came entirely under Soviet control in 1940 and constitute the northernmost of the three Baltic republics. They are traditionally Lutheran Protestants and have long been under the influence of Germanic culture. The next group, the Karelians, number only about one fourth of the 1,000,000 Estonians. They are very closely related to the true Finns, whose language they speak, but are of Russian culture and traditionally Russian Orthodox. In conjunction with the true Finns, who are few in numbers (19,467 in 1926) in the U.S.S.R., the Karelians constitute, since 1940, the Karelo-Finnish S.S.R. To the north of this union republic, in the Kola Peninsula, lives the Soviet section of the Lapps (known as *Saamy* in the official Soviet terminology), constituted in a national *raion* of Murmansk *oblast* of the Russian S.F.S.R. Finally, the Western Finns comprise a number of small splinter groups in the vicinity of Lake Ladoga and Lake Onega. These are the Veps, the Vote, and the Izhora (Inger), numbering no more than 50,000 in 1926.

The two southern Baltic states, Latvia and Lithuania, are inhabited by peoples of the Baltic language subfamily. The Lutheran Latvians (or Letts), like the Estonians influenced by a Germanic cultural veneer, are associated in their republic with the closely related Roman Catholic Latgalians of Polish culture. This latter cultural development, typical also of the Lithuanians, dates from the long period of Polish rule in these regions after the sixteenth century.

Following southward along the relatively narrow European isthmus between the Baltic and the Black Sea, we find at its southern end another important non-Slavic minority—the Moldavians. The century-long control by Russia over the Moldavians in Bessarabia after 1812 has added some Russian strains to their essentially Latin and Romanian background. As a result the Moldavians use the Romanian language written in the Cyrillic script. After the First World War only about 250,000 Moldavians remained within the U.S.S.R. and constituted the Moldavian Autonomous S.S.R. within the Ukraine, on the left bank of the Dniester River, then the Soviet-Romanian frontier. Following the acquisition of Bessarabia in 1940, the number of Moldavians under Soviet control rose to about 2,000,000 and the political organization was raised to that of a union republic.

By far the greatest ethnic diversity, exceeding even that of the middle Volga Region, exists in the Caucasus. Russian settlement having progressed predominantly in the steppes of the Northern Caucasus, the largest minority groups are found on the southern slopes, in Transcaucasia. Here, in addition to the Azerbaijani Turks, are the major Armenian and Georgian groups, each constituted as a union republic. The Armenians form a distinct linguistic group of the Indo-European family, related by some to the Caucasian languages. Settled traditionally around Mount Ararat within the territories of Russia, Turkey, and Persia, the Armenians were greatly decimated between 1894 and 1915 by systematic Turkish policies of extermination. As a result of these trials, the bulk of the population remained in Russian Armenia, a considerable minority in northwestern Iran, and the rest scattered through the lands of the Middle East and other parts of the world. Of the present estimated Armenian world population of 3,500,000, two thirds live in the U.S.S.R. However, only 40 per cent of the Soviet Armenians live in the Armenian S.S.R. proper, with the rest scattered through the rest of the Soviet Union. After World War II, the Soviet Government invited Armenian emigrés to return to their homeland, more specifically Soviet Armenia. By 1948, 100,000 emigré Armenians had returned, chiefly from the Middle East. In addition to their own union republic, the Armenians also constitute the majority population (89 per cent in 1926) of an exclave

—the Nagorno-Karabakh Autonomous Oblast—within the Azerbaijan S.S.R.

The Georgians, like the Armenians, number somewhat more than 2,000,000 persons in the U.S.S.R. They are concentrated in their relatively homogeneous republic and constitute the leading member of the Caucasian language group. Within the Georgian S.S.R., the Mingrelian, Svanetian, and Adzhar groups are associated with Georgian in the South Caucasian languages. The Adzhars, of Moslem religion and influenced by Turkish culture, form a separate autonomous republic within Georgia. Another Georgian dependent unit—the Abkhaz Autonomous S.S.R.—is the chief representative of the North Caucasian languages on the southern slopes of the mountains. The other members, considerably dissected by Russian areas of settlement, are the Cherkess (Circassian) people, also known by their own native appellation of Adyge, the related Kabardians (or Kabardinians), and the diverse mountain groups of Dagestan, including the Lesghians, Avars, Darghins, Laks, and Andi. The Chechen and Ingush peoples, who lost their ethnic identity after the Second World War, also were members of the North Caucasian group.

Several peoples of the Caucasus are members of the Iranian group of the Indo-European language family. These are primarily the Ossetians, settled in the central part of the Caucasus, where they constitute the North Ossetian Autonomous S.S.R. of the Russian S.F.S.R. and the South Ossetian Autonomous Oblast of the Georgian S.S.R. The Ossetians are believed to be descendants of the ancient Alans, a steppe people of the Northern Caucasus, last reported at the time of the Mongol-Tatar raids of the thirteenth century. Smaller Iranian splinter groups are the Talysh, in the Talysh (or Lenkoran) lowland adjoining the Caspian Sea, the Tats, at the eastern foot of the Caucasus in Azerbaijan, and the Kurds, on the slopes of Mount Ararat in Armenia.

Alone among the leading ethnic groups of the Soviet Union, the Jews have no political autonomous division commensurate with their numbers. Reported at 3,020,141 in 1939 (then the seventh largest group), the Jews are estimated to have reached a total of 5,000,000 on the eve of World War II, as a result of the annexation by the U.S.S.R. of areas in eastern Poland with large Jewish elements. However, following the systematic massacre of the Jews by the Germans during the war, their postwar number dropped to an estimated 2,000,000. This physical extermination of a great section of Soviet Jews was followed in the years after the war by a cultural "extermination" within the Soviet Union. Though nominally still recognized by the Soviet Government as a distinct ethnic group, the Jews were gradually deprived through the period 1945-48 of their schools, newspapers, books, and other cultural institutions ordinarily associated with cultural autonomy within the U.S.S.R. No official Soviet explanation of these restrictions has been given. Possible reasons for this policy may lie in the traditional association of the Jews with "cosmopolitanism," an internationalist ideology attacked by the U.S.S.R. during the postwar period. The fear of possible Jewish interests and ties with the new state of Israel has also been offered as an explanation for the Soviet reversal in policy.

As apparent proof of the continued nominal recognition of the Jews as a distinct cultural group, the Soviet regime has kept in existence the Jewish Autonomous Oblast (commonly known as Birobidzhan), on the banks of the Amur River in the Soviet Far East. This administrative unit, originally set up in 1930 as a national *raion*, was raised to the status of autonomous *oblast* in 1934. Although the unit had been created to encourage concentrated Jewish settlement in the area, no mass migration developed from the traditionally Jewish settlement areas of Belorussia and the western Ukraine, as well as from the large urban Jewish population scattered through the cities of the U.S.S.R. Today no more than 50,000 to 75,000 Jews are believed to have settled in the autonomous region, but it is doubtful whether the customary Soviet cultural autonomy, such as use of the Yiddish language in schools, newspapers, and books, is still sanctioned to any extent.

Concept of Autonomy

It has been seen that with the possible exception of the Jews and of the disfranchised peoples accused of collaboration during World War II, the peoples of the U.S.S.R. enjoy cultural autonomy, at least within their own national autonomous units. This autonomy manifests itself primarily through the existence of schools, newspapers, books, and other information media in the indigenous language, the use of the language in official local government matters, and the promotion of the native cultural development in literature and the arts within the very narrow limits of Soviet ideology.

This cultural autonomy must be understood in the light of two trends that dominate the entire life of the U.S.S.R. These phenomena are the Soviet ideology and way of life, as well as Russification, a more recent, though increasingly important factor in the life of the peoples of the Soviet Union.

A thorough analysis of what is meant by the Soviet ideology and way of life would go beyond the scope of this chapter. Suffice it to say that this imposed cultural force involves the application of the strictest type of governmental control to all phases of the public and private life of the Soviet citizen. This supervision, whose severity is appreciated only with difficulty by peoples of the West, applies not only to the political and economic sphere, but also to all cultural activities of the many different ethnic groups of the country. This results in a stereotyped, uniform layer of Soviet ideology over all indigenous civilizations. The Soviets have described this phenomenon as the development of cultures that are "national in form,—Socialist in content."

Side by side with Sovietization, the trend toward Russification has begun to appear. The Russians, who represent the dominant ethnic group in the country, dominate all phases of life among the non-Russian groups. Russian is taught as a requisite in all non-Russian schools, Russian books and newspapers appear in non-Russian areas, and Russians fill many of the responsible government posts in non-Russian territorial units.

The history of the languages of the U.S.S.R. well illustrates the Russification trend, particularly in the development of the alphabets. In the early years of the Soviet regime the eradication of illiteracy was one of the most pressing problems facing the struggling new government. Many of the non-Russian languages were then written in the Cyrillic and Arabic scripts, which it was felt, would retard progress toward literacy. Consequently, a campaign was begun to introduce the Latin alphabet into many of the non-Russian tongues, particularly those of the Turkic peoples who had had an Arabic tradition. Even those Turkic peoples of Siberia who had acquired the Cyrillic alphabet under Tsarist rule were given modified Latin scripts. After the Azerbaijani Turks had adopted the new alphabet in 1922 (they had previously used the Arabic script), the latinization movement swept the country through the 1920's. Only the Slavic peoples and the Finnic and Turkic tribes of the European U.S.S.R., who had been long exposed to Russian culture, escaped the impact, as did the Georgians and Armenians with their own traditional scripts.

However, the tide turned after the successful completion of the campaign against illiteracy in the 1930's. The new policy desired a closer integration of the peoples of the U.S.S.R. around the Russian leading group and the over-all introduction of the Cyrillic script was ordered in order to facilitate the study of the Russian language by other ethnic groups. In 1935, the Kabardian-Balkar Autonomous S.S.R. in the Northern Caucasus was the first to heed the call, converting its existing Latin alphabet into the Cyrillic. The conversion proceeded with great speed and by 1940 most Latin alphabets used in the U.S.S.R. had been converted. At the present time, the only non-Cyrillic scripts are the Latin, used by the three Baltic states and the Karelo-Finnish S.S.R., the Georgian script, which dates from the fourth century, and the Armenian alphabet, in use since the same period. The extent of the use of the Hebrew alphabet in the Yiddish language is problematical and is closely tied to the entire question of the Jewish culture in the U.S.S.R.

While the question of alphabets has been considered in some detail to illustrate the Russification of non-Russian cultures, this trend is also evident in the Russification of the native vocabulary and other linguistic elements.

Religion

Before the Bolshevik Revolution of 1917, the Russian Orthodox Church was the state church of the Russian Empire, with the Tsar as its head. Other religious denominations were merely tolerated. An abrupt change took place after the revolution, with the separation of state and church and the expropriation of all church property. Atheism, formerly a crime against the state, was welcomed by the new Soviet regime and supported by active antireligious propaganda.

Public places of worship had been a characteristic feature of the urban and rural settlements of Russia. This applied not only to the characteristic bulbous church towers of the Russian Orthodox Church but also to the mosques and minarets of Central Asia, and the Lamaist monasteries of Buryat-Mongolia. After the revolution, this feature of the landscape remained in part, though many churches were demolished, and a great number of these places of worship became public buildings, clubs, theaters, libraries, or museums. Moreover, the house of worship was not considered a necessary element in the planning of collective farm settlements or new industrial and mining towns and has remained only as a reminder of the past in older centers.

The intense antireligious propaganda that swept the Soviet

scene during the 1930's was temporarily abandoned during the Second World War in order to remove any obstacle to the marshalling of all forces against the German invader. The Russian Orthodox Church resumed some of its former authority, but merely as a voice of the Soviet Government, and is credited with a considerable share in the mobilization of the Soviet people during the war. Its position was again weakened after the war when antireligious propaganda was resumed, but it appears that the semblance, at least, of the major religious denominations of the U.S.S.R., together with their hierarchic structure, has been maintained in the postwar period.

Thus, while religion has definitely been relegated to a very minor position, the church has not been abolished and it may prove useful to survey briefly the religious affiliations of the major ethnic groups of the U.S.S.R.

By far the dominant church is the Russian Orthodox Church, which embraces not only all the Slavs but also the Finnic and Turkic peoples of the European U.S.S.R. that have been long exposed to Russian culture. Among the Belorussians and Ukrainians, however, there is a considerable Roman Catholic minority, particularly among the people of western Belorussia and the western Ukraine annexed from Poland in 1939. Also among the Ukrainians, notably in former Ruthenia or Carpatho-Ukraine, there are numerous adherents to the Uniate rite of the Roman Catholic Church. Roman Catholicism is the predominant denomination of the Lithuanians and the Latgalians, both peoples of Polish cultural background. Lutheran Protestantism is prevalent among the Latvians and the Estonians, as well as among the few true Finns in the U.S.S.R., whose religion is the chief distinction from their Russian Orthodox Karelian co-linguists.

The Armenians and the Georgians each have their own independent church. The Armenian, also known as Gregorian, is an independent Christian church with Western and Eastern elements in its rites, while the Georgian is one of the oldest Orthodox churches of Byzantine heritage. Islam is important in the European U.S.S.R. only among the Azerbaijani Turks, while a greater number of adherents may be found among the Turkic peoples of Central Asia. Unlike the Shiite Azerbaijanis, however, the Moslems of Central Asia belong largely to the Sunnite sect. Mention should be made, finally, of the Buryat-Mongols of southern Siberia, who are the only representatives of Lamaist Buddhism in the U.S.S.R.

The Soviet Economy

Before the Bolshevik Revolution, Russia had a primarily agrarian economy. Today it is an industrial power second only to the United States. While it would be academic to discuss the question—one that is sometimes raised—whether Russia would not have made the same progress under the old regime, it is pertinent to examine some of the major developments of Soviet economic history since the revolution.[7]

A period of war communism (1917-21) followed in the wake of the overthrow of Tsarist power. It was a period of extremist and ruthless measures necessitated by the chaos of civil war and foreign intervention. State control spread rapidly over all phases of the economy; all land and its mineral resources were nationalized, industries, means of transportation, and all buildings were declared state property, private banks were merged into the state bank, and a government monopoly over foreign trade was instituted. At the same time, however, arbitrary food requisitions, mounting inflation, and a confused economic administration created dissatisfaction among the peasants, which, coupled with a decline in industrial discipline among the workers, endangered the very existence of the struggling young state.

In order to appease the peasantry and revive the economy, Lenin initiated the New Economic Policy (NEP), which was in effect a temporary concession to capitalism. Domestic commerce and small and medium industry were partly returned to private hands, with the government retaining control over all key industries and means of transport. Under this mixed economy the U.S.S.R. gradually raised its production and by 1928 had regained or exceeded the output of 1913. At the same time the state had expanded its share in the economy and gradually reduced the role of private enterprise through a variety of restrictive measures, such as high profit taxes, discrimination in the supply of raw materials and in the use of transportation facilities.

In 1928 the Soviet regime initiated the first of its five-year plans aimed at a sharp increase of industrial output under conditions of strict government control and planning. Shortly thereafter began the process of agricultural collectivization. This forcible consolidation of individual farms into cooperatives reached its climax in the early 1930's in one of the most tempestuous periods of Soviet history, marked by the deportation of rich peasants (kulaks), the

[7] For statistical information, see Appendix III.

slaughter of cattle, and a drop in agricultural production with a resulting famine in 1931-32.

However, the government won. Under planned conditions, industrial output soared during the first (1928-32) and second (1933-37) five-year plans. Emphasis was placed on the producer industries at the cost of consumer goods. New industries were created and their geographical distribution marked a gradual eastward shift of the industrial center of gravity of the U.S.S.R. At the same time, agricultural production began to increase, after the upheaval of collectivization, through the application of modern farming methods, mechanization, and similar measures facilitated by the creation of the large collectives.

The third five-year plan (1938-42) was interrupted by the German invasion in June, 1941. Although the principal economic regions of the U.S.S.R. fell to the invader in 1941 and 1942, the results of the forced industrial expansion of the 1930's bore fruit. On the basis of the industrial production of the eastern part of the U.S.S.R., which dated chiefly from the period of the five-year plans, and as a result of the removal of some 1,300 plants from the path of the German forces, the Soviets were able to stem the Nazi advance. This, and the subsequent expulsion of the enemy from the U.S.S.R., were aided in no small measure, it should be added, by the vital shipments of Allied aid.

The postwar period was dominated by the fourth five-year plan of "reconstruction and development of the national economy" (1946-50), the completion of which on schedule was announced in April, 1951. In the following sections we shall survey the present situation in the various branches of the Soviet economy, agriculture, mining, industry, transportation and trade.

Agriculture

As we have already indicated, the present organization of Soviet agriculture is the result of a long process of evolution and revolution. Dominated by conditions of serfdom and feudalism until the partial emancipation of 1861, later modified by the reforms of 1906, agriculture in Russia before the revolution was mainly in the hands of 10.5 million poor peasants owning about 200,000,000 acres, and of 30,000 big landowners, whose estates aggregated about 185,000,000 acres. In addition, there were about 1,000,000 wealthier peasants, who averaged 40 acres each and 1,500,000 rich farmers, who in the aggregate owned as much land as the big estate owners.

Following the expropriation of the estate owners as a result of the revolution and the consequent redistribution of the land among the peasants, there emerged about 25,000,000 individually owned farms. Medium-wealthy peasants were in the majority (about 60 per cent), followed by about 8,000,000 poor peasants, and about 1,000,000 rich peasants (kulaks), who employed outside labor.

In 1928, only 1.7 per cent of the total number of farms were of the collective type. In the succeeding years (1929-32) occurred the agricultural revolution of collectivization. As a result of collectivization, the 25,000,000 individually owned farms of the 1920's were, in the course of the 1930's, welded into one hundredth of their former number.

The Soviet agricultural revolution was repeated on a smaller scale in the areas annexed by the U.S.S.R. in 1939-40. The redistribution of largely expropriated estates was begun soon after the assumption of Soviet control, was partly cancelled under German occupation during World War II, and resumed by the Soviets after the war. Unlike the period of grace of nearly a decade that had been granted the Soviet farms under the New Economic Policy, the newly annexed areas underwent the process of collectivization within a few years of the redistribution of land and by early 1950 nearly all peasant families had been collectivized.

At this point began the consolidation of collective farms, which resulted in the halving of their number during 1950. This process took place primarily in areas where the average acreage per collective farm had traditionally been small: in the central, western, and northern sections of the European U.S.S.R., in the Caucasus, and in the irrigated areas of Central Asia. This process was to be followed, as has been seen, by the concentration of the rural population in central collective farm settlements. The program is still continuing and it is vain to speculate on its success or on the ultimate number of consolidated farms and rural settlements planned by the Soviet regime.

While the collective farm (*kolkhoz*) dominates the agricultural picture of the Soviet Union and produces the great bulk of the agricultural output, the actual work of raising crops and livestock is also done by two other types of farms, the state farm (*sovkhoz*) and the individually owned peasant farm. The state farms occupy a special position in the agricultural organization of the country. Unlike the collective farmers, who receive a share of the collective net income in proportion to their labor input and can also carry on some private production, the peasants on the state farms are simply employees of the state. Payment is on a straight piece-work basis, with the farmers obtaining the highest crop yield per acre or the most production from their livestock at the top of the income scale.

Soviet state farms have from their beginnings in the early 1920's served as model farms for the education of the surrounding peasantry. They are, moreover, located in areas presenting particularly difficult agricultural conditions because of either climate or soils. One of their principal tasks is the experimentation with new crops and livestock breeds. Their average size was two to three times that of the average collective farm, but has been roughly that of the new consolidated collective units. Their number is only about 5,000 and they are engaged primarily in the raising of livestock for milk, meat, and wool production, accounting for about one fourth of the total output, and in the cultivation of lesser proportions of sugar beets, cotton, and grain.

Individually owned peasant farms represent a negligible factor in the Soviet agricultural economy. Their number had been reduced to 1,300,000 by 1938, when the government took further measures to eliminate them. In 1946, 3,000,000 peasant farms existed in the U.S.S.R., most of them in areas annexed after 1939, and these were collectivized during the late 1940's so that the individually owned farm has become an insignificant quantity in the U.S.S.R.

In addition to the collective and state farms, the actual producing units of Soviet agriculture, the system of organization of farming in the U.S.S.R makes provision for the existence of an additional unit—the machine tractor station (MTS). These stations own most of the complex agricultural machinery used by the collective farms and supply considerable technical aid through agronomists attached to the stations. The services rendered to the collective farms are paid for in kind, usually a share of the crop. In early 1950, there were about 8,000 machine tractor stations throughout the U.S.S.R., serving 30 collective farms each on the average, and 10 to 15 since the consolidation.

Under conditions of planned economy, the trend in Soviet agriculture has been the gradual increase of production through higher yields and through increased sown acreage or increase in livestock. In order to increase yields, the Soviet regime has introduced the common use of mineral fertilizer, improved agricultural methods, such as moisture conservation and rotation. Quick-ripening and drought-resistant types of grains, for example, have been developed in order to enable the extension of the sown area into areas of ordinarily unfavorable climatic conditions.

Particular attention has been given to the irrigation of arid areas, most common in Central Asia. However, in the southeastern part of the European U.S.S.R., adjoining the Caspian Sea, great progress has also been made toward the extension of agriculture to arid or semiarid areas. In the Northern Caucasus, for example, the Nevinnomyssk Canal (completed in 1947) diverts water from the Kuban River to the dry steppe of the Stavropol region, ultimately joining the Western Manych canal system. At the eastern end of the Caucasus, water from the Samur River of Dagestan has been diverted southeast along the Caspian shore to the arid Apsheron Peninsula, site of the Baku oilfield. This so-called Samur-Divichi Canal, begun in 1940, was being completed during the postwar five-year plan.

A new series of projects aimed at irrigating the dry steppe north of the Caspian Sea and in the southern Ukraine and the Crimea was announced by the Soviet Government in August and September, 1950, for completion by 1957. This program envisages the construction of dams at Kuibyshev and Stalingrad on the Volga River and at Kakhovka on the Dnieper River, as well as a network of irrigation canals. Finally, additional areas of the Northern Caucasus will be irrigated by canals connected with the Volga-Don Canal and the associated Tsimlyanskaya dam and reservoir on the Don River.

A different type, though nevertheless equally important type of drought-combating program is the planting of forest shelter belts. Begun on a local scale in the 1930's, the planting of shelter belts was originally aimed at aiding snow and moisture retention, particularly in the dry steppe east of the lower Volga River. In 1948, however, a comprehensive program for combating drought was announced for the period 1949-65. It provides for a number of huge state shelter belts extending for a total length of 3,500 miles generally northeast-southwest between the southern Urals and the Northern Caucasus. In addition to these great belts, intended to protect the agricultural areas of the southeastern European U.S.S.R. from the hot, dry winds of Kazakhstan and Central Asia, the plan provides for the systematic local planting of shelter belts by individual state and collective farms. The possible success of this ambitious program, particularly in areas where insufficient precipitation normally prohibits tree growth, has been the subject of considerable debate outside the U.S.S.R.

Not content with irrigation and shelter-belt programs, the Soviet regime ordered, in 1950, the complete revamping of the existing irrigation system. Like so many other features of Soviet organization, this program was aimed at centralized control. The existing irrigation system was condemned chiefly for the high density of canals per unit of irrigated area and the small average size of the fields. The new program proposed the permanent maintenance of the trunk canals, but ordered the filling-in of the old feeder canals, which were also condemned as focal points of weed and insect infestation. Instead, the plan envisages temporary feeder canals to be dug and filled in annually with a view to reducing their number and increasing the average size of the irrigated fields. The new scheme is to go into effect by 1953.

While these ambitious measures may ultimately result in a gradual southeastward shift in the agricultural center of gravity, similar to the eastward shift in industry, the Leningrad-Odessa-Urals triangle of the European U.S.S.R., encompassing the mixed forests, the forest-steppe, and the true steppe zones, remains the chief agricultural belt of the U.S.S.R. In this agricultural triangle, we can differentiate regional specialization areas or surplus-production areas for individual crops (Figure 148).

Wheat is by far the leading grain in acreage and output, followed by rye among the bread grains and by oats and barley among the feed grains. In 1937, food grains (wheat, rye) accounted for two thirds of all grain output, with wheat in turn composing two thirds of the food grains. The surplus production area for wheat in Europe is not, as popularly supposed, the Ukraine, but a broad belt oriented southwest-northeast and extending from the Crimea, southern Ukraine, and the northern Caucasus through the trans-Volga steppes to the southern Urals. Winter wheat is grown mainly at the southwestern end of this belt, while the reduced snow cover and more extreme winter temperatures toward the east necessitate the sowing of spring wheat.

While wheat is produced primarily in the chernozem and chestnut soils of the steppe, rye grows best in the lighter podsols of the cooler north and northwest. Oats, destined chiefly for horse feed, give their highest yield in the central European U.S.S.R., but attain their greatest acreages in the Urals and Siberia. Barley, whose production goes primarily into brewing and the fattening of hogs, is grown widely in the Ukraine and in the Caucasus, as well as in areas of extreme climatic conditions and a short growing season. Similarly, millet is produced in areas of Central Asia and Kazakhstan, though it is also rotated with wheat in some areas of the chernozem zone. Corn is also grown in the Ukraine and in the Caucasus, as well as in the Moldavian S.S.R. (Bessarabia), where its porridge (*mamalyga*) is a national dish. The only rice-producing

FIGURE 148. Agricultural specialty belts of the European U.S.S.R.

area of the European U.S.S.R. is the Talysh district in the southern Azerbaijan S.S.R. on the Caspian Sea. It is cultivated much more widely, however, in southern Kazakhstan, Central Asia, and the Ussuri region of the Soviet Far East.

While the Ukraine is no longer the bread basket of the U.S.S.R., it can certainly be dubbed its sugar bowl. About 70 per cent of the sugar-beet production of the U.S.S.R. comes from the western Ukraine, with another 20 per cent coming from the adjoining chernozem areas in the Russian S.F.S.R. (Kursk, Voronezh). Under the Soviet regime, the sugar beet has been introduced into the Altai *krai* of Western Siberia and into the Kazakh and Kirghiz republics, but the great bulk of the production continues to come from the European U.S.S.R. The production of sugar cane is still in its early experimental stages, with some effort at acclimatization being made along the Amu Darya in the Uzbek S.S.R.

Soviet attempts to expand cotton growing to the nonirrigated lands of the northern Caucasus and the southern Ukraine have been only partly successful. Although the new areas occupy nearly 25 per cent of the total Soviet acreage under cotton, they contribute less than 10 per cent to the total cotton production of the country. Highest yields still come from the irrigated cotton lands in Central Asia, particularly in the Uzbek S.S.R., where long-staple fibers are increasingly planted. The European U.S.S.R. does, however, have areas of intensive, irrigated cotton production in Transcaucasia, in the Kura and Aras plains.

The northwestern part of the European U.S.S.R., in the forested podsol belt, has conditions most favorable to the production of fiber flax, a plant that flourishes under cloudy, humid climate with a July mean below 70° F. Because of the plant's high demands on the soil, it is generally cultivated in rotation with alfalfa, which furnishes the link with the raising of dairy cattle. Hemp, another important Soviet fiber, requires more warmth and is grown south of the flax belt, mainly in the Orel and Bryansk *oblasts* of the Russian S.F.S.R., in southern Belorussia, and also in the middle Volga region. A number of fiber plants were introduced for the first time by the Soviet regime into Central Asia; however, their production is of minor importance. These fibers are ramie or Chinese nettle, which furnishes a silky fiber, kendyr, which is used in the making of resistant cloth, and kenaf, a substitute for jute.

The sunflower is the predominant oil-bearing plant grown in the European U.S.S.R. where its area of major production coincides closely with the wheat surplus areas in the dry steppe of the southeast. Another oil-bearing plant, sesame, is produced chiefly in Central Asia. The Soviet Union cultivates a number of rubber-bearing plants, including the Mexican guayule and the native Central Asian *kok-sagyz* and *tau-sagyz*. However, the relative importance of natural plant rubber with respect to the synthetic rubber output of the U.S.S.R. is quite negligible.

While no tropical products such as coffee, cacao, and bananas are found in the Soviet Union, its subtropical areas do produce tea, citrus fruit, wine, and tobacco. Most of these products are grown in Transcaucasia and on the southern coast of the Crimea. The cultivation of tea and citrus fruit, particularly, is concentrated along the Black Sea littoral of Transcaucasia in the Georgian S.S.R., where humid subtropical conditions prevail. Wine is also produced at the northern foot of the Caucasus, as well as in the oases of Central Asia. In the case of tobacco, the Russian *makhorka* type stems mainly from the chernozem belt, with chief production areas in the Ukraine (near Poltava and Chernigov), and in the central European Russian S.F.S.R. (near Tambov and Saratov). The better-grade Turkish tobacco, on the other hand, is grown in the Caucasus region.

Just as the European U.S.S.R. contains the greater part of the sown acreage in the entire country, it harbors the greater proportion of livestock, with the emphasis on hogs toward the west, on dairy cattle toward the north, and on sheep toward the southeast. Semi-nomadic grazing prevails in the desert areas of Kazakhstan, Central Asia, and in the arid valleys of Transcaucasia.

Dairying is best developed in the central and northern parts of the European U.S.S.R. as well as in Western Siberia, with the emphasis on fresh-milk supply in the vicinity of urban centers and on butter and cheese in more remote regions. Beef cattle is concentrated in the steppe belt, where it is fed on root crops and the by-products of food processing and on pasture land.

Hog raising flourishes in the potato-growing areas of Belorussia and the chernozem belt of the central European U.S.S.R., as well as on by-products of food processing in the Ukraine and the Northern Caucasus. Sheep are raised predominantly in the arid sections of Kazakhstan and Central Asia, while horses are bred in the steppe belt.

Among other nonindustrial activities in the U.S.S.R., hunting and fishing play a major role in the economy. The hunting of fur-bearing animals has been a traditional source of riches in the history of Russian expansion. The U.S.S.R. continues to be the leading world supplier of furs, with the principal regions in Eastern Siberia, the Soviet Far East, and the northern European U.S.S.R. Fur farming has also been introduced.

The majority of Soviet fisheries are located in the Caspian Sea in Europe and in Far Eastern waters in Asia. The Caspian fisheries, concentrated near the mouth of the Volga River, furnish about 35 per cent of the total Soviet catch. They are favored by their nearness to the consumption centers of the European U.S.S.R. and to the salt deposits of Lake Baskunchak, two factors that work to the disadvantage of the remote Far Eastern fisheries, whose products are therefore largely exported. In Europe, other fisheries are along the Barents Sea coast of the Kola Peninsula, favored by the warm waters of the North Atlantic Drift, with their base at Murmansk. Mention should be made also of the vast Rybinsk Reservoir on the upper Volga where fish were introduced following its completion in 1940-41. As a result fishing has become of considerable importance among the lakeside population, which had been formerly engaged in a purely agricultural economy.

Mining and Industry

Since the start of the first five-year plan in 1928, through the 1930's and 1940's, the Soviet Union has experienced a remarkable growth of industrial production. New factories, power stations, and mines have been put into operation and modern machinery and techniques have been introduced. In accordance with the drive for an industrialized economy, emphasis was laid on the rapid growth of heavy industry, such as the production of machinery, industrial chemicals, power-generating and transportation equipment, as well as the related mining activities. The production of consumer goods, on the other hand, though increasing, lagged proportionately behind the development of heavy industry.

Typical of this tendency is the emphasis on the production of trucks in the automobile industry. The 1950 goal for the production of motor vehicles was set at 500,000, of which 428,000 were trucks. In general terms, the part of heavy industry in the total Soviet industrial output rose from 40 per cent in 1928 to 60 per cent in 1940, and a further relative increase took place during the 1940's.

And it was precisely within the sphere of the producer industries that the U.S.S.R. initiated the output of goods that had never been produced before within the country. Thus, it was able to curtail or greatly reduce the import of motor vehicles, tractors, various types of machinery (metallurgical, textile, printing, paper-making), steam hydraulic turbines, excavators, and similar equipment that would be needed by a country in full process of industrialization. New techniques were developed to use raw materials at hand. These included improved hydraulic methods for the use of the vast Russian peat deposits as power-station fuel, the underground conversion of coal into gas, and the development of synthetic rubber production.

At the same time there took place a considerable shift in the geographic distribution of industry and mining. Before the revolution and through the 1920's, there was a heavy concentration of these activities in four areas of the European U.S.S.R.: the Donets Basin, the Urals, Moscow, and Leningrad. Outlying European regions, including the Kola Peninsula, the northeastern Pechora region, and the arid southeast, were entirely undeveloped. Beyond the Urals, intensive exploitation of the natural resources was restricted to the narrow forest-steppe and steppe zone along the Trans-Siberian Railroad, and in Kazakhstan and Central Asia, only the long-settled oases could be considered as playing any major role in the economy.

The gradual shift of the industrial center of gravity toward the east became noticeable during the prewar five-year plans, particularly in the case of the Ural-Kuznetsk combine. This much-publicized Soviet industrial experiment involved the exchange of Kuznetsk coking coal and Urals iron ore over a distance of 1,200 miles and resulted in the creation of two of the Soviet Union's leading new steel centers—Magnitogorsk in the Urals and Stalinsk in the Kuznetsk Basin.

The gradual eastward shift of industry received a sudden impetus during the emergency period of the Second World War. This drastic change was the result not only of the removal of some 1,300 industrial plants from the war-threatened areas west of the Leningrad-Moscow-Stalingrad line but also of the accelerated building of industries and mines in the east. During the war industrial output in the Urals, in Siberia, as well as in the Volga Region rose three to four times. A further indication of the urban, and therefore, industrial growth of the east is the increase of cities during the war period. Of the total number of 67 new cities created in the U.S.S.R. during the years 1942-45, 53 were situated east of the Volga River. Following the end of the war, the eastern industries remained in their new location, while the destroyed areas of the west were rehabilitated during the postwar five-year plan, in part with the aid of machinery removed by the U.S.S.R. from Germany and Manchuria. The European U.S.S.R. thus continues to harbor by far the greater share of Soviet industries, but the industrial center of gravity has moved appreciably closer to the Urals.

In pursuing this policy of geographic decentralization, the Soviet regime has been motivated by a number of factors. There was the urge to move some of the industries nearer to the sources of raw materials as well as some of the outlying markets. Typical of the former situation was the shipment of Central Asian cotton to the mills of the Moscow-Ivanovo region and the long return haulage of the finished textiles to the consumers of the cotton-growing area. This the Soviets attempted to avoid through the building of large cotton mills in the very heart of the Central Asian cotton belt.

Another factor in dispersion was the desire to provide industries to theretofore nonindustrial areas with the ultimate aim of obtaining regional self-sufficiency to the greatest extent possible. According to a policy first stated in 1939, the Soviet Union seeks to organize districts with their independent fuel industry, production of building materials, as well as of mass consumption goods in the food and light industries. Such a policy, if successful, would result in considerable economic savings, such as reducing railroad hauls over great distances, as well as strategic advantages in minimizing the vulnerability of the U.S.S.R. to industrial disruption from military attack.

Power Resources. The distribution of Soviet power resources is uneven throughout the entire country. In the approximate order of their importance, these resources are coal, water power, firewood, petroleum and natural gas, peat, and oil shale. East of the Urals, for example, there is relatively little petroleum according to present data, and in the south there is little timber. However, following the principle of regional self-sufficiency, the Soviets are attempting to develop one type of fuel base or another in all the major economic areas of the country.

Within the European U.S.S.R., the richest power resources are (a) the coal of the Donets Basin, (b) the oil of the Caucasus, and the water power of the Dnieper River and the Caucasian torrents in the south, and (c) the Vorkuta coal, Ukhta oil, peat and water power of the far north. It is, therefore, the central part of the European U.S.S.R. that lacks abundant power supplies. And it is precisely here, in the highly industrial heart of the country, that about half of the power-consuming industries are located in the areas of Moscow, Ivanovo, and Gorki. These areas have come to be dependent on local power reserves, such as the lignitic coal of the Moscow Basin, the abundant peat east of Moscow, and timber. In order to reduce further the need for long-distance hauls of power fuels to this industrial region, a great effort has been made to raise locally available supplies. This effort has already borne fruit in the great hydroelectric stations of the upper Volga (at Uglich and Shcherbakov), to be supplemented in the future by the stations of Gorki and Kuibyshev. The further development of the vast oil-bearing region of the Second Baku between the Volga and the Urals may also reduce the power shortage in the central European U.S.S.R.

COAL. The predominant Soviet fuel resource is coal (Figure 149), supplying about two thirds of the needs of the economy. The well-known Donets Basin (Donbas) in the eastern Ukraine and the Lower Don region of the Russian S.F.S.R. is the leading producer. However, as a result of the development of new coal basins since the beginning of the Soviet regime, the share of the Donbas in the Soviet coal output has dropped from 87 per cent in 1913 to 35 per cent in 1950. At the same time, it should be noted that the absolute production of the Donbas rose from 25.3 million tons in 1913 to 95 million tons in 1950. The coal of the Donbas supplies the metallurgical and chemical industries of the southern European U.S.S.R., as well as the region's power stations and railroads. Of all the coal basins of the European U.S.S.R., the Donbas suffered the greatest damage during the Second World War (1945 production was 36.7 million tons), but has been completely rehabilitated during the postwar plan (1946-50).

Next in importance among the Soviet coal producers is the Kuznetsk Basin (Kuzbas) of southern Siberia. The third-ranking supplier of high-grade coking coal is the Karaganda Basin of central Kazakhstan, whose development also dates from the 1930's. Among the remaining major coal basins, all in the European U.S.S.R., are those of Moscow, the Urals, and Vorkuta. The Moscow Basin is of importance chiefly because of its nearness to the industrial heart of the country. Its lignitic coal of low caloric value and unsuitable for coking is employed primarily in the local power stations, of which the largest are at Stalinogorsk and Kaganovich near Kashira. It is also a raw material for the nitrate fertilizer production of Stalinogorsk.

Of the various coal fields of the Urals, the leading producers are the Kizel Basin of medium-grade coking coal and the lignite basin of Chelyabinsk. The Vorkuta basin of coking coal was developed during the 1940's after the laying of the North Pechora railroad

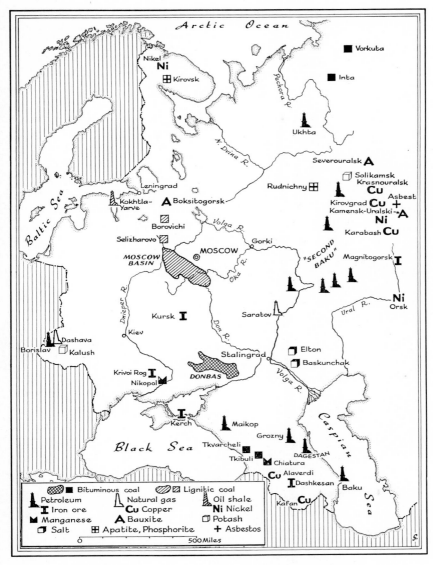

FIGURE 149. Mineral resources of the European U.S.S.R.

was completed in 1942. It supplies the Leningrad industrial area, and may in the future be linked directly with the northern Urals.

PETROLEUM. The Soviet Union is believed to have among the largest oil reserves in the world, if potential oil-bearing regions are taken into account. Its proven reserves, however, are less than 10 per cent of those of the world. The Baku oil field on the Apsheron Peninsula in the Azerbaijan S.S.R. can be termed the Donets Basin of the Soviet oil industry. Like the Donbas, it once had an overwhelming share of the production (85 per cent in 1913), which has dropped to 45 per cent in 1950 as a result of the development of new oil-bearing areas. Chief among these is the Second Baku, so called because of its vast potential resources rivaling those of Baku, but a misnomer if its vast area between the Volga and the Urals is compared to the concentrated reserves at Baku. Development began in the 1930's and in 1950 it produced just over one quarter of the total Soviet oil output.

In addition to these two leading fields, there are lesser fields near Grozny and Maikop in the Northern Caucasus, as well as the Ukhta area in the northern European U.S.S.R. and the former Polish field at the foot of the Carpathians in the western Ukraine.

PEAT. No other country has such vast peat reserves as the U.S.S.R. Although peat is of very low calorific value, the location of the peat bogs near the great industrial centers of the central European U.S.S.R. has enhanced the importance of peat as power station fuel. Confronted with this abundant, though uneconomic fuel, the U.S.S.R. has developed many processes to mechanize and speed the laborious processes of peat extraction, dehydration, and transportation to the power plants, all of which lie in the immediate vicinity of the peat bogs.

NATURAL GAS AND OIL SHALE. The natural gas industry of the U.S.S.R. developed only during the Second World War. While natural gas is associated with virtually all oil-producing regions, its use during the prewar five-year plans was in local power plants and for municipal and household needs. During the war, however, natural gas was found at Yelshanka, a suburb of Saratov on the Volga, and a pipeline to Moscow was completed in 1947. This was followed after the war by a pipeline from Dashava near Stry in the western Ukraine to Kiev, and one from Sultangulovo near Buguruslan to Kuibyshev.

Another major pipeline carrying oil-shale gas was completed in 1948 between Kokhtla-Yarve (Kohtla-Järve) in Estonia and Leningrad. The Estonian oil-shale field is the most important in the U.S.S.R., the product being converted into gasoline, fuel oil, as well as gas. Other installations of the oil-shale industry are just east of the Estonian field in the Leningrad Oblast of the Russian S.F.S.R. at Slantsy, and in the Middle Volga Region at Kashpirovka (southern suburb of Syzran), Gorny, and Ozinki in Saratov Oblast.

WATER POWER. Although most of the great potential water power resources of the U.S.S.R. lie outside the European portion of the nation, most of the hydroelectric development has been taking place in Europe, in the vicinity of the great production centers. The main water power producing areas are the Caucasus, particularly Transcaucasia, the Dnieper and the Volga in the middle reaches of the European U.S.S.R., and the Leningrad area and Kola Peninsula in the north. Construction scheduled under the present five-year plan includes the mammoth stations of Kuibyshev and Stalingrad on the Volga.

A characteristic feature of the Soviet power industry has been the creation of large regional interconnected systems supplying the main industrial areas. The major power systems—Moscow, Leningrad, Gorki-Ivanovo, Dnieper, Donets, Baku, Urals, and Kuzbas— are eventually to be connected into one unified national power system. Electrification of the economy has been a major objective since the very beginning of the Soviet regime and was expressed in the initial electrification plan adopted in 1920 and fulfilled within fifteen years. Production in kilowatt-hours rose from an insignificant two billion in 1913 to 40 billion in 1938 and 90 billion in 1950.

Iron and Steel. Historically, the first ironworks appeared in Russia in the early seventeenth century in the region between Tula and Moscow, using local iron ore and charcoal. During the reign of Peter the Great, the Russian ferrous metallurgy shifted abruptly to the Urals where higher-quality iron ore and timber reserves were abundant. During the late nineteenth century the center of production shifted again—to the southern European U.S.S.R., where the proximity of Krivoi Rog iron ore and Donbas coking coal furnished the basis of a new expanded industry.

This southern region is the leading producer of iron and steel although, as in coal and oil production, its once predominant position has been greatly reduced. In 1913, the south produced nearly 75 per cent of the iron and steel of Russia; in 1950, its output was one half of the total pig iron, but only one third of the total steel. This disparity in production is explained by the fact that the newer metallurgical centers are able to produce high-quality steel, but lack the optimum conditions for producing pig iron present in the south.

The southern metallurgical plants are grouped in three clusters —two near the sources of iron ore and one near the source of coking coal. The latter is the Donets Basin, which also has large reserves of limestone and contains the large integrated iron and steel centers of Voroshilovsk, Yenakiyevo, Makeyevka, and Stalino. The second cluster, situated in the vicinity of Krivoi Rog iron ore, consists of the metallurgical plants of Dnepropetrovsk, Dneprodzerzhinsk, Zaporozhe, and Krivoi Rog itself. The third cluster, which is based on Kerch iron ore, consists of the plants of Zhdanov (former Mariupol) and Kerch, which are linked by water across the Sea of Azov.

The so-called central metallurgical region includes the steel plants of the Moscow, Leningrad and Gorki areas, all of which are primarily dependent on scrap iron for their steel production. The region also includes the metallurgical centers of Tula and Lipetsk, whose iron production goes largely into cast-iron products.

Although it lies outside the European portion of the U.S.S.R., mention should be made of the eastern metallurgical region. This region has as its principal feature the Ural-Kuznetsk link, which gave rise in the 1930's to the great steel centers of Magnitogorsk and Stalinsk through a long-distance exchange of iron ore and coking coal. The link has since been considerably weakened by the development of other resources, such as Karaganda coal and the Kizel coal of the Urals, which is being made available more and more for coking purposes. In the Urals, there are, in addition to Magnitogorsk, the new metallurgical plants of Nizhni Tagil and Chelyabinsk, as well as numerous smaller reconstructed works, producing high-quality steels on a charcoal basis. Locally available manganese, chrome, and nickel ores are widely used by these plants.

Since World War II, the U.S.S.R. has completed metallurgical plants in many outlying areas of the country that previously lacked their own iron and steel resources.

Closely associated with the production of iron and steel in the U.S.S.R. is the ferroalloys industry. Ferromanganese, the most important of the ferroalloys, is produced at Zaporozhe on the basis of the nearby Nikopol manganese deposits, and at Zestafoni in Georgia on the basis of the Chiatura deposits, the two leading manganese-producing areas of the U.S.S.R. Other ferroalloy plants are in Siberia, at Chelyabinsk, using chrome and tungsten, and at Aktyubinsk, using chrome and nickel.

Nonferrous Metallurgy. Before the Bolshevik Revolution, the production of nonferrous metals was at a very low level although it had begun in the time of Peter the Great. Only small amounts of copper, lead, and zinc were produced, and no nickel, aluminum or tin. In its drive for self-sufficiency, the Soviet regime greatly increased the output or, in some areas, developed native resources of these metals, in many cases beyond the limits of the European portion of the U.S.S.R.

The chief centers of the copper industry were until recently in the Urals, where production dates from the early eighteenth century. Until the late 1930's, the Urals smelted the bulk (84.2 per cent in 1937) of Soviet copper. At that time, however, began the great development of the Kazakhstan deposits, which comprise more than half of the total U.S.S.R. deposits and are more than three times as large as those of the Urals. The rising production of the giant smelters at Balkhash and Dzhezkazgan placed Kazakhstan in the lead in copper production during the 1940's. The third copper-producing area of the U.S.S.R. is Armenia, where ores from Kafan and Alaverdi are smelted electrolytically at Alaverdi. The construction of a fourth copper-production base in the Uzbek S.S.R., whose reserves nearly equal those of the Urals, was begun in 1947 at Almalyk near Tashkent.

Lead and zinc are commonly found in conjunction with silver, gold, and copper in the so-called polymetallic ores. As in the case of copper, the largest Soviet reserves of lead and zinc are found in Kazakhstan—62 and 42 per cent respectively. While the smelting of lead could proceed in the Kazakh centers of Leninogorsk and Chimkent, the republic lacked zinc-smelting facilities until the construction, in the 1940's, of the electrolytic smelter at Ust-Kamenogorsk. Until that time, Kazakh zinc had to be shipped thousands of miles to smelters at Belovo in the Kuznetsk Basin, Chelyabinsk in the Urals, Konstantinovka in the Donets Basin, or even Dzaudzhikau in the Northern Caucasus. Of these centers outside of Kazakhstan, only Dzaudzhikau has a well developed raw-material base in the nearby Sadon deposits and Belovo gets its ores from the nearby Salair mine. Another lead-zinc center is situated in the Soviet Far East at Tetyukhe, with only lead-smelting facilities according to latest data.

The first Soviet aluminum was produced in 1933 at Volkhov on the basis of bauxite mined near by at Boksitogorsk (near Tikhvin). A second aluminum plant was opened later in Zaporozhe (also based on Boksitogorsk bauxite) and a third at Kamensk-Uralski, on the basis of local deposits. During World War II, however, with Volkhov and Zaporozhe in German hands, new aluminum sources were developed in the Urals, Armenia, and in the Kuznetsk

Basin. In addition to bauxite and alunite, the U.S.S.R. also converts nephelite from Kirovsk (Kola Peninsula) into aluminum at Kandalaksha.

The first nickel production began in the Urals in 1934 in Verkhni Ufalei and 1935 in Rezh near Sverdlovsk. Later plants were built at Orsk, Monchegorsk in the Kola Peninsula, and Norilsk in northern Siberia. After the war, the U.S.S.R. acquired from Finland the former Canadian-owned mine at Nikel near Pechenga.

Most of the mining and processing of other nonferrous metals and rare metals—tin, mercury, tungsten, molybdenum, and gold— takes place in the Asiatic U.S.S.R., particularly in Transbaikalia, Central Asia, and the Altai.

Manufacturing Industry. The machine-building industry occupies the foremost position in Soviet manufacturing (Figure 150), a development that is in line with the policy of all-out industrialization adopted in the early period of the Soviet regime. Within the machinery industry, emphasis was put on machine tools, agricultural implements, metallurgical equipment, electrical machinery, tractors, motor vehicles, river and ocean-going vessels and railroad rolling stock. Principles of rational location guided the U.S.S.R. in the erection of new machinery plants. Heavy machine tools and metallurgical equipment are produced in the Donets Basin and the Urals, precision instruments are made in old machinery centers (Moscow, Leningrad) where skilled manpower is available, and agricultural machinery plants naturally gravitate toward the major farming areas of the country.

The leading machine-building centers of the U.S.S.R. continue to be in the metropolitan areas of Moscow and Leningrad, as before the revolution. To these have been added the new machinery industries in the Donets Basin and elsewhere in the Ukraine, the Urals, and the Volga region.

The machine industry of the Urals received a strong impetus during World War II, as a result of the relocation of war-threatened plants and the building of new establishments. The leading center is Sverdlovsk. Nearly all large cities in the Volga region and those situated on the other leading waterways of the European U.S.S.R. have acquired machine industries during the last two decades.

The manufacture of fertilizer plays the greatest role in the chemical industry of the Soviet Union. This emphasis is motivated by the Soviet desire to increase the yield of the agricultural areas of the country and to bring new less fertile areas under cultivation. The leading types are phosphate, nitrate, and potash fertilizers. Phos-

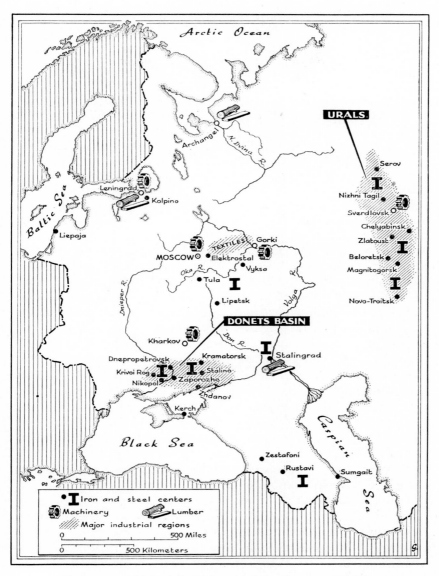

FIGURE 150. Major industrial areas of the European U.S.S.R.

phate fertilizers are based on the rich apatite deposits at Kirovsk on the Kola Peninsula and on the phosphorite deposits found at Rudnichny (Kirov Oblast) and Fosforitny (Moscow Oblast). There are superphosphate plants using these raw materials at Leningrad, Voskresensk (Moscow Oblast), Dzerzhinsk (near Gorki), Molotov, and Konstantinovka.

The production of synthetic nitrate fertilizers is derived mainly from coke by-products or by conversion from carbon monoxide. The major plants of this category are situated in the great coal-mining and metallurgical regions of the U.S.S.R. Outstanding examples are Stalinogorsk (Moscow Basin), Gorlovka (Donets Basin), Magnitogorsk (Urals), and Kemerovo (Kuznetsk Basin). Potash fertilizer is produced on the basis of the rich deposits of the Solikamsk-Berezniki area on the western slopes of the Urals and of Borislav-Drogobych in the western Ukraine.

Other notable chemical raw materials found in the U.S.S.R. are rock salt (at Artemovsk in the Donbas), which is found also in association with potash; mirabilite or Glauber salt (in the Kara-Bogaz-Gol inlet of the Caspian), sulphur in Turkmenistan, pyrite and chromite in the Urals, and borate in northwestern Kazakhstan.

The production of synthetic rubber plays a very important role in the chemical industry, since Soviet needs have got to be met from native rubber-bearing plants and rubber imports cannot be assured in time of war. Most Soviet production of synthetic rubber is based on the butadiene process, which uses potato alcohol as raw material. The first such plant was completed in 1932 in Yaroslavl, followed later by Voronezh, Yefremov (Tula Oblast), and Kazan. Another method, based on limestone and calcium carbide, is used by the synthetic rubber plant of Yerevan.

In view of the immense amount of new industrial construction in the U.S.S.R., much importance has been attached to the industry of building materials. The trend has been to provide each major economic area with its local production and no concentration of this industry is therefore evident. However, the production of cement has been traditionally associated with two major centers—Volsk on the middle Volga and Novorossisk on the Black Sea. Other localized products are chalk (at Belgorod, north of Kharkov), granite and diabase in the Karelo-Finnish S.S.R., and volcanic tuff and basalt in the Armenian S.S.R. Refractory materials needed by the metallurgical industry are generally located near the centers of demand, such as the Donets Basin, the Urals, the Kuznetsk Basin, and the Moscow Basin.

The bulk of Soviet timber resources (about 70 per cent) is found east of the Urals in Siberia and the Far East. Yet, because of the distance of these areas from the chief consuming centers and because of the lack of means of transportation, the center of gravity of the timber industry and its processing branches remains in the European U.S.S.R. Soviet timber resources yield construction lumber, wood for the furniture industry, paper, and a great variety of wood-distillation products, such as rosin and turpentine. Sawmills and plywood mills are typically located in the forested zone of the north, at the crossings of river and railroad. However, timber is also floated for great distances to the south and is then sawn at southern sawmilling centers for later shipment by railroad. Such a southern sawmilling center, situated in the treeless steppe, is Stalingrad, which receives its timber via the Volga River. The greatest northern sawmilling centers, working primarily for export, are Archangel in the European North and Igarka on the lower Yenisei River in northern Siberia.

The plywood industry, which uses the deciduous birch and alder as raw material, is concentrated in the mixed-forest belt, in the middle and western reaches of the European U.S.S.R. Furniture factories meet local requirements and are widely scattered through the country. Paper mills, in contrast, are large integrated plants located predominantly in the European North. These are situated north of the line Kiev-Moscow-Gorki-Molotov, with the older pre-revolutionary centers toward the west and the newer plants toward the east.

The match industry requires soft light wood (chiefly aspen) of the mixed-forest zone. Its main centers are all situated in the middle and western reaches of the European U.S.S.R. Finally, the distillation of wood has found its greatest development in the Urals, where it has been traditionally associated with charcoal production.

Cotton milling leads in the Soviet textile branch of the consumer industries. It continues to be concentrated in the old production centers of the Moscow-Ivanovo region and at Leningrad, but under the Soviet regime new mills have been opened in Central Asia and Transcaucasia, where most of the cotton is grown, and in Western Siberia, where the cotton is obtained in return for grain shipped to Central Asia via the Turksib Railroad.

The linen industry has also been concentrated in the Central Industrial Region, with Vyazniki and Kostroma the chief production centers. Under Soviet rule, new mills have also been located in the flax-growing region proper.

The woolen industry was located before the revolution in the areas of Moscow and Leningrad (fine cloths) and in the Central Chernozem Region and the Middle Volga (coarse cloths). During the Soviet regime, the tendency has been to bring the mills nearer the source of raw material, i.e., the sheep-raising regions of Kazakhstan and Transcaucasia.

Hemp, jute, and its substitute, kenaf, are used in the manufacture of fishing and marine equipment (ropes, sails, nets), and for other industrial products. New mills have been built at Murmansk and Archangel, but the bulk of the industry continues to be located in the middle reaches of the European U.S.S.R., near the hemp-growing areas and in the vicinity of large industrial centers.

The silk industry also is concentrated in the Central Industrial Region, although important mills are located near the raw-silk producing areas in Transcaucasia and Central Asia. Artificial silk and other fibers are increasingly produced.

Tanning and the production of shoes and leather products is fairly well scattered through the country, with the traditional centers at Kimry (Kalinin Oblast), Bogorodsk (Gorki Oblast), and the Kirov-Slobodskoi district. The latter area and Kazan also do most of the fur processing of the U.S.S.R.

In the food-processing sphere, the U.S.S.R. occupies a leading place in the world in the production of wheat flour and beet sugar. The food industry is widely distributed, with a view to local self-sufficiency. The largest food-processing centers are located both with respect to the large centers of consumption and the agricultural producing regions. Meat-packing plants, for example, are found not only at Moscow, Leningrad, Gorki, and Sverdlovsk but also in the Volga region, Kazakhstan, and Siberia, where the livestock is raised. Dairying has two favored locations—the Vologda region in the northern European U.S.S.R. and the Omsk-Novosibirsk belt of Western Siberia. Fish processing is naturally done at the great fishing centers—Murmansk and Archangel in the north, Kerch, Astrakhan, and Guryev in the south, and in the Far East. The canning of fruit and vegetables has important centers in the Northern Caucasus, the Ukraine, and the Moldavian S.S.R. Dried fruit, however, is a specialized product of Central Asia.

Transportation and Trade

In a country of the size of the Soviet Union, where production and consumption centers are frequently separated by thousands of miles, a major role is attached to means of transportation. This importance has been reduced very little by the policy of the establishment of nearly self-sufficient economic regions.

Certain fundamental factors have shaped the transport situation of the U.S.S.R. The predominant lowland topography of the country has offered little obstacle to the building of railroads. Most of the rivers, in contrast, are frozen from three to nine months every year. Moreover, the largest rivers flow through the sparsely populated Siberian part of the Soviet Union into seas of the Arctic Ocean that are also frozen most of the year. Highway transportation has played a negligible role because of the lack of good roads and the small number of motor vehicles. Coastwise shipping, while of some importance, is possible only where raw materials and consumers are located near the seaboard. As a result of these factors, it will be easily understood to what extent railroads predominate in the transportation picture of the Soviet Union. Under the plan for 1950, 80 per cent of all freight carried in the U.S.S.R. was to be handled by the railroads.

A glance at a railroad map of the European U.S.S.R. (Figure 151) shows an extremely uneven distribution of rail lines, with a relatively dense net (approaching the density found in Western Europe) west of a line Kharkov-Moscow-Leningrad, a progressive thinning out toward the Urals, and east of the Urals only isolated strands, seemingly lost in the vast regions they traverse. In the European U.S.S.R., where Moscow is the natural center of the net, the greatest density of rail lines is found to be in the Central Industrial Region and in the Ukraine, notably in the Donets Basin.

Since the Revolution, when the new state inherited about 40,000 miles of track, the length of the railroads has nearly doubled. Tsarist rail construction has been almost exclusively in the European part, with only the Trans-Siberian and the Trans-Caspian railroads extending into the outlying regions of Siberia and Central Asia. Soviet rail construction, in contrast, was motivated by the desire to begin the industrial exploitation of precisely these outlying regions. As a consequence, the overwhelming majority of new lines were laid there.

In the European U.S.S.R., rail construction completed after 1940 includes (1) the Vorkuta line, linking Leningrad with the oil and coal of the European North, (2) the Volga lateral line between Kazan and Stalingrad, (3) the direct link between the lower Volga and the Caucasus along the Caspian Sea between Astrakhan and Kizlyar, and (4) the shorter Black Sea route for trains to Transcaucasia.

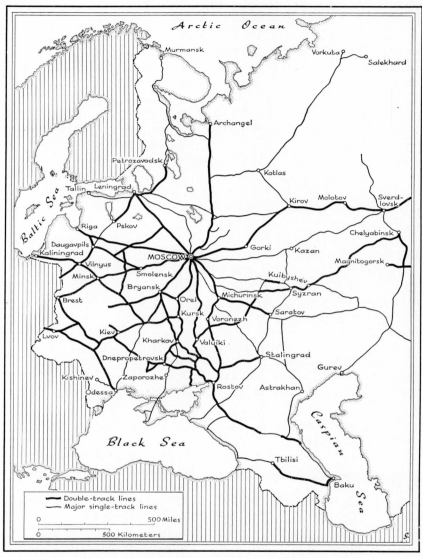

Arctic Ocean

Murmansk

Vorkuta

Salekhard

Archangel

Petrozavodsk

Kotlas

Baltic Sea

Tallin
Leningrad

Kirov
Molotov
Sverd-
lovsk

Riga
Pskov

Gorki
Kazan

Chelyabinsk

Daugavpils
Kaliningrad

MOSCOW

Magnitogorsk

Vilnyus
Smolensk

Kuibyshev

Minsk
Bryansk

Michurinsk
Syzran

Brest
Orel

Kursk
Saratov

Kiev
Voronezh

Lvov
Kharkov
Valuiki

Dnepropetrovsk
Stalingrad

Gurev

Kishinev
Zaporozhe

Odessa
Rostov
Astrakhan

Caspian Sea

Black Sea

Tbilisi

Baku

Double-track lines
Major single-track lines

0   500 Miles
0   500 Kilometers

FIGURE 151. Chief railroads of the European U.S.S.R.

654

In spite of the natural handicap inherent in the long winter
season, the waterways of the European U.S.S.R. (Figure 152) play
a considerable part in the carrying of freight during the open season.
Of a total length of 250,000 miles of waterways, about 60,000 miles
are navigable. Although much of this navigable length is accounted
for by the rivers of Siberia, they play as yet a minor role in the
river traffic. About half the traffic is handled by the Volga River
and its affluents. If the northwestern rivers (including the Neva
River) are included in the Volga system, we find that less than one
quarter of the navigable waterway net of the U.S.S.R. carries 70
per cent of the river traffic.

The dominating position of the Volga system in the river-freight
turnover is explained by the fact that the Volga River, the longest
of the European U.S.S.R., traverses with its tributaries one of the
most populated and economically developed sections of the country. At its widest spread the Volga system, if joined with the Neva,
extends from the Baltic at Leningrad to the Caspian at Astrakhan
and from Moscow to the Urals. In bulk, most of the freight consists of timber (downstream) and of petroleum (upstream). In
addition the system carries grain from the southern steppes, fish
from Astrakhan, and salt from Lake Baskunchak.

The Volga's position has been further enhanced by the construction of major connecting canals during the Soviet period. The
eighteenth-century Mariinsk system, repeatedly enlarged since the
revolution, links the Volga's Rybinsk Reservoir at Cherepovets with
the Neva River and Leningrad. Leningrad, in turn, is linked with
the White Sea by the Baltic-White Sea Canal, completed during
the early 1930's. The upper Volga is connected with Moscow by
the former Moscow-Volga Canal, completed in 1937 and since 1947
simply called Moscow Canal. These routes have linked the Caspian Sea with the Baltic Sea and the White Sea of the Arctic
Ocean. The final touch to this network was added in mid-1952
with the opening of the Volga-Don Canal, linking the Volga at
Stalingrad with the Don at Kalach. The completion of this long-
projected waterway tied in the Sea of Azov and the Black Sea, with
all their tributary streams, with the basic waterways of the European U.S.S.R.

In view of the continental character of the country, maritime
shipping plays a secondary role in the U.S.S.R. However, the bulk
of Soviet foreign trade is sea-borne and from this point of view
shipping is of some importance. The Black Sea handles more than
half of Soviet overseas trade, particularly oil, grain, and coal. The
leading Black Sea ports are Odessa, Nikolayev, Zhdanov (on the

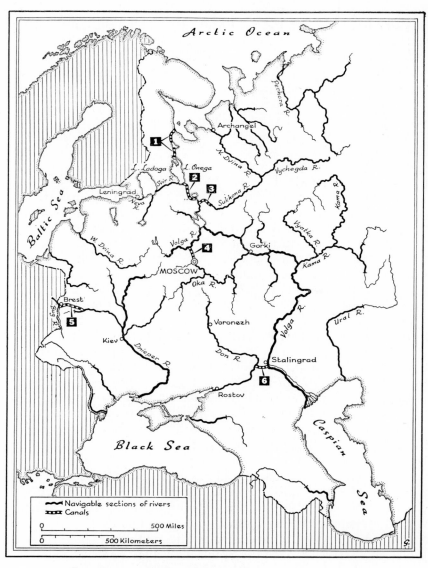

FIGURE 152. Chief waterways of the European U.S.S.R.

1. Baltic–White Sea Canal
2. Mariinsk Waterway
3. North Dvina Canal
4. Moscow Canal
5. Dnieper–Bug Canal
6. Volga–Don Canal

Sea of Azov), Novorossisk, and Batumi. On the Caspian Sea, the coastwise shipping of petroleum and petroleum products from Baku, and to a lesser extent from Makhachkala, to Astrakhan and up the Volga constitutes one of the leading water-freight routes of the U.S.S.R. Caspian shipping also handles the minor Soviet trade with Iran. The Baltic Sea constitutes the nearest route from the Soviet Union to the Atlantic Ocean. Some of the ports, such as Leningrad, Tallin, and Riga, are frozen in during part of the winter, but others (Liepaja, Kaliningrad) can be kept open. The Arctic seacoast of the U.S.S.R. is accessible all year round in the area of Murmansk, thanks to the North Atlantic Drift. Archangel, the other major northern port on the White Sea, is frozen in during the winter. Although the remainder of the Arctic coast, east of Novaya Zemlya, is frozen for nine months every year, some ships use the so-called Northern Sea Route during the navigation season, which is sometimes extended with the aid of icebreakers. The development of this northern route has long been a pet project of the Soviet planners, but even under optimum conditions it is only of minor significance as a maritime route between the European and Asiatic parts of the U.S.S.R.

Road transport, or trucking, plays a minor role in the Soviet freight-forwarding scheme. Trucks handle primarily short-distance hauls from and to railroad stations and river landings, as well as between nearby urban centers. Longer distances are covered, however, in areas lacking railroad and water transportation.

Air transportation in such a vast country as the U.S.S.R. is of relatively great importance, since it reaches many remote areas that are difficult of access by land or water. This is true particularly of all northern Siberia. The total length of Soviet air routes is said to exceed that of the United States. However, service on some of the northern routes is relatively infrequent and is also hampered by extreme winter conditions. Nor has night flying been perfected to such an extent as in the United States, which has a greatly superior net of radio installations serving the air lines.

The Prospect

Out of the industrial backwardness of the prerevolutionary Russia, the Soviet rulers of the country have created the second most powerful industrial nation in the world today. This remarkable achievement has been obtained at great cost to the personal freedom of the Soviet peoples and to their standard of living. In its effort of all-out industrialization, the Soviet regime has emphasized the production of heavy machinery, chemicals, iron and steel, and similar requirements of a modern industrial power, but has been neglecting the output of consumer goods on a proportionate level. It has thus maintained a standard of living considerably below that of the countries of Western Europe, whose standard of living, in turn, is lower than that of the United States.

The Soviet Union has repeatedly described its economic goal as the equalling and ultimate exceeding of the production levels of the industrial capitalist nations. This it has now achieved, with the notable exception of the United States. It is more than doubtful whether the U.S.S.R. will be able to overtake the industrial production of the United States in the foreseeable future. The announced long-range goals for the production of pig iron, steel, coal, and oil by 1960 merely would roughly equal the United States output of these materials in 1940 or 1941. Moreover, during and since the Second World War, the United States has been able to raise its production still further. Thus, while continued increases in the production of the U.S.S.R. can be anticipated in the future, it is unlikely that the United States will lose its world leadership in this respect.

The continued development of the Soviet Union will more and more be based on the natural resources of Siberia, the vast Asiatic part of the country in which only the beginnings in industrialization have been made. Power for the expanding industries will be furnished by the Angara and Yenisei rivers, whose long-planned hydroelectric projects still await realization. New railroad lines, particularly the Baikal-Amur trunk line, will have to be built, new cities founded along these new transportation routes, and more mineral deposits placed into exploitation. Agricultural areas, such as the Baraba and Kulunda steppes of Western Siberia will have to be turned into great food-producing areas to feed the additional industrial population.

In the European U.S.S.R., future development is closely linked with the current construction of the great dams at Kuibyshev and Stalingrad on the Volga and at Kakhovka on the lower Dnieper River. The two Volga dams and associated power plants will supply additional billions of kilowatt-hours to the Central Industrial Region around Moscow (Figure 153), to the developing industries of the Volga Region itself, and will be used to irrigate and place under cultivation vast new areas of the arid steppes of the southeast. Similarly, the Kakhovka dam will divert water into the dry South Ukrainian and Crimean steppes and consequently raise the yield of these regions.

FIGURE 153. Major physico-economic regions of the European U.S.S.R.

All these projects, of course, assume continued peace in the world. The outbreak of a major war would cancel many of these plans, as happened during the Second World War, and would again force the Soviet Union to harness all its resources for the production of war materials and the associated heavy industries. Whatever the future may hold for the country, it has much room for expansion in all phases of its economy as well as in its population, which would enable it to develop many of the untouched resources of one of the richest areas in the world.

BIBLIOGRAPHY

A. Books in English

Balzak, S. S., Vasyutin, V. F. and Feigin, Ya. G. *Economic Geography of the U.S.S.R.* American edition edited by Chauncy D. Harris. New York: The Macmillan Co., 1950.

Berg, L. S. *The Natural Regions of the U.S.S.R.* New York: The Macmillan Co., 1950.

Cressey, George B. *The Basis of Soviet Strength.* New York: McGraw-Hill Book Co., Inc., 1945.

Gray, G. D. B. *Soviet Land; the Country, Its People, and Their Work.* London: London, A. and C. Black, Ltd., 1947.

Gregory, J. S., and Shave, D. W. *The U.S.S.R.; a Geographical Survey.* New York: John Wiley & Sons, Inc., 1946.

Jorré, Georges. *The Soviet Union, the Land and Its People.* New York: Longmans, Green & Co., Inc., 1950.

Lorimer, F. *The Population of the Soviet Union: History and Prospects.* Geneva: League of Nations, 1946.

Mirov, N. T. *Geography of Russia.* New York: John Wiley & Sons, Inc., 1951.

Schwartz, Harry. *Russia's Soviet Economy.* New York: Prentice-Hall, Inc., 1950.

Shabad, Theodore. *Geography of the U.S.S.R.; a Regional Survey.* New York: Columbia University Press, 1951.

B. Books in Foreign Languages

Baranskiy, N. N. *Ekonomicheskaya Geografiya S.S.S.R.* (Economic Geography of the U.S.S.R.), 11th ed. Moscow: Uchpedgiz, 1950.

Chefranov, S. V. *Fizicheskaya Geografiya S.S.S.R.* (Physical Geography of the U.S.S.R.), 9th ed. Moscow: Uchpedgiz, 1950.

Dobrynin, B. F. *Fizicheskaya Geografiya S.S.S.R.* (Physical Geography of the U.S.S.R.). Moscow: Uchpedgiz, 1948.

George, Pierre. *U.R.S.S., Haute Asie, Iran.* Paris: Presses Universitaires de France, 1947.

Leimbach, Werner. *Die Sowjetunion: Natur, Volk, Wirtschaft* (The Soviet Union; The Land, Its People, and the Economy). Stuttgart: Franck'sche Verlag, 1950.

chapter 10

EUROPE IN THE WORLD'S ECONOMY

THE PRECEDING chapters have discussed the regions of Europe. In this concluding chapter its more recent economic history, its total resource pattern, and its position in international trade will be analyzed. The concluding pages of the chapter summarize what appear to be some of the more important facets of the problems of Europe of today and tomorrow.

Europe in the Victorian Age

The broad outline of Europe's historical geography has been given in Chapter 1, but we may pick up the thread of the discussion beginning with that remarkable period of modern history from the Industrial Revolution to the outbreak of World War I, during which modern capitalism and technology changed the institutional pattern of the world and formed the basis of our modern society. The Industrial Revolution provided the material basis for the important position which Europe was to achieve during the nineteenth century. Toward the end of the eighteenth century a political, economic, and social awakening began to sweep the Western World, superseding the tradition of an all-powerful state such as existed under mercantilism in countries like Britain or an already declining feudalism and absolute monarchy in other countries. In politics as well as economics there was an assertion of freedom of the individual, which gave birth to our modern concept of democracy as well as to that of capitalism. One has only to realize that such events as the signing of the Declaration of Independence in the United States and the publication of Adam Smith's

Wealth of Nations in Britain took place in the same year, 1776, only shortly before the French Revolution in 1789, to see the widespread nature of these changes.

The absence of war among the major powers for most of the period from 1815 to 1914, the Hundred Years' Peace, was unique in Europe's history. This was an essential condition for the development of the self-regulating market mechanism of capitalism, i.e., the operation of economic forces through the market place with a minimum of interference from the government. It also facilitated the spreading of the material gains made.

One special feature of this period is of particular relevance to our discussion of the trade of Europe. During this time a monetary system—the gold standard—was developed under which domestic currencies were freely convertible into gold at a fixed price. This meant, of course, that currencies were convertible into each other, also at a fixed price. Thus, there were no financial impediments to the transfer of money from one country to another.

What were some of the more salient features of Europe's economy just before the outbreak of the First World War? Europe had reached the pinnacle of her power position in the world. The importance of the United States in the economic and political affairs of the world had only recently been fully felt. The full sovereignty of the British Dominions under the common crown was just being recognized; Tsarist Russia had just started to feel the rumblings of the eventual breakdown of her feudal order. The industrial countries that were able to produce the material goods necessary for a higher standard of living, as well as for political power, were largely European. The degree and speed with which various European countries were affected by these broad changes differed widely. In this respect, the hegemony of Great Britain can be seen in the position which the British pound and the Bank of England occupied during this period in the field of international finance, the handmaiden of international trade.

Great Britain. Britain was in a particularly favorable position to adopt these new ideas and methods, which made her the first among the family of nations. During the eighteenth century the guilds had lost much of the influence they had enjoyed a century earlier. As long as they were still powerful, they had been quite successful in suppressing the use of machinery in an attempt to preserve jobs. The decline of the guilds and the development of machinery coincided with the introduction of mechanical power in the eighteenth century, a *sine qua non* of modern industry.

The availability of this power stimulated the invention of James Watt's steam engine and of such mechanical, power-driven devices as Hargreaves's spinning jenny, Arkwright's waterframe, Crompton's mule, and Cartwright's powerloom, and revolutionized transportation by making possible steam engines on railroads and ships. Britain was in a good position to develop these new inventions. As the leading colonial power she had the markets which could absorb the ever-increasing stream of goods which was soon to pour out of her workshops. At the same time the need for iron (later steel) for those machines stimulated the development of the iron, coal, and steel industries. Fortunately for Britain, she was well supplied with the necessary coal and iron deposits suitably located to make these developments possible. Her resources of iron ore and coal of coking quality have been one of the basic pillars of British economic development. Darby's development of coal for coke, which replaced charcoal in the eighteenth century, was followed by other improvements such as the Bessemer process of steel making in 1856, and the Thomas-Gilchrist process which made it possible to use phosphorous iron ore.

The development of Great Britain was further aided by the opening of the vast food resources of the New World. With the improvements in transportation made possible by this mechanical age, the produce from these new regions could be sold more cheaply in Britain than it could be produced there. The abundance of food and raw materials which thus became available allayed, at least temporarily, the Malthusian fear of an eventual overpopulation of the Western World. Consequently, Britain gave up the protection of her agriculture by such means as the abolition of the Corn Laws in 1846, and developed her industries to sell the products of her factories in exchange for the food and raw materials of the overseas world which she controlled. The outpouring of the British workshops was large enough not only to provide the income to buy the needed produce from overseas, but also to provide a substantial excess income which was invested abroad. These investments, in turn, soon yielded handsome returns. In fact, by the end of the nineteenth century these returns were large enough to permit Britain to import more goods than she exported, pay for this import surplus with the income from investments, and have enough left over to make still further investments!

It must be remembered that Britain had not been ravaged by war since 1066. The damage done by her civil wars was small in comparison with the devastation of war which had occurred on the continent. To be sure, Britain's navy had fought battles, her soldiers had been fighting on foreign battlefields, and she had had to finance foreign armies. But her domestic industries, social institutions, and economic life were not interrupted, as they had often been on the continent. Thus, the period following the Napoleonic Wars, which had created a serious inflationary problem on the continent, was for her a century of exceptional economic expansion and tranquillity.

In the fall of 1914 a truly remarkable century came to an end. At that time products from the far corners of the earth could be bought and sold freely in the major trading centers of Europe, with Britain as the trading center par excellence. The staples of the United States' plains, the tropical fruits of Asia or South America, the spices of the East, or the silks of the Orient—all were available to anyone with the money to pay for them. There was a feeling of contentment and economic security despite the gathering war clouds. It seemed as if the future could bring only further progress. Not only could goods be shipped from the far corners of the earth, but travel was equally free and unhampered. Money could be taken along without restrictions, or could be invested wherever it might suit the fancy of the investor. This was regarded as the "normal" state of affairs.

However, difficulties had begun to appear on the horizon. A large percentage of the population had a low standard of living. Although many people seemed reasonably content with their lot and their chances for advancement, the ferment of unrest was clearly evident in the rise of the Labor Party in Britain and the Social Democrats on the continent. Political struggles between the rising industrial powers became more and more intensive. This was accompanied by, and in part caused by, the competition for markets. The rapidly increasing population of Europe created greater pressures for the importation of food and an increasing reliance on foreign trade. At the same time, the increase in population overseas still further increased the demand for food and resulted in rising prices of food relative to those of the industrial products of Europe, a worsening of Europe's terms of trade. In other words, forces which eventually destroyed the illusion of stability were present, but not dominant, even during the Victorian Age.

Although the Industrial Revolution centered in the British Isles, it spread overseas and southeastward through Europe, a development which is still in progress. The impact of this development differed, of course, from country to country in its intensity and the time of occurrence. Many of the essentially agricultural countries of East Central and Southern Europe, with their rapidly increasing population, have only recently begun any large-scale efforts at industrialization.

France. Although the industrialization of France had started several decades earlier, the Thomas-Gilchrist process of making steel in 1878 made the minette ore of France the basis for an important expansion of its industrial development. The rate of progress was not high enough, however, to overcome the nation's lag behind her neighbor across the Channel. Economically, France was handicapped by a shortage of coal, large quantities of which had to be imported, and the absence of vast markets in her empire. Furthermore, France had deliberately maintained a policy of protecting her agriculture from foreign competition, thereby retarding the shift of productive resources from agriculture to industry. This meant a high-cost food supply and a retardation of industrialization. French population growth had been slight since the Napoleonic Wars, and agriculture had been handicapped by the inefficiency resulting from the exceedingly small plots of land owned by individual farmers.

Psychologically, France has not had a tradition of commerce such as existed in Britain. Law and politics rather than industry and trade seemed to present the most desirable careers. Many Frenchmen, therefore, did not invest their savings in equity capital where it might help the development of industry. They preferred "sound" government bonds. Foreign government bonds, especially those of Russia, became favorite French investments. Thus, industrialization, as compared with its development in the British Isles, was greatly retarded. The underlying belief in the stability of the status quo was as evident in France as it was across the Channel.

Germany. Modern Germany traces its origin to the German customs union which eliminated the trade barriers between the many small but sovereign states which were a heritage of the Holy Roman Empire. This customs union led to the foundation of the German Empire after the war with France in 1871. After this unification, industrialization advanced rapidly, directly fostered by the protective policies of the German government. Industrial development was greatest in the Ruhr district, near the abundant coal supplies. With this good quality coal, the iron ore of the Lorraine, and a helping hand from the government, Germany rapidly became the industrial and economic hub of the continent. Her lack of extensive overseas territories and her late start in entering the race for industrialization were compensated by her trade with Europe. The very fact that Germany was a late-comer gave her certain advantages. Her industrial plant was the most up to date technologically, her industries could be located in conformity with newer methods, and she could profit by the mistakes of others. Indeed, the industrial reparations imposed on Germany after World War I gave her the same advantage in the interwar period, and the widespread destruction of World War II may again have similar effects. Germany's location in the heart of the continent, astride many of the main transportation routes, favored such a development. Progress was so rapid that by the time World War I broke out "Germany was the best customer of Russia, Norway, Holland, Belgium, Switzerland, Italy, and Austria-Hungary; she was the second best customer of Great Britain, Sweden, and Denmark; and the third best customer of France. She was the largest source of supply to Russia, Norway, Sweden, Denmark, Holland, Switzerland, Italy, Austria-Hungary, Roumania, and Bulgaria; and the second largest source of supply to Great Britain, Belgium, and France."[1] This very rapid expansion of the industrial economy of Germany may in large part be responsible for the political instability or immaturity of Germany.[2] It also created a desire for overseas markets and political expansion.

The elements of instability and change which were to make the interwar period so different from the preceding century were present when the holocaust of World War I tore apart the economic and social structure of Europe to such an extent that the countries of Europe never really recovered from its aftermath.

Europe Since 1918

When Germany surrendered in 1918, both victor and vanquished were exhausted. The destruction of life and property was great. Previously existing channels of trade were disrupted. The United States, a relative newcomer, emerged as a great industrial nation in the New World. Belief in the stability and future of the economic and social order was greatly shaken in some coun-

[1] John M. Keynes, *The Economic Consequences of the Peace* (New York: Harcourt, Brace & Howe, 1920) p. 17.

[2] Thorstein Veblen in his *Imperial Germany and the Industrial Revolution* (New York: The Macmillan Co., 1924) suggests that one of the important factors distinguishing developments in England from those in Germany was that in the former the changes from a feudal to an industrial society were slow enough to permit an adjustment, while in the latter industrialization was compressed into a short period and adopted from England without concomitant changes in the social and political order.

tries and destroyed in others. Thus, World War I ushered in an era of uncertainty.

To help finance her war expenditures, Britain had sold a large part of her foreign investments with concomitant loss of income. Many foreign investments, especially in East Central Europe and Eastern Europe, became worthless. The gold standard, which had been suspended at the outbreak of hostilities in 1914, remained suspended except for a few years from 1926 to 1931 in Great Britain and a few years longer in some other countries such as France, Switzerland, Belgium and the Netherlands. Inflation swept the continent and currency values fluctuated widely. By 1920 prices had increased by more than 200 per cent in the Netherlands, by almost 300 per cent in Sweden, by 400 per cent in France, 500 per cent in Italy, and were about ten times their prewar level in Germany. Compare this inflation with the slightly more than doubling of prices which took place in the United States and the United Kingdom. A little later hyperinflation or extreme inflation completely destroyed the existing currency in countries like Germany and Hungary, a condition unimaginable only a few years earlier.

This inflation, of course, resulted from (a) the destruction of goods and facilities for producing goods, (b) the increased demand for goods destroyed during the war, (c) the population's desire to purchase the things they were deprived of during the war, (d) the large increase in the money supply and the purchasing power which had been created as a result of war financing, and (e) the need for exports and the difficulty of obtaining imports.

The economic upheaval resulting from this inflation was accompanied by political and social unrest. The revolution of 1918 put the Soviet government into power. Similar uprisings occurred throughout East Central Europe and were temporarily successful in some countries, such as Hungary. Strife and unrest, if not revolution meant that industrial Europe fell still further behind the United States in improving its methods and increasing its volume of production.

It was not until the middle of the 1920's that a semblance of economic stability reappeared. Germany put its currency on a new basis in 1923, the British pound went back on a gold standard at the prewar parity in 1926, France regained stability in 1928. As in the United States, the prevailing opinion in Europe during the middle 1920's was that stability and progress were at last returning. This was true despite the fact that many of Europe's long-established industries, especially its export industries, were losing to foreign competitors, and despite the fact that there was unemployment in most of the industrialized countries. Living standards, especially in the agricultural countries, remained at a low level. The reliance of Europe on capital investment by the United States [3] increased the dependence of the former on the latter. The keeping of exchange reserves in London, the so-called gold exchange standard, meant that any disturbance in one European country would spread rapidly to others. Except for a short-lived price inflation after the end of hostilities in 1918, agricultural prices started to decline relative to industrial prices. This gave the industrial countries some advantage and for a time obscured the decline of the world position which industrial Europe had enjoyed. Thus, the 1920's produced only a partial recovery from the aftermath of the war.

At the close of the third decade all hope of lasting prosperity was shattered. The first spectacular sign, although not the cause, of the collapse [4] was the stock market crash in the United States in 1929, after which the flow of American capital to Europe ceased except for a brief period in 1930. Early in 1931, one of the leading Austrian banks failed and precipitated the collapse of the international structure. This was followed by the failure of a leading German bank, whereupon the crisis spread rapidly all over Europe. In an attempt to save their own economies from the spreading paralysis, nearly all countries imposed sharp restrictions on international trade and finance. During this period exchange controls, import quotas, export subsidies, and similar measures were introduced on a large scale. Tariffs, the traditional weapon of commercial policy, were also raised substantially, although they became relatively less important in the control over trade. These restrictions were not only in the form of government restrictions. Private controls in the form of domestic and international restrictions through cartels and similar devices were also intensified. This return to autarchy and restrictive trade practices was combined with upsurges of nationalism. Perhaps the most important of these was the rise of German nationalism and the attempt to increase her political power by making such areas as the Balkans increasingly dependent on Germany economically. German nationalism also provided a threat to political security on the continent.

[3] Although the bulk of these investments were made in Central and East Central Europe in the first instance, the dollars so obtained were diffused throughout Europe.
[4] The level and pattern of economic activity and employment varied substantially from country to country, which meant that depressed domestic conditions existed in many cases even before the fall of 1929.

Some recovery from the low ebb of economic activity in most industrial countries as well as some recovery of the very low price level of agricultural products was evident in the middle and later 1930's. Innumerable efforts were made, with only limited success, to reduce trade barriers which had only recently been introduced. The rearmament boom, of course, did not get under way in most countries except Germany until late in the decade, mostly after Munich in 1938. Progress toward recovery had been made toward the end of the 1930's, but in 1939, war was again imposed on the economic system of a Europe still suffering from the effects of the earlier conflict and the more recent depression.

Postwar Europe

Some of the major consequences of this second conflagration can perhaps be summarized under five points.[5] In the first place, the loss of life among soldiers and civilians was great. The loss of life was concentrated in the younger age brackets of men. When this younger generation takes over from its elders, its ranks will be severely thinned and many of the best men will be gone. In fact, this particular aftereffect of World War I is felt very severely right now by such countries as Great Britain and France. The loss of life during World War II was, for some countries, on a smaller scale than in the earlier war. It is estimated that the losses of Great Britain and France during World War II were 400,000 and 650,000 men, respectively. On the other hand the loss of life in the U.S.S.R., Poland, and Germany was high. Estimates of German losses vary greatly, but probably exceeded 5 million people. This has been partially offset by a large influx of refugees.

At the same time, birth rates went up during the decade 1939-50, while deaths from natural causes, especially infant mortality, continued to decline. The population of Europe actually increased 10 per cent during this period. This increase was a reversal for some countries, particularly for France. The annual French increase of 500,000 during the years 1946-50 was the largest for any five-year period since population figures were first compiled in that country in 1811. For other countries, many of which were overpopulated, this increase in population still further aggravated the economic problem of raising the standard of living. Higher production was now needed simply to maintain existing levels.

[5] Most of these points were suggested by the Bank for International Settlements, *Twenty-First Annual Report*, 1950-1951 (Basel, Switzerland), pp. 7-13.

The second major point is the extensive destruction of property —much greater than in the earlier wars—not only in Europe itself but also in the overseas possessions such as the Malay Peninsula and Indonesia. To the physical destruction must be added the absence of repairs and replacements which permitted the physical plant to deteriorate during the war. As an offset against this great destruction we must take into account the new technological improvements which increased the potential for speedy recovery. Another type of destruction, widely publicized, was the loss of foreign investments which it will be difficult, if not impossible, to recover. France almost lost her creditor position. Great Britain suffered a further sharp decline in her holdings of foreign securities, and at the same time acquired a large short-term indebtedness.

The third major difficulty to be emphasized is the disorganization of trade resulting from the war. This took the form of diversion of trade from its normal channels, distorted price standards and structures, and the undermining of monetary systems. This disorganization may well turn out to be one of the most serious consequences of the war. The shortages of goods and the increased money supply resulting from the war created inflationary problems all over Europe. In many countries (Greece is a good example) hyperinflation almost completely destroyed the value of money. In only a few countries, such as Belgium and Germany, did the government reduce the money supply drastically. In still others (the United Kingdom, for example) the government tried to suppress inflation by price control and increased taxation.

The only basic solution to this problem, of course, is higher productivity, not just higher production, and this takes time.[6] Such higher productivity could result either from a more intensive use of capital equipment in domestic industries or from a greater domestic and international specialization, i.e., a substantial relaxation of the barriers to trade. The immediate effects of the greater production of capital goods tend to be inflationary, however, because they create purchasing power—wages, etc.—without providing more consumable goods. This imbalance between goods for sale and purchasing power is one of the major reasons for the almost desperate need of Europe for imports.

The fourth major postwar problem is the survival of ideas from the 1930's which are not applicable to the problem of reconstruction. The depression years and the twin specters of unemployment

[6] Productivity refers to output per unit of a factor of production such as land and labor used, while production is the total amount produced.

and falling prices still dominate the thinking of many policy makers, despite the fact that these were not the problems of the inflationary 1940's and are even less the problems of the 1950's. The expected postwar depression never materialized, despite a minor delayed recession in the United States in 1949. Nevertheless, the haunting fear of a repetition of the depression years still stalked Europe.

Finally, the changed attitude of the United States in international affairs, particularly economic matters, has been of the greatest significance to Europe. After World War I the United States had remained aloof from all international organizations, political or economic. This time, the United States government not only took part in the various organizations and attempts to re-create order out of chaos, but actually took the initiative in many of the postwar programs.

During the later 1940's great strides were made in the rehabilitation of Europe. Production in most countries exceeded the prewar output by substantial margins. Attempts to liberalize trade were moderately successful, at least as far as intra-European trade was concerned. The unbalance in Europe's international accounts was greatly reduced, despite difficulties resulting from the East-West split. By 1952, however, much of the hard-won progress which had been made was again jeopardized by the great burdens imposed on Europe by the rearmament program. The grim cycle had entered a new and yet tragically familiar stage.

The foregoing brief summary of European economic history should have made clear several significant points. Ever since World War I, Europe has lived in an era of uncertainty and instability. Two major wars and a severe depression disrupted the European economic structure to the point where it is impossible to discern any condition which might be considered "normal." Severe trade restrictions were imposed by the governments in an attempt to insulate their own countries, while producer organizations tried to stem the tide of deflation by reducing competition among themselves and by restricting output in the hope of preventing prices from falling. At the same time the agricultural countries were much less successful in maintaining the price level of primary products, thus creating economic havoc in the countries depending on agricultural and mineral exports. Unless these basic trends are fully appreciated, current developments in Europe cannot be understood. It is against this general background that the total resource pattern and trade of Europe will be examined.

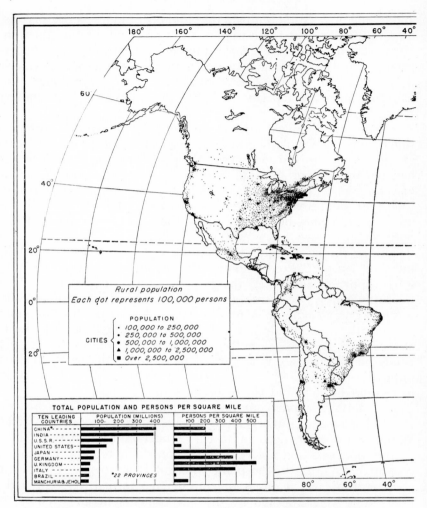

FIGURE 154. World population, according to an official map of the United States distribution obtains for the postwar world.

Europe's Resources

Human Resources. The human resources of Europe are one of its greatest assets, and at the same time form the basis for one of its major problems. The continent is densely populated (Figure 154 and Table 7).[7] This has been true for a long time, with the result that labor is abundant relative to the other factors of pro-

[7] All tables are to be found in Appendix III. The reader will need to refer to them while reading the balance of this chapter.

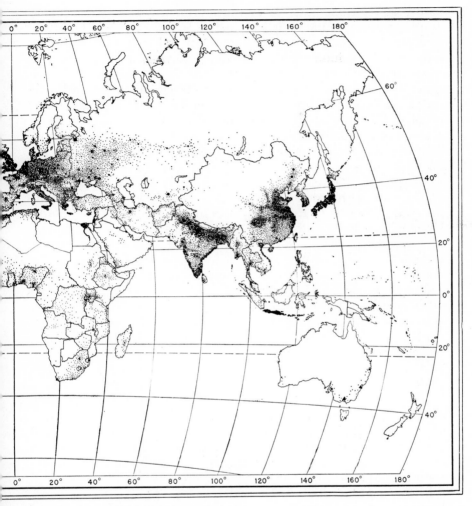

tment of Agriculture. Although this map is based on prewar data, much the same pattern of

duction—land and capital. It has also meant that, in the competitive struggle for advancement, the individual had to develop specialized skills. The net result of this, particularly in industrial Europe, is a tradition of relatively cheap, i.e., low paid, artisans and technicians which has enabled Europe to become the workshop it is. At the same time, the high concentration of population has made it impossible for Europe to produce enough food, and trade became the lifeblood of many countries. In the predominantly agricultural parts of Europe, primarily East Central and Southern Europe, industrialization has lagged. A typical illustration of this is Italy, particularly southern Italy with its high birth rate, its lack of industrialization, and its low living standards. In these countries suitable employment and the development of non-agricultural skills have of necessity been extremely limited, with the result that overpopulation on the farm has been a most serious problem. The pressure of these increasing populations has meant a very low standard of living and frequently a desire to emigrate. This explains the paradox that the human resources of Europe are one of its main assets and at the same time one of its chief problems.

Despite its dominant role in the world, Europe has only about 25 per cent of the total population. This ratio is declining as the population growth in Europe lags behind that of other continents. Even within Europe there are significant differences in the rate of increase. Generally speaking, the countries with the highest standard of living seem to show the lowest increase. Although the rate of increase has declined, the population of Europe has continued to increase, with the remarkable acceleration toward the end of the first half of this century we have mentioned above. Whether this is a temporary phenomenon resulting from the war or a permanent change, remains to be seen. Europe's population increased by some 20 million people during the decade from 1939 to 1949.[8] This continuous demographic expansion represents a very real challenge to the economic capacity of Europe.

The age distribution of a population is of great significance in evaluating the potential of an area. After all, it is only in certain age brackets that people are most productive. The very old and the very young are primarily consumers and not producers. An analysis of the data will show that Europe has a smaller concentration in the youngest age brackets than the world as a whole and a heavier concentration in the older group. This pattern is more typical of the industrialized parts of Europe, while agricultural Europe more closely resembles the world pattern. Several factors account for this difference. As Europe's population growth is arrested, or in some countries actually declines, the percentage of people in the younger age brackets declines while the percentage of older people increases. This tendency is accentuated by the fact that mortality rates (including infant mortality) decline in the

---

[8] This is a U.N. estimate: *U.N. Demographic Yearbook, 1949/1950* (New York, 1950), p. 10. The Bank for International Settlements, *op. cit.*, p. 7, estimates that the population of Europe increased by 10 per cent from 1939 to 1950. On the basis of U.N. population figures, this would mean an increase of 57 million.

industrial areas with a high standard of living, as a result of better sanitary conditions, nutritional standards, and medical attention. This means that more people live to middle and old age. It also means, of course, increased productivity and an extension of the useful span of life.

This aging of the population may have some serious consequences. It is not only in terms of productivity, and thereby in terms of the standard of living, that an aging population can lead to a decline. An older people tends to become more conservative and less willing to accept new ideas and changes. This can easily lead to what may be called a hardening of the arteries of the social and economic system. One of the reasons why countries which are expanding through immigration are making such rapid progress is that their population increase is concentrated in the most productive age brackets without the immediate concomitant increase in nonproductive infants and old folks. The experience of the United States during her period of rapid growth is a good illustration of this fact. The reverse also holds true. Emigration does not present the simple panacea to the overpopulation of Europe that many seem to think, because the emigrants generally come from that part of the population which is most productive because of age or other characteristics. This difficulty has been recognized in only a very few emigration schemes under which whole villages, instead of just a few of the more productive individuals, have been resettled overseas. Thus, the problem of the age distribution deserves more attention than it is frequently given. In the study of the resource pattern of a continent the human resources are all-important. It is only in conjunction with the study of these human resources that a study of the nonhuman resources, including technology, makes any sense.

Industrial Resources. Iron and steel are still the basis of present-day manufacturing. Despite the rising importance of such industries as light metals, plastics, and the chemical industries, Europe's importance in this respect is significant, although its relative importance has declined. When the percentage distributions of the world's manufacturing from 1870 to 1936-38 and of mining and industrial production from 1937 to 1952—to bring the former series roughly up to date—are compared, it is apparent that the relative position of both Great Britain and France has declined. Germany's importance was increasing before World War I, but its relative position has declined since that time, although it has already recovered somewhat from the low position imposed by its defeat and industrial disorganization. On the other hand, the relative importance of the United States and the Soviet Union has risen sharply. At the same time, rising industrial centers overseas, such as Canada, have also increased their share of the world's production.

Comparisons of production by specific industries are difficult but a comparison of production in terms of the basic ingredients of industry will be useful. In 1952, the three major industrial powers of Europe (Great Britain, France, and Germany) produced about one fifth of the world's mining and industrial production, compared to over 10 per cent for the U.S.S.R. and close to 50 per cent for the United States. Of the world production of steel, Europe (excluding the U.S.S.R.) at present produces about 35 per cent of the world total, the United States about 45 per cent, and the U.S.S.R. is estimated to produce about 15 per cent. Within Europe, Great Britain, France, and Germany are the most important producers and among them they account for over two thirds of Europe's production.

Europe is an important producer of other basic raw materials. Here again the productive capacity of Europe is underlined by the fact that in many cases the continent's relative importance as a producer of the refined metal is much larger than its importance as a producer of the basic ore. This is illustrated by the fact that Europe in 1949 produced one third of the world's tin while it produced practically no tin ore. It should be noted that the production of most of these basic materials is concentrated in a few countries. This uneven distribution of the available resources again emphasizes the need for trade.

COAL AND STEEL. In view of the importance of coal, iron, and steel a somewhat more detailed discussion of these industries is called for. Even a cursory examination of Figure 155 discloses the very uneven distribution of the continent's resources of iron ore and coal. The map shows two areas of concentration, one in Britain and one on the continent in a triangle stretching northwestward from the coal fields of the Ruhr through the Netherlands and Belgium to the coal fields of northern France, and pointing southward to include the iron ore deposits of Lorraine.[9]

In 1937, a representative prewar year, the coal fields of Great Britain and western Germany produced about two thirds of all

---

[9] This discussion relies heavily on the article "The Coal and Steel Industries of Western Europe," U.N. Economic Commission for Europe, *Economic Bulletin for Europe*, II, No. 2 (October, 1950), 18-51.

coal consumed in Europe (excluding the U.S.S.R.). If the production from the coal fields now located in Poland were included, this figure would mount to 75 per cent. The same general pattern has prevailed in the postwar period. Countries like Denmark, Italy, Luxembourg, Norway, Sweden, and Switzerland have always been almost entirely dependent upon imported coal. Most of these countries have made a great effort to develop hydroelectric power. France, the third largest producer of coal on the continent, was also the largest importer of coal. The steel industry of France was particularly dependent upon metallurgical coal imported from her neighbors, especially Germany; France, in return, was able to supply Germany with iron ore. The importance of trade is underlined by Belgium and the Netherlands, who both import and export coal of different qualities for different purposes. All of this re-emphasizes the importance of coal to modern industry and focuses attention on the need for an expansion of coal production for an expanding industrial economy.

The steel-producing "triangle" on the continent presents two distinct patterns of development. The first pattern is based on the local availability of iron ore, used in conjunction with imported coal and coke. This pattern prevails in the Lorraine iron and steel center, which (in 1937) produced about 70 per cent of the pig iron production and about 60 per cent of the crude steel of France. The same pattern is true of Luxembourg. The reverse pattern, the importation of the iron ore for use with the local coal supplies, prevails in the Ruhr, which has the most abundant high quality coking coal in Europe. The same is true in Belgium, northern France, the Netherlands, and the Saar. These facts emphasize the extent to which Europe depends upon international trade.

The interdependence of Europe in this basic industry is not a recent phenomenon. France, despite its large production of coal, much of which is of low quality, imported 30 per cent of her coke in 1937 and over 40 per cent in 1949, mainly from Germany. For France (including the Saar), imports of coke have averaged between 25 and 30 per cent both before the war and in 1950. The Saar is almost completely self-sufficient in coking coal, while Luxembourg is almost entirely dependent upon coking coal from Germany.

The German Ruhr depended heavily on imports of iron ore. Before the war over 60 per cent of the iron ore it needed came from foreign countries, while in 1950 only one third of its need was foreign ore. This decline resulted largely from the lower production of steel. Domestic production of iron ore was close to pre-

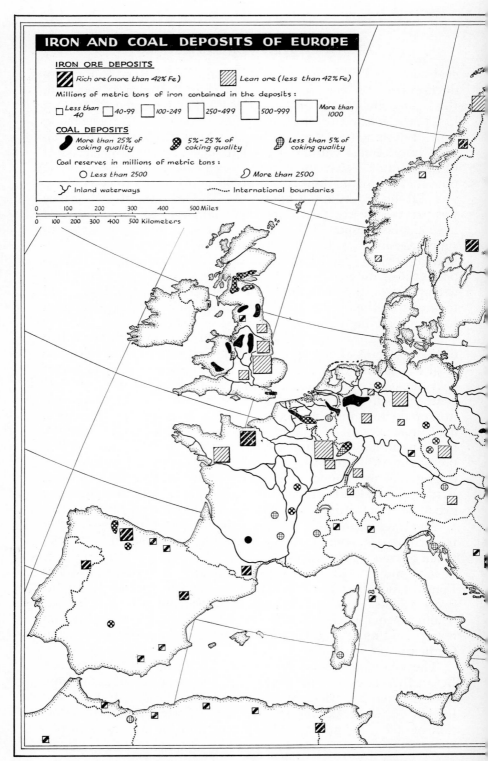

FIGURE 155. Iron and coal deposits of Europe. (Modified from a map in *European Steel Tre*

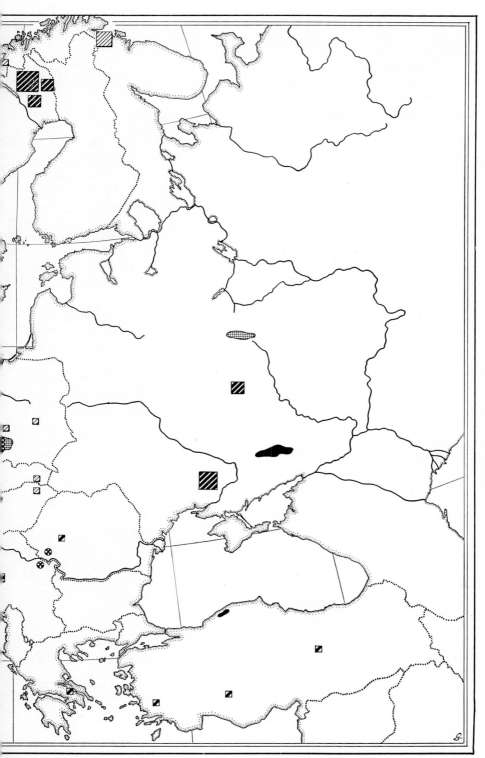

he *Setting of the World Market*, United Nations Economic Commission for Europe, 1951.)

679

war production.[10] Whereas, before the war only little more than half of Germany's ore imports came from Sweden, almost all her present imports come from that country.

In contrast to this trade structure on the continent, the British were less dependent upon trade for the maintenance of their steel industry. While Britain was a large exporter of coal before 1913, largely for the generation of steam and not for coking, the importance of these exports continuously declined as coal was replaced by other fuels. Thus, British production and exports of coal, of which bunker coal formed a large part, had reached their peak in 1913.

In summary, the prewar pattern of the heavy industry of Europe showed a definite dependence upon coal from the United Kingdom and Germany; an exchange of iron ore for metallurgical fuel from the countries forming the industrial triangle of the Ruhr-Lorraine; a heavy dependence upon outside supplies of iron ore by such areas as the Ruhr and the United Kingdom; and decreasing and relatively little competition by the major producers of steel products in each other's home market as a result of the cartelization of the coal and steel industry.

The production of crude steel in Europe (excluding the U.S.S.R.) in 1951 was 67.6 million metric tons.[11] This compares with a prewar average (1936-38) of 53 million. The remarkable recovery which has taken place is emphasized by the fact that total production in 1947 was only 36.7 million tons. Among the major changes in the steel production of the major European producers are the significant increase in production in East Central Europe, the increase in production in France and Luxembourg, and the very substantial increase in Great Britain, which is largely the result of new capacity such as the new plant at Port Talbot in Wales.

One conspicuous change in the production of iron ore is the decline in France, Germany, and Luxembourg from their prewar levels. By 1950 this production had again reached 30, 11, and 4 million metric tons, respectively, and West German recovery has been rapid since then. Note, however, that the French ore has the higher iron content. Another conspicuous change is the reduced volume of imports of iron ore by West Germany, particularly from overseas. Here again, Germany is making a comeback. The increased use of scrap, however, has meant that the total production

[10] In terms of iron content the import figures are 80 per cent for prewar and 50 per cent now. The higher percentages reflect the lower iron ore content of domestic production.

[11] A table of conversions will be found in Appendix III.

of steel has declined less than the reduced availability of iron ore might indicate. Despite the removal of much productive capacity and the imposition of production ceilings during the early postwar years, the West German production of steel has risen from the low postwar levels to 15.8 million metric tons in 1952, compared with 18 million before the war. This lower production has decreased the need for iron ore imports and has increased the amount of coking coal available for export. Production in France has risen from 7 to 9.8 million, in Great Britain from 12 to 16.4, in Luxembourg from 2 to over 3 million, in Belgium from 3 to over 5 million, in Czechoslovakia from less than 2 to over 3 million, in Poland from less than 2 to 2.8 million, and in Sweden from 1 to 1.5 million tons. This increase in production is a result not only of better technology but also the result of large new capacity. The installation of such new capacity has been particularly noticeable in Great Britain, Eastern, and East Central Europe. Germany's industrial production increased rapidly after the currency reform of 1948, and by 1953 she was rapidly regaining her place as the industrial leader of the continent.

There are significant differences in the productivity of the various countries. This results from at least five factors: first, the varying richness of the ore and coal deposits; second, the countries of earliest development, especially Great Britain, have exhausted their best iron ore deposits and have had to tap lower-grade ores; third, the accessibility and general location of the deposits varies greatly, and greater depths have to be reached as the top layers are worked off; fourth, costs of transportation vary with the type of transportation available and the length of the haul; and fifth, labor costs vary from country to country. In the production of coal the output per manshift in 1950 varied from 0.69 tons in Belgium to 1.42 tons in the Netherlands. The price of iron ore likewise varies from a low of $3.27 in the United Kingdom through $5.97 for Lorraine, $6.71 for Western France, $7.00 for Luxembourg, to $14.67 for Western Germany.[12] Imported iron ores usually are expensive to the importing country, despite the fact that they have a very high iron content, usually well above 50 per cent. All of this results in substantial differences in the price of steel.

It is against this background of interdependence and substantial productivity differences that Robert Schuman, then Foreign Minister of France, proposed what has now become known as the Schuman Plan: that the coal and steel industries of Western Eu-

---

[12] These prices refer to April, 1950, quotations per ton of iron content.

rope, excluding those of Great Britain, be pooled under one central authority, eliminating trade barriers on both raw materials and finished steel. A start has been made on making the Plan a reality. It should result in a more rational allocation of resources in the iron and steel industry, and thus help to allay political strife between France and Germany. At the same time, the Plan is a step toward a general integration of the economy of Western Europe. It can reduce the cost of steel, one of the basic ingredients of modern industry, provided the low-cost producers are able to expand their production, while at the same time the high-cost producers make the necessary internal adjustments in reducing output. Obviously, this is not going to be accomplished without some difficulty. There have been a good many objections to the Plan on the ground that it involves the surrender of some sovereignty. Countries are reluctant to give up their individual control, even if unexercised at the moment, over a basic industry such as this. Fear has also been expressed that this Plan could easily become just another bigger and larger cartel. If successful, however, it will be a most significant step in the direction of integrating Europe's economy or at least that of Western Europe.

OTHER INDUSTRY. Apart from these changes in industrial Europe, significant changes are occurring at a rapid rate in East Central Europe.[13] The satellites of the Soviet Union, with a population of less than half that of the U.S.S.R., produce half as much hard fuel and electric power, a third as much steel, and a fifth as much petroleum. The per-capita industrial production of these countries is claimed to be as high as that of the U.S.S.R. The increase in industrial production claimed in 1950 over the preceding year is substantial: 16 per cent in Czechoslovakia, 22 in Bulgaria, 31 in Poland, 34 in Hungary, and 39 in Romania, while the officially reported increase in the U.S.S.R. was 23 per cent. At present the industrial output per capita of Czechoslovakia is said to be equal to that of France, while that of Poland and Hungary is equal to that of Italy.

A partial indication of the industrialization which has taken place is the fact that whereas 61 per cent of the population of Poland in 1931 was employed in agriculture, the 1950 census showed a

[13] The data in this paragraph are from "The Rise of Industrial Middle Europe," by Ian Wszelaki, *Foreign Affairs*, October, 1951, pp. 123-34. The reader should be cautioned, however, that statistical information from East Central and Eastern Europe may be substantially less accurate than is desirable. It should also be noted that relatively small increases in production on a small base show up as large percentage increases.

figure of only 45 per cent. This latter figure, of course, includes the highly industrialized parts of Silesia incorporated into Poland after World War II, and excludes the agricultural areas ceded by Poland to the U.S.S.R. Not only has there been substantial industrialization, but the plans for the future call for still further developments. If these plans come to fruition the differences in the structure of the economies on both sides of the Iron Curtain will be greatly reduced.

Despite these great strides in industrialization very significant differences still exist, and industrial production has risen unevenly since the war. As a general rule, it can be said that as we move south and east across the continent of Europe we get into areas which are less and less industrialized. There are exceptions, such as northern Italy and Czechoslovakia, which are much more industrialized than the above generalization indicates. It is noteworthy that the political East-West split virtually coincides with the industrial-agricultural division with the additional exception of Greece, the Iberian peninsula, and Yugoslavia if we count that country on the side of the West. Among the countries of Northern Europe, Norway is more agricultural than industrial although shipping and allied industries and services are more important than either industry or agriculture, and Denmark really has an "industrialized" agriculture. As we have also seen, the intensity of industry, even within the industrialized nations, is very unevenly distributed.

One of the keynotes of postwar Europe is the great effort to industrialize, whether that means intensification of existing industrialization or the beginning of industrialization. Quite apart from the effort to become increasingly independent from imports of manufactured goods, many countries feel that industrialization should raise the standard of living. There is also a feeling that to be agricultural is to be "inferior." A very real question is whether the wholesale attempt to establish heavy industries everywhere is the best way of using available resources. It is quite likely that some specialization in the race for industrialization, i.e., different countries producing different industrial products, would bring beneficial results. Likewise, in some countries the "industrialization of agriculture" may be more promising. The fact remains that practically all agricultural countries are struggling, frequently against heavy odds, to establish heavy industries.

In many respects, considerations of productivity are more important than those of total production. Over the long pull, increasing agricultural or industrial productivity is the key to a higher standard of living, which after all, is the main purpose of industrialization.[14] In this respect Europe comes out only second best, in comparison with the United States. While this is true as a general proposition, productivity even within Europe varies greatly. Exact comparisons are extremely difficult to make, yet from all studies which have been made it is quite clear that productivity— even in the most industrialized country of Europe, the United Kingdom—has lagged behind the United States, sometimes by a substantial margin.[15]

Among the factors usually given for the great difference between the two continents are the following: The traditionally low man–land ratio in the United States means that the available supply of labor is relatively scarce and therefore expensive. In other words, wages are relatively high. This has encouraged the large-scale use of capital equipment in the production process in order to minimize labor costs. This was facilitated by the availability in the United States of most of the necessary raw materials and encouraged by the existence of a large and rapidly expanding market. The generally expanding economy and the frontier developments certainly further encouraged the experimentation with and the use of new processes and techniques, while the more settled industrialists of Europe tended to be more conservative and reluctant to introduce new methods and machines. To this day many of the basic inventions made in Europe are first applied to industrial use in the United States and not in the countries where they were first developed.

Still another factor related to the size of the market is the fact that whereas the United States has specialized in the production of mass-produced articles, European countries with their smaller national markets have emphasized quality and specialty products, where the efficiencies of mass production are not possible. It is significant in this context that some European countries are able to export certain types of high-grade specialty steels to the United States. This raises the question whether it would be wise for Europe to compete with the United States in the field of mass-produced articles or whether Europe would not be better off if it tried to develop the production and stimulate the sale of specialty products. By 1950, productivity was barely 10 per cent above prewar

[14] Productivity can, of course, be raised by producing those commodities which can be produced most efficiently in a country and trading those commodities for goods which could not be produced as efficiently. Productivity can also be raised by simply increasing the efficiency in all sectors of the economy, if trade is not possible or desirable.

[15] See the recent studies of the Anglo-American Council on Productivity.

levels, while total production has increased by about 40 per cent. Productivity in the United States during the same period has risen very sharply. A very substantial further increase in productivity is absolutely essential if Europe is to increase her standard of living and if she is to be competitive in the world markets.

Apart from the willingness to introduce new methods and techniques and to work with machines, higher productivity means the production of and the investment in capital equipment, i.e., machines and equipment, to produce other goods. It is for this reason that all European countries have allocated large proportions of their national income to the production of capital equipment, despite the fact that this raises at least two important and related problems. First, as productive capacity is diverted to the manufacture of capital equipment, the output of immediately available consumers' goods either declines or certainly is not increased immediately. This may well be unpopular with people who have gone without these goods for many years. Second, the production of capital goods creates purchasing power (wages, etc.) while it does not immediately produce goods for consumption. This means added oil to the flames of inflation which is already a serious problem in Europe. To the extent which the capital equipment can be obtained by grant or loan from the outside, e.g., the United States, or to the extent which consumers' goods can be obtained the same way, this inflationary problem can be avoided. This is one of the ways in which the large-scale American aid helped Europe in the postwar period. Despite these difficulties, the overall problem of industrial productivity must be solved if Europe is not to lose its place in the working world.

Another factor which retards the industrialization of Europe is the shortage of many of the industrial raw materials; this shortage is extremely acute in the light of the difficulties which Europe has encountered in balancing its overseas accounts. It is enough to note here that the unavailability of essential raw materials such as aluminum, zinc, copper, and many of the ferroalloys, whether due to world-wide shortages or to an inability to pay for them, is a serious problem for European manufacturing industries. Industrial production in 1951 for Europe (excluding the U.S.S.R.) increased by 40 per cent over 1938. While this is a substantial and significant increase, production in the U.S.S.R. increased by an alleged 68 per cent and more than doubled in the United States.[16] It is again ap-

---

[16] The increase in the United States somewhat overstates the changes which have occurred, because in the United States 1938 still was a year of substantial unemployment.

parent that the best Europe could do in the way of recouping production, remarkable as it was considering the postwar difficulties, was not enough to retain the position of an industrial leader.

A special word about the role which coal plays as one of the basic energizers. While it is true that coal has become less important with the development of new sources of energy, it should be noted that about two thirds of the total European production of electricity is based on coal (lignite and coal). New uses for coal in the chemical industries have been found even though these industries use relatively small quantities. It is true, furthermore, that coal is still an important source for industrial energy and at present new processes are being developed to convert coal not only into electricity but also into liquid and gaseous fuel. Europe in the past has produced all the coal it needed. Its production potential in this basic fuel is extremely high, yet in the postwar period there have been several years during which it was necessary to import coal from the United States. Europe needs to do more than maintain its prewar production, because an expanding coal supply is necessary for an expanding economy.

The production of electricity has increased from 172 billion kw-hr for Europe (excluding the U.S.S.R.) before the war to 336 billion in 1951. About one third of this amount is hydroelectric power and about two thirds thermoelectric power. Great efforts are still being made to increase the production of electricity.

Europe, outside the U.S.S.R., is not so fortunate with respect to petroleum. Production increased from 9 million tons crude in 1938 to 11 million tons in 1950. Further substantial expansion in this production, of course, is limited to further discoveries of oil deposits, although synthetic production may well become significant. In 1950, about half of the production of the German Federal Republic was of this type. Europe imported about 84 per cent of its consumption of this increasingly important fuel. Again we see Europe's dependence on foreign trade and the limitations imposed by a shortage of raw materials.

Agricultural Resources. Notwithstanding the importance of certain European countries as workshops of the world, Europe, including most of the industrialized countries, is extremely important agriculturally. In 1950, Europe (excluding the U.S.S.R.) produced 24 per cent of the world's wheat, more than 40 per cent of the world's rye, 10 per cent of the world's corn, 30 per cent of the world's barley, and 56 per cent of the world's potatoes. The

U.S.S.R. produced about a quarter of the world's total production of wheat, over half of the rye, and a third of the potatoes.

Agriculture constitutes a large part of the total economy in much of Southern and East Central Europe. While it is difficult to draw an exact dividing line between an agricultural and an industrial country, either the percentage of national income produced by agriculture or the number of people employed in agriculture may serve as a guide.[17] Table 6 clearly indicates the relatively small number of essentially industrialized countries and emphasizes the agricultural aspect of Europe as a whole.

One of the most significant aspects of these agricultural economies is that their standard of living is uniformly below, and frequently substantially below, that of the industrialized countries. How can this be explained? In agriculture the output per worker is frequently less than in industry because the human effort is not as heavily, and in some cases not at all, supplemented by inanimate energy. Countries like Denmark, which have "industrialized" their agriculture, not only are exceptions to the inverse relationship between agriculture and the standard of living but also illustrate the effect of the use of industrial methods in agriculture. The use of mechanical devices such as tractors has been extremely limited in Europe, although significant increases in their use have been made since the war. The small landholdings in many countries have in the past retarded the introduction of these mechanical devices. Animals are still common as an important source of energy for work on the farm and many outmoded methods are still widely used.

Because of climate and relief, the land is frequently not suited to good agricultural yields. In addition, many parts of Europe have long and severe winters with relatively short summers. In many countries these locational difficulties are aggravated by a semifeudal political and social order. The population problem, particularly acute in the agricultural countries, has already been discussed. Overpopulation on the farm, or underemployment as it is frequently called, results in the inefficient use of labor and subsequently a low standard of living.

Wide differences in productivity result from all this. By way of illustration, let us again refer to wheat.[18] The latest postwar figures show average yields ranging as high as 61 bushels per acre

[17] These data are estimates for different years, depending on the availability of data. It should be noted that in some cases prewar data were used.

[18] More complete figures for wheat and figures for other crops are given in Table 12.

in the Netherlands, over 50 bushels in Belgium and Denmark, 40 bushels in the United Kingdom to such low yields as 9 bushels in Portugal, 11 bushels in Spain and Bulgaria, and 12 bushels in Romania. This compares with an average yield of 15 bushels per acre in the United States. The very high yields are a reflection of intensive agriculture, while the low yields reflect poor production methods and/or adverse physical conditions; in the United States and the U.S.S.R., they reflect an intensive mechanization of agriculture.

The raising of the level of agricultural productivity is, indeed, one of the more pressing and often overlooked problems of Europe. In contrast to the remarkable recovery which has taken place in the industrial production in Europe since the war, agriculture in 1952 barely reached its prewar level. Much remains to be done. Land reforms in Central and Southern Europe and collectivization of farming in East Central Europe during the postwar years were undertaken with the hope that they would increase agricultural production. The increasing use of inanimate power such as tractors may help.[19] Industrialization could also help to alleviate the agricultural problem by absorbing some of the excess rural population in urban industries.

Agriculture thus remains an important sector in Europe's economy, despite the efforts toward industrialization. No program looking toward the rehabilitation of Europe can afford to be so preoccupied with the problem of industrialization that it overlooks the agricultural problems.

The Service Industries. In addition to industrial and agricultural production there are the tertiary or service industries which are typical of countries with a high standard of living. With increasing industrialization and urbanization, more and more functions of a community are provided on a commercial basis. One has only to think of such services as laundry and baking bread to realize that while those functions are performed in the home in an agrarian community, they are performed commercially in an industrial urban society. Furthermore, an industrial society is more complex. As more trade takes place, more service functions in connection with this trade and transportation are required, and as the standard of living rises, more services can be afforded. In the more industrialized countries of Europe these services have long played an important role. They not only have been important in the

[19] The use of tractors in 23 countries for which we have data more than trebled from 1939 to 1950; United Nations, *Economic Survey of Europe 1950*, p. 184.

domestic trade of these countries but also have enabled these countries to perform service functions for the rest of the world. Here, as elsewhere, the United States is more and more challenging the position of Europe.

What do these services consist of? London and to lesser extent Paris, Amsterdam, and Zürich have long been financial centers where international trade was financed. The capital for the development of overseas territories, including the United States at an earlier period, came from those centers. Foreign exchange transactions were effected there. The insurance business, including re-insurance, flourished in countries like the United Kingdom and Switzerland. Much of the world's commerce has long been negotiated and transacted in these European cities or by Europeans. They also provided the training ground for many of the world's doctors, scientists, engineers, and other technical and scientific specialists. Again, as we have found in other areas of activity, the relative importance of Europe for all of these is declining.

It is unnecessary to emphasize the importance of a highly developed transportation system for such a continent. A dense railroad system has been complete since the turn of the century. Electrification of the railroads is making rapid strides in many countries. The railroads are still the most important single carrier, although motor vehicles are giving the railroads ever-increasing competition for the transportation of both passengers and freight. This competition is even more serious in Europe than in the United States because the shorter distances increase the advantages of trucking. Inland waterways, both natural and canals, have long been a mainstay of intra-European transportation. The world's ocean-going merchant marine has long been centered in Europe, and despite heavy wartime losses, Europe has more than restored its tonnage to prewar levels. In this field, also, postwar competition from the United States has been greater than it had been in the 1930's. While Europe is the hub of an extensive international network of airways, and intra-European air transportation is developing, the distances are much too small to expect a development comparable to the airways of the United States.

It has been in these service industries that the losses of Europe during the war have been extremely severe, and perhaps the most irreparable. Overseas investments were lost. The confidence in Europe, so necessary for her to act as trustee and agent for the rest of the world, was severely shaken. "Service" competition from other areas, especially the United States, grew increasingly important.

These changes will require some difficult adjustments. Either those European countries which have sold services to the world must again sell these services to the world, which seems extremely difficult, or they must provide other employment for the resources formerly used in these service industries. The difficulties of this adjustment are demonstrated by the experience of Vienna after World War I. Before that war she was the service center for a large empire. After the breakup of the empire she remained a service center primarily for a small country, with the result that the occupational pattern of Austria's capital was top-heavy with people in the professions and commercial pursuits. The same unbalance will exist for Europe if it permanently loses its position as the service center of the world. These tertiary industries are an area in which the European countries affected will perhaps find it most difficult of all to regain anything like their prewar position.

Europe's Commerce

Merchandise Trade. Europe's position in the world's commerce is of such significance both to the world at large and to Europe itself as to deserve special consideration.[20] In considering a country's position in international commerce one should look for her total international transactions and her balance of payments, rather than just her merchandise transactions, as is so frequently done.

Before the war Europe's trade (excluding the U.S.S.R.) amounted to slightly more than half the world's trade, despite the fact that Europe had only 19 per cent of the world's population and 4 per cent of the area. While the approximate distribution of population and land remained the same, Europe's share in international trade declined to about 43 per cent in 1949.

This large share of international trade means that the per-capita trade of Europe must be relatively high. In 1935, 28 per cent of the aggregate imports of European countries consisted of foodstuffs, 45 per cent of raw materials, and 27 per cent of manufactured goods. Of their exports, 57 per cent consisted of manufactured goods, 25 per cent of raw materials and semimanufactured goods, and the remainder of foodstuffs. While comparable figures for

[20] It is true, of course, that the political unit is an arbitrary unit for the consideration of trade. For many purposes, trade within a country is more important. For other purposes it might be argued that the trade of a unit larger than a country, say Europe as a whole, should be considered. Because of the difficulty of combining data gathered by individual countries we must rely, in a few instances, on prewar data for very basic relationships.

the postwar period are available for individual countries only, the basic pattern seems unchanged. Europe, particularly Great Britain and the other nations of Western Europe, is one of the workshops of the world where raw materials are imported and the finished manufactured goods are exported. This basic composition of the foreign trade resembles that of the United States for much the same reason.

In addition, Europe must import substantial food supplies to feed its dense population. This food, too, must be paid for by exports. In 1950, 47 per cent of Europe's imports came from overseas, the main source of raw materials, while only 40 per cent of its exports went overseas, other European markets providing a more important market for manufactured goods. Another characteristic of Europe's trade is its excess of imports over exports. This again is a characteristic which predates World War I and was possible, as we shall see, because of the substantial income from services.

Within Europe, ten industrial countries [21] accounted for about 80 per cent of the total trade of Europe before the war and little less in 1950. The per-capita trade of these countries is also high. The importance of the industrial countries is significant. It is frequently argued that the export of capital goods, goods used to produce other goods, is undesirable because it will destroy the export trade when these export goods are put to work. Here we find, however, that the industrial countries which have long been exporters of capital goods remain the most important trading countries and are also the countries with the highest living standards. To be sure, the specific type of goods will have to change, and much of the success of an exporting country depends on whether or not it can adapt itself to these changes.

In 1935, the ten most highly industrialized countries of Europe [22] had a net import surplus of foodstuffs of $2.3 billion while the rest of Europe had a net export surplus of $0.55 billion. In raw and semimanufactured materials, industrial Europe had an import surplus of $2.8 billion with a negligible figure for the rest of Europe. In manufactured goods the picture was reversed, with industrial Europe showing an export surplus of $2.7 billion and the rest of Europe showing an import surplus of $1 billion. The United Kingdom alone accounted for about two thirds of the food imports of

[21] The League of Nations included the following countries in this group in the order of their importance in the import trade of Europe: United Kingdom, Germany, France, Belgium, Luxembourg, Netherlands, Italy, Sweden, Switzerland, Czechoslovakia, Austria.

[22] League of Nations, *Europe's Trade* (Geneva, 1941), p. 7.

industrial Europe, one third of the imports of raw and semi-manufactured materials, and over a third of the exports of the manufactured goods. This emphasizes the importance of the United Kingdom within the group of industrial countries.

For its imports of primary products, industrial Europe depended to a very large degree on other continents. Agricultural Europe was a net importer of raw materials, and its net exports of foodstuffs did not cover a quarter of industrial Europe's net imports of foodstuffs. The relative importance of agricultural Europe to the industrial sector is greater if we exclude Great Britain, which relied more heavily on its empire trade. In terms of the interdependence of East Central and Western with Central Europe it is important to point out that in 1935 the countries of industrial Europe (footnote 20, p. 690) derived 34 per cent of their imports from each other, 51 per cent from other continents, and only 15 per cent from the rest of Europe. In 1950, these same ten industrial countries derived 34 per cent of their imports from industrial Europe, 53 per cent from other continents, and 13 per cent from the rest of Europe, including the U.S.S.R. On the other hand, in 1935, the rest of Europe obtained approximately two thirds of its imports from the countries of industrial Europe, and consigned three fourths of their exports to them.[23]

Among the more salient features of the changes which have occurred in the postwar trade pattern of Europe are the substantial increase in the trade within each of the two parts of Europe and a decline in the trade with each other and the increase of the trade deficit of Europe with the United States. At the same time, the large role which Europe played in the total trade of the world and the export surplus of continental Europe with the British Isles were continued.

The basic structure of the trade pattern has provided the framework for the present problems of Europe's trade. Some of the more pressing problems will be discussed below. First, Europe, particularly industrial Europe, has long depended on imports of foodstuffs to feed its increasing population. For several reasons, these became more difficult to acquire in the postwar period:

1. As a result of the destruction and dislocation of the war, domestic production of food decreased and by 1950 production had barely reached prewar levels despite a population increase of about 10 per cent.

[23] This paragraph is taken almost verbatim from League of Nations, *Europe's Trade* (Geneva, 1941), pp. 7-8.

2. Imports became more difficult to obtain because of Europe's difficulty in obtaining the necessary foreign exchange to buy goods abroad.

3. As a result of the East-West split, the amount of foodstuffs obtained by Western and Central Europe from East Central Europe declined. East Central Europe had less to export, and trade as such became more difficult because of the political tensions.

4. The Eastern zone of Germany, a large food-producing area, was cut off from Western Germany.

5. Many foods in the world at large were in short supply; this was particularly true of fats.

6. Ever since before the war the price level of food has risen sharply, relative to the price of manufactured goods. Europe's terms of trade have deteriorated because more of her domestic production of manufactured goods must be allocated to exchange for foodstuffs from abroad. All of this clearly explains why the traditional reliance of Europe on the importation of foodstuffs from abroad has created one of her major problems.

The second problem, aside from foodstuffs, is the dependence of Europe on the importation of raw materials. Here again we find increasing physical shortages and sharply increased prices, both aggravated by the rearmament program in Western Europe and the United States. In addition, the Soviet sphere has also been buying raw materials in the world markets.

Third, the loss of political control of overseas territories, such as in Southeast Asia, and the increasing independence of practically all overseas territories further reduced the import potential of the European mother countries. Possibly, as these areas develop, they may again become important to Europe.

Fourth, comparable difficulties arose on the export side. The corollary of these changes is that the prices of manufactured goods, the standard exports of Europe, declined relative to import prices. Many traditional overseas export markets switched to other sources of supply, such as the United States, during the war and in the immediate postwar period when the industrial production of Europe was being rebuilt. Even within Europe changes have taken place in that Germany has not yet been able to recover her prewar place as an exporter, and other European countries have stepped into her place. The war also stimulated the production of manufactured goods in practically all overseas areas, creating increasing competition for the exports of Europe in those products. The production and productivity in the United States, in particular, continued to outstrip that of Europe. This latter fact has created its own set of difficulties, because Europe had to buy increasing amounts of raw materials, foodstuffs, and even industrial machinery from the United States, without being able to sell equally increased exports to the United States.

Under these circumstances it is not surprising to find that practically every European country has taken severe measures to limit its imports to make sure that only absolute essentials are bought from abroad, particularly the United States, while at the same time doing everything possible to increase exports. In fact, most European countries had to hold their physical volume of imports close to prewar levels while increasing exports substantially. Thus the physical volume of imports in the United Kingdom in 1951 was at about the prewar level, while exports had almost doubled.[24] French imports had increased about 10 per cent and exports about 90 per cent. Many other countries were not as successful. Countries with the greatest war-caused destruction fared the worst. The imports of Western Germany were about 25 per cent above prewar, while exports stood at about 135 per cent. Italy's imports stood at 140 per cent of prewar while her exports had increased by only 25 per cent.

The substantial deterioration of the position in international trade in the face of traditional dependence on that trade has shaped Europe's economic policy in the postwar period. A policy of complete autarchy would be simply impossible without complete deterioration of living standards, yet some steps in that direction have been taken in an attempt to become self-sufficient in agriculture and raw materials even though this entails higher costs. These common difficulties have also given impetus to greater efforts toward increasing economic collaboration within Europe, or more correctly, within the two Europes—East and West. Trade within East Central Europe has increased substantially since the war, despite the great difficulties which this area has had in obtaining the manufactured goods it so badly needs in its attempts to industrialize.

The countries participating in the European Recovery Program (the Marshall Plan) have made substantial progress in encouraging trade among themselves. This was done partly on the insistence of the United States, which heavily subsidized Western Europe in the postwar period.[25] This cooperation has taken the form of

[24] International Monetary Fund, *International Financial Statistics*, May, 1952.

[25] Total grants and loans by the United States government to Europe, from July 1, 1945 to March 31, 1952, exceeded $25 billion. U. S. Department of Commerce, *Foreign Transactions of the U. S. Government, Foreign Aid*, June, 1952.

greatly reduced quota barriers between the European countries under the auspices of the Organization for European Economic Cooperation (OEEC) in Paris. This same agency sponsored a plan, the European Payment Union (EPU), which facilitates the international payments among the participating countries. All of this has resulted in a substantial increase in intra-European trade and a relaxation of trade barriers among the Marshall Plan countries.

Among other measures contemplated are customs unions between several pairs of countries. The only one of these to take concrete form, so far, is that between Belgium-Luxembourg and the Netherlands (Benelux); even this union has encountered many difficulties in fully integrating two diverse economies. Tariffs have been substantially reduced on a world-wide basis, again under United States sponsorship by the General Agreement on Tariffs and Trade (GATT) with headquarters in Geneva.

The Schuman Plan, which has been discussed earlier, is an attempt to integrate the coal and steel industries of France, Italy, the German Federal Republic, and the Benelux countries to reduce both political and economic frictions and create a more efficient European industry. Similar plans have been proposed for agriculture and investments. On the political side, the Council of Europe has been set up in Strasbourg as a parliament of Europe. To date this organization has been no more than a debating society, but it is too early to say whether this is an abortive attempt at integration or if it is the first stage of a really new development.

In other words, the Europe on this side of the Iron Curtain is trying to solve the problems created by the difficulties arising from its precarious position in international trade partly by greater control over the volume and direction of its trade, partly by greater autarchy, and partly by a greater integration of its various national economies. While these policies may be partially conflicting, no real alternatives seem to be available at the moment.

Nonmerchandise Trade. Trade in merchandise presents only a partial picture of a country's international position, and this is particularly true of Europe. It has already been mentioned that Europe as a whole, especially industrial Europe, has imported more merchandise than it has exported. This is not the whole story, because Europe has also sold to overseas areas many services such as transportation, insurance, banking, etc. In addition, Europe has had substantial income from overseas investments. In fact, these investments long provided Europe with a reserve fund it could draw upon in time of stress. This was done extensively during World War I, when many investments abroad were sold. Some countries had to continue to do so in the interwar period and again during World War II. The loss of these investments is probably an irreparable damage of the war, at least irreparable for a long time.

Let us now examine the over-all international transaction picture of Europe. From 1938 to 1950 the import surplus of Europe increased from $1.8 billion to $2.9 billion, while the import surplus from the United States alone almost trebled from $0.7 billion to $2.0 billion. At the same time the income from services decreased from $1.8 billion to $0.4 billion, half of this decline being attributable to a loss of investment income. The total deficit of Europe in 1950 amounted to almost $2.0 billion. Since the dollar and gold reserves had previously been seriously depleted, this deficit was made possible by almost $3.0 billion in aid from the United States.

Very roughly, Europe acquired dollars in two ways with which to pay for her import surplus. First, the United States loaned substantial sums to Europe, especially Central Europe, in the 1920's. Second, Europe had an export surplus with the overseas areas, which in turn had an export surplus with the United States. As these overseas areas, especially in the sterling area, were paid in dollars they could pay for their deficits with their mother country in dollars. When these capital movements ceased in the 1930's gold exports from Europe to the United States partly replaced them. Thus we see once more that the unbalance in the international accounts of Europe at the present time is nothing new but merely an accentuation of an earlier trend.

Let us again emphasize that two problems should be clearly distinguished. First, there is the problem of Europe's total balance of payments, the problem of selling enough goods and services to the world to buy the goods, and to a lesser extent the services, Europe needs to buy from the rest of the world. Failing this, other means of financing must be found. Second, there is the problem of the relations with the dollar area, i.e., primarily the United States. Even though the over-all account of Europe may be brought into balance, it could still mean a severe deficit with the United States and a surplus with other areas whose currency may not be convertible into dollars and who cannot themselves maintain a surplus with the United States. This is, of course, what is commonly referred to as the problem of "the dollar shortage." As long as the United States maintains an export surplus, this problem can be solved only by United States grants or loans. The only other alternative for Europe, regardless of the cost involved and regardless of the undesirability of such action, is to reduce purchases from the United States and thus eliminate the American export surplus. This emphasizes the need of the United States to buy goods or services—freight, insurance, tourism, etc.—or to make loans to foreign areas. The alternative is reduced exports. Thus, in a very real sense, the European balance of payments problem is also an American problem.

Other Factors. Apart from discussing the resources—human, industrial, and agricultural—and the external commerce of Europe, there are several other factors of present-day Europe which must be considered. The aftermath of World War I, the depression in the interwar period, and yet another war have left their mark on the political as well as the economic thinking of Europeans. Let us also remember that such opposition movements to the status quo as the Social Democrats on the continent and the Labor Party in Britain antedate the First World War. Thus, instability, insecurity, and uncertainty have long since become the "normal" state of affairs.

Relatively low living standards have long contributed to the social and political unrest in Europe. One way of comparing living standards is in terms of the consumption of basic foods and other consumer goods.[26] In terms of calories consumed per person per day we find that the average in 1950-51 in Europe (O.E.E.C.) was 2,740 calories compared with about 3,200 in the United States. The consumption of proteins per person per day was 79 grams in Europe and about 95 in the United States, for animal proteins the figures were 33 and 60 respectively, while for all fats they were 88 grams for Europe and about 136 for the United States. This is one indication of the difference in consumption levels between Europe and the United States. Even within Europe there are marked differences, however. The British Isles and Scandinavia rate high, while consumption in Southern, East Central, and Eastern Europe is the lowest. These same regional differences appear even more markedly in the consumption of such durable consumer goods as automobiles and radios.

The deterioration of the agricultural situation in Europe is clearly indicated by the generally lower level of caloric consumption in the postwar period. The differences between countries are greatest in the consumption of animal proteins and fats, both of which are typically scarce in low standard of living communities. The production of animals is an expensive process of food conversion,

26 For detailed data see *Economic Survey of Europe*, 1949, pp. 25 ff.

since most animals consume a substantial part of the food consumed for energy expended in their own locomotion.

An analysis of the level of the consumption of some typical commodities such as potatoes, tobacco, wheat, etc., also shows rather significant differences in the tastes and preferences of different peoples. The most significant fact which emerges from all this is again the substantial difference in the standard of living between the more industrial and more agricultural parts of Europe.

Retrospect and Prospect

Europe as a Unit. We now are in a position to view the totality of the European scene. Three questions should be asked at this point: First, in what sense, if any, is Europe a unit? Second, would it be more useful to think of Europe as being polarized into two camps, East and West? Or third, is Europe so divided into independent states that it would be best not to think of Europe as a unit at all?

Europe can be perceived as a unit only in the very broadest sense. The various chapters of this book have shown vast cultural, political, and economic differences. Yet it remains true that for some centuries Europe has been the center of the world. In spite of differences, many of its people have thought of themselves as "Europeans." While it has not been the population center, it has certainly been the hub from which human activity and progress spread. It has contained the nucleus for the higher standard of living of Western mankind. Only in the last half century has Europe been seriously challenged in that position. Europe certainly provides the basis for a unified economic unit, if and when political rivalries can be eliminated to make that possible. The many long and proud traditions of sovereign peoples jealously guarding their political as well as their cultural and economic independence will certainly prevent Europe from becoming a unit for a long time to come. Thus, in a sense, the stumbling block to Europe's integration is its history, conditioned as this history has been by geography.

Today two Europes are clearly evident, divided by the so-called Iron Curtain. This division, of course, is essentially political and tends to polarize Europe into two camps. We have seen that the Iron Curtain very roughly coincides with the dividing line between Europe's industrial and agricultural countries.[27] This also means

---

[27] Except for Southern Europe, probably Czechoslovakia, and perhaps Poland.

differences in the standard of living and in demographic, cultural, and sociological patterns—all of which have for a long time accentuated this polarization. Nevertheless it should not be overlooked that these two parts are not only economically different; to a large extent they are complementary. This complementarity has meant that the decline in the trade relationships between the two areas has been a serious blow to many countries. It also explains why trade continues at all, despite the political impediments. The elimination of these barriers, whenever that becomes politically feasible, will certainly be a contribution to the general level of economic activity.

This extreme political polarization has had at least one by-product which should be noted here. As a result of the "cold war" with one another, each area has tended to unify and solidify more rapidly than might have been the case otherwise. In a very real sense, Europe is hardening into two camps. In this connection we should also recall the peculiar position of Great Britain. Because of her close economic, political, and cultural ties with her empire overseas, and because of the influence which this empire has on the affairs of the United Kingdom, that country in many respects does not consider itself as part of Europe.

There is still the third way of looking at Europe. The current attempts at consolidation, at least within the two spheres, imply that no such unity exists. The countries differ in their individual traditions and aspirations. They have intense national rivalries between themselves. It is in this sense that Europe is completely disunited. It is probably unnecessary to point out that the further this disunity is permitted to go or the longer it is permitted to exist, the more difficult it will be for each individual nation to put its economic house in order, and especially to raise its standard of living.[28]

Thus the totality of Europe presents a somewhat confusing picture, varying from a completely disorganized area to a unified continent. Nevertheless, forces have been shown to be at work which would increasingly integrate the economies, if not of Europe, of its two parts.

Summary. After analyzing the European picture one cannot help being impressed with the great accomplishments of the peoples of Europe, crowded as they are on a subcontinent. The domi-

[28] It should be noted that actually only a very limited amount of detailed analysis of the real implications of economic unification has been published to date and that difficulties of effecting such a unification are considerable.

nant position which Europe has held for several centuries was the result of many diverse factors. No doubt Europe had geographical advantages—its moderate climate, severe enough to have marked seasonal swings; its long seacoast stimulating the movement of persons and ideas to other continents; and its agricultural and mineral resources—but its early cultural start was also one of the main factors.

In a more specific way, any summary must again point out that Europe had reached the pinnacle of her relative power position in the world at the close of the Victorian Age which came to an end with the outbreak of World War I. Global empire relations were most intimate then. Three empires covered much of the continent. Material welfare was improving. Both science and the fine arts were making unprecedented progress. Much of this came to an end with the war.

Europe's overpopulation is still one of its basic problems. Food could once be easily bought for these people from overseas territories; today, this is a difficult process. The rate of population increase in many parts of Europe has been slowing down, with resultant aging and in many cases more conservative population. This is true in spite of the increasing radicalism engendered by unsettled conditions and a low standard of living. Substantial population upheavals have occurred as a result of the late war. Casualties were high in some countries, resulting in abnormal demographic patterns. Substantial migrations, primarily from east to west, took place. Large movements of people had occurred, of course, as they left their homes moving with the tides of war.

On the positive side of the ledger, the immense resources of the people of Europe must be emphasized. They are energetic and resourceful, as their history proves. They have developed a backlog of industrial, scientific, and artistic skill and training that is unequalled anywhere in the world. If all these latent abilities are put to the best use, there is no reason why Europe could not literally produce a cultural and economic renaissance, despite the fact that it no longer can be *the* center of the scheme of things.

Industrially, Europe still is one of the great workshops. Its industrial potential is greater than its actual position. This is true even though Europe is handicapped in depending on overseas supplies of many of its basic raw materials, and its productivity is lagging behind that of the United States. Among Europe's great assets have been its quality products produced by skilled craftsmen. Even in such industries as steel, where the United States is justly proud of its production record, European specialty steels have long been used in this country. Its future may to a large extent lie in making such specialty products. To be sure, Europe has a lot to make up for, but with diligence, hard work, a belief in its own recuperative powers, and a little patience Europeans are still capable of producing great things, both material and nonmaterial.

Agriculturally, Europe is faced with the same basic problem of raising its productivity. However, this is complicated by the fact that Europe has long practiced a very intensive form of agriculture which will make further improvements, though needed, more difficult. Much can be done, though, by greater use of inanimate power, by better social organization, by increased use of irrigation, and by related projects aimed at the improvements of the soil and fertility of the land now used for agricultural purposes. Europe's population problem on the farm will have to be solved in conjunction with the industrial problem. The only solution is migration from the farm to industries in the same country or abroad. Only over a long period will a downward revision of the birth rate stabilize the population.

With severe restrictions on trade, the standard of living in most countries is low compared with American standards. It varies significantly from country to country. A higher standard of living, of course, can be achieved only as the industrial and agricultural problems are worked out. At the same time Europe depends to a very large extent on foreign commerce. International trade, intra-European and overseas trade, are its lifeblood. There are great obstacles in this field. Europe needs more in the form of goods and services from foreign countries than those countries are willing to buy from Europe. This problem is particularly acute in relations with the United States. However, Europe must keep its international accounts in balance. Exports must pay for imports. The help Europe is now receiving from the United States cannot be counted on indefinitely. It is in this field of foreign economic relations that perhaps the greatest ingenuity and adaptability to changed conditions is required if Europeans are to regain their position as a prosperous and independent people.

The Future. It is always dangerous to speculate about the future, but an attempt must be made to evaluate the basic forces at work and to draw some conclusions as to what the future may hold in store for Europe.

It is evident that Europe's relative position in the world has long since passed its peak, i.e., it has lost its place as *the* center of commerce, industry, and culture. This will remain true even if Europe can again show a large increase in its own production. Its absolute position need not decline. Every effort must be made to increase productivity in both industry and agriculture. Substantial progress along this line is possible simply by the adaptation of known methods and processes—to say nothing of new inventions and discoveries. Much has already been accomplished since the end of the war. The seeds for much more have been planted, and much more progress can be expected.

A more intractable problem is Europe's balance of payments, especially with the United States. Without cooperation from the United States the only solution would mean reduced imports from the United States. This would mean substantial sacrifices and difficulties because the products now obtained from North America are essential to Europe's economy. Perhaps at some time in the future Europe can obtain even more of its raw materials and foodstuffs from the newly developing areas in the world, including South America, and in turn supply them with the manufactures these areas so badly need. That, however, does not solve the immediate problem. Above all, Europe must have a period of political—and social—stability within which to develop its potential. It is true, of course, that Europe has long since become accustomed to the fact that the only thing which is certain is uncertainty itself; yet this uncertainty is not conducive to any long-range development. This instability has rather widespread significance in the political and social attitudes of people. Unless the people of Europe themselves again fully believe in their own future, that future will not be a rosy one.

The rearmament program presents an additional and severe strain on the already overtaxed resources of Europe. Although it may help to increase the confidence of the people in their own future political security, it is diverting resources—human and inanimate—into nonproductive channels. Unless this can be compensated for by higher production, a cut in the standard of living is the inevitable result of the rearmament program. The European contribution to the joint rearmament program must come either from increased production, or from cuts in European consumption, nonmilitary government expenditures, investment, or exports.[29] Balance-of-payment difficulties are accentuated as a result of higher imports of raw materials and higher import prices. Greater austerity is the fate of many countries. Inflation is again on the rise. Manpower

[29] See Committee for Economic Development, *Economic Aspects of North Atlantic Security* (New York, 1951), pp. 14 ff.

is again diverted into the armed forces. Exports again receive a priority second to the needs of rearmament.

It is easy to see why this burden, necessary as it is in view of the political tensions, is difficult to bear. Rather careful thought must be given to the question just how much of an armament effort can be supported without completely destroying the whole fabric of Europe's economy. This state of preparedness for war may well continue for a decade or more.

These problems resulting from the rearmament program in large part merely aggravate and focus some of the issues facing Europe. They have again given rise to attempts at greater unification. The military situation seems to necessitate some form of allocation of scarce raw materials on an international level. The efforts to create a unified defense point to the increasing need for European integration and attempts along that line are under way.

Quite apart from these aspects of Europe's present position, which are directly related to the East-West split, the fundamental world relations, and thereby the position of Europe, are shifting. When Europe rose to its peak position, there were large undeveloped areas to exploit. Today even the underdeveloped countries, or most of them, are politically independent states jealously guarding their sovereignty against outside interference. It is also true that economic development, i.e., the development of industries, is proceeding much more rapidly than in earlier decades. As this development becomes accelerated and light industries, at first, begin to appear in undeveloped areas, the adjustments necessary in the industrial areas also have to be accelerated. This means that the underlying world relationships of which Europe is a part are constantly shifting with a marked acceleration in the rate of change.

Thus, the future of Europe is fraught with increasing difficulties and dangers, but there also remains a large reservoir of hope, strength, and very real potential.

BIBLIOGRAPHY

LEAGUE OF NATIONS
Europe's Trade
Industrialization and Foreign Trade
Network of World Trade

UNITED NATIONS
Demographic Yearbook 1949/50
Economic Commission for Europe
Economic Bulletin for Europe (three times a year)
Economic Survey for Europe (yearly)

European Steel Statistics (quarterly)
Monthly Bulletin of Coal Statistics
Annual Bulletin of Transport Statistics
European Steel Trends in the Setting of the World Market

UNITED STATES

CASSELS, JOHN M. *The Sterling Area, an American Analysis.* Economic Cooperation Administration, Special Mission to the United Kingdom, London, 1951. Washington, D. C.: Government Printing Office, 1952.
U.S. Department of the Interior, Bureau of Mines, *Minerals Yearbook*
U.S. Department of Agriculture, *Agricultural Statistics* (annual)

FOOD AND AGRICULTURAL ORGANIZATION OF THE UNITED NATIONS

Yearbook of Food and Agriculture Statistics

INTERNATIONAL MONETARY FUND

Balance of Payment Yearbook (annual)
International Financial Statistics (monthly)

BANK FOR INTERNATIONAL SETTLEMENTS

Annual Report

ORGANIZATION FOR EUROPEAN ECONOMIC COOPERATION

General Statistics (bimonthly bulletin)
Foreign Trade Statistical Bulletin, with commodity supplement (monthly)
Economic Progress and Problems of Western Europe
Europe—The Way Ahead

BOOKS

CLOUGH, S. B., and COLE, C. W. *Economic History of Europe*, rev. ed. Boston: D.C. Heath & Co., 1946.
DIEBOLD, W., JR. *Trade and Payments in Western Europe.* New York: Harper & Bros., 1952.
HEATON, H. *Economic History of Europe*, rev. ed. New York: Harper & Bros., 1948.
KAHN, A. *Great Britain in the World Economy.* New York: Columbia University Press, 1946.
ZIMMERMAN, E. *World Resources and Industry*, rev. ed. New York: Harper & Bros., 1951.

APPENDIX

TABLE OF GEOLOGICAL TIME

Eras	Periods	Epochs	Estimated Per Cent of Geologic Time	Orogenic Events
CENOZOIC	QUATERNARY	RECENT ⎫ PLEISTOCENE ⎬	0.5	Glaciations (Great Ice Age)
CENOZOIC	TERTIARY	PLIOCENE ⎫ MIOCENE ⎪ OLIGOCENE ⎬ EOCENE ⎪ PALEOCENE ⎭	3.00	Uplift of the great young mountains of Europe: Pyrenees, Jura, Alps, Carpathians, Caucasus, and renewed uplift of older mountains to moderate heights. The term "Alpine" thus applies to this period of mountain building in Europe. It was markedly concentrated in late Oligocene and Miocene.
MESOZOIC	CRETACEOUS ⎫ JURASSIC ⎬ TRIASSIC ⎭		7.00	The earlier phase of Alpine mountain building marked the close of the Cretaceous.
PALEOZOIC	PERMIAN ⎫ CARBONIFEROUS * ⎪ DEVONIAN ⎪ ⎬ SILURIAN ⎪ ORDOVICIAN ⎪ CAMBRIAN ⎭		17.00	*Hercynian* mountains: Vosges, Black Forest, Harz, Sudeten, Urals; all are of approximately same age, late Paleozoic. Also western Ireland, southern Wales, southern France, and northwestern France. *Caledonian* mountains: Early uplifts of the Kjölen Mountains of Scandinavia and the igneous plateau of Finland.
PROTEROZOIC, ARCHEOZOIC or ARCHEAN	PRE-CAMBRIAN		72.00	Mountain-building forces at work, but subsequent erosion and later uplifts caused the replacement of the structures by mountains now existent.

* The *Carboniferous* of European geologists includes the Pennsylvanian and Mississippian systems recognized in North America.

CLIMATIC DATA OF SELECTED STATIONS IN EUROPE *

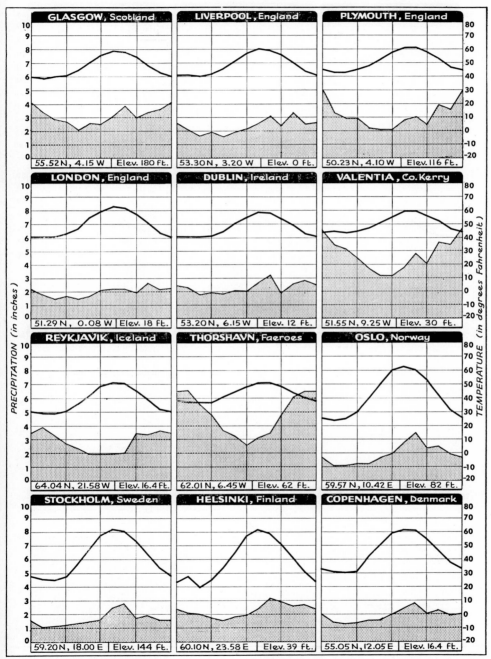

PRECIPITATION (in inches)

TEMPERATURE (in degrees Fahrenheit)

GLASGOW, Scotland — 55.52 N, 4.15 W | Elev. 180 ft.

LIVERPOOL, England — 53.30 N, 3.20 W | Elev. 0 ft.

PLYMOUTH, England — 50.23 N, 4.10 W | Elev. 116 ft.

LONDON, England — 51.29 N, 0.08 W | Elev. 18 ft.

DUBLIN, Ireland — 53.20 N, 6.15 W | Elev. 12 ft.

VALENTIA, Co. Kerry — 51.55 N, 9.25 W | Elev. 30 ft.

REYKJAVIK, Iceland — 64.04 N, 21.58 W | Elev. 16.4 ft.

THORSHAVN, Faeroes — 62.01 N, 6.45 W | Elev. 62 ft.

OSLO, Norway — 59.57 N, 10.42 E | Elev. 82 ft.

STOCKHOLM, Sweden — 59.20 N, 18.00 E | Elev. 144 ft.

HELSINKI, Finland — 60.10 N, 23.58 E | Elev. 39 ft.

COPENHAGEN, Denmark — 55.05 N, 12.05 E | Elev. 16.4 ft.

* Data from W. G. Kendrew, *Climates of the Continents* (3d ed.; New York: Oxford University Press, 1942).

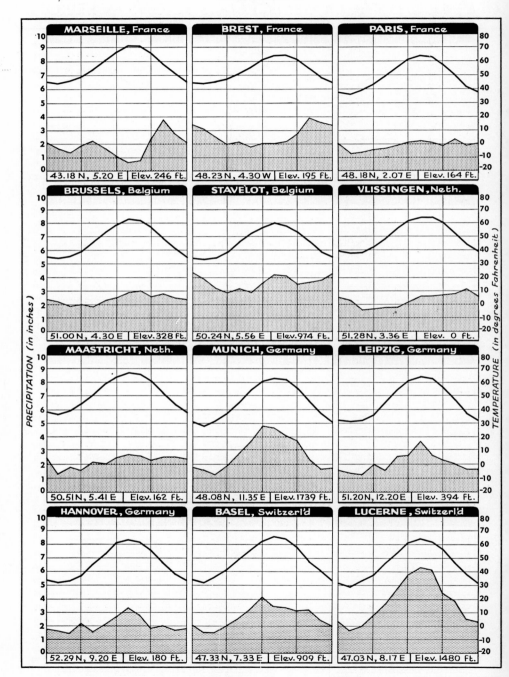

PRECIPITATION (in inches)

TEMPERATURE (in degrees Fahrenheit)

MARSEILLE, France   43.18 N, 5.20 E   Elev. 246 ft.

BREST, France   48.23 N, 4.30 W   Elev. 195 ft.

PARIS, France   48.18 N, 2.07 E   Elev. 164 ft.

BRUSSELS, Belgium   51.00 N, 4.30 E   Elev. 328 ft.

STAVELOT, Belgium   50.24 N, 5.56 E   Elev. 974 ft.

VLISSINGEN, Neth.   51.28 N, 3.36 E   Elev. 0 ft.

MAASTRICHT, Neth.   50.51 N, 5.41 E   Elev. 162 ft.

MUNICH, Germany   48.08 N, 11.35 E   Elev. 1739 ft.

LEIPZIG, Germany   51.20 N, 12.20 E   Elev. 394 ft.

HANNOVER, Germany   52.29 N, 9.20 E   Elev. 180 ft.

BASEL, Switzerl'd   47.33 N, 7.33 E   Elev. 909 ft.

LUCERNE, Switzerl'd   47.03 N, 8.17 E   Elev. 1480 ft.

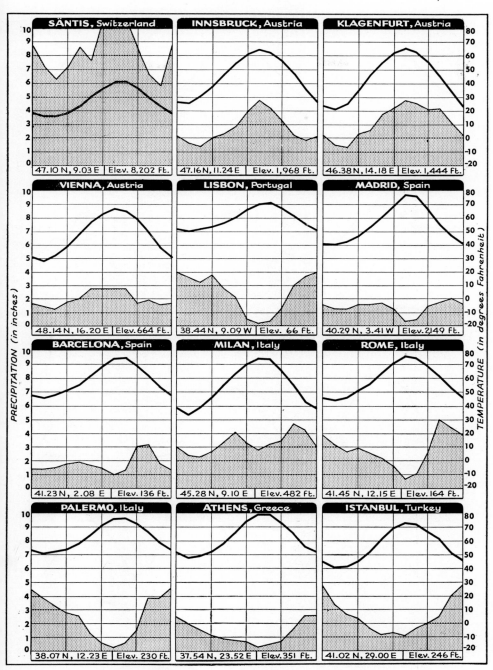

PRECIPITATION (in inches)

TEMPERATURE (in degrees Fahrenheit)

SÄNTIS, Switzerland — 47.10 N, 9.03 E | Elev. 8,202 Ft.
INNSBRUCK, Austria — 47.16 N, 11.24 E | Elev. 1,968 Ft.
KLAGENFURT, Austria — 46.38 N, 14.18 E | Elev. 1,444 Ft.
VIENNA, Austria — 48.14 N, 16.20 E | Elev. 664 Ft.
LISBON, Portugal — 38.44 N, 9.09 W | Elev. 66 Ft.
MADRID, Spain — 40.29 N, 3.41 W | Elev. 2,149 Ft.
BARCELONA, Spain — 41.23 N, 2.08 E | Elev. 136 Ft.
MILAN, Italy — 45.28 N, 9.10 E | Elev. 482 Ft.
ROME, Italy — 41.45 N, 12.15 E | Elev. 164 Ft.
PALERMO, Italy — 38.07 N, 12.23 E | Elev. 230 Ft.
ATHENS, Greece — 37.54 N, 23.52 E | Elev. 351 Ft.
ISTANBUL, Turkey — 41.02 N, 29.00 E | Elev. 246 Ft.

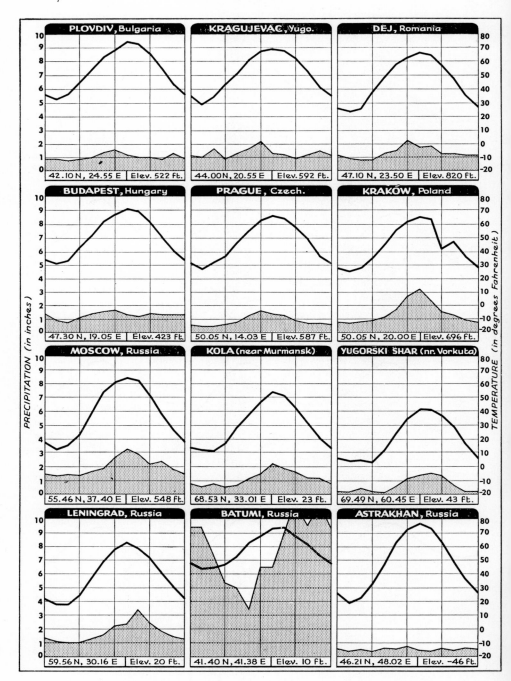

PRECIPITATION (in inches)

TEMPERATURE (in degrees Fahrenheit)

PLOVDIV, Bulgaria — 42.10 N, 24.55 E | Elev. 522 ft.

KRAGUJEVAC, Yugo. — 44.00 N, 20.55 E | Elev. 592 ft.

DEJ, Romania — 47.10 N, 23.50 E | Elev. 820 ft.

BUDAPEST, Hungary — 47.30 N, 19.05 E | Elev. 423 ft.

PRAGUE, Czech. — 50.05 N, 14.03 E | Elev. 587 ft.

KRAKÓW, Poland — 50.05 N, 20.00 E | Elev. 696 ft.

MOSCOW, Russia — 55.46 N, 37.40 E | Elev. 548 ft.

KOLA (near Murmansk) — 68.53 N, 33.01 E | Elev. 23 ft.

YUGORSKI SHAR (nr. Vorkuta) — 69.49 N, 60.45 E | Elev. 43 ft.

LENINGRAD, Russia — 59.56 N, 30.16 E | Elev. 20 ft.

BATUMI, Russia — 41.40 N, 41.38 E | Elev. 10 ft.

ASTRAKHAN, Russia — 46.21 N, 48.02 E | Elev. –46 ft.

STATISTICAL TABLES

THE FOLLOWING statistical tables have been compiled from various sources. The reader should be warned about the difficulty of making international comparisons, especially if the statistics are prepared by different agencies, and he is reminded of the fact that the reliability of the data varies greatly. Even for those countries where reasonably reliable statistics are available the figures obtained by different collecting agencies vary in quality.

The precise definition of commodities, areas, and other classifications varies from country to country and from source to source. For details the reader should consult the sources cited in each table. In most cases, more recent data will be found in later issues of the sources given. In many cases data are available only for a limited number of countries. In the case of the U.S.S.R. and Turkey, statistics generally include both the Asiatic as well as the European parts and separate figures for the European part are not available.

An effort has been made to present the data in the most comparable form. This has meant that data frequently had to be converted from one unit of measurement into another (e.g., kilometers into miles) and that many of the figures were rounded off. The Tables of Measures and Weights on the following page will be found useful.

MEASURES AND WEIGHTS

UNITS OF LENGTH

1 millimeter (mm) = 0.0394 inch	
1 centimeter (cm) = 0.3937 inch	1 inch = 2.540 centimeters
	1 foot = 0.3048 meter
1 meter (m) = 3.2808 feet	1 yard = 0.9144 meter
1 kilometer (km) = 0.62137 mile	1 statute mile = 1.609 kilometers
	= 5,280 feet
	1 nautical mile = 1.853 kilometers
	= 6,080 feet

UNITS OF AREA

1 square meter = 10.7639 square feet 1 square yard = 0.8361 square meter
1 hectare (ha) = 2.471 acres 1 acre = 0.4047 hectare
1 square kilometer = 0.3861 square mile 1 square mile = 2.590 square kilometers

UNITS OF WEIGHT

1 metric ton	= 1.1023 short tons	1 short ton = 2,000 pounds
		= 0.9072 metric ton
	= 0.9842 long ton	1 long ton = 2,240 pounds
		= 1.0160 metric tons
1 quintal	= 220 pounds	1 U.S. hundredweight (cwt) = 100 pounds
		1 U.K. hundredweight (cwt) = 112 pounds
		1 gross registered ton = 100 cubic feet

UNITS OF DRY MEASURE

1 liter (l) = 0.9081 quart
= 0.02837 bushel   1 quart = 1.1012 liters
1 bushel = 35.2383 liters

UNITS OF LIQUID MEASURE

1 liter = 1.0567 quarts   1 quart = 0.9463 liter
= 0.264 gallon   1 gallon (U.S.) = 3.785 liters
1 gallon (imperial) = 1.2 gallons (U.S.)

1 metric ton (petroleum) = 264.4175 U.S. barrels

MISCELLANEOUS

1 board foot (fbm) = 144 cubic inches
1 barrel (42 gallons) crude petroleum   = 306.6 pounds = 139.07 kilograms
= 158.984 liters

LIST OF STATISTICAL TABLES

EUROPE AND THE WORLD

THE PEOPLES OF EUROPE

LAND USE AND AGRICULTURE

INDUSTRIAL AND RAW MATERIALS PRODUCTION

COMMERCE

TRANSPORTATION

TABLE 1. POPULATION, AREA, AND DENSITY OF THE WORLD

(By continents, 1950)

	Estimated Population (in millions)	Area (sq. mi.) (in millions)	Population (per sq. mi.)
Europe	396.0	1,910	207
Africa	198.0	11,610	18
North America	216.3	9,370	23
South America	111.4	6,860	16
Asia (except U.S.S.R.)	1,272.0	10,380	122
U.S.S.R.	201.0	8,610	23
Oceania	12.9	3,300	3
Total	2,407.6	51,800	47

Source: United Nations, *Demographic Yearbook, 1951,* New York, 1952. Figures for the U.S.S.R. are taken from Theodore Shabad, *Geography of the USSR* (New York: Columbia University Press, 1951).

TABLE 2. PERCENTAGE AGE DISTRIBUTION, REGIONS OF THE WORLD, 1947

	Est. Percentages of Population		
	Under 15 Years	15–59 Years	60 Years and Over
EUROPE			
North-West-Central Europe	24	62	14
Southern Europe [1]	30	59	11
Eastern Europe (inc. all of U.S.S.R.) [2]	34	59	7
AFRICA	40	55	5
AMERICA			
U.S. and Canada	25	64	11
Latin America	40	55	5
ASIA			
Near East [3]	40	54	6
South Central Asia [4]	40	56	4
Japan	37	55	8
Remaining Far East [5]	40	55	5
OCEANIA	28	62	10
WORLD	36	57	7

[1] Spain, Portugal, Italy, Greece, Andorra, San Marino, Vatican, Malta, Trieste, Gozo.
[2] Albania, Bulgaria, Czechoslovakia, Hungary, Poland, Romania, Turkey in Europe, Yugoslavia, U.S.S.R.
[3] Arabian Peninsula, Iran, Afghanistan and all Asia west of these.
[4] India, Pakistan, Ceylon, Maldive Is. and adjacent areas of Nepal, and French and Portuguese India.
[5] All the rest of Asia, except Japan and U.S.S.R.

Source: United Nations, *Demographic Yearbook, 1949-1950,* New York, 1950, p. 15.

Country		Year			
Italy	42,024	1936	46,272	116,235	398
Liechtenstein	13	1950	13[2]	67	194
Luxembourg	290	1947	297	1,000	297
Monaco	20	1951	20	.4	
Netherlands	9,625	1947	10,250	12,450	823
Norway	3,156	1950	3,156[2]	124,556	25
Spitsbergen	3.5	1950	3.5[2]	25,000	1.4
Poland	24,976	1950	24,976[2]	121,131	206
Portugal	8,490	1950	8,490[2]	35,466	239
Romania	15,872	1948	16,094[1]	91,584	176
Saar	889	1946	943	992	950
San Marino	13		13[1]	24	541
Spain	25,877	1940	28,287	189,400	149
Sweden	7,047	1950	7,047[2]	173,035	41
Switzerland	4,714	1950	4,714[2]	15,900	296
Trieste	344	1936	298	287	
Turkey	20,934	1950	20,934	287,000	73
Turkey in Europe	1,626		1,626	9,250	176
United Kingdom	50,210	1951	50,210[2]	94,205	533
England & Wales	43,744	1951	43,744	58,343	750
N. Ireland	1,369	1951	1,369	5,451	251
Scotland	5,096	1951	5,096	30,411	167
U.S.S.R.	170,467	1939	201,000	5,986,787	34
Vatican City	1	1948	1	2	500
Yugoslavia	15,772	1948	16,250	95,558	170

[1] Estimate. [2] Census figures. [3] Eastern Zone is estimated.

Sources: United Nations, *Demographic Yearbook, 1951,* New York, 1952, and national statistics of individual countries.

TABLE 8. VITAL STATISTICS

	Crude Birth Rate per 1,000		Crude Death Rate per 1,000		Natural Increase	
	1931–35	1947–50	1931–35	1947–50	1931–35	1947–50
Albania	30.2	—	*	*	—	—
Austria	14.4	17.2	13.5	12.6	0.9	4.6
Belgium	16.8	17.2	12.9	13.0	3.9	4.2
Bulgaria	29.3	24.0	15.5	13.4	13.8	10.6
Czechoslovakia	19.6	23.2	13.8	11.8	5.8	11.4
Denmark	17.7	19.0	10.9	9.1	6.8	9.9
Finland	19.5	26.0	13.4	11.0	6.1	15.0
France	16.5	21.7	15.7	12.9	0.8	8.8
Germany	16.6		11.2	*	5.4	
Eastern		*		*		*
Western [1]		16.7		10.7		6.0
Greece	29.5	26.6	16.5	10.8	13.0	15.8
Hungary	22.5	19.7	16.0	12.0	6.5	7.7
Iceland	23.5	27.8	11.1	8.2	12.4	19.6
Ireland	19.4	21.9	14.0	13.0	5.4	8.9
Italy	23.8	20.8	14.1	10.5	9.7	10.3
Luxembourg	16.9	14.6	12.4	12.1	4.5	2.5
Netherlands	21.2	24.8	8.9	8.8	12.3	16.0
Norway	15.2	19.7	10.4	9.1	4.8	10.6
Poland	27.6	22.7	14.6	11.2	13.0	11.5
Portugal	29.1	25.3	17.0	13.1	12.1	12.2
Romania	32.8	22.4	20.6	21.1	12.2	1.3
Spain	26.9	21.5	16.2	11.4	10.7	10.1
Sweden	14.1	17.8	11.6	10.2	2.5	7.6
Switzerland	16.4	18.7	11.8	10.7	4.6	8.0
United Kingdom	15.5	17.9	12.2	11.7	3.3	6.2
U.S.S.R.	33	25	22	10	11	15
Yugoslavia	31.8	29.2	17.9	13.3	13.9	15.9

* Not available.
[1] 1945-49.

Source: United Nations, *Demographic Yearbook, 1951*, New York, 1952, pp. 161 ff, 203 ff, and national statistics.

TABLE 9. CITIES WITH OVER 1,000,000 INHABITANTS

Name of City, Country	Date of Census of Latest Enumeration	Total Population (in thousands)
Greater London, U.K.	1951	8,417
Moscow, U.S.S.R.	1951 [1]	5,600
Paris, France	1950	5,008
Berlin, Germany	1950	
West sector		2,145
East sector		1,189
Leningrad, U.S.S.R.	1951 [1]	3,100
Vienna, Austria	1951	1,760
Rome, Italy	1950	1,665
Hamburg, Germany	1950	1,605
Budapest, Hungary	1951 [1]	1,600
Madrid, Spain	1950	1,512
Athens, Greece	1951	1,368
Milan, Italy	1950	1,289
Barcelona, Spain	1950	1,286
Copenhagen, Denmark	1951	1,185
Birmingham, U.K.	1951 [1]	1,184
Glasgow, U.K.	1951 [1]	1,087
Istanbul, Turkey	1951 [1]	1,080
Bucharest, Romania	1948	1,041
Naples, Italy	1950	1,029

[1] Latest estimate.

Sources: Compiled from different national statistics.

TABLE 10. FOOD CONSUMPTION AND DOMESTIC PRODUCTION (SELECTED COUNTRIES)

	Wheat and Rye		Rice and Millet		Other Cereals		Potatoes		Sugar (Refined)		Dry Legumes		Meat		Fats and Oils	
	1934-1938	1949-1950	1934-1938	1949-1950	1934-1938	1949-1950	1934-1938	1949-1950	1934-1938	1949-1950	1934-1938	1949-1950	1934-1938	1949-1950	1934-1938	1949-1950
Austria	1,304 / 74	1,208 / 60	29	27	1,403 / 66	914 / 68	2,859 / 99	2,010 / 100	163 / 99	167 / 37	25 / 76	18 / 56	330 / 84	213 / 92	133 / 47	123 / 39
Belgium-Luxembourg	1,986 / 44	1,622 / 56	48 / 2	31 / —	2,086 / 40	1,735 / 50	2,310 / 97	2,357 / 93	239 / 99	258 / 119	89 / 52	54 / 50	392 / 93	383 / 87	246 / 39	250 / 38
Czechoslovakia		2,744 / 92		5 / —		2,576 / 87		6,516 / 100		346 / 168		32 / 100		422 / 87		153 / 45
Denmark	1,077 / 60	831 / 93	8 / —	3 / —	3,207 / 91	3,583 / 93	1,324 / 102	1,703 / 105	195 / 101	132 / 228	10 / 82	34 / 79	277 / 192	277 / 190	134 / 127	118 / 115
Finland	683 / 78	686 / 79	13 / —	— / —	1,020 / 92	956 / 97	1,325 / 100	1,172 / 99	103 / 10	118 / 19	19 / 100	14 / 100	119 / 103	111 / 104	56 / 86	71 / 61
France	9,017 / 99	7,838 / 112	560 / 45	68 / 19	7,508 / 88	5,886 / 86	15,006 / 105	11,744 / 98	1,012 / 86	1,001 / 83	357 / 67	224 / 58	2,219 / 99	2,428 / 102	842 / 39	675 / 49
Germany [1]	12,880 / 97	8,627 / 69	190 / —	93 / —	11,790 / 91	5,975 / 71	48,470 / 100	21,225 / 98	1,620 / 106	1,159 / 48	627 / 82	260 / 75	3,450 / 94	1,562 / 93	1,984 / 50	803 / 49
Greece	1,298 / 63	1,321 / 67	31 / 8	28 / 46	614 / 100	571 / 100	149 / 98	408 / 97	73	73	92 / 78	90 / 89	136 / 80	94 / 79	115 / 117	139 / 182

	1	2	3	4	5	6	7	8	9	10	11	12	13	14	15	16
Ireland	607 / *30*	550 / *67*	3 / *—*	3 / *—*	1,025 / *69*	1,040 / *70*	2,550 / *101*	2,679 / *102*	113 / *66*	105 / *86*	2 / *—*	8 / *38*	103 / *233*	158 / *196*	54 / *108*	63 / *89*
Italy	7,893 / *94*	8,708 / *86*	377 / *136*	280 / *144*	4,084 / *93*	3,062 / *93*	2,774 / *102*	2,578 / *101*	306 / *99*	510 / *91*	935 / *96*	524 / *94*	840 / *95*	803 / *98*	720 / *77*	580 / *71*
Netherlands	1,568 / *62*	1,516 / *62*	74 / *—*	32 / *—*	1,570 / *29*	1,330 / *48*	2,780 / *110*	4,032 / *119*	250 / *84*	359 / *100*	110 / *128*	65 / *140*	320 / *110*	293 / *109*	266 / *56*	306 / *58*
Norway	419 / *16*	420 / *16*	5 / *—*	2 / *—*	468 / *67*	525 / *49*	892 / *100*	1,098 / *100*	88 / *—*	82 / *—*	8 / *25*	11 / *9*	110 / *99*	114 / *99*	92 / *257*	100 / *251*
Poland	8,094 / *105*	6,657 / *119*	42 / *—*	— / *—*	3,756 / *108*	3,769 / *103*	34,969 / *100*	25,506 / *101*	312 / *125*	418 / *149*	389 / *104*	95 / *100*	894 / *103*	453 / *114*	205 / *98*	200 / *86*
Sweden	1,069 / *103*	868 / *112*	12 / *—*	15 / *—*	2,158 / *94*	1,806 / *92*	1,852 / *100*	1,724 / *101*	275 / *98*	388 / *72*	41 / *100*	37 / *108*	309 / *104*	311 / *91*	171 / *51*	194 / *91*
Switzerland	699 / *32*	701 / *50*	17 / *—*	27 / *—*	518 / *9*	538 / *30*	780 / *95*	893 / *86*	160 / *6*	180 / *13*	8 / *—*	6 / *17*	236 / *96*	210 / *91*	92 / *38*	68 / *31*
United Kingdom	7,253 / *24*	6,853 / *33*	92 / *—*	55 / *—*	7,077 / *41*	8,042 / *73*	5,483 / *97*	9,529 / *100*	2,186 / *21*	1,824 / *26*	167 / *16*	172 / *73*	2,876 / *48*	2,578 / *46*	1,387 / *12*	1,519 / *10*
Yugoslavia	2,460 / *110*	2,095 / *101*	24 / *12*	— / *—*	4,956 / *105*	4,395 / *105*	1,616 / *100*	750 / *107*	68 / *100*	58 / *134*	119 / *125*	80 / *125*	340 / *111*	239 / *100*	122 / *110*	81 / *99*

Upper figures represent consumption in 1,000 metric tons. Lower figures, *in italics*, show percentage which is domestically produced.

[1] 1949-50 for Western Zone only.

Source: United Nations, *Statistical Yearbook, 1951*, New York, 1952, pp. 286 ff.

TABLE 11. LAND USE

	Total Area (millions of acres)	(Percentage of total area)			
		Arable Land	Meadows and Pastures	Forests	Other [1]
Albania	7.1	17	29.5	30	23.5
Austria	20.6	22	27	37	14
Belgium	7.6	33	24	17	26
Bulgaria	27.4	38.5	2.5	33	26
Czechoslovakia	31.2	43	16	32	9
Denmark	10.6	76	9	8	7
Finland	93.2	7	2	64	27
France	136.1	39	22	20	19
E. Germany	26.5	47.5	12	27.5	13
W. Germany	60.3	36	22	27	15
Greece	32.4	27	38.5	15.5	19
Hungary	22.9	60	17	12	11
Iceland	25.4	1	17	1	81
Ireland	17.4	21.5	46	1.5	31
Italy	74.4	51.5	17	19.5	12
Luxembourg	0.6	32	22	27	19
Netherlands	8.7	31	37	7	25
Norway	80.1	2	1	23	73
Poland [2]	77.0	54	14	22	10
Portugal	22.0	39		28	33
Romania	59.1	39	14	27	19
Saar	0.6	31	19	32	18
Spain	114.2	38	47	10	5
Sweden	111.0	9	1	53	37
Switzerland	10.2	11	41	25	22
Turkey	194.2	19	56	15	10
United Kingdom	60.3	34	48	6	12
U.S.S.R.	5,500.0	11	18	37	34
Yugoslavia	61.1	30	22	35	13

[1] Wasteland, inland water bodies, buildings, roads, any area not specifically shown.
[2] Data for present boundaries based on prewar statistics.

Source: United Nations, *Statistical Yearbook, 1951,* New York, 1952, pp. 86-87, and national statistics.

TABLE 12. ACREAGE, PRODUCTION, AND YIELDS OF MAJOR CROPS

	Acreage (million acres)						
	Wheat	Rye	Barley	Oats	Maize	Potatoes	Sugar Beets
Eastern Europe							
1934-1938	26.2	22.5	10.6	13.1	26.5	12.11	1.73
1939-1950	26.43	20.7	9.8	11.8	19.0	11.37	2.47
Western Europe							
1934-1938	20.3	8.6	6.9	19.0	0.99	9.9	1.97
1949-1950	18.4	6.9	7.9	16.3	0.99	8.9	2.47
Mediterr. Europe							
1934-1938	26.9	2.2	5.9	3.9	6.4	2.2	0.5
1949-1950	25.4	2.7	5.4	3.9	5.9	2.2	0.5
	Production (1,000 metric tons)						
Eastern Europe							
1934-1938	14.1	12.2	5.9	7.5	12.3	66.1	18.1
1939-1950	13.3	11.3	4.9	6.2	7.7	50.2	19.6
Western Europe							
1934-1938	15.2	6.1	5.6	14.0	0.7	58.1	24.3
1949-1950	16.0	5.6	7.5	12.5	0.4	59.2	30.0
Mediterr. Europe							
1934-1938	12.9	0.9	2.8	1.4	4.3	8.3	5.0
1949-1950	11.8	0.8	2.1	1.2	3.2	7.1	5.8
	Yields (cwts. per acre)						
Eastern Europe							
1934-1938	11.8	11.9	12.3	12.7	12.5	120	236
1939-1950	11.1	12.0	10.8	11.6	8.9	96	182
Western Europe							
1934-1938	16.4	15.5	18.2	16.0	14.9	130	257
1949-1950	19.3	17.9	20.6	17.0	10.4	144	280
Mediterr. Europe							
1934-1938	10.2	8.3	10.7	80.0	14.8	82.7	220
1949-1950	10.2	6.9	8.7	6.7	11.9	68.5	230

Eastern Europe: Albania, Bulgaria, Finland, Hungary, Romania, Yugoslavia, Czechoslovakia, Poland, East Germany.

Western Europe: Austria, Belgium, Denmark, France, West Germany, Ireland, Luxembourg, Netherlands, Norway, Sweden, Switzerland, United Kingdom.

Mediterranean Europe: Greece, Italy, Portugal, Spain.

Sources: Adapted from United Nations, *Economic Bulletin for Europe*, Vol. III, No. 2, 1951, p. 27. Based on: *International Yearbook of Agricultural Statistics*, IIA, Rome, Italy; *Yearbooks of FAO Statistics*, Washington, D. C.; national statistics.

Due to rounding, totals do not necessarily add.

TABLE 13. INDEX NUMBERS OF AGRICULTURAL PRODUCTION (SELECTED COUNTRIES)

1934-1938 = 100

	1950-1951		1950-1951
Austria	98	Norway	118
Belgium-Luxembourg	111	Poland	71
Bulgaria	87 [1]	Portugal	102
Czechoslovakia	81 [2]	Romania	91 [1]
Denmark	126	Spain	86
Finland	115	Sweden	113
France	10	Switzerland	120
E. Germany	71 [2]	United Kingdom	130
W. Germany	104	Yugoslavia	96 [2]
Greece	99		
Hungary	87 [2]	Total East Central Europe	80 [2]
Ireland	106	Other Europe	110
Italy	109	Total Europe	96 [2]
Netherlands	123		

[1] 1948-1949.
[2] 1949-1950.

Source: United Nations, *Economic Survey of Europe in 1951*, Geneva, 1952, p. 179.

TABLE 14. DIETS OF SELECTED COUNTRIES

	Calories per Capita per Day		Total Proteins (grams)		Fats (grams)	
	Prewar	1950-51	Prewar	1950-51	Prewar	1950-51
Austria	2,990	2,685	88	77	103	85
Belgium-Luxembourg	2,820	2,910	84	85	93	106
Denmark	3,415	3,300	91	100	150	141
Finland [1]	3,000	3,100	95	99	*	*
France	2,830	2,700	93	92	88	85
German Fed. Rep.	2,960	2,800	83	78	113	97
Greece	2,600	2,510	94	79	69	65
Iceland [1]	3,164	3,231	111	124	*	*
Ireland	3,400	3,465	99	97	107	114
Italy	2,515	2,450	82	78	60	55
Netherlands	2,915	3,025	80	81	109	119
Norway	3,205	3,160	90	104	120	133
Sweden	3,120	3,190	95	94	118	130
Switzerland	3,140	3,300	95	101	108	113
United Kingdom	3,125	3,085	83	90	125	126

[1] Postwar figures are for 1948-49.
* Not available.

Source: Organization for European Economic Cooperation, *General Statistics*, May, 1952, pp. 18, 67, and national statistics.

TABLE 15. PERCENTAGE DISTRIBUTION OF AGRICULTURAL AND INDUSTRIAL PRODUCTION (SELECTED COUNTRIES)

	Agricultural 1934–1938	Industrial 1950
Austria	1.9	1.6
Belgium		2.8
Belgium-Luxembourg	1.8	
Bulgaria	1.6	0.5
Czechoslovakia	4.1	3.8
Denmark	2.0	1.6
Finland	1.0	0.6
France	16.1	11.3
E. Germany [1]	3.9	5.8
W. Germany [1]	10.7	15.4
Greece	1.8	0.6
Hungary	2.9	1.6
Ireland	1.3	0.5
Italy	10.3	5.8
Luxembourg		0.2
Netherlands	2.5	2.8
Norway	0.6	1.0
Poland	10.5	4.4
Portugal	1.5	0.4
Romania	3.1	1.1
Saar		0.3
Spain	5.3	3.3
Sweden	2.0	3.7
Switzerland	1.3	
United Kingdom	6.0	29.7
Yugoslavia	3.3	

Note: While exact postwar figures for agriculture are not available, the basic structure has not changed substantially.

Industrial percentages are based on total European production, except Switzerland and Yugoslavia.

[1] Postwar boundaries.

Sources: United Nations, *Economic Survey of Europe in 1950*, Geneva, 1951, p. 30; United Nations, *Economic Survey of Europe in 1951*, Geneva, 1952, p. 179.

TABLE 16. PRODUCTION OF INDUSTRIAL RAW MATERIALS (SELECTED COUNTRIES)

(All figures in thousand metric tons unless otherwise indicated. All figures are based on prewar boundaries.)

	Bauxite		Coal[10]		Copper Ore		Electric Energy[2]		Iron Ore		Lead Ore		Manganese		Crude Petro.[10]	
	1937	1950	1937	1951	1937	1950	1937	1951	1937	1951	1937	1950	1937	1950	1937	1951
Austria	*	3.0	0.2	0.2[11]	*	1.7	2.9	7.4	0.6	0.7	8.7	4.8[12]				1.5[11]
Belgium			29.9	29.6			5.6	9.5	0.1							
Bulgaria	3[5]		0.1	0.1[8]			0.2	0.5[8]								
Czechoslovakia			16.7	17.9	0.7	*	4.1	10.3	0.6	0.6	3.9	2.2[9]		*		0.1[11]
Finland					14.3	11.9	2.8	4.4			0.4	0.3				
France	691	805	44.4	52.9	0.6	*	20.1	36.1	12.5	11.6	4.6	10.8[12]			0.1	0.3
Germany	93	*	171.1	123.8	30.4		49.0		2.5	3.7	78.9				0.5	
E. Germany			6.0	3.1					0.1	0.1						
W. Germany				120.7		1.4		51.4	2.4	3.6		50.4[12]				1.4
Greece		45[7]					0.2	0.6[7]	0.1		8.5	2.4[7]				
Hungary	533	340	0.9	1.2[6]			1.1	1.2[9]	0.1	0.2	0.5	0.2[8]	10.1	23.6[8]		0.5
Iceland			0				0	0.2[11]								
Ireland			0.1	0.2[11]			0.3	0.9[11]								
Italy	387	153	1.3	1.0[11]	1.0	0.2	15.4	29.1	0.5	0.2	35.0	38.4[12]	10.9	4.9		

Country															
Luxembourg															0.7
Netherlands	14.3	12.5			3.5	7.5	2.3	1.7							
Norway	0.8	0.4	20.7	15.5	9.0	17.3	0.6	0.2	0.4	0.2					
Poland	36.2	81.8			3.6	11.1		0.3						0.5	0.1 [8]
Portugal	0.3	0.4 [7]			0.4	0.9 [11]			0.2	0.3					
Romania	0.3	0.2 [7]			1.1	2.1 [11]	0.1	0.2	7.4 [4]	3.3 [8,4]	18.3	21.4 [7]	7.2	3.8 [8]	
Saar	13.4	16.3													
Spain	6.9 [3]	11.0 [11]			3.3 [3]	8.0		1.1	61.7 [3]	35.9	1.5 [3]	7.3			
Sweden	0.5	0.3 [11]	7.2	16.1	8.0	19.4	6.9	9.8	9.3	16.8 [12]	2.1	1.9			
Switzerland					6.8	10.3									
Turkey (all)	2.3	4.4 [11]	0.7 [4]	11.7 [4]	0.3 [5]	0.8 [11]	0.1		7.6	0	0.2	15.2			
United Kingdom	244.3	226.4			24.2	60.0	4.3	4.5	41.9 [3]	4.4 [12]			0	0	
U.S.S.R.	250	*	100	185	92.5	*	36.4	90.2 [11]	*	*	*	41.9 [3]	*	2,752	*	28.5	37.9
Yugoslavia	354	201	0.4	1.2 [11]	41.9	43.3	0.9	2.4 [11]	0.3	0.3	65.9	84.0	1.5	4.1	0.2

731

Sources: United Nations, *Statistical Yearbook, 1951*, New York, 1952; United Nations, *Monthly Bulletin of Statistics*, July, 1952; United Nations, *General Statistics*, July, 1952; United Nations, *Quarterly Bulletin of Steel Statistics*, No. 8, September, 1952; Organization for European Economic Cooperation, *General Statistics*, July, 1952; national statistics.

* Not available.

1 Anthracite and bituminous. 2 Figures in billion kw.-hrs. 3 1935. 4 Smelter production. 5 1938. 6 1948. 7 1949. 8 1947. 9 1946. 10 Million metric tons. 11 1950. 12 1951.

TABLE 17. INDUSTRIAL PRODUCTION (SELECTED COUNTRIES AND COMMODITIES)

	Cotton Fabrics (thousand metric tons)		Woolen Fabrics (thousand metric tons)		Nitrogen (not incl. industrial) (thousand metric tons)		Cement (million metric tons)		Crude Steel (million metric tons)	
	1937	1950	1937	1950	1938-39	1950-51	1937	1951	1937	1951
Austria	13	14[8]	10.8	7.2	1.5[7]	75.0	0.4	1.5	0.7	1.0
Belgium	53	109	15.6[2]	26.4	93.0[15]	171.0[15]	3.0	4.4	3.9	5.1
Czechoslovakia	56	60[12]	17.2	19.6[12]	24.5[2,17]	30.0	1.3	1.7[1]	2.3	3.3
Denmark	5	6[1]	2.6	4.6[1]			0.7	1.0		0.1[6]
Finland	9	7	3.6	4.7[1]		1.0	0.4	0.7[5]		0.1
France	159[2]	196[8]	79.8[2]	80.0	196.0	238.0	4.3	8.1	7.9	9.8[4]
Germany									19.8	
E. Germany	204[7]	217[8]			478.0	*	2.5[2]	*		1.6
W. Germany	26[3]	65[1,3]	7.5[3]	60.2[1,3]	354.0	612.0	11.5[2]	12.3		13.5
Greece	148[2,3]	128[3,12]	20.0[2,3]	10.9[1,3]			0.3	0.3[13]		
Hungary				*			0.4	0.2[12]	0.7	1.2
Ireland			3.2[10]	5.2[10]		4.0	0.1[2]	0.4[5]		
Italy	90	123[8]			109.0	169.0	4.3	5.6	2.1	3.0[5]
Luxembourg							0.1	0.1[5]	3.5	3.1
Netherlands					99.0	189.0	0.4	0.7		0.6
Norway	4	4[1]	3.3	4.6[1]	90.0	160.0	0.3	0.7	0.1	0.1
Poland	51	69[8]	20.9	28.1[1]	51.0	65.0	1.3	2.7	1.5	2.8
Portugal	16[2]	28	5.3[3,11]	2.1[3]			0.3	0.6		
Romania							0.5	0.7[5]	0.2	0.6[5]
Saar									2.4	2.6
Spain					4.0	7.0	0.6[2]	2.1	0.6[9]	0.8
Sweden	20	23			8.0	26.0	0.9	2.0	1.1	1.5
Switzerland			11.5[7]	14.0	10.0	14.0	0.6	1.1[5]		
Turkey (all)	15	23[8]	3.0[3]	4.4	1.0	1.0	0.2	0.4		0.1
United Kingdom	3,328[3,9]	202[8]	290.0[3]	376.0[3]	123.0	262.0	7.4	10.4	13.2	15.9
U.S.S.R.[5]	2,612[3,9]	3,900[3]	100.0[3]	165.0[3]	*	*	5.8[7]	10.5[6]	17.7	31.3[5]
Yugoslavia	115[10,11]	144[10]	9.8[10,11]	24.4[1]	8.0	3.0	0.6	1.2[5]	0.2	0.4

1 1949. 2 1938. 3 Millions of meters. 4 Secondary production. 5 Estimate. 6 1950. 7 1936. 8 1951. 9 1935. 10 Millions of square meters. 11 1939.
12 1947. 13 1948. 14 Leather uppers only. 15 Belgium and Luxembourg. 16 1940. 17 1937. 18 Primary production only.

	Copper (smelter prod.) (thousand metric tons)		Lead (smelter prod.) (thousand metric tons)		Aluminum (thousand metric tons)		Footwear (million pairs)		Lumber (million cubic meters)	
	1937	1951	1937	1951	1937	1951	1937	1950	1937	1950
Austria	2	5	11	9	4	27	5.5[14]	4.2[14]	1.9	2.7
Belgium	90	142[2]	85	71	1	1	18.0[2]	15.1	0.5	0.4
Czechoslovakia	1	*	5	8[13]			55.0	64.4[13]	2.4	*
Denmark							4.6	8.1[1]	0.8	0.4
Finland	11	21	13[2,4]	21[4]			2.9	5.5[1]	6.4	4.1
France	6[4]	6[4]	38	48	35	91	152.7[2]	141.1	3.4	4.9
Germany	122[7]		166		146		143.3		14.0	*
E. Germany								*		*
W. Germany	69[4,7]	58[4]	140	118[6]	49[7]	74		81.0		8.8
Greece			5	1[1]			10.5	13.0[1]	0.4	0.1
Hungary	1	*	5	*	1	14[1]	3.5[2]	3.7[13]	0.2	*
Ireland							4.6	5.0[1]		0
Italy	2	10[6]	39	36[1]	23	50	*	*	2.1	1.8
Luxembourg			7[4]	18[1,4]					*	*
Netherlands					23	51	15.1	20.4[1]	0.2	0.3
Norway	8	9	18	17[13]			3.2	4.7[1]	2.7	1.6
Poland							1.5	7.3[1]	4.6	*
Portugal	1						2.8[2]	0.9	1.4	0.6
Romania	1		7	3[12]					3.3	*
Saar										
Spain	10[9]	9[6]	71[9]	41	1[9]	4	*	16.6[1]	0.4	0.9[1]
Sweden	10	21[1]		17[6]	2	7	8.9	11.9	6.6	5.7
Switzerland					25	28			0.6	1.0
Turkey (all)	1	18	1	*					*	0.1
United Kingdom	8	209[4]	10[18]	75[4]	19	28	132.5[9]	138.1	0.5	1.7
U.S.S.R.[5]	94	*	55	*	45	*	170.0	200.0	176.0	240.0
Yugoslavia	39	32	4	57	2[11]	3	4.0[11]	9.0	2.8	2.8

Footnotes on opposite page.

Sources: United Nations, *Statistical Yearbook, 1951,* New York, 1951, pp. 207-66; United Nations, *Recent Changes in Production, Supplement to World Economic Report, 1950-51,* New York, 1952; United Nations, *Economic Bulletin for Europe,* Vol. IV, No. 1, Geneva, 1952; Organization for European Economic Cooperation, *General Statistics,* July, 1952, Paris, 1952; United Nations, *Monthly Bulletin of Statistics,* July, 1952, New York, 1952.

TABLE 18. CHANGES IN INDUSTRIAL PRODUCTION AND OUTPUT PER MAN IN INDUSTRY (SELECTED COUNTRIES)

	Industrial Production (1938 = 100)		Output per Man in Industry (1935–1938 = 100)
	1950	1951	1950
Austria	145 [1]	166 [1]	87 [1]
Belgium	125	143	96
Bulgaria	290	345	
Czechoslovakia	146 [1]	168 [1]	126 [1]
Denmark	157	161	100
Finland	145	171	114
France	121	134	100
E. Germany	94	115	
W. Germany	94	113	87
Berlin W.	28	40	63
Greece	113	130	
Hungary	206	267	124
Iceland			
Ireland	168	178	128
Italy	117	134	106
Luxembourg	146	175	
Netherlands	139	145	86
Norway	151	157	99
Poland	223 [2]	270 [2]	141
Portugal	122	125	
Romania	160	206	
Saar	88	107	
Spain	144	147	
Sweden	164	171	126
Switzerland			
Turkey	159	*	
United Kingdom	151	156	126
Yugoslavia	338	348	
Total of Countries Listed	126	141	

[1] 1937 = 100.
[2] Current production compared with 1938 production in prewar area: medium and large-scale industries.

Sources: United Nations, *Economic Survey for Europe in 1950*, Geneva, 1951, p. 57; United Nations, *Economic Bulletin for Europe,* Vol. IV, No. 2, Geneva, 1952, and national statistics

TABLE 19. EUROPE'S BALANCE OF PAYMENTS, CURRENT TRANSACTIONS

(In U.S. dollars—billions)

	1938			1950			Transactions of OEEC Countries Only 1951		
	U.S.	Other Non-Europe	Total	U.S.	Other Non-Europe	Total	U.S.	Other Non-OEEC	Total
Current Transactions:									
Merchandise Imports	1.3	4.2	5.5	3.6	8.9	12.5	5.1	13.2	18.3
Merchandise Exports	0.6	3.1	3.7	1.6	8.0	9.6	2.0	12.0	14.0
Balance on merchandise account	0.7	1.1	1.8	2.0	0.9	2.9	3.1	1.2	4.3
Service Transactions:									
Income from Investments	0.1	1.1	1.2	0.1	0.4	0.5	*	*	*
Transportation }	0.2	0.4	0.6	—	0.5	0.5	*	*	*
Other Services }				0.3	0.9	0.6	*	*	*
Total Service Transactions	0.3	1.5	1.8	0.4	—	0.4	0.1	0.1	0.2
Total Current Transactions	0.4	0.4	—	1.6	0.9	2.5	3.0	1.1	4.1
Other Transactions:									
Government grants and credits			*	2.7	0.2	2.9	2.2	—	2.2
Gold movements			*	1.3	0.4	1.7	0.3	0.2	0.5
Use of sterling balances			*	—	0.9	0.9	—	0.3	0.3
Other			*	—	0.4	0.4	0.5	0.6	1.1
				1.4	1.1	2.5	3.0	1.1	4.1

Note: Figures in *italics* indicate imports (deficits). Figures for all of Europe for 1951 or figures for prewar for OEEC countries only are not available.

Sources: Adapted from International Monetary Fund, *Balance of Payments Yearbook, 1938, 1946, 1947,* Washington, D.C., 1949, p. 48; International Monetary Fund, *International Financial Statistics,* May, 1951, p. ii; and *International Monetary Fund,* preliminary reports.

TABLE 20. EXPORTS AND IMPORTS

	Exports (millions of dollars)			Imports (millions of dollars)		
	1938	1951	Per Capita 1951	1938	1951	Per Capita 1951
Austria	171	453.6	65.9	263	652.8	94.86
Belgium-Luxembourg	721	2,634.6	304.5	702	2,527.2	292.1
Bulgaria	62	133 *	18.4 *	46	178 *	24.6 *
Czechoslovakia	358	800 *	64.2 *	262	653 *	52.4 *
Denmark	335	825.6	193.5	307	1,004.4	235.4
Finland	181	354 *	87.9 *	163	359	89.1 *
France	863	4,225.2	99.6	1,198	4,592.4	108.31
Germany	2,023	3,474	50.34	1,863	3,502.8	50.76
Greece	90	102	12.81	120	398.4	50.05 *
Hungary	147	257 *	27.6 *	116	116	12.5 *
Iceland	17	44.4	308.33	10	56.4	391.66
Ireland	118	228	77.07	183	572.4	193.5
Italy	549	1,629.6	35.21	519	2,118	45.77
Netherlands	579	1,926	187.9	732	2,516.4	245.5
Norway	193	619	196.2	262	874.8	277.18
Poland	223	631 *	25.3 *	231	844 *	33.8 *
Portugal	59	262.8	30.95	95	328.8	38.72
Romania	160	239 *	14.9 *	125	213 *	13.2 *
Spain	101	389 *	13.8 *	130	370 *	13.1 *
Sweden	463	1,777	251.5	472	1,774	251.9
Switzerland	301	1,078.8	228.8	340	1,360	288.4
Turkey	122	276	13.1 *	121	324 *	15.5 *
United Kingdom	2,291	7,578	150.9	3,732	10,060	218.27
U.S.S.R.	365	1,141 *	5.7 *	328	1,049 *	5.2 *
Yugoslavia	130	154 *	9.5	124	217 *	13.4 *

* 1950.

Source: United Nations, Economic Bulletin for Europe, Geneva, 1950.

TABLE 21. PERCENTAGE DISTRIBUTION OF FOREIGN TRADE, POPULATION, AND AREA

(All figures are approximations)

	Trade		Population		Area
	1938	1950	1938	1950	
Europe, excl. U.S.S.R.	51	40	19	17	4
U.S.S.R.	1	1	8	8	16
Asia, excl. U.S.S.R.	15	15	53	52	20
Africa	7	6	7	8	23
North America	14	23	7	7	15
South America	9	11	6	7	16
Oceania	3	4	.5	.5	6

Sources: League of Nations, Europe's Trade, Geneva, 1941, p. 9; International Monetary Fund, International Financial Statistics, Vol. IV, No. 8, Washington, D.C., 1951, pp. XXIV-XXVII; United Nations, Demographic Yearbook, 1949–50, New York, 1950, pp. 79-83.

TABLE 22. IMPORTS OF GRAINS BY WESTERN EUROPEAN COUNTRIES

(1,000,000 metric tons)

Exporting Area	Bread Grains [2]		Coarse Grains [3]		Total	
	1934–38	1951	1934–38	1951	1934–38	1951
U.S.S.R.	0.8	0.5	0.5	0.9	1.3	1.4
Other East European Countries [1]	1.6	0.1	1.5	0.1	3.1	0.2
Total from Eastern Europe	2.4	0.6	2.0	1.0	4.4	1.6
Imports from all countries	12.1	14.5	11.1	7.4	23.2	21.9
Percentage share of Eastern Europe in total imports of Western Europe....	20	4	18	14	19	7

[1] Including Yugoslavia, excluding Czechoslovakia.
[2] Wheat and rye including flour in grain equivalent.
[3] Maize, barley, and oats.

Sources: United Nations, Economic Bulletin for Europe, Vol. III, No. 2, Geneva, 1951, p. 55, and Economic Commission for Europe.

TABLE 23. IMPORTS OF SELECTED COMMODITIES INTO TEN WESTERN EUROPEAN * COUNTRIES FROM EASTERN EUROPE

(1,000 metric tons)

	1938	1951
Coal	11,825	10,715
of which: Sweden	2,715	3,542
Austria	1,864	1,825
Denmark	295	1,935
Italy	2,198	1,320
France	1,724	1,125
Norway	456	158
Timber (1,000 cubic meters)	6,117	793
of which: United Kingdom	2,786	505
W. Germany	1,838	9
Belgium	343	141
Netherlands	949	117
France	183	10
Steel	214	
Sugar	221	
Meat	160	59
of which: United Kingdom	41	39
W. Germany	102	10
Eggs	72	15
of which: United Kingdom	42	3
W. Germany	20	5
Tobacco	26	—

* Belgium-Luxembourg, France, the three western zones of Germany (for 1938 whole of prewar Germany), Italy, Netherlands, Norway, Sweden, Switzerland, Turkey, the United Kingdom.

Sources: United Nations, *Economic Bulletin for Europe*, Vol. III, No. 2, Geneva, 1951, p. 54, and Economic Commission for Europe.

TABLE 24. EXPORTS OF 11 WESTERN EUROPEAN COUNTRIES TO EASTERN EUROPE

(Millions of dollars at constant prices)

	By Countries	
	1938	1950 [1]
Belgium-Luxembourg	103	66
Denmark	16	23
Finland	1	101 [2]
France	107	50
Netherlands	84	37
Norway	18	30
Sweden	51	99
United Kingdom	220	99
Western Germany	397 [3]	88

	By Commodities	
	1938	1950
Food, drink, and tobacco	72	30
Raw materials	202	108
Metals and manufactures	234	106
Machinery	200	255
Vehicles and other transport equipment	82	61
Chemicals	89	44
Textiles	121	35
Other manufactures	97	35
Unspecified	40	38
	1,137	712

[1] Annual rate based on first nine months (in 1949 prices).
[2] Including war reparations.
[3] Three western zones for all years.

Source: United Nations, *Economic Bulletin for Europe,* Vol. III, No. 2, Geneva, 1951, pp. 50, 52.

TABLE 25. TRADE OF WESTERN EUROPE WITH EASTERN EUROPE

(Millions of dollars at current prices, f.o.b.) [1]

		Czechoslovakia		Poland		Hungary		Romania		Bulgaria		U.S.S.R.		Yugoslavia	
		1938	1951 [5]	1938	1951 [5]	1938	1951 [5]	1938	1951 [5]	1938	1951 [5]	1938	1951 [5]	1938	1951 [5]
United Kingdom	Imp.	32	27	41	59	11	—	18	2	2	—	119	129	11	23
	Exp.	11	9	26	24	3	4	6	3	1	1	55	13	6	21
France	Imp.	9	8	9	7	3	1	8	—	1	—	17	4	2	4
	Exp.	12	6	9	9	1	2	10	1	2	—	8	1	3	5
Netherlands	Imp.	15	17	10	8	2	5	2	1	—	1	22	9	2	4
	Exp.	7	15	7	6	1	4	1	1	—	1	17	2	1	11
Belgium-Luxembourg	Imp.	7	10	10	7	1	2	4	—	—	—	26	17	5	4
	Exp.	6	25	10	9	1	11	4	3	1	—	18	10	1	8
Switzerland	Imp.	12	21	5	9	5	8	6	—	1	—	7	6	2	4
	Exp.	10	23	5	8	3	11	3	6	1	1	6	7	3	8
Italy	Imp.	13	13	12	27	10	8	10	1	5	—	—	29	7	12
	Exp.	7	14	6	14	9	9	7	3	4	1	2	17	12	28
Turkey	Imp.	10	10	2	1	1	6	2	—	1	1	4	—	—	1
	Exp.	4	14	2	2	1	8	2	—	1	2	4	—	—	1
Denmark	Imp.	2	4	3	35	1	2	2	—	1	—	6	10	—	1
	Exp.	1	4	2	20	—	1	3	—	1	—	2	—	—	4

		1	2	3	4	5	6	7	8	9	10	11	12	13	14
Sweden	Imp.	10	20	14	65	3	1	1	1	—	—	5	11	1	3
	Exp.	9	20	9	44	1	1	1	1	—	—	9	22	1	3
Norway	Imp.	5	4	3	7	1	1	—	—	—	—	4	9	—	1
	Exp.	2	7	2	6	—	1	—	—	—	—	2	13	—	1
Finland [2]	Imp.	4	3	4	37	—	2	—	5	—	1	4	41	—	1
	Exp.	—	5	1	14	—	2	—	1	—	1	2	113	—	1
W. Germany [3]	Imp.	59	6	44	11	44	16	30	—	35	1	53	—	42	22
	Exp.	55	23	48	21	35	16	40	4	23	1	48	—	35	37
Austria	Imp.	19	21	11	22	28	15	12	3	5	1	2	—	24	8
	Exp.	8	19	8	16	15	6	8	3	2	1	3	—	11	10
Others [4]	Imp.	1	7	4	10	1	1	17	—	1	—	15	—	4	1
	Exp.	3	3	1	2	1	—	2	—	—	—	5	2	2	—
Total	Imp.	198	171	172	305	111	68	112	12	52	4	284	265	102	88
	Exp.	135	187	136	195	71	76	87	25	35	7	181	200	75	138

[1] C.i.f. figures have been converted to f.o.b. values by reducing c.i.f. figures at varying rates up to 10 per cent. See Source for details.
[2] Including war reparations to the U.S.S.R., which amounted to $85 million, $72 million and $34 million respectively in 1948, 1949, and 1950.
[3] For 1938: whole of prewar territory.
[4] Iceland, Ireland, Greece, Spain, and Portugal.
[5] Annual rates based on first 6 months; 5 months for Spain and Turkey; 3 months for Greece.

Source: United Nations, *Economic Bulletin for Europe,* Vol. III, No. 2, Geneva, 1951, p. 58

TABLE 26. IMPORTS AND EXPORTS OF EIGHTEEN EUROPEAN COUNTRIES AND THE UNITED STATES ACCORDING TO AREAS OF ORIGIN AND DESTINATION

(Millions of dollars at current prices; imports c.i.f., exports, f.o.b.)

Area	Year	United Kingdom Imp.	United Kingdom Exp.	Ireland Imp.	Ireland Exp.	Iceland Imp.	Iceland Exp.	France Imp.	France Exp.	Netherlands Imp.	Netherlands Exp.	Belgium-Luxembourg Imp.	Belgium-Luxembourg Exp.	Switzerland Imp.	Switzerland Exp.	Italy Imp.	Italy Exp.	Portugal Imp.	Portugal Exp.
United Kingdom, Ireland, Iceland	1938	113	102	99	110	3	3	74	104	65	131	55	93	18	34	30	32	16	16
	1951	214	288	269	189	17	11	166	34	218	322	215	280	94	54	83	224	52	54
Western Europe, Industrial Countries [1]	1938	353	209	9	2	0	1	171	197	136	103	180	214	79	52	51	57	17	10
	1951	1,057	606	39	10	4	6	402	621	615	433	606	819	303	199	248	311	68	31
Mediterranean and Iberian Countries [2]	1938	80	103	1	0	1	4	35	33	15	18	15	28	30	26	30	26	3	4
	1951	1,445	335	19	4	3	7	225	225	63	81	78	155	121	126	47	114	12	11
Scandinavian Countries [3]	1938	433	198	3	2	4	6	40	29	37	38	31	42	7	19	21	17	5	5
	1951	1,126	703	31	5	9	6	231	208	188	188	136	233	58	65	113	90	16	3
Germany and Austria	1938	143	107	7	0	2	2	93	58	169	87	91	92	91	54	141	107	16	10
	1951	252	164	14	3	5	2	306	231	344	297	237	193	235	127	319	160	20	8
Eastern European Countries [4]	1938	115	53	1	0	3	0	32	37	27	17	27	23	33	25	49	45	1	13
	1951	90	34	6	0	1	3	37	34	25	25	20	38	7	50	57	40	1	0
U.S.S.R.	1938	119	55	2	0	3	0	17	8	22	17	26	18	7	6	0	2	0	2
	1951	169	10	0	0	0	0	12	5	14	2	17	13	5	5	22	24	0	1
Total Europe	1938	1,356	827	122	117	10	16	462	470	475	411	425	510	263	216	330	286	58	42
	1951	3,385	2,140	376	209	41	34	1,383	1,714	1,462	1,347	1,309	1,731	850	627	769	963	169	123
United States and Dependencies	1938	1,476	101	23	9	1	1	134	54	72	31	77	42	25	58	58	10	11	11
	1951	1,067	383	72	7	7	8	520	250	283	112	409	213	220	139	442	103	50	35
Canada and Newfoundland	1938	311	111	7	0	0	0	16	5	12	4	10	6	5	3	2	7	0	1
	1951	730	384	25	1	1	0	51	22	25	9	82	36	35	17	46	10	7	2
Latin American Republics	1938	310	177	7	0	1	0	78	46	54	22	57	54	20	20	35	43	3	3
	1951	934	460	14	0	0	1	337	279	160	99	155	173	100	127	199	141	19	17
Overseas Sterling Area	1938	990	873	14	3	2	0	119	23	31	29	60	45	11	16	39	21	12	0
	1951	3,649	3,268	58	0	0	0	928	177	232	147	251	209	51	77	383	253	16	8
Dependent Overseas Territories [5]	1938	114	58	5	0	0	3	322	239	69	69	59	35	5	5	31	36	16	7
	1951	393	122	11	0	0	0	1,032	1,577	83	59	251	145	36	24	74	42	54	73
Other Overseas Countries [5]	1938	175	144	5	0	1	0	87	26	19	13	14	29	11	20	24	119	19	3
	1951	729	413	12	1	1	0	345	189	315	162	98	129	80	77	203	140	37	17
Total Overseas Countries	1938	2,376	1,464	61	1	6	4	736	393	257	168	277	211	77	85	189	263	37	17
	1951	7,503	5,039	191	15	16	11	3,214	2,495	1,096	586	1,235	905	522	461	1,349	721	160	140
Total World	1938	3,732	2,291	183	118	16	20	1,198	863	732	579	702	721	340	301	519	549	95	59
	1951	10,894	7,179	567	223	57	45	4,597	4,209	2,558	1,933	2,544	2,636	1,372	1,088	2,118	1,684	329	263

Footnotes on opposite page.

		Greece, Spain, Turkey		Denmark		Sweden		Norway		Finland		W. Germany[6]		Austria		U.S.	
		Imp.	Exp.	Imp.	Exp.	Imp.	Exp.	Imp.	Exp.	Imp.	Exp.	Imp.	Exp.	Imp.	Exp.	Imp.	Exp.
United Kingdom, Ireland, Iceland	1938	49	33	77	187	59	116	41	55	27	82	108	144	6	8	103	499
	1951	139	126	262	326	232	355	203	125	99	245	123	224	77	41	473	949
Western Europe, Industrial Countries[1]	1938	37	27	18	19	63	49	28	27	19	20		425	17	19	148	308
	1951	185	151	167	81	314	299	131	86	129	119	670	1,084	116	81	721	1,259
Mediterranean and Iberian Countries[2]	1938	22	31	6	1	9	16	8	12	4	6		254	22	27	89	104
	1951	84	43	36	47	79	99	31	48	33	29	319	383	73	99	331	898
Scandinavian Countries[3]	1938	9	7	37	31	9	75	42	30	30	17		271	4	6	79	128
	1951	71	48	163	114	124	218	156	94	77	72		484	23	20	228	320
Germany and Austria	1938	123	114	82	67	110	84	51	31	34	27		46	46	32	66	150
	1951	166	140	150	135	263	200	69	57	74	61	412	119	117	69	251	616
Eastern European Countries[4]	1938	49	19	40	6	29	21	9	4	8	1	56	236	99	52	53	76
	1951	21	23	6	23	98	80	10	10	61	24	254	64	64	56	39	3
U.S.S.R.	1938	17	8			5	9	4	2	4	2	53		2	3	27	74
	1951	0	2		0	13	33	10	12	41	68	53	48	2	0	32	0
Total Europe	1938	296	242	235	313	319	370	183	161	126	155	1,136	1,424	196	147	565	1,339
	1951	665	533	827	726	1,183	1,284	609	432	519	618	1,653	2,358	469	365	2,075	4,046
United States and Dependencies	1938	33	43	25	5	64	42	27	1	12	17	130	63	20	3		
	1951	224	147	107	19	167	93	110	45	41	58	651	237	145	27		
Canada and Newfoundland	1938	4	2	2	2	5	2	8	1	1	0	25	10	2	0	260	468
	1951	4	9	2	8	11	10	32	3	1	0	51	25	2	2	2,265	2,516
Latin American Republics	1938	9	8	22	32	50	20	17	5	10	3	221	214	19	4	453	494
	1951	52	79	35	3	136	197	32	58	57	69	333	370	21	25	3,308	3,609
Overseas Sterling Area	1938	13	14	9	21	21	14	13	3	9	3	136	120	13	6	254	267
	1951	53	1	13		139	130	37	55	35	38	473	282	6	14	1,641	1,231
Dependent Overseas Territories[5]	1938	9	7	9	14	6	3	8	1	3	0	101	41	6	2	121	119
	1951	83	90	7	2	72	15	26	4	10	4	123	40	3	3	333	288
Other Overseas Countries[5]	1938	7		5	4	7	12	6	7	2	3	87	151	7	3	286	417
	1951	106	60	20	15	69	51	32	24	11	27	242	162	7	18	1,175	1,608
Total Overseas Countries	1938	75	71	72	22	153	93	79	32	37	26	700	599	67	24	1,374	1,765
	1951	518	359	184	105	592	495	268	188	162	194	1,869	1,116	183	89	8,722	10,026
Total World	1938	371	313	307	335	472	463	262	193	163	181	1,836	2,023	263	171	1,939	3,104
	1951	1,183	893	1,010	831	1,775	1,779	877	620	677	812	3,503	3,474	652	454	10,797	13,298

1 France, Netherlands, Belgium-Luxembourg, Switzerland. 2 Italy, Greece, Spain, Portugal, Yugoslavia (in 1951 but not in 1938), Turkey, and miscellaneous countries. 3 Denmark, Sweden, Norway, Finland. 4 Czechoslovakia, Poland, Romania, Hungary, Bulgaria, Yugoslavia in 1938 only. 5 In 1951 Indonesia has been shifted from "Dependent Overseas Territories" to "Other Overseas Countries." 6 1938 prewar Germany.

Note: Due to rounding, totals may not add.

Source: United Nations, Economic Bulletin for Europe, Vol. IV, No. 2, and Vol. III, No. 2.

TABLE 27. RAILWAYS

(1950)

	Railway Lines (in thousands of miles)	Railway Tracks (in thousands of miles)	Line-Miles per Square Mile	Passenger Miles (in billions of miles)	Freight Ton-Miles (in billions of miles)
Albania	0.1		0.05		
Austria	3.8		0.12	2.7	3.4
Belgium	3.1	8.2	0.27	1.9	3.4
Bulgaria	2.0 [7]			1.6 [2]	0.8 [2]
Czechoslovakia	8.7 [8]		0.05	11.6 [3]	8.1 [3]
Denmark		3.0	0.18 [1]	2.1 [3]	0.7 [3]
Finland				1.3	2.1
France	25.7	52.2	0.12	16.4	24.2
Germany	18.8		0.14	18.2	29.9
W. Germany	18.9	43.8	0.20		
Greece	1.5	1.8	0.03	0.2 [4]	0.1 [3]
Hungary	3.5		0.10	3.3 [4]	2.0 [4]
Iceland					
Ireland				0.3	
Italy	9.8	17.1	0.08	13.8 [4, 3]	6.2
Luxembourg	0.2	0.6	0.24	0.1	0.3
Netherlands	2.0	4.3	0.16	3.8	1.9
Norway	2.8	3.1	0.02	0.9	0.9
Poland	14.5		0.12	16.4	19.9
Portugal				0.9 [3]	0.4 [3]
Romania	6.0		0.07	3.4 [5]	2.4 [5]
Spain				4.4	4.0
Sweden	10.3	12.8	0.06	4.1	5.4
Switzerland	1.8	3.9	0.11	4.0	1.1 [3]
Turkey	4.5	5.1	0.02	1.3	1.6
United Kingdom	19.5	52.0	0.21	24.0	22.5
U.S.S.R.		70.0	0.01 [1]		373.4
Yugoslavia	5.0 [7]			5.0	6.2

[1] Tracks per square mile.   [2] 1947.   [3] 1949.   [4] 1948.   [5] 1946.   [6] 1935.   [7] 1938.   [8] 1936.

Sources: United Nations, *Annual Bulletin of Transport Statistics, 1949*, Geneva, 1950; United Nations, *Annual Bulletin of Transport Statistics, 1950*, Geneva, 1951; United Nations, *Statistical Yearbook, 1951*, New York, 1931, pp. 314-15; national statistics.

TABLE 28. AUTOMOBILES

	Passenger Automobiles (in thousands)		Commercial Vehicles (in thousands)		Miles of Road Network per Sq. Mi. of Area
	1937	1950	1937	1950	1950
Austria	32.4	51.3	16.2	42.0	0.57
Belgium	144	78.3	274	145	2.43
Bulgaria	90.9	105 [1]	31.5	63 [1]	*
Czechoslovakia	90.9	105 [1]	31.5	63 [1]	*
Denmark	101.1	117.7	41.4	60.9	*
Finland	24.4	26.0	18.8	35.3	0.16
France	2,020 [2]	1,520 [3]	285 [2]	770	2.10
W. Germany .	1,108 [4]	598	381 [4]	522	1.92
Greece	8.7 [2]	7.2 [3]	8.6 [2]	18.0 [3]	*
Hungary	25.9	4.1 [3]	36.4	11.9 [5]	*
Iceland	0.8	6.0	1.1	4.7	*
Ireland	48.8	91.9	11.1	26.4	*
Italy	271	341	82.1	229	1.04
Luxembourg ..	7.5	9.5	4.3	4.4	2.49
Netherlands ..	90.8	138.6	50.7	83.7	0.59
Norway	47.3	65.0	32.4	51.2	*
Poland	20.3 [4]	23.1	7.1 [4]	90.2	*
Portugal	30.7	57.4 [5]	11.2	16.7 [5]	*
Spain	*	88.5	*	85.5	
Sweden	134	252	57.7	92.5	*
Switzerland ..	71.5	147	21.2	40.5	1.79
Turkey	3.8	10.1 [3]	3.7	16.4 [3]	0.09
United Kingdom ..	1,833	2,317	526	967	1.95
U.S.S.R.	760 [6]	*	*	*	*
Yugoslavia ...	11.3	7.2	3.9	17.1	0.21

[1] 1948. [2] 1939. [3] 1949. [4] Prewar boundary. [5] 1947. [6] Including commercial.

* Not available.

Sources: United Nations, *Statistical Yearbook, 1951,* New York, 1952; United Nations, *Annual Bulletin of Transport Statistics, 1950,* Geneva, 1951; national statistics.

TABLE 29. CIVIL AVIATION IN SELECTED COUNTRIES

Scheduled Services (in millions)

	Passenger Miles		Cargo Tons	
	1938	1950	1938	1950
Belgium	11.2	146	0.4	6.8
Bulgaria	4.9 [3]	*	*	*
Czechoslovakia	13.5	25.5 [1]	0.5	1.8 [1]
Denmark	3.5	92.6	0.1	3.4
Finland	2.1	16.7	0.1	0.5
France	45.6	694.7	1.0	32.6
Hungary	6.8	4.9 [2]	0.4	0.2 [2]
Ireland	0.1	49.8	*	0.8
Netherlands	37.7	479.8	1.2	24.3
Norway	1.5	99.6	*	4.9
Poland	1.2	1.5 [1]	10.7	21.8 [1]
Romania	7.5	*	*	*
Spain	7.0	71.9 [1]	*	0.4 [1]
Sweden	8.6	139.0	0.4	5.3
Switzerland	6.8	91.5	0.1	2.5
United Kingdom	53.4	793.8	1.6	35.8
Yugoslavia	1.7	*	*	*

[1] 1949.   [2] 1948.   [3] 1940.

Sources: United Nations, *Statistical Yearbook, 1951,* New York, 1952, and national statistics.

TABLE 30. MERCHANT MARINE

| | Merchant Marine (in million gross tons) | | International Sea-Borne Shipping (in million metric tons) | | | |
	1938	1950	Loaded 1938	Loaded 1950	Unloaded 1938	Unloaded 1950
Belgium	0.4	0.5	11.3	11.6	15.0	11.9
Denmark	1.1	1.3	2.0	2.2	10.6	12.4
Finland	0.5	0.5	6.7	6.0	3.8	4.0
France	2.9	3.2	12.6	18.7	35.9	31.0
Ger. Fed. Rep.	4.2	0.5	15.0	9.9	28.8	13.4
Greece	1.9	1.3	0.7	0.2 [2]	2.6	0.3 [2]
Iceland		0.1				
Italy and Trieste	3.3	2.6	3.8 [3]	3.5	20.1 [3]	20.2
Netherlands	2.9	3.1	19.5	15.0	33.1	23.9
Norway	4.6	5.5				
Poland	0.1	0.2	13.2 [3]	12.5	3.1 [3]	3.2
Portugal	0.3	0.5	0.2 [4]	0.4	0.7 [4]	1.4
Romania	0.1	0.1				
Spain	0.9	1.2	2.1	4.1	2.4	5.0
Sweden	1.6	2.0	12.0	13.7	12.2	10.6
Turkey	0.2	0.4				
United Kingdom	17.7	18.2				
U.S.S.R.	1.6	2.0				
Yugoslavia	0.4	0.2	1.5	2.0	0.6	1.1

[1] 1947. [2] 1949. [3] Prewar boundaries. [4] 1940.

Sources: United Nations, *Statistical Yearbook, 1951*, New York, 1952, pp. 321, 372, and national statistics.

INDEX